Geometry Formulas

PARALLELOGRAM

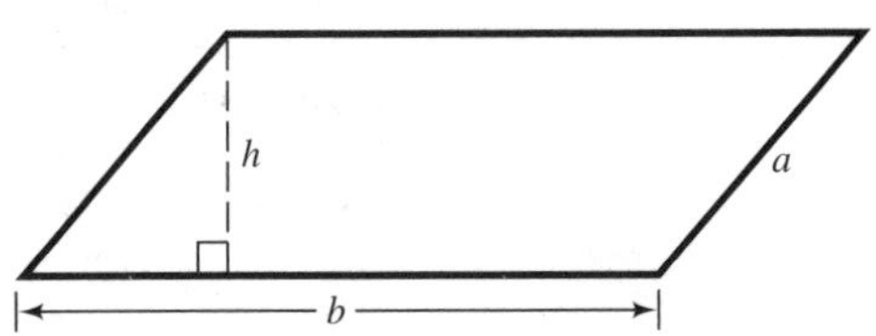

b = base; h = altitude; a = side

Area: $A = bh$

Perimeter: $P = 2a + 2b$

b_2

a h c

b_1

b_1, b_2 = bases; h = altitude; a, c = sides

Area: $A = \frac{1}{2}(b_1 + b_2)h$

Perimeter: $P = a + b_1 + b_2 + c$

Sets of Numbers (1.1, 2.2, 10.7)

Natural	$\{1, 2, 3, 4, 5, \ldots\}$
Whole	$\{0, 1, 2, 3, 4, \ldots\}$
Integers	$\{\ldots, -3, -2, -1, 0, 1, 2, 3, \ldots\}$
Rational	$\left\{x \mid x = \frac{a}{b}, \text{ where } a \text{ and } b \text{ are integers with } b \neq 0\right\}$
Irrational	$\{x \mid x$ cannot be expressed as the quotient of two integers$\}$
Real	$\{x \mid x$ is rational or irrational$\}$
Complex	$\{x \mid x = a + bi$ where a and b are real and $i^2 = -1\}$

Axioms of the Real Numbers (2.3, 2.4, 2.5)

Commutative Properties	$a + b = b + a$
	$ab = ba$
Associative Properties	$a + (b + c) = (a + b) + c$
	$a(bc) = (ab)c$
Additive Identity	$a + 0 = a = 0 + a$
Multiplicative Identity	$a \cdot 1 = a = 1 \cdot a$
Negatives	$a + (-a) = 0 = (-a) + a$
Reciprocals	$a\left(\frac{1}{a}\right) = 1 = \left(\frac{1}{a}\right)a, \quad a \neq 0$
Distributive Laws	$a(b + c) = ab + ac$
	$a(b - c) = ab - ac$

THIRD EDITION

Elementary Algebra

THIRD EDITION

Elementary Algebra

L. MURPHY JOHNSON
ARNOLD R. STEFFENSEN
Northern Arizona University

HarperCollins*CollegePublishers*

To Barbara, Barbara, Becky, Roy, Cindy, John, and Pam

FOR THE STUDENT To help you study and understand the course material, a *Student's Solutions Manual* is available from your college bookstore. This book provides complete, step-by-step solutions to all the Exercises in the text and to all Chapter Review and Chapter Test Exercises.

Sponsoring Editor: Karin E. Wagner
Development Editor: Elizabeth Lee
Project Editor: Randee Wire
Design Administrator: Jess Schaal
Text and Cover Design: Lesiak/Crampton Design Inc
Text and Cover Illustration: Heidi Younger
Compositor: York Graphic Services, Inc.
Printer and Binder: R.R. Donnelley & Sons Company
Cover Printer: The Lehigh Press, Inc.

Elementary Algebra, Third Edition

Library of Congress Cataloging-in-Publication Data

Johnson, L. Murphy (Lee Murphy)
Elementary algebra / L. Murphy Johnson, Arnold R. Steffensen. — 3rd ed.
p. cm.
Includes index.
ISBN 0-673-46645-0
1. Algebra. I. Steffensen, Arnold R. II. Title.
QA152.2.J6 1994
512′.9—dc20 93-10109
CIP

93 94 95 96 9 8 7 6 5 4 3 2 1

Contents

CHAPTER 3 *Linear Equations and Inequalities*

CHAPTER 4 *Graphing*

CHAPTER 5 *Systems of Linear Equations*

CHAPTER 6 *Exponents and Polynomials*

CHAPTER 10 *Quadratic Equations*

Preface

ELEMENTARY ALGEBRA, THIRD EDITION, is designed for college students who have had one year of high school algebra, who have not been exposed to college algebra, or who require further review before taking additional courses in mathematics, science, business, or computer science. The primary objective of the course is to gain familiarity with mathematical symbols and operations in order to formulate and solve first- and second-degree equations.

The hallmarks of the book include informal yet carefully worded explanations; key definitions, rules, and procedures set off in colored boxes; detailed examples with accompanying annotations; enhanced graphs and figures employing color; abundant graded exercises; and comprehensive chapter reviews. Each chapter opens with a full-page introduction including an illustrated application that serves as an overview of and motivator for upcoming material. The text's organization allows instructors maximum flexibility to select topics to fit individual needs.

An annotated instructor's edition, testing manual, solutions manual, and test generator are provided for the instructor. Supplements for students include interactive tutorial software, a set of text-specific instructional videotapes, and a solutions manual written by the authors available for student purchase.

New to This Edition

- Conceptual and writing exercises have been added, in accordance with the NCTM guidelines.
- The quantity of real-world and geometry applications has been increased and integer and age problems have been reduced considerably.
- A special strategy for solving word problems, the ATTACK method, is given in Section 3.5. Section 2.1 introduces material on translating words into mathematical symbols, also in accordance with the NCTM guidelines.
- The format of the section exercises has been modified into three separate sets: Exercises, Parallel Exercises, and Enrichment Exercises, the latter of which include writing, conceptual, calculator, and challenging exercises.
- Chapter 1 has been extensively revised by being split into two chapters to provide greater flexibility for those who require differing amounts of arith-

metic review. A Chapter 1 pretest has been added to enable instructors to determine students' needs relative to this basic material. Students who are well prepared can begin with Chapter 2 and get into the algebra immediately.

- Integer exponents and scientific notation have been moved from Chapter 1 to Chapter 6 on polynomials, a more logical location.
- The section on solving literal equations and formulas has been moved forward, to Chapter 3 (Section 3.4), to help students prepare for applied problems that follow.
- Compound inequalities have been moved from an appendix to Section 3.8, and designated as optional.
- Former Chapter 3 has been split into two chapters, Chapter 4, Graphing, and Chapter 5, Systems of Linear Equations. This change keeps graphing early in the text and allows greater coverage for topics like systems and problem solving with systems.
- Quadratic equations are introduced briefly in Chapter 7 for those who do not cover Chapter 10, where the topic is given full treatment.
- Additional material on 30°–60° right triangles and 45°–45° right triangles has been added to Section 9.7 in response to several state skills requirements.
- The discussion of graphing quadratic equations, in Section 10.6, has been expanded to include finding the vertex of a parabola more directly.
- New Student Guideposts at the beginning of each section give learning objectives for the section.
- Chapter Reviews summarizing Key Terms and Key Concepts are new student aids.
- Chapter Review Exercises have been expanded and divided into two parts. Part I consists of exercises that are ordered and section referenced. Part II exercises are thoroughly mixed to help students prepare for examinations.
- A new full-color format has been used in this edition to improve the book pedagogically and visually.

Features

The following three pages illustrate important features, which are designed to assist students in the learning process. Pedagogical features have been enhanced to increase interest and accessibility.

Chapter Openers

Each chapter opens with a full-page introduction including an illustrated application that serves as an overview of and motivator for upcoming material. Each Chapter Opener will be solved in an example somewhere within the chapter.

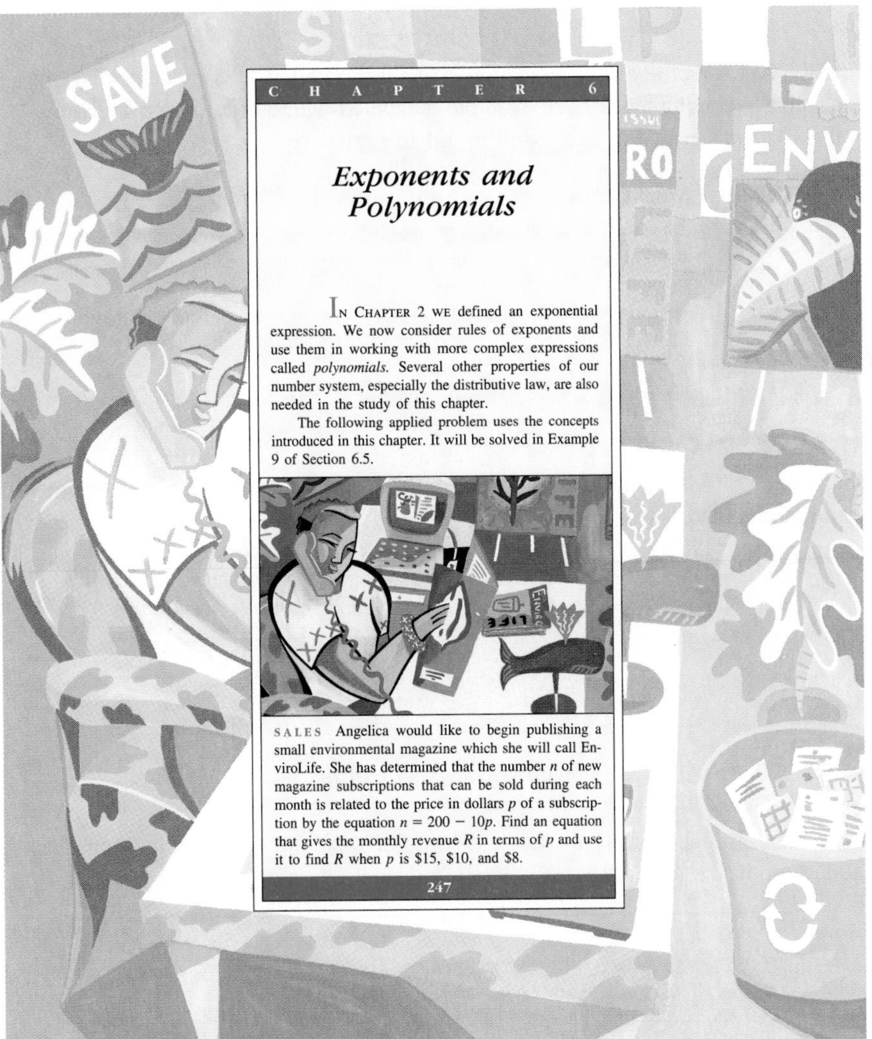

CHAPTER 6

Exponents and Polynomials

In Chapter 2 we defined an exponential expression. We now consider rules of exponents and use them in working with more complex expressions called *polynomials*. Several other properties of our number system, especially the distributive law, are also needed in the study of this chapter.

The following applied problem uses the concepts introduced in this chapter. It will be solved in Example 9 of Section 6.5.

SALES Angelica would like to begin publishing a small environmental magazine which she will call EnviroLife. She has determined that the number n of new magazine subscriptions that can be sold during each month is related to the price in dollars p of a subscription by the equation $n = 200 - 10p$. Find an equation that gives the monthly revenue R in terms of p and use it to find R when p is \$15, \$10, and \$8.

247

Student Guideposts

This new feature, which consists of a list of objectives for each section, helps students locate important concepts as they study or review. Guideposts specify major topics, rules, and procedures, and are listed at the beginning of each section, then repeated as the corresponding material is discussed in that section.

SECTION 6.2 **Scientific Notation**

Student guideposts
- ▶ *Scientific notation*
- ▶ *Calculations using scientific notation*

Examples

More than 650 carefully selected examples include detailed, step-by-step solutions and descriptive side comments. Each example is labeled with a title to help students focus on the concept being developed and to aid in review.

EXAMPLE 9 **Working with a Sales Application**

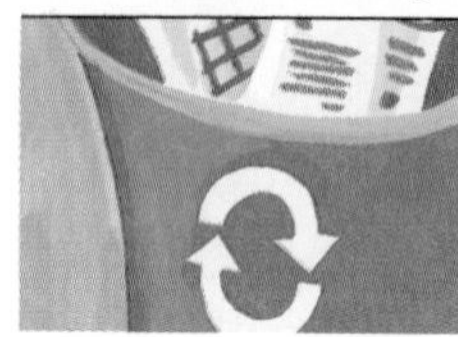

Angelica would like to begin publishing a small environmental magazine which she will call EnviroLife. She has determined that the number n of new magazine subscriptions that can be sold during each month is related to the price in dollars p of a subscription by the equation $n = 200 - 10p$. Find an equation that gives the monthly revenue R in terms of p and use it to find R when p is \$15, \$10, and \$8.

Cautions

This feature calls students' attention to common mistakes and special problems that should be avoided.

CAUTION Notice in Example 3(f) that the sum of two squares cannot be factored. Do not make the mistake of giving $(a + b)^2$ as the factors of $a^2 + b^2$.

$$(a + b)^2 = a^2 + 2ab + b^2 \neq a^2 + b^2$$

Also, $(a - b)^2 \neq a^2 - b^2$.

Definitions and Rules

Major definition and rules are outlined in color boxes to stress their importance as students study the material.

To Factor $x^2 + bx + c$

1. Write $x^2 + bx + c = (x + \_\_)(x + \_\_)$.
2. List all pairs of integers whose product is c.
3. Find the pair from this list whose sum is b (if there is one).
4. Fill in the blanks with this pair.

Notes

Important procedures or concepts are given special attention.

> NOTE In Example 4 we used the symbol $\approx$ to represent the phrase "is *approximately equal* to." It is important to use $\approx$ whenever an approximate or rounded number is indicated.

Exercises

As a key feature of this text, more than 6000 exercises, including approximately 1000 review exercises, 650 conceptual exercises, 100 writing exercises, and 400 additional enrichment exercises, are provided. All applications have been improved and updated to better reflect uses of mathematical concepts in the real world. More than 600 applications drawn from such diverse areas as business, engineering, physics, chemistry, agriculture, sports, and recreation are included in the chapter introductions, examples, and exercises. Calculator exercises marked with the calculator symbol, ▦, are also provided throughout the book.

Section exercises are provided in three sets: **Exercises, Parallel Exercises,** and **Enrichment Exercises.** Answers for all exercises in the first set are given at the back of the book, but none are given for the Parallel Exercises, which mirror the first set. This gives an opportunity for student practice without answers provided. Both the Exercises and Parallel Exercises include a subset of exercises called **For Review.** Their purpose is to encourage continuous review of previously covered material, and to provide special review for topics covered in the upcoming section. The third set of exercises, Enrichment Exercises, includes challenging, conceptual, writing, and calculator exercises. Answers for selected exercises, marked with the ⚠ symbol, are given in this set.

Chapter Review Exercises and a practice **Chapter Test** conclude each chapter. The Chapter Review Exercises are divided into two parts: the problems in Part I are ordered and marked by section, but those in Part II are thoroughly mixed to help students prepare for examinations. Answers to all Chapter Review and Chapter Test exercises are provided at the end of the text.

Comprehensive **Chapter Reviews** include **Key Terms,** listed by section with brief definitions, and **Key Concepts** that summarize the major points of each section.

Supplements

For the Instructor

The **Annotated Instructor's Edition** provides instructors with immediate access to the answers for every exercise in the text, with the exception of writing exercises, for which more than one correct answer may be possible. All the exercises from the student's edition are reprinted in the special Instructor's Answer Section at the end of the text, with answers printed in color next to the corresponding text exercise. Symbols are used to identify the writing, ✍, and conceptual, ◉, exercises to assist in making homework assignments. Each section of the instructor's edition also includes a Resources list, cross-referencing each relevant supplement to the respective text sections. The book also includes Exploration Guides, new writing/exploration/discussion problems that emphasize conceptual understanding and writing to learn mathematics.

The **Instructor's Test Manual,** written by the authors, contains a series of ready-to-duplicate tests, a placement test, six different but equivalent tests for each chapter (four open-response and two multiple-choice), and two final examinations, all with answers provided in an easy-to-use format. More than 1000 additional problems, grouped by section, are supplied in the Exercise Bank, available for in-class exams, quizzes, or tests. Included in these exercises are a selection of writing exercises (new) that may be used by those instructors who wish to do so. Section-by-section teaching tips provide suggestions for content implementation that an instructor, tutor, or teaching assistant might find helpful.

The **Instructor's Solutions Manual,** written by the authors, contains complete worked-out solutions to the Parallel Exercises and Enrichment Exercises given in the text.

HarperCollins Test Generator/Editor for Mathematics with QuizMaster is available in IBM and Macintosh versions and is fully networkable. The test generator enables instructors to select questions by objective, section, or chapter, or to use a ready-made test for each chapter. The editor enables instructors to edit any preexisting data or to easily create their own questions. The software is algorithm driven, allowing the instructor to regenerate constants while maintaining problem type, providing a nearly unlimited number of available test or quiz items in multiple-choice or open-response format. The system features printed graphics and accurate mathematics symbols. QuizMaster enables instructors to create tests and quizzes using the Test Generator/Editor and save them to disk so that students can take the test or quiz on a stand-alone computer or network. QuizMaster then grades the test or quiz and allows the instructor to create reports on individual students or classes.

For the Student

The **Student's Solutions Manual** (ISBN 0-673-46905-0), written by the authors, contains complete, worked-out solutions to every exercise in the first set of Exercises in each section, to all Chapter Review Exercises, to all exercises in the Chapter Tests, and to all Final Review Exercises.

Interactive Tutorial Software with Management System. This innovative package is also available in IBM and Macintosh versions and is fully networkable. As with the Test Generator/Editor, this software is algorithm driven, which automatically regenerates constants so that a student will not see the numbers repeat in a problem type if he or she revisits any particular section. The tutorial is self-paced and provides unlimited opportunities to review lessons and to practice problem solving. When students give a wrong answer, they can request to see the problem worked out. The program is menu-driven for ease of use, and on-screen help can be obtained at any time with a single keystroke. Students' scores are automatically recorded and can be printed for a permanent record. The optional Management System lets instructors record student scores on disk and print diagnostic reports for individual students or classes.

Videotapes. A new videotape series has been developed to accompany *Elementary Algebra,* Third Edition. These text-specific videotapes have been produced in consultation with a task force of academicians from both two-year and four-year colleges. In a separate lesson for each section of the book, the tapes cover all objectives, topics, and problem-solving techniques within the text.

Acknowledgments

We extend our sincere gratitude to the students and instructors who used the previous editions of this text and offered many suggestions for improvement. Also, we would like to express our appreciation to the Northern Arizona University administration, especially President Eugene M. Hughes, who has given us generous support and encouragement for many years.

We also express our thanks to the following instructors and reviewers for their countless beneficial suggestions and criticisms at various stages of the book's revision:

Sam Borah
Pima Community College

Judith Covington
University of Southwestern Louisiana

Lynn Darragh
San Juan College

Carol Sue Huffman
Iowa Western Community College

Mary Johnson
Inver Hills Community College

Debra Madrid-Doyle
Santa Fe Community College

Giles Wilson Maloof
Boise State University

Carol Jean Martin
Dodge City Community College

Robert Maynard
Tidewater Community College

Elaine M. Parks
Laramie County Community College

Ann C. Parsons
Northeastern University

Sandra Sher
Marymont College

Patricia C. Treloar
University of Mississippi

Lenore Vest
Lower Columbia College

We extend special appreciation to Joseph Mutter and Michael Ratliff for their assistance and support over the years.

To our editors and designer, Liz Lee, Randee Wire, and Jess Schaal, we are greatly indebted. Special thanks goes to Anne Kelly and Karin Wagner, whose support and efforts can never be adequately recognized.

Finally, we appreciate the encouragement and support of our families, especially our wives, Barbara and Barbara, who have contributed greatly to our endeavors in so many ways.

L. Murphy Johnson
Arnold R. Steffensen
Northern Arizona University

To the Student

OVER THE YEARS, WE have taught elementary algebra to thousands of students. Often our students have made comments such as: "I never did do well in math, but now my major requires algebra." "I really don't like math, why does it have to be required for graduation?" "I can't do word problems!" If you have ever made a similar statement, now is the time to begin thinking positively, and to start down the road toward success in algebra. Don't be frightened of the course as a whole. The material in the text is presented in a way that allows you to take one small step at a time. As you begin your course, try to keep in mind the following guidelines.

General Guidelines

1. Motivation and dedication are basic requirements for mastering algebra. Just as an athlete does not improve without commitment to his or her goal, an algebra student must be prepared to work hard and spend time studying. Keep up with your assignments. Don't procrastinate and let things slide until the night before your exam. If you need extra help, ask for it right away. In mathematics you will often discover that comprehension of one topic depends on understanding a previous one making it very difficult if you are behind in your work.
2. Students often have the impression that their homework consists only of the written exercises assigned by their instructor. Actually, you will take a tremendous leap toward success if you recognize that the written homework exercises are only a part of your homework assignment. In reality, your homework should consist of studying your class notes, reading the appropriate section in your text, and finally, testing yourself to see if you really have mastered the material by working the assigned written exercises.
3. Algebra is not learned simply by watching, listening, or reading; *it is learned by doing*. Use your text, use your pencil, and practice. When your thoughts are organized and written in a neat and orderly way, you will have taken a giant step toward success. Do not try to take shortcuts, be complete and write out all details. This is especially true when working word problems. Try to pattern your work after the work given in the

examples. The following are samples of two students' work on an applied problem. Which student do you think was the more successful in the course?

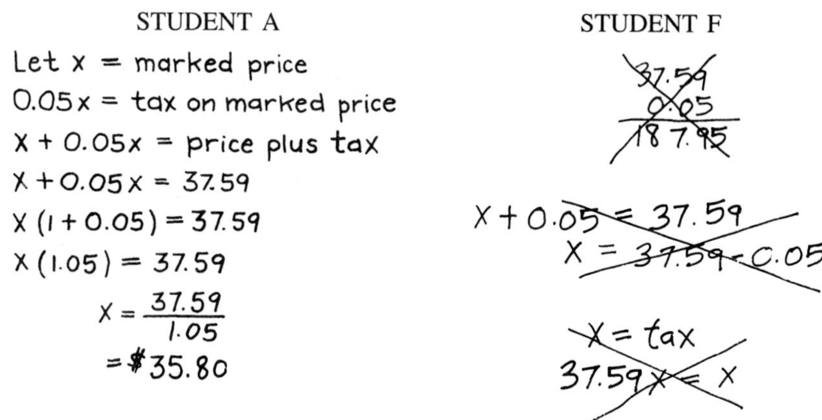

4. If you are allowed to use a calculator in your course, consult your owner's manual to become familiar with its features. When you are computing with decimals or approximating irrational numbers, a calculator can be a time-saving device. On the other hand, you should not be so dependent on a calculator that you reach for it to perform simple calculations that can be done more quickly mentally. For example, it would be foolish to use a calculator to evaluate $8 \div 2$, but a calculator would be appropriate if you needed to compute $7343.84 \div 1.12$. It is important that you learn when to use and when not to use your calculator; some exercises for which a calculator may be especially helpful are marked with a calculator symbol, ▦.

Specific Guidelines

1. As you begin to study each section, look ahead through the material for a preview of what to expect.
2. Return to the beginning of the section and start reading slowly; study the explanations carefully. The **STUDENT GUIDEPOSTS** will help you find important concepts as you progress. Pay close attention to the definitions, rules, and procedures in the colored boxes.
3. Read each example and make sure that you understand each step. The side comments given in color will help you if something is not quite clear.
4. Periodically you will see a **CAUTION** or **NOTE.** The **CAUTION** warns you of common mistakes and special problems to avoid. The **NOTE** provides pertinent information or additional important explanation.
5. After you finish the material in the body of the section, you need to check your understanding of the topics and begin to practice, practice, practice!

Work all of the exercises assigned by your instructor. Answers to all exercises in the first set at the end of each section are given at the back of the text. Complete solutions to all of these exercises, as well as to the Chapter Review Exercises, Chapter Tests, and Final Review Exercises are available in the *Student's Solutions Manual.*

6. To help retain what you've learned and to prepare you for topics in the next section, be sure to work the exercises marked *For Review,* located at the end of most exercise sets.

7. After you have completed all of the sections in the chapter, read the **CHAPTER REVIEW** that contains Key Words and Key Concepts. The Review Exercises provide more practice before you take the Chapter Test. Answers to the Review Exercises and Chapter Test exercises are given at the back of the text. Solutions are also provided in the *Student's Solutions Manual* if you need more help.

8. To help you study for your final examination, we have concluded the book with a comprehensive set of **FINAL REVIEW EXERCISES.**

If you follow this advice and work closely with your instructor, your chances of success in algebra will be greatly improved. We wish you the best of luck in your course.

L. Murphy Johnson
Arnold R. Steffensen

Applications Index

Numbers give the pages where applications are found. If a number is in parentheses, it is an exercise number on the indicated page.

CHAPTER 1 PRETEST

1.1

1. Express 1950 as a product of primes.

2. Reduce $\frac{105}{120}$ to lowest terms.

3. Supply the missing denominator. $\frac{3}{7} = \frac{12}{\quad}$

1.2

Perform the indicated operations.

4. $\frac{6}{11} \cdot \frac{22}{15}$

5. $\frac{2}{9} \div \frac{8}{3}$

6. $\frac{1}{3} + \frac{7}{5}$

7. $\frac{5}{14} - \frac{4}{21}$

8. Change $\frac{127}{5}$ to a mixed number.

9. A wire $3\frac{1}{3}$ feet long is to be cut into equal pieces each of length $\frac{1}{6}$ feet. How many pieces can be cut?

1.3

10. Express 15.69 in expanded notation.

Perform the indicated operations.

11. $13.5 + 1.28 + 201.003$

12. $403.27 - 28.004$

13. $(0.004)(1.35)$

14. $0.012\overline{)0.0516}$

1.4

15. Convert $\frac{4}{25}$ to a decimal.

16. Convert 1.25 to a fraction.

17. Convert 36% to a decimal.

18. Convert 2.5 to a percent.

19. Convert $\frac{5}{8}$ to a percent.

20. There were 480 people at a concert. If 60% of those in attendance were children, how many children were at the concert?

CHAPTER 1

Prealgebra

ARITHMETIC SERVES AS A foundation for algebra. Thorough knowledge of the operations in arithmetic is essential for understanding operations in algebra since, very simply stated, algebra involves arithmetic operations on letters that are used to represent numbers. In this chapter we study the basic sets of numbers and review the four basic operations on fractions and decimals. These operations can be considered in a variety of ways, but we will present techniques that are especially helpful when we turn our attention to algebra. Well-prepared students might skip this material and begin their work with Chapter 2. The Chapter 1 Diagnostic Pretest might be used to help determine a student's particular needs.

Throughout the text, we will be considering a variety of applied problems that show how algebra can be used in practical and useful ways. The following example, solved in Example 7 of Section 1.4, illustrates one such application.

SPORTS During a recent homecoming game at Northern Arizona University, quarterback Greg Wyatt completed 28 passes in 40 attempts. What fraction of his attempts did he complete? What percent of his attempts did he complete?

We begin this chapter by considering the fundamental sets of numbers including properties and operations with fractions. Next we review decimals, operations on decimals, and the notion of percent. We conclude by examining conversions between fractions, decimals, and percents.

SECTION 1.1 Fractions

Student guideposts

- *Sets of numbers*
- *Properties of fractions*
- *Reducing to lowest terms*
- *Prime numbers and factors*

Sets of numbers

Two terms that are used repeatedly in algebra are *set* and *element.* A **set** is a collection of objects. These objects, the **elements** of the set, are often listed within braces { }.

Most sets we deal with are sets of *numbers.* A **number** is a human invention, an idea formed when questions about "how many" or "in what order" are asked. Symbols for numbers are called **numerals.** For example, "4" is a symbol or numeral that represents the number four. The most basic numbers are the **natural** or **counting numbers.**

$N = \{1, 2, 3, 4, \ldots\}$ Natural (counting) numbers

We use three dots to mean that a sequence or pattern continues on in the same manner. When zero is included with the natural numbers, we obtain the set of **whole numbers.**

$W = \{0, 1, 2, 3, 4, \ldots\}$ Whole numbers

Properties of fractions

Numbers written as the quotient of a whole number and a natural number, such as

$$\frac{1}{2}, \quad \frac{3}{4}, \quad \frac{7}{3}, \quad \frac{5}{5}, \quad \frac{5}{1}, \quad \frac{0}{1}, \quad \frac{15}{1}, \quad \frac{61}{21},$$

are called **fractions.** The **numerator** of a fraction is the number above the fraction bar, and the **denominator** is the number below the fraction bar. In the fraction $\frac{3}{4}$, 3 is the numerator and 4 is the denominator.

When the numerator is a smaller number than the denominator, the fraction is called a **proper fraction;** otherwise it is an **improper fraction.** For example, $\frac{1}{2}$ and $\frac{3}{4}$ are proper fractions, while $\frac{7}{5}$, $\frac{5}{5}$, $\frac{5}{1}$, and $\frac{61}{27}$ are improper fractions.

Every whole number can be written as a fraction by letting the whole number be the numerator and 1 be the denominator. For example,

$$5 = \frac{5}{1}, \qquad 2 = \frac{2}{1}, \qquad 0 = \frac{0}{1}, \qquad \text{and} \qquad 15 = \frac{15}{1}.$$

Five could also be written as $\frac{10}{2}$, $\frac{15}{3}$, $\frac{20}{4}$, etc. Similarly, the fraction $\frac{1}{4}$ could be expressed as $\frac{1}{4}$, $\frac{2}{8}$, $\frac{3}{12}$, $\frac{4}{16}$, $\frac{5}{20}$, and so on. We can always find another name for a fraction by multiplying both the numerator and the denominator by the same nonzero number. Fractions that are names for the same number or have the same value are called **equivalent fractions.**

Fundamental Principle of Fractions

If both the numerator and denominator of a fraction are multiplied or divided by the same nonzero number, the resulting fraction is equivalent to the original fraction.

▶ *Reducing to lowest terms*

We **build up** fractions when we multiply both the numerator and denominator by the same natural number other than 1 and **reduce** fractions when we divide both by the same natural number other than 1. For example,

$$\frac{3}{4} = \frac{3 \cdot 2}{4 \cdot 2} = \frac{6}{8}, \qquad \frac{3}{4} = \frac{3 \cdot 5}{4 \cdot 5} = \frac{15}{20}, \qquad \frac{3}{4} = \frac{3 \cdot 10}{4 \cdot 10} = \frac{30}{40}.$$

Thus, $\frac{3}{4}$ has been built up to the equivalent fractions $\frac{6}{8}$, $\frac{15}{20}$, $\frac{30}{40}$. Also,

$$\frac{12}{18} = \frac{12 \div 2}{18 \div 2} = \frac{6}{9}, \qquad \frac{12}{18} = \frac{12 \div 3}{18 \div 3} = \frac{4}{6}, \qquad \frac{12}{18} = \frac{12 \div 6}{18 \div 6} = \frac{2}{3}.$$

Thus, $\frac{12}{18}$ has been reduced to the equivalent fractions $\frac{6}{9}$, $\frac{4}{6}$, and $\frac{2}{3}$.

NOTE When we use the fundamental principle of fractions and multiply or divide the numerator and denominator of a fraction by the same nonzero number, we are simply multiplying the fraction by the number 1. For example,

$$\frac{3}{4} = \frac{3}{4} \cdot 1 = \frac{3}{4} \cdot \frac{2}{2} = \frac{3 \cdot 2}{4 \cdot 2} = \frac{6}{8}$$

and

$$\frac{12}{18} = \frac{2 \cdot 6}{3 \cdot 6} = \frac{2}{3} \cdot \frac{6}{6} = \frac{2}{3} \cdot 1 = \frac{2}{3}.$$

Reducing Fractions

A fraction is **reduced to lowest terms** when 1 is the only natural number that divides both numerator and denominator.

▶ *Prime numbers and factors*

We reduced $\frac{12}{18}$ to $\frac{6}{9}$, $\frac{4}{6}$, and $\frac{2}{3}$ above. Notice that $\frac{6}{9}$ and $\frac{4}{6}$ can each be reduced further, while $\frac{2}{3}$ cannot. Thus, $\frac{2}{3}$ is reduced to lowest terms. The concept of a *prime number* is useful for reducing fractions to lowest terms. A **prime number** is a natural number greater than 1 whose only divisors are 1 and itself. Since 1 and 5 are the only divisors of 5, 5 is prime; since 2 and 3 are divisors of 6 along with 1 and 6, 6 is not prime.

The first few primes are

$$2, \quad 3, \quad 5, \quad 7, \quad 11, \quad 13, \quad 17, \quad 19, \quad 23, \ldots.$$

Prime Numbers and Factors

Every natural number greater than 1 either is prime or can be expressed as a product of primes.

The primes in the product are called **prime factors,** and the process of expressing a number as a product of primes is called **factoring into primes.**

EXAMPLE 1

Factoring into Primes

Express as a product of primes.

(a) $15 = 3 \cdot 5$ Why not $15 = 15 \cdot 1$?

(b) $28 = 2 \cdot 2 \cdot 7$ Why not $28 = 4 \cdot 7$?

(c) $41 = 41$ 41 is a prime ■

To Reduce a Fraction to Lowest Terms

1. Factor the numerator and denominator into products of primes.
2. Divide both the numerator and denominator by all common factors.
3. Multiply remaining factors in the numerator and multiply the remaining factors in the denominator.

Dividing both the numerator and denominator of a fraction by common factors is sometimes called **canceling factors.** This is shown by crossing out the common factors. For example,

$$\frac{9 \cdot \overset{1}{\cancel{5}}}{\underset{1}{\cancel{5}}} = \frac{9}{1} = 9 \quad \text{and} \quad \frac{\overset{1}{\cancel{2}} \cdot \overset{1}{\cancel{7}}}{\underset{1}{\cancel{2}} \cdot 3 \cdot \underset{1}{\cancel{7}}} = \frac{1}{3}.$$

Notice that when we cancel *all* of the factors out of a numerator or a denominator, it makes the numerator or denominator 1, *not* 0.

EXAMPLE 2 **Reducing Fractions**

Reduce the fractions to lowest terms.

(a) $\dfrac{6}{15} = \dfrac{2 \cdot \cancel{3}^{1}}{\cancel{3}_{1} \cdot 5} = \dfrac{2}{5}$ Divide out or cancel common factor 3 from both numerator and denominator

(b) $\dfrac{12}{42} = \dfrac{\cancel{2}^{1} \cdot 2 \cdot \cancel{3}^{1}}{\cancel{2}_{1} \cdot \cancel{3}_{1} \cdot 7} = \dfrac{2}{7}$ Divide out or cancel common factors 2 and 3 from both numerator and denominator

(c) $\dfrac{14}{15} = \dfrac{2 \cdot 7}{3 \cdot 5}$ There are no common factors, so $\frac{14}{15}$ is already reduced to lowest terms ■

CAUTION Divide out or cancel only *factors* (numbers that are multiplied) and never cross out parts of sums. For example,

$$\frac{2 \cdot 7}{2} = \frac{\cancel{2} \cdot 7}{\cancel{2}} = 7, \quad \text{but} \quad \frac{2 + 7}{2} \text{ is } \textit{not} \text{ equal to } \frac{\cancel{2} + 7}{\cancel{2}}.$$

With practice, we often shorten the process of reducing fractions by dividing out common factors without first factoring into primes. For example, if we notice that 6 is a common factor of both 12 and 42, we can write

$$\frac{12}{42} = \frac{2 \cdot \cancel{6}^{1}}{7 \cdot \cancel{6}_{1}} = \frac{2}{7}.$$

Fractions describe parts of quantities in many applied situations. If a baseball player got three hits in five times at bat, we would say he had a hit $\frac{3}{5}$ (three-fifths) of the time. Thus, fractions are used to indicate what part one number is of another.

EXAMPLE 3 **Calculating Fractional Parts**

A group of 100 students was made up of 60 girls and 40 boys. Exactly 75 students were taking math, and exactly 35 students were taking history.

(a) What fractional part of the total number of students were girls?

There were 60 girls among 100 students for a fractional part of $\frac{60}{100}$, or $\frac{3}{5}$, reduced to lowest terms.

(b) What fraction of the students were taking math?

There were 75 math students out of the 100 total for a fraction of $\frac{75}{100}$, or $\frac{3}{4}$, reduced to lowest terms.

(c) What fraction of the students were *not* taking history?

Since 35 students were taking history, 65 were not. Thus, $\frac{65}{100}$, or $\frac{13}{20}$, of the students were not taking history. ■

1.1 EXERCISES

Answer true *or* false *in Exercises 1–6. If the statement is false, tell why.*

1. A collection of objects is also called a set of objects.

2. The name or symbol for a number is a numeral.

3. If the numerator of a fraction is a smaller number than the denominator, it is a proper fraction.

4. Two fractions with the same value are called equivalent fractions.

5. A natural number other than 1 that is divisible only by itself and 1 is called prime.

6. The process of canceling factors from a numerator and denominator is really the process of adding common factors.

7. Consider the fractions $\frac{1}{5}, \frac{3}{8}, \frac{9}{9}, \frac{10}{2}, \frac{6}{6}, \frac{13}{15}$, and $\frac{8}{1}$.
(a) Which of these are proper fractions? **(b)** Which of these are improper fractions?

Write three fractions that are equivalent to each fraction in Exercises 8–10.

8. $\dfrac{2}{5}$ **9.** 4 **10.** $\dfrac{105}{2}$

11. List all prime numbers between 1 and 20.

Express as a product of primes in Exercises 12–14.

12. 70 **13.** 47 **14.** 1470

Reduce to lowest terms in Exercises 15–20.

15. $\dfrac{9}{36}$ **16.** $\dfrac{25}{30}$ **17.** $\dfrac{12}{35}$ **18.** $\dfrac{72}{16}$ **19.** $\dfrac{72}{72}$ **20.** $\dfrac{120}{162}$

21. Write an equivalent fraction for $\frac{7}{8}$ with 32 as the denominator.

22. Write an equivalent fraction for $\frac{6}{5}$ with 36 as the numerator.

Supply the missing numerator in Exercises 23–25.

23. $\dfrac{3}{4} = \dfrac{}{12}$ **24.** $\dfrac{5}{7} = \dfrac{}{28}$ **25.** $\dfrac{10}{3} = \dfrac{}{24}$

Supply the missing denominator in Exercises 26–28.

26. $\dfrac{3}{7} = \dfrac{6}{}$ **27.** $\dfrac{2}{11} = \dfrac{10}{}$ **28.** $\dfrac{21}{2} = \dfrac{63}{}$

29. A softball pitcher struck out 12 of the 21 batters she faced. What fractional part of the total number of batters **(a)** did she strike out? **(b)** did she not strike out?

30. Marvin received \$150 from his dad. He spent \$55 for a coat and deposited the rest into his savings account. What fractional part of the \$150 went for **(a)** the coat? **(b)** savings?

1.1 PARALLEL EXERCISES

Answer true *or* false *in Exercises 1–6. If the statement is false, tell why.*

1. The objects that belong to a set are called the elements of the set.

2. The denominator of the fraction $\frac{5}{7}$ is 5.

3. If the numerator of a fraction is equal to or larger than the denominator, it is a proper fraction.

4. We reduce a fraction when we divide both numerator and denominator by a natural number other than 1.

5. The process of dividing common factors from a numerator and denominator is sometimes called reducing common factors.

6. A number expressed as a quotient of a whole number and a natural number is called a fraction.

7. Consider the fractions $\frac{1}{7}$, $\frac{3}{11}$, $\frac{8}{8}$, $\frac{15}{3}$, $\frac{17}{17}$, $\frac{21}{23}$, and $\frac{5}{1}$.
(a) Which of these are proper fractions? **(b)** Which of these are improper fractions?

Write three fractions that are equivalent to each fraction in Exercises 8–10.

8. $\frac{7}{2}$ **9.** 8 **10.** $\frac{1}{1000}$

11. List all prime numbers between 20 and 40.

Express as a product of primes in Exercises 12–14.

12. 42 **13.** 625 **14.** 2541

Reduce to lowest terms in Exercises 15–20.

15. $\frac{7}{42}$ **16.** $\frac{15}{77}$ **17.** $\frac{60}{35}$ **18.** $\frac{88}{16}$ **19.** $\frac{90}{147}$ **20.** $\frac{168}{228}$

21. Write an equivalent fraction for $\frac{5}{8}$ with 48 as the denominator.

22. Write an equivalent fraction for $\frac{8}{5}$ with 32 as the numerator.

Supply the missing numerator in Exercises 23–25.

23. $\frac{2}{3} = \frac{\quad}{12}$ **24.** $\frac{3}{7} = \frac{\quad}{35}$ **25.** $\frac{12}{5} = \frac{\quad}{45}$

Supply the missing denominator in Exercises 26–28.

26. $\frac{4}{7} = \frac{28}{\quad}$ **27.** $\frac{8}{11} = \frac{24}{\quad}$ **28.** $\frac{52}{3} = \frac{104}{\quad}$

29. A basketball player hit 21 free throws in 28 attempts during a recent tournament. What fractional part of the attempts **(a)** did he make? **(b)** did he miss?

30. Bill received \$250 from his grandmother. He spent \$120 to repair his car and the rest went for gasoline. What fractional part of the \$250 went for **(a)** car repairs? **(b)** gasoline?

1.1 ENRICHMENT EXERCISES

Reduce each fraction in Exercises 1–3 to lowest terms.

1. $\frac{632}{492}$ **2.** $\frac{246}{1230}$ △ **3.** $\frac{780}{5005}$

4. When told to reduce the fraction $\frac{6}{30}$ to lowest terms, Burford gave the following.

$$\frac{6}{30} = \frac{\cancel{3} \cdot \cancel{2}}{\cancel{3} \cdot \cancel{2} \cdot 5} = \frac{0}{5} = 0 \qquad \text{Wrong!}$$

What is wrong with Burford's work? What is the correct answer?

5. When Burford was told to build up the fraction $\frac{2}{3}$ so that the denominator was 9, he gave the following.

$$\frac{2}{3} = \frac{2+6}{3+6} = \frac{8}{9} \qquad \text{Wrong!}$$

What is wrong with Burford's work? What is the correct answer?

6. It might be said that the number $\frac{1}{2}$ has many different names. Explain in your own words what is meant by this statement.

7. Explain what is meant by the term *prime number,* and tell how such numbers are used relative to reducing fractions.

8. Using complete sentences, define what is meant by *a fraction is in lowest terms* and discuss the process of reducing a fraction to lowest terms.

SECTION 1.2 Operations on Fractions

Student guideposts

- ▶ *Division by zero*
- ▶ *Multiplying fractions*
- ▶ *Reciprocals*
- ▶ *Dividing fractions*
- ▶ *Least common denominator*
- ▶ *Adding fractions*
- ▶ *Mixed numbers*
- ▶ *Subtracting fractions*

▶ *Division by zero*

The four basic operations on fractions are addition (+), subtraction (−), multiplication (·), and division (÷ or a fraction bar). We assume that these four operations applied to whole numbers are well understood. Division by zero, however, causes a problem. Why? The quotient of two numbers such as 8 and 2, written $8 \div 2$ or $\frac{8}{2}$, is the number which, when multiplied by 2, equals 8.

That is, $\frac{8}{2} = 4$ because $8 = 2 \cdot 4$.

Similarly, $\frac{20}{4} = 5$ because $20 = 4 \cdot 5$.

If $\frac{20}{0} = (\text{a number})$, then $20 = 0 \cdot (\text{a number})$.

But zero times any number is zero, not 20, so there is no number equal to $\frac{20}{0}$. Since we could have used any number in our example, no number can be divided by zero (except possibly zero itself). What would $\frac{0}{0}$ equal?

$$\frac{0}{0} \text{ could be } 5 \quad \text{since} \quad 0 = 0 \cdot 5$$

$$\frac{0}{0} \text{ could be } 259 \quad \text{since} \quad 0 = 0 \cdot 259$$

$$\frac{0}{0} \text{ could be (any number)} \quad \text{since} \quad 0 \cdot \text{(any number)} = 0$$

Since $\frac{0}{0}$ cannot be determined, we agree never to divide 0 by 0. Thus, *any division by 0 is said to be undefined* and is excluded from mathematics. However, $0 \div 5$ or $\frac{0}{5}$ does make sense, and in fact $\frac{0}{5} = 0$ (why?).

▶ *Multiplying fractions*

We now review the four operations on fractions starting with multiplication.

To Multiply Two (or More) Fractions

1. Factor all numerators and denominators into products of primes.
2. Place all numerator factors over all denominator factors.
3. Divide out or cancel all common factors from both numerator and denominator.
4. Multiply the remaining factors in the numerator and multiply the remaining factors in the denominator.
5. The resulting fraction is the product (reduced to lowest terms) of the original fractions.

EXAMPLE 1

Multiplying Fractions

Multiply.

(a) $\frac{3}{8} \cdot \frac{20}{9} = \frac{3}{2 \cdot 2 \cdot 2} \cdot \frac{2 \cdot 2 \cdot 5}{3 \cdot 3}$ Factor all numerators and denominators

$= \frac{3 \cdot 2 \cdot 2 \cdot 5}{2 \cdot 2 \cdot 2 \cdot 3 \cdot 3}$ All numerator factors over all denominator factors

$= \frac{\not{3} \cdot \not{2} \cdot \not{2} \cdot 5}{\not{2} \cdot \not{2} \cdot 2 \cdot \not{3} \cdot 3}$ Divide out common factors

$= \frac{5}{6}$ Multiply the remaining factors

(b) $\frac{3}{7} \cdot 14 = \frac{3}{7} \cdot \frac{14}{1} = \frac{3}{7} \cdot \frac{2 \cdot 7}{1} = \frac{3 \cdot 2 \cdot \not{7}}{\not{7} \cdot 1} = \frac{6}{1} = 6$ ■

NOTE With practice we can shorten our work by not factoring completely to primes when larger common factors can be recognized. For example, in Example 1 (a) we might multiply as follows:

$$\frac{\overset{1}{\cancel{3}}}{\underset{2}{\cancel{8}}} \cdot \frac{\overset{5}{\cancel{20}}}{\underset{3}{\cancel{9}}} = \frac{5}{6}. \qquad \text{Divide out 4 and 3}$$

▶ *Reciprocals* To divide fractions, we need to understand the idea of a *reciprocal.* The **reciprocal** of a fraction is the fraction formed by interchanging its numerator and denominator. Some fractions and their reciprocals are given in the following table.

Fraction	*Reciprocal*
$\frac{2}{3}$	$\frac{3}{2}$
$\frac{7}{8}$	$\frac{8}{7}$
$5 \left(\text{or } \frac{5}{1}\right)$	$\frac{1}{5}$
$\frac{1}{3}$	$3 \left(\text{or } \frac{3}{1}\right)$

Any fraction multiplied by its reciprocal gives us the number 1. For example,

$$\frac{2}{3} \cdot \frac{3}{2} = 1, \quad \frac{7}{8} \cdot \frac{8}{7} = 1, \quad \frac{5}{1} \cdot \frac{1}{5} = 1, \quad \frac{1}{3} \cdot \frac{3}{1} = 1.$$

▶ *Dividing fractions* When one number is divided by a second, the first is the **dividend,** the second is the **divisor,** and the result is the **quotient.** In $10 \div 2 = 5$, 10 is the dividend, 2 the divisor, and 5 the quotient.

To Divide Two Fractions

1. Replace the divisor with its reciprocal and change the division sign to multiplication.
2. Multiply the fractions.

EXAMPLE 2 **Dividing Fractions**

Divide.

(a) $\frac{13}{15} \div \frac{39}{5} = \frac{13}{15} \cdot \frac{5}{39}$ Replace divisor with its reciprocal and multiply

$= \frac{13}{3 \cdot 5} \cdot \frac{5}{3 \cdot 13}$ Factor

$= \frac{\cancel{13} \cdot \cancel{5}}{3 \cdot \cancel{5} \cdot 3 \cdot \cancel{13}}$ Indicate products and divide out common factors

$= \frac{1}{9}$ A 1, not 0, remains in the numerator

(b) $\frac{4}{5} \div 44 = \frac{4}{5} \cdot \frac{1}{44}$

$= \frac{2 \cdot 2}{5} \cdot \frac{1}{2 \cdot 2 \cdot 11}$

$= \frac{\cancel{2} \cdot \cancel{2} \cdot 1}{5 \cdot \cancel{2} \cdot \cancel{2} \cdot 11} = \frac{1}{55}$

(c) $\frac{3}{7} \div \frac{3}{7} = \frac{3}{7} \cdot \frac{7}{3} = \frac{\cancel{3} \cdot \cancel{7}}{\cancel{7} \cdot \cancel{3}} = \frac{1}{1} = 1$ Does this answer seem reasonable? ■

To add or subtract fractions with the same denominators, add or subtract numerators and place the result over the common denominator. For example,

$$\frac{3}{7} + \frac{5}{7} = \frac{3 + 5}{7} = \frac{8}{7}.$$

> **CAUTION** When adding fractions, we add numerators but *not* denominators.

▶ *Least common denominator*

To add or subtract fractions with different denominators, change the fractions to equivalent fractions having a common denominator. For this it is a good idea to find the **least common denominator (LCD)** of the fractions, that is, the *smallest* number that has both denominators as factors. For example,

$$\frac{1}{2} + \frac{1}{3} \quad \text{can be changed to} \quad \frac{3}{6} + \frac{2}{6}.$$

Here 6 is the least common denominator of $\frac{1}{2}$ and $\frac{1}{3}$ since there is no smaller number that has both 2 and 3 as factors. Notice we could have used 12 or 18 as a common denominator, but 6 is the *least* common denominator.

To Find the LCD of Two (or More) Fractions

1. Factor each denominator into a product of primes.
2. If there are no common factors in the denominators, the LCD is the product of *all* denominators.
3. If there are common factors in the denominators, each factor must appear in the LCD as many times as it appears in the denominator where it is found the *greatest number of times.*

EXAMPLE 3 **Finding the LCD**

Find the LCD of the fractions.

(a) $\frac{1}{6}$ and $\frac{4}{15}$

Factor the denominators: $6 = \overset{1}{2} \cdot \overset{1}{3}$ and $15 = \overset{1}{3} \cdot \overset{1}{5}$. The LCD must consist of **one** 2, **one** 3, and **one** 5. Thus, the LCD $= 2 \cdot 3 \cdot 5 = 30$.

(b) $\frac{13}{90}$ and $\frac{7}{24}$

Factor the denominators: $90 = \overset{1}{2} \cdot \overset{2}{3 \cdot 3} \cdot \overset{1}{5}$ and $24 = \overset{3}{2 \cdot 2 \cdot 2} \cdot \overset{1}{3}$. The LCD must consist of **three** 2's, **two** 3's, and **one** 5. Thus, the LCD $= 2 \cdot 2 \cdot 2 \cdot 3 \cdot 3 \cdot 5 = 360$. ■

NOTE To see why the rule above works, let us look again at the fractions $\frac{1}{6}$ and $\frac{4}{15}$ in Example 3(a). By definition, each denominator must be a factor of the LCD. Since 6 is a factor of the LCD, the LCD must contain the factors 2 and 3. Also, with 15 a factor of the LCD, the LCD must contain the factors 3 and 5. Since we already have 3 as a factor from the denominator 6, we only need to supply the factor 5. Thus,

$$\text{LCD} = 2 \cdot 3 \cdot 5 = 30,$$

which is what we found in Example 3(a) using the rule above.

▶ *Adding fractions* We now use the LCD to add fractions with different denominators.

To Add Two (or More) Fractions with Different Denominators

1. Rewrite the sum with each denominator expressed as a product of primes.
2. Find the LCD.
3. Multiply the numerators and denominators of each fraction by all those factors present in the LCD but missing in the denominator of the particular fraction.
4. Place the sum of all numerators over the LCD.
5. Simplify the resulting numerator and reduce the fraction to lowest terms.

EXAMPLE 4 **Adding Fractions**

Add.

(a) $\frac{5}{6} + \frac{7}{15} = \frac{5}{2 \cdot 3} + \frac{7}{3 \cdot 5}$ Factor denominators the LCD is $2 \cdot 3 \cdot 5$

$= \frac{5 \cdot 5}{2 \cdot 3 \cdot 5} + \frac{7 \cdot 2}{3 \cdot 5 \cdot 2}$ Multiply numerators and denominators by missing factors

$= \frac{25 + 14}{2 \cdot 3 \cdot 5}$ Simplify and add over LCD

$= \frac{39}{2 \cdot 3 \cdot 5}$ Simplify

$= \frac{\not{3} \cdot 13}{2 \cdot \not{3} \cdot 5}$ Factor numerator and divide out common factors

$= \frac{13}{10}$ The desired sum

(b) $\frac{1}{2} + \frac{5}{6} + \frac{7}{25}$

$= \frac{1}{2} + \frac{5}{2 \cdot 3} + \frac{7}{5 \cdot 5}$ Factor: the LCD $= 2 \cdot 3 \cdot 5 \cdot 5$

$= \frac{1 \cdot 3 \cdot 5 \cdot 5}{2 \cdot 3 \cdot 5 \cdot 5} + \frac{5 \cdot 5 \cdot 5}{2 \cdot 3 \cdot 5 \cdot 5} + \frac{7 \cdot 2 \cdot 3}{5 \cdot 5 \cdot 2 \cdot 3}$ Multiply numerators and denominators by missing factors

$= \frac{75 + 125 + 42}{2 \cdot 3 \cdot 5 \cdot 5}$ Simplify and add over LCD

$= \frac{242}{2 \cdot 3 \cdot 5 \cdot 5}$ Simplify

$= \frac{\not{2} \cdot 11 \cdot 11}{\not{2} \cdot 3 \cdot 5 \cdot 5}$ Factor numerator and divide out common factors

$= \frac{121}{75}$ The desired sum ■

▶ *Mixed numbers* It is sometimes helpful to write an improper fraction, such as $\frac{121}{75}$, as a *mixed number.* A **mixed number** is the sum of a whole number and a proper fraction. For example,

$$\frac{121}{75} \text{ can be written as } 1 + \frac{46}{75} \text{ or } 1\frac{46}{75}.$$

This is read ‘‘one and forty-six seventy-fifths.’’

> NOTE To change an improper fraction to a mixed number, reduce the fraction to lowest terms and divide the denominator into the numerator. The quotient is the whole number part of the mixed number, and the fractional part is the remainder over the divisor.

EXAMPLE 5

Changing an Improper Fraction to a Mixed Number

Change each improper fraction to a mixed number.

(a) $\dfrac{13}{4}$

Divide 4 into 13.

$$\begin{array}{r} 3 \\ 4\overline{)13} \\ \underline{12} \\ 1 \end{array} \begin{array}{l} \leftarrow \text{Whole number} \\ \\ \\ \leftarrow \text{Numerator of fraction} \end{array}$$

The mixed number is $3\frac{1}{4}$, read "three and one-fourth."

(b) $\dfrac{27}{6}$

Reduce $\frac{27}{6}$ to lowest terms and then divide.

$$\frac{27}{6} = \frac{9 \cdot \not{3}}{2 \cdot \not{3}} = \frac{9}{2} \qquad \begin{array}{r} 4 \\ 2\overline{)9} \\ \underline{8} \\ 1 \end{array}$$

Thus, $\frac{27}{6} = 4\frac{1}{2}$. ■

To change a mixed number to an improper fraction, we can think of the mixed number as a sum of two fractions. For example, the mixed number $2\frac{11}{18} = 2 + \frac{11}{18}$. Adding, we have

$$\frac{2}{1} + \frac{11}{18} = \frac{2}{1} + \frac{11}{2 \cdot 3 \cdot 3} = \frac{2 \cdot 2 \cdot 3 \cdot 3}{2 \cdot 3 \cdot 3} + \frac{11}{2 \cdot 3 \cdot 3} = \frac{36 + 11}{2 \cdot 3 \cdot 3} = \frac{47}{18}.$$

Rather than going through all of these steps, we can use a shortcut. Consider $2\frac{11}{18}$ again. Notice that if we multiply the denominator, 18, by the whole number, 2, and add the numerator, 11, we obtain

$$(18 \cdot 2) + 11 = 47.$$

When we put this result over the denominator, 18, we have the desired improper fraction $\frac{47}{18}$. We can show this as

$$\frac{(\textbf{denominator} \times \textbf{whole number}) + \textbf{numerator}}{\textbf{denominator}}.$$

EXAMPLE 6 **Changing a Mixed Number to an Improper Fraction**

Change each mixed number to an improper fraction.

(a) $$4\frac{3}{5} = \frac{(5 \cdot 4) + 3}{5} = \frac{20 + 3}{5} = \frac{23}{5}$$

(b) $$6\frac{7}{10} = \frac{(10 \cdot 6) + 7}{10} = \frac{60 + 7}{10} = \frac{67}{10}$$ ■

To add two or more mixed numbers or mixed numbers and proper fractions, convert all mixed numbers to improper fractions and proceed as before.

EXAMPLE 7 **Adding Mixed Numbers**

Add.

$$3\frac{1}{4} + 6\frac{7}{10} + \frac{1}{3} = \frac{13}{4} + \frac{67}{10} + \frac{1}{3}$$ Convert to improper fractions

$$= \frac{13}{2 \cdot 2} + \frac{67}{2 \cdot 5} + \frac{1}{3}$$ The LCD = $2 \cdot 2 \cdot 3 \cdot 5$

$$= \frac{13 \cdot 3 \cdot 5}{2 \cdot 2 \cdot 3 \cdot 5} + \frac{67 \cdot 2 \cdot 3}{2 \cdot 5 \cdot 2 \cdot 3} + \frac{1 \cdot 2 \cdot 2 \cdot 5}{3 \cdot 2 \cdot 2 \cdot 5}$$

$$= \frac{195 + 402 + 20}{2 \cdot 2 \cdot 3 \cdot 5}$$

$$= \frac{617}{60} \text{ or } 10\frac{17}{60}$$ ■

▶ *Subtracting fractions* The fourth operation we consider is subtraction.

To Subtract Two Fractions

1. Rewrite the difference with each denominator expressed as a product of prime factors.
2. Find the LCD.
3. Supply missing factors just as when adding.
4. Place the difference of the numerators over the LCD.
5. Simplify the resulting numerator and reduce the fraction to lowest terms.

EXAMPLE 8

Subtracting Fractions

Subtract.

(a) $\frac{7}{12} - \frac{5}{9} = \frac{7}{2 \cdot 2 \cdot 3} - \frac{5}{3 \cdot 3}$ Factor; LCD is $2 \cdot 2 \cdot 3 \cdot 3$

$= \frac{7 \cdot 3}{2 \cdot 2 \cdot 3 \cdot 3} - \frac{5 \cdot 2 \cdot 2}{3 \cdot 3 \cdot 2 \cdot 2}$ Supply missing factors

$= \frac{21 - 20}{2 \cdot 2 \cdot 3 \cdot 3}$ Subtract and simplify

$= \frac{1}{36}$ The difference in reduced form

(b) $4\frac{1}{2} - 3\frac{7}{8}$

First convert the mixed numbers to improper fractions.

$$4\frac{1}{2} - 3\frac{7}{8} = \frac{9}{2} - \frac{31}{8} = \frac{9 \cdot 4}{2 \cdot 4} - \frac{31}{8} = \frac{36 - 31}{8} = \frac{5}{8}$$ ■

NOTE In Example 8(b) we took a shortcut and did not factor denominators into primes. It was clear that the LCD of the two fractions is 8, so we simply supplied the factor of 4 to both numerator and denominator of $\frac{9}{2}$. With practice, shortcuts such as this can save time.

The rules for adding and subtracting fractions can be extended to include combinations of these operations, as shown in the next example.

EXAMPLE 9

Combining Operations

Perform the indicated operations.

$2\frac{1}{15} + 4\frac{1}{5} - 3\frac{1}{2}$

$= \frac{31}{15} + \frac{21}{5} - \frac{7}{2}$ Convert to improper fractions

$= \frac{31}{3 \cdot 5} + \frac{21}{5} - \frac{7}{2}$ The LCD $= 2 \cdot 3 \cdot 5$

$= \frac{31 \cdot 2}{3 \cdot 5 \cdot 2} + \frac{21 \cdot 2 \cdot 3}{5 \cdot 2 \cdot 3} - \frac{7 \cdot 3 \cdot 5}{2 \cdot 3 \cdot 5}$ Supply missing factors

$= \frac{62 + 126 - 105}{2 \cdot 3 \cdot 5}$

$= \frac{83}{30}$ or $2\frac{23}{30}$ ■

Many applications involve mixed numbers.

EXAMPLE 10 **Solving a Retailing Problem**

The Fine Fabric Shop had $3\frac{1}{4}$ yards of an expensive fabric and sold $1\frac{1}{2}$ yards. How much of the fabric was left?

We just subtract $1\frac{1}{2}$ yards from $3\frac{1}{4}$ yards to find the number of yards left. First we convert the mixed numbers to fractions.

$$3\frac{1}{4} = \frac{3 \cdot 4 + 1}{4} = \frac{13}{4}$$

$$1\frac{1}{2} = \frac{1 \cdot 2 + 1}{2} = \frac{3}{2}$$

To find the material left we subtract $\frac{3}{2}$ from $\frac{13}{4}$.

$$\frac{13}{4} - \frac{3}{2} = \frac{13}{2 \cdot 2} - \frac{3 \cdot 2}{2 \cdot 2} = \frac{13 - 6}{4} = \frac{7}{4} = 1\frac{3}{4}$$

Thus, $1\frac{3}{4}$ yards of material remain. ■

1.2 EXERCISES

1. $\frac{0}{3} =$ ______
2. $\frac{3}{0} =$ ______
3. $\frac{0}{0} =$ ______

Multiply in Exercises 4–6.

4. $\frac{1}{3} \cdot \frac{6}{5}$
5. $4\frac{2}{5} \cdot \frac{3}{11}$
6. $2\frac{2}{3} \cdot 1\frac{1}{8} \cdot \frac{1}{6}$

Divide in Exercises 7–9.

7. $\frac{3}{7} \div \frac{9}{28}$
8. $\frac{\frac{20}{9}}{\frac{2}{3}}$
9. $3\frac{1}{3} \div 1\frac{3}{5}$

Find the LCD of the fractions in Exercises 10–12.

10. $\frac{2}{7}$ and $\frac{4}{33}$
11. 7 and $\frac{9}{2}$
12. $\frac{1}{9}$, $\frac{5}{6}$, and $\frac{1}{75}$

Add in Exercises 13–15.

13. $4 + \frac{3}{5}$
14. $2\frac{1}{5} + 1\frac{2}{3}$
15. $\frac{2}{3} + \frac{1}{6} + \frac{3}{4}$

Change each improper fraction to a mixed number in Exercises 16–18.

16. $\frac{23}{8}$
17. $\frac{135}{4}$
18. $\frac{142}{11}$

Change each mixed number to an improper fraction in Exercises 19–21.

19. $4\frac{2}{5}$ **20.** $66\frac{2}{3}$ **21.** $9\frac{7}{11}$

Subtract in Exercises 22–24.

22. $\frac{19}{2} - 3$ **23.** $5\frac{1}{3} - 2\frac{3}{4}$ **24.** $11\frac{4}{5} - 5\frac{2}{3}$

Perform the indicated operations in Exercises 25–27.

25. $\frac{7}{20} + \frac{3}{8} - \frac{1}{4}$ **26.** $\frac{14}{15} - \frac{2}{5} - \frac{1}{3}$ **27.** $\frac{7}{3} + \frac{1}{7} - 2$

28. A piece of rope 20 m long is to be cut into pieces, each of whose length is $\frac{2}{3}$ m. How many pieces can be cut?

29. A fuel tank holds $12\frac{1}{2}$ gallons when it is $\frac{3}{4}$ full. What is the capacity of the tank?

30. Alphonso hiked from Whiskey Creek to Bald Mountain, a distance of $2\frac{1}{3}$ mi. From there he hiked to Spook Hollow, a distance of $4\frac{1}{5}$ mi. How far did he hike?

31. To get the right shade of paint for her living room, Tracy Bell mixed $\frac{7}{8}$ of a gallon of yellow paint with $\frac{2}{3}$ of a gallon of light blue paint. How much paint did she have?

32. The weight of one cubic foot of water is $62\frac{1}{2}$ lb. How much do $3\frac{1}{5}$ cubic feet of water weigh?

33. Fahrenheit temperature can be found by multiplying Celsius temperature by $\frac{9}{5}$ and adding 32°. If Celsius temperature is 15°, what is Fahrenheit temperature?

FOR REVIEW

34. Write an equivalent fraction for $\frac{7}{8}$ with **(a)** 21 for the numerator and **(b)** 72 for the denominator.

35. Max received $125 for doing a particular job. If he had to pay $15 for income tax, what fractional part of the $125 went for tax?

1.2 PARALLEL EXERCISES

1. $\frac{7}{0} =$ _____ **2.** $\frac{0}{0} =$ _____ **3.** $\frac{0}{7} =$ _____

Multiply in Exercises 4–6.

4. $\frac{11}{4} \cdot 8$ **5.** $4\frac{4}{5} \cdot \frac{1}{12}$ **6.** $1\frac{1}{3} \cdot 3\frac{3}{8} \cdot \frac{2}{3}$

Divide in Exercises 7–9.

7. $\frac{2}{7} \div \frac{6}{28}$ **8.** $\dfrac{\frac{15}{8}}{\frac{3}{4}}$ **9.** $2\frac{2}{3} \div 1\frac{1}{5}$

Find the LCD of the fractions in Exercises 10–12.

10. $\frac{5}{12}$ and $\frac{2}{27}$ **11.** $\frac{1}{3}, \frac{3}{4}$, and $\frac{2}{7}$ **12.** $\frac{1}{6}, \frac{5}{9}$, and $\frac{7}{30}$

Add in Exercises 13–15.

13. $\frac{1}{8} + 2$ **14.** $4\frac{1}{5} + 2\frac{1}{3}$ **15.** $\frac{1}{3} + \frac{5}{6} + \frac{1}{5}$

Change each improper fraction to a mixed number in Exercises 16–18.

16. $\frac{81}{10}$ **17.** $\frac{245}{9}$ **18.** $\frac{167}{11}$

Change each mixed number to an improper fraction in Exercises 19–21.

19. $10\frac{1}{5}$ **20.** $42\frac{3}{10}$ **21.** $8\frac{4}{11}$

Subtract in Exercises 22–24.

22. $5 - \frac{1}{9}$ **23.** $6\frac{2}{3} - 1\frac{3}{4}$ **24.** $11\frac{3}{5} - 4\frac{1}{3}$

Perform the indicated operations in Exercises 25–27.

25. $\frac{9}{20} + \frac{5}{8} - \frac{3}{4}$ **26.** $\frac{13}{15} - \frac{1}{5} - \frac{1}{3}$ **27.** $\frac{8}{3} + \frac{2}{7} - 2$

28. When Fred Vickers pounds a nail into a board, he sinks it $1\frac{1}{4}$ inches with each blow. How many times will he have to hit a 5-in nail to drive it completely into the board?

29. After driving 285 miles, the Stotts had completed $\frac{5}{8}$ of their trip. What was the total length of the trip?

30. In July, Memphis had two rain storms, one that dropped $1\frac{1}{4}$ in of rain and another that dropped $\frac{3}{5}$ in. How much rain did Memphis receive in July?

31. It took Burford $8\frac{1}{2}$ hr to fix his car himself. If he had had the money, he could have hired a mechanic to do the job in $1\frac{1}{3}$ hr. How many hours of work could Burford have saved?

32. Cindy Brown is paid $4\frac{1}{2}$ dollars per hr to type a manuscript. If she types for a period of $20\frac{2}{3}$ hr, how much is she paid?

33. Celsius temperature can be found by subtracting 32° from Fahrenheit temperature and multiplying the result by $\frac{5}{9}$. If Fahrenheit temperature is 122°, what is the corresponding Celsius temperature?

FOR REVIEW

34. Write an equivalent fraction for $\frac{8}{9}$ with **(a)** 32 as the numerator, and **(b)** 81 as the denominator.
35. A farmer collected 280 bushels of grain from his field. If he had to give 40 bushels to his landlord for rent, what fractional part of the 280 bushels went for rent?

1.2 ENRICHMENT EXERCISES

Perform the indicated operations in Exercises 1–3.

△ **1.** $22\frac{5}{8} + 17\frac{3}{10} - 8\frac{3}{4}$ **2.** $42\frac{7}{15} - 18\frac{5}{6} - 11\frac{3}{10}$ **3.** $125\frac{16}{25} + 37\frac{2}{15} - 83\frac{7}{20}$

Exercises 4–5 show Burford's work on two problems involving operations with fractions. What is wrong with his work? What is the correct answer to each?

4. $\frac{2}{7} + \frac{4}{5} = \frac{2+4}{7+5} = \frac{6}{12} = \frac{1}{2}$ △ **5.** $\frac{1}{2} \cdot \frac{4}{6} = \frac{3}{6} \cdot \frac{4}{6} = \frac{3 \cdot 4}{6 \cdot 6} = \frac{12}{36} = \frac{1}{3}$

6. In Chicago, the Chess Cab Company charges \$2.15 for the first half mile and \$0.75 for each additional half mile. If John Lenchek took a cab from his hotel to a restaurant 4 miles away, gave the driver a \$10.00 bill telling him to keep the change, how much did John tip the driver?

7. Explain the difference between multiplying fractions and dividing fractions.

8. In your own words, explain the method for adding two fractions.

9. Discuss how to change a mixed number into an improper fraction, and how to change an improper fraction into a mixed number.

SECTION 1.3 Decimals

Student guideposts

▶ *Place-value number system*
▶ *Decimal notation*
▶ *Operations on decimals*

▶ *Place-value number system*

Remember that our number system is a **place-value system.** That is, each **digit** (0, 1, 2, 3, 4, 5, 6, 7, 8, or 9) in a numeral has a particular value determined by its location or place in the symbol. For example, the numeral

$$125.378$$

is a shorthand symbol for the **expanded numeral**

$$100 + 20 + 5 + \frac{3}{10} + \frac{7}{100} + \frac{8}{1000},$$

or

$$1 \cdot 100 + 2 \cdot 10 + 5 \cdot 1 + 3 \cdot \frac{1}{10} + 7 \cdot \frac{1}{100} + 8 \cdot \frac{1}{1000},$$

where each of the digits, 1, 2, 5, 3, 7, and 8 is multiplied by 100, 10, 1, $\frac{1}{10}$, $\frac{1}{100}$, or $\frac{1}{1000}$, depending upon the location of the digit in the symbol 125.378. We read 125.378 as "one hundred twenty-five *and* three hundred seventy-eight thousandths." This results from thinking of the number as a mixed number

$$125 + \frac{378}{1000}, \quad \text{or} \quad 125\frac{378}{1000}.$$

▶ *Decimal notation*

The numeral 125.378, representing the mixed number $125\frac{378}{1000}$, is in **decimal notation,** and numbers expressed in this manner are referred to simply as **decimals.** Decimal notation is based on the number 10, and the period used in a decimal is the **decimal point.** If there are no digits to the right of the decimal point we usually omit it; we write 53 rather than 53., for example. The diagram below gives the value of each position. Notice that the decimal point separates the ones digit from the tenths digit.

Hundreds	Tens	Ones	Decimal Point	Tenths	Hundredths	Thousandths
1	2	5	.	3	7	8

The following table expresses each decimal in expanded notation, as a mixed number, and as a proper or improper fraction.

Decimal	*Expanded Notation*	*Mixed Number*	*Fraction*
1.25	$1 + \frac{2}{10} + \frac{5}{100}$	$1\frac{25}{100}$	$\frac{125}{100}$
23.46	$20 + 3 + \frac{4}{10} + \frac{6}{100}$	$23\frac{46}{100}$	$\frac{2346}{100}$
43.278	$40 + 3 + \frac{2}{10} + \frac{7}{100} + \frac{8}{1000}$	$43\frac{278}{1000}$	$\frac{43{,}278}{1000}$
562.34	$500 + 60 + 2 + \frac{3}{10} + \frac{4}{100}$	$562\frac{34}{100}$	$\frac{56{,}234}{100}$
0.23	$\frac{2}{10} + \frac{3}{100}$	$0\frac{23}{100}$	$\frac{23}{100}$
47 or 47.0	$40 + 7$ or $40 + 7 + \frac{0}{10}$	47 or $47\frac{0}{10}$	$\frac{47}{1}$ or $\frac{470}{10}$

▶ *Operations on decimals*

We have already reviewed the operations of adding, subtracting, multiplying, and dividing numbers in fractional notation. Now we review these operations when the numbers are in decimal notation.

To Add Two (or More) Decimals

1. Arrange the numbers in a column so that the decimal points line up vertically.
2. Add in columns from right to left as if there were no decimal points.
3. Place the decimal point in the sum in line with the other decimal points.

EXAMPLE 1

Adding Decimals

Add.

(a)
```
   21.3
+   4.2
   ----
   25.5
```

(b)
```
  123.417
   45.
+   1.14
  -------
  169.557
```
■

NOTE Obviously, with the availability of a calculator, most decimal operations will be performed on it. However, it is important to review the mechanics of the operations since, for example, lining up numbers in the appropriate columns has a direct relationship to operating on algebraic expressions later.

To Subtract Two Decimals

1. Arrange the numbers in a column so that the decimal points line up vertically.
2. Subtract in columns from right to left as if there were no decimal points. (Additional zeros may be placed to the right of the decimal points if desired.)
3. Place the decimal point in the difference in line with the other decimal points.

EXAMPLE 2

Subtracting Decimals

Subtract.

(a)
```
   27.5
-   2.4
   ----
   25.1
```

(b)
```
  421.3000
-   8.9999
  --------
  412.3001
```

(In (b), the three zeros to the right of 3 have been supplied.) ■

We will agree to say that 42.7 has *one decimal place,* 12.16 has *two decimal places,* 5.006 has *three decimal places,* and so forth.

To Multiply Two Decimals

1. Ignore the decimal points and multiply as if the numbers were whole numbers.
2. Place the decimal point so the product has the same number of decimal places as the *sum* of the number of decimal places in the factors.

EXAMPLE 3

Multiplying Decimals

Multiply.

(a)

1.23	2 decimal places
× 2.1	1 decimal place
123	
246	
2.583	2 + 1 = 3 decimal places

(b) (0.02)(0.013) = 0.00026 5 decimal places ■

NOTE In Example 3(b), multiplication was indicated without using the multiplication sign ×. This is common notation in algebra.

To Divide One Decimal into Another

1. Move the decimal point in the divisor (the dividing number) to the right until the divisor becomes a whole number.
2. Move the decimal point in the dividend (the number divided into) to the right the same number of places adding zeros as necessary.
3. Divide as if the numbers were whole numbers.
4. Place the decimal point in the quotient directly above the decimal point in the dividend.

EXAMPLE 4

Dividing Decimals

Divide.

(a) $0.12\overline{)14.4}$

$0.12\overline{)14.40}$ (decimal point moved 2 places in each) becomes

$$\begin{array}{r} 120 \\ 12\overline{)1440} \\ \underline{12} \\ 24 \\ \underline{24} \\ 0 \end{array}$$

(b) $0.003\overline{)42.3}$

$0.003\overline{)42.300}$ becomes $\begin{array}{r} 14{,}100 \\ 3\overline{)42{,}300} \end{array}$ ■

(decimal moved 3 places in divisor and 3 places in dividend)

> NOTE Again, we need to know how to operate on decimals since these techniques are used often in algebra. However, using a calculator can eliminate much of the tedious, time-consuming work with decimal operations. If you have a calculator, be sure to read the instruction manual that comes with your model. You might use a calculator to check part of your work in some of the following exercises.

1.3 EXERCISES

Express in expanded notation in Exercises 1–3.

1. 3.47 **2.** 107.28 **3.** 203.005

Express in decimal notation in Exercises 4–6.

4. $400 + 20 + 7 + \frac{3}{10}$ **5.** $500 + 3 + \frac{2}{10} + \frac{8}{1000}$ **6.** $4000 + 30 + \frac{2}{100} + \frac{5}{1000}$

Add in Exercises 7–9.

7. $\begin{array}{r} 31.4 \\ +\ 1.07 \\ \hline \end{array}$ **8.** $\begin{array}{r} 403.1 \\ +\ 21.08 \\ \hline \end{array}$ **9.** $15.0001 + 9.3 + 0.004$

Subtract in Exercises 10–12.

10. $\begin{array}{r} 4.0003 \\ -\ 1.1 \\ \hline \end{array}$ **11.** $\begin{array}{r} 427.006 \\ -\ 135.04 \\ \hline \end{array}$ **12.** $47.2 - 0.0003$

Multiply in Exercises 13–15.

13. $\begin{array}{r} 3.42 \\ \times\ 2.1 \\ \hline \end{array}$ **14.** $\begin{array}{r} 15.207 \\ \times\ 3.12 \\ \hline \end{array}$ **15.** $(0.02)(0.02)(0.02)$

Divide in Exercises 16–18.

16. $0.007\overline{)38.717}$ **17.** $8\overline{)7.0}$ **18.** $9\overline{)1.0}$

19. Before leaving on a trip, Harley's odometer read 23,411.8. If he drove 723.9 mi on the trip, what did it read when he returned?

20. The Northern Arizona four-mile relay team members recorded times of 4.23, 4.17, 3.99, and 4.08 minutes. What was their combined time for the race?

21. Roseanne Strauch buys a pair of hose for \$3.95. If she pays with a \$20 bill and the sales tax amounts to \$0.20, how much change should she receive?

22. When Kimmie was sick, she ran a temperature of 103.2° Fahrenheit. If normal body temperature is 98.6° Fahrenheit, how many degrees above normal was her temperature?

23. Jose is paid \$7.35 per hr. If he worked a total of 35.2 hr last week, how much was he paid?

24. How many months will it take to pay off a loan of \$6562.80 if the monthly payments are \$182.30?

FOR REVIEW

Perform the indicated operations in Exercises 25–28.

25. $\frac{2}{9}+\frac{5}{12}$ 26. $\frac{23}{36}-\frac{4}{9}$ 27. $\frac{3}{4}\cdot\frac{16}{27}$ 28. $1\frac{1}{12}\div 9\frac{3}{4}$

29. Nancy Chandler plans a two-day hike from Gopher Gulch to Aspen Glen by way of North Face. It is $7\frac{3}{4}$ mi from Gopher Gulch to North Face and $9\frac{1}{8}$ mi from there to Aspen Glen. If she plans to travel half the total distance on each day, how far will she hike on the first day?

30. Julio has a rope $26\frac{2}{3}$ meters in length. He wishes to cut the rope into 3 pieces of equal length. What will be the length of each piece?

1.3 PARALLEL EXERCISES

Express in expanded notation in Exercises 1–3.

1. 35.6 2. 257.663 3. 3215.802

Express in decimal notation in Exercises 4–6.

4. $700+30+8+\frac{6}{10}$ 5. $4000+6+\frac{7}{100}$ 6. $300+40+\frac{2}{100}+\frac{7}{1000}$

Add in Exercises 7–9.

7. $\begin{array}{r} 52.3 \\ +\ 2.09 \\ \hline \end{array}$ 8. $\begin{array}{r} 602.9 \\ +\ 43.07 \\ \hline \end{array}$ 9. $12.0003+7.2+0.003$

Subtract in Exercises 10–12.

10. $\begin{array}{r} 6.0004 \\ -\ 2.3 \\ \hline \end{array}$ 11. $\begin{array}{r} 637.008 \\ -\ 123.05 \\ \hline \end{array}$ 12. $39.4-0.0006$

Multiply in Exercises 13–15.

13. $\begin{array}{r} 2.91 \\ \times\ 3.4 \\ \hline \end{array}$ 14. $\begin{array}{r} 17.603 \\ \times\ 4.15 \\ \hline \end{array}$ 15. (0.0002)(0.00002)

Divide in Exercises 16–18.

16. $4.2\overline{)94.5}$ 17. $30.1\overline{)6.52267}$ 18. $4\overline{)1.0}$

19. The Saturday and Sunday receipts at Waldo's Waffle Palace were \$621.13 and \$743.19, respectively. How much money did Waldo take in on that weekend?

20. What is the **perimeter** of (the distance around) a four-sided figure with sides of 6.031 m, 5.411 m, 4.003 m, and 5.772 m?

21. Sam Passamonte had a balance of \$635.86 in his checking account when he wrote a check for \$249.93. What was his new balance?

22. When George filled the gas tank on his Bronco, the odometer read 62,421.8. The next time he filled it, the odometer read 62,914.2. How far had he driven?

23. Betty Sue bought 13.4 pounds of peaches at \$0.55 per pound. How much did she pay for the peaches?

24. Kate Williams paid \$58.00 to rent a car for two days. If the rental fee amounts to \$12.50 per day plus \$0.15 per mile driven, how far did she drive the car?

FOR REVIEW

Perform the indicated operations in Exercises 25–28.

25. $\frac{12}{15} + \frac{8}{35}$ **26.** $\frac{13}{24} - \frac{3}{8}$ **27.** $1\frac{2}{3} \cdot 4\frac{1}{5}$ **28.** $\frac{6}{5} \div \frac{24}{45}$

29. A wheel on a child's car is turning at a rate of $40\frac{1}{2}$ revolutions per minute. If the car is driven for $3\frac{1}{9}$ minutes, how many revolutions does the wheel make?

30. Marguerite is proofing a computer program that is $14\frac{1}{3}$ pages in length. If she has completed $10\frac{1}{5}$ pages, how much remains to be done?

1.3 ENRICHMENT EXERCISES

Perform the indicated operation in Exercises 1–2. A calculator would be useful for these problems.

1.
```
    374.26
  × 8.603
```

2. $0.0257\overline{)0.02584392}$

Find the error in Burford's work in Exercises 3–4. What is the correct answer?

3.
```
    4.21
  × 3.5
    2105
    1263
   3.368
```

4.
```
        2.14
  3.8)81.32
      76
       5 3
       3 8
       1 52
       1 52
          0
```

5. Use estimation to approximate the answers in Exercises 3–4. Can you see from these estimations that the answers that Burford obtained must be wrong? Explain.

6. Using complete sentences, explain why moving the decimal point in the divisor right until we have a whole number, then moving the decimal point in the dividend the same number of places, is an appropriate procedure when dividing decimals. [*Hint:* Try writing the division problem as a fraction and use the fundamental principle of fractions.]

SECTION 1.4 Converting Fractions, Decimals, and Percents

Student guideposts

- *Converting fractions to decimals*
- *Rational and irrational numbers*
- *Converting terminating decimals to fractions*
- *Conversions involving percent*

▶ *Converting fractions to decimals*

Every fraction can be converted to a decimal. Several problems in the previous section gave a preview of this process.

To Convert a Fraction to a Decimal

1. Divide the denominator of the fraction into the numerator.
2. Place the decimal point as in any decimal division problem.

EXAMPLE 1

Converting a Fraction to a Decimal

Convert each fraction to a decimal.

(a) $\frac{3}{20}$ We divide 20 into 3 as follows:

$$\begin{array}{r} .15 \\ 20\overline{)3.00} \\ \underline{2\,0} \\ 1\,00 \\ \underline{1\,00} \\ 0 \end{array} \qquad \frac{3}{20} = 0.15$$

(b) $\frac{1}{3}$

$$\begin{array}{r} .333\ldots \\ 3\overline{)1.000} \\ \underline{9} \\ 10 \\ \underline{9} \\ 10 \\ \underline{9} \\ 1 \end{array}$$

It is clear that we will continue to obtain "3" on each division. When this happens we write $\frac{1}{3} = 0.333\ldots = 0.\overline{3}$, where the bar denotes the digit (sometimes digits) that continues to repeat. For the mixed decimal number $3\frac{1}{3}$ we write $3.\overline{3}$ (not $\overline{3}$).

(c) $\frac{2}{7}$

$$\begin{array}{r} .285714285714\ldots \\ 7\overline{)2.000000000000} \end{array}$$

$$\begin{aligned} \frac{2}{7} &= 0.285714285714\ldots \\ &= 0.\overline{285714} \quad \blacksquare \end{aligned}$$

It is a property of every fraction that in decimal notation, the digits after the decimal either terminate, as in

$$\frac{1}{2} = 0.5, \qquad \frac{3}{20} = 0.15, \qquad \frac{13}{40} = 0.325,$$

or contain a block of digits that repeats without ending, as in

$$\frac{1}{3} = 0.\overline{3}, \qquad \frac{2}{7} = 0.\overline{285714}, \qquad \frac{2}{3} = 0.\overline{6}.$$

Rational and irrational numbers

It is also true that if a number has a decimal representation that terminates or repeats, the number can always be expressed as a fraction. This fact is often used to define the set of **rational numbers** or fractions. The rational numbers include all of the numbers we have considered thus far. Numbers that are not rational numbers, called **irrational numbers,** have decimal representations that neither terminate nor repeat. One of the most famous irrational numbers is π (the ratio of the circumference of a circle to its diameter). Rational and irrational numbers are discussed in more detail in Chapter 2.

Converting terminating decimals to fractions

We now turn our attention to converting a terminating decimal to a fraction. For example,

$$0.5 \quad \text{is} \quad \frac{5}{10},$$

$$0.23 \quad \text{is} \quad \frac{2}{10} + \frac{3}{100} = \frac{20}{100} + \frac{3}{100} = \frac{23}{100},$$

$$0.537 \quad \text{is} \quad \frac{5}{10} + \frac{3}{100} + \frac{7}{1000} = \frac{500}{1000} + \frac{30}{1000} + \frac{7}{1000} = \frac{537}{1000}.$$

To Convert a Terminating Decimal to a Fraction

1. Express the decimal in expanded notation.
2. Add the whole number terms and add the fractional terms to obtain a mixed number.
3. Convert the mixed number to a single fraction by addition.

EXAMPLE 2

Converting a Decimal to a Fraction

Convert each decimal to a fraction.

(a) $0.47 = \frac{4}{10} + \frac{7}{100} = \frac{40}{100} + \frac{7}{100} = \frac{47}{100}$

(b) $2.35 = 2 + \frac{3}{10} + \frac{5}{100} = 2 + \frac{30}{100} + \frac{5}{100}$

$= 2 + \frac{35}{100} = \frac{2 \cdot 100}{100} + \frac{35}{100} = \frac{235}{100}$

(c) $43.619 = 40 + 3 + \frac{6}{10} + \frac{1}{100} + \frac{9}{1000} = 43 + \frac{619}{1000} = \frac{43{,}619}{1000}$ ■

▶ *Conversions involving percent*

The concept *percent* is closely related to decimals and is used in a variety of applied problems. The word **percent** literally means *per hundred;* it refers to the number of parts in one hundred parts. A five percent tax means five parts per one hundred parts, or a tax of 5¢ on every 100¢. Five percent would be written

$$5\%.$$

Since the % symbol means "divide by 100" or "multiply by $\frac{1}{100} = 0.01$,"

$$5\% = 5(0.01) = 0.05 \quad \text{or} \quad 5\% = \frac{5}{100} = \frac{1}{20}.$$

To Convert a Percent to a Decimal

Remove the % symbol and multiply by 0.01. Or remove the % symbol and move the decimal point two places to the *left,* adding zeros as necessary.

To Convert a Percent to a Fraction

Remove the % symbol and divide by 100. Reduce the resulting fraction to lowest terms.

EXAMPLE 3

Converting Percent to a Decimal

Convert each percent to a decimal.

(a) $43\% = (43)(0.01) = 0.43$ $\qquad 43\% = 0.43$

(b) $325.5\% = (325.5)(0.01) = 3.255$ $\qquad 325.5\% = 3.255$

(c) $0.05\% = (0.05)(0.01) = 0.0005$ $\qquad 0.05\% = 0.0005$

(d) $0.2\% = (0.2)(0.01) = 0.002$ $\qquad 0.2\% = 0.002$ ■

EXAMPLE 4

Converting Percent to a Fraction

Convert each percent to a fraction.

(a) $28\% = \frac{28}{100} = \frac{\not{4} \cdot 7}{\not{4} \cdot 25} = \frac{7}{25}$

(b) $37.5\% = \frac{37.5}{100} = \frac{(37.5)(10)}{(100)(10)}$ Clear decimal by multiplying by 10

$$= \frac{375}{1000}$$

$$= \frac{3 \cdot \cancel{125}}{8 \cdot \cancel{125}}$$

$$= \frac{3}{8}$$ Reduce fraction

(c) $66\frac{2}{3}\% = \left(66\frac{2}{3}\right)\left(\frac{1}{100}\right)$ Dividing by 100 is the same as multiplying by $\frac{1}{100}$

$= \left(\frac{200}{3}\right)\left(\frac{1}{100}\right)$ $66\frac{2}{3} = \frac{(3 \cdot 66) + 2}{3} = \frac{200}{3}$

$= \frac{2 \cdot \cancel{100}}{3 \cdot \cancel{100}} = \frac{2}{3}$ Reduce fraction

(d) $100\% = \frac{100}{100} = 1$ ■

To Convert a Decimal to a Percent

Multiply by 100 and attach the % symbol. Or move the decimal point two places to the *right,* adding zeros as necessary, and attach the % symbol.

To Convert a Fraction to a Percent

Convert the fraction to a decimal by dividing the numerator by the denominator. Then change the resulting decimal to a percent.

EXAMPLE 5 **Converting a Decimal to Percent**

Convert each decimal to a percent.

(a) $0.37 = (0.37)(100)\% = 37\%$ $0.37 = 37.\% = 37\%$

(b) $5.81 = (5.81)(100)\% = 581\%$ $5.81 = 581.\% = 581\%$

(c) $0.0004 = (0.0004)(100)\% = 0.04\%$ $0.0004 = 000.04\% = 0.04\%$

(d) $0.\overline{3} = (0.\overline{3})(100)\% = (0.333\ldots)(100)\%$

$= 33.33\ldots\%$

$= 33.\overline{3}\%$ or $33\frac{1}{3}\%$ $0.\overline{3} = \frac{1}{3}$ ■

EXAMPLE 6 **Converting a Fraction to Percent**

Convert each fraction to a percent.

(a) $\frac{3}{4} = 0.75$ Divide 4 into 3

$= (0.75)(100)\% = 75\%$ $0.75 = 075.\% = 75\%$

(b) $\frac{1}{8} = 0.125$ Divide 8 into 1

$= (0.125)(100)\% = 12.5\%$ $0.125 = 012.5\% = 12.5\%$

(c) $\frac{5}{3} = 1.\overline{6}$ Divide 3 into 5

$= (1.\overline{6})(100)\%$

$= (1.666\ldots)(100)\%$

$= 166.666\ldots\%$

$= 166.\overline{6}\%$ or $166\frac{2}{3}\%$ $0.\overline{6} = \frac{2}{3}$ ■

> **NOTE** Keeping a simple example in mind will help you remember whether you should multiply by 0.01 or by 100 when making percent conversions. 50% of some quantity is 0.5 or $\frac{1}{2}$ of that quantity. Thus, to convert
>
> 50% to 0.5, multiply by 0.01
>
> and to convert 0.5 to 50%, multiply by 100.

Many applied problems involve finding a percent of some number. For example, we might ask

What is 5% of $40.00?

To solve such problems we change the percent to a decimal or fraction and then multiply it by the given number. The word *of* means "multiply" or "times" in this setting.

5%	of	$40.00
↓	↓	↓
(0.05)	·	(40.00)

Thus, 5% of $40.00 is (0.05)(40.00) = $2.00.

In other applied problems, we might first obtain a fraction then convert the fraction to a percent. This is illustrated in the next example, which was presented in the chapter introduction.

EXAMPLE 7

Sports Problem

During a recent homecoming game at Northern Arizona University, quarterback Greg Wyatt completed 28 passes in 40 attempts. What fraction of his attempts did he complete? What percent of his attempts did he complete?

Since Greg completed 28 passes in 40 attempts, the desired fraction is

$$\frac{\text{passes completed}}{\text{passes attempted}} = \frac{28}{40} = \frac{\cancel{4} \cdot 7}{\cancel{4} \cdot 10} = \frac{7}{10}.$$

Change $\frac{7}{10}$ to a decimal, 0.7, then convert to a percent.

$$0.7 = (0.7)(100)\% = 70\%$$

Thus, Greg's completion percent was 70%. ■

> **NOTE** In some cases it is easy to convert a fraction to a percent more directly. In Example 7 we could have started with the fraction $\frac{7}{10}$. Multiply the numerator and denominator by 10 to obtain $\frac{70}{100}$. Remembering that *percent* means *per hundred,* we then have 70 per 100, or 70%. This technique works nicely when the denominator of the fraction is easy to convert to 100.

1.4 EXERCISES

Convert each fraction to a decimal in Exercises 1–3.

1. $\frac{1}{8}$ **2.** $\frac{5}{9}$ **3.** $2\frac{1}{7}$

Convert each decimal to a fraction in Exercises 4–6.

4. 0.48 **5.** 3.207 **6.** 25.001

Convert each percent to a decimal in Exercises 7–9.

7. $\frac{1}{2}\%$ **8.** 200% **9.** $8\frac{1}{4}\%$

Convert each percent to a fraction in Exercises 10–12.

10. 100% **11.** $3\frac{2}{3}\%$ **12.** 1000%

Convert each decimal to a percent in Exercises 13–15.

13. 0.005 **14.** $0.6\overline{23}$ **15.** 1.1

Convert each fraction to a percent in Exercises 16–18.

16. $\frac{1}{2}$ **17.** $\frac{6}{5}$ **18.** $\frac{50}{3}$

19. A basketball player made 15 shots in 20 attempts during a recent game. What fractional part of his shots did he make? What percent of his shots did he make?

20. Jess Schaal earned $24,000 last year and gave $3000 to charity. What fractional part of his income was given to charity? What percent of his income was given to charity?

21. There were 5000 votes cast in an election. Mr. Gomez received 55% of the votes. How many votes did he receive?

22. Snow, Montana has a normal annual snowfall of 120 in. This year the city received 150% of normal. How many inches of snow fell this year?

FOR REVIEW

23. Express 32.51 in expanded notation.

24. Add:
$$\begin{array}{r} 403.2 \\ 1.006 \\ +\ \ 0.04 \\ \hline \end{array}$$

25. Subtract: 3.21 − 0.0005

26. Multiply:
$$\begin{array}{r} 0.0014 \\ \times\ \ 1.06 \\ \hline \end{array}$$

27. Divide: $0.004\overline{)0.086}$

28. Jay Beckenstein rented an Escort for 3 days. If the rental fee was \$8.95 per days plus \$0.14 per mi, how much was he charged if he drove a total of 185.5 mi?

1.4 PARALLEL EXERCISES

Convert each fraction to a decimal in Exercises 1–3.

1. $\frac{5}{16}$ **2.** $\frac{11}{15}$ **3.** $\frac{1}{6}$

Convert each decimal to a fraction in Exercises 4–6.

4. 0.002 **5.** 31.85 **6.** 35.001

Convert each percent to a decimal in Exercises 7–9.

7. $3\frac{1}{2}\%$ **8.** $7\frac{3}{4}\%$ **9.** $\frac{2}{3}\%$

Convert each percent to a fraction in Exercises 10–12.

10. 500% **11.** $4\frac{1}{3}\%$ **12.** $\frac{1}{100}\%$

Convert each decimal to a percent in Exercises 13–15.

13. 4.29 **14.** 0.01 **15.** $0.57\overline{3}$

Convert each fraction to a percent in Exercises 16–18.

16. $\frac{9}{50}$ **17.** $\frac{5}{8}$ **18.** $\frac{25}{3}$

19. A football quarterback completed 21 passes in 35 attempts during a game last fall. What fraction of his attempts did he complete? What percent of his attempts did he complete?

20. Amy received \$12,000 from her grandfather. She spent \$8000 on a new car. What fraction of the money went for the car? What percent of the money went for the car?

21. There are 0.2% impurities in a laboratory solution weighing 485 grams. What is the weight of the impurities?

22. Diane Gray received a raise giving her a salary equal to 120% of her previous salary. If she earned \$16,000 last year, how much will she earn this year?

FOR REVIEW

23. Express 29.65 in expanded notation.

24. Add:
$$\begin{array}{r} 209.6 \\ 4.007 \\ +\ 0.01 \\ \hline \end{array}$$

25. Subtract: $4.81 - 0.0002$

26. Multiply:
$$\begin{array}{r} 0.0015 \\ \times\ 1.08 \\ \hline \end{array}$$

27. Divide: $0.003\overline{)0.1488}$

28. Ben Whitney rented a midsize car for two days. If the rental fee was \$11.95 per day plus \$0.18 per mi, how much was he charged if he drove a total of 230.5 mi?

1.4 ENRICHMENT EXERCISES

Solve in Exercises 1–2. A calculator would help in solving these problems.

1. A retailer paid \$92.00 for a dress and marked it up 30% to sell in her store. When the dress did not sell, she sold it at a 25% discount on the marked price. What was the percent profit or loss based on the original cost?
2. A salesman receives a 3% commission on all sales of \$50,000 or less and a 4% commission on the amount he sells over \$50,000. What is his commission on sales of \$85,000? What is the effective total commission rate, a single rate on \$85,000, to give the same total commission on the \$85,000 sales?

In this section we review converting a terminating decimal to a fraction. Decimals that have a repeating block of digits can also be changed to fractions. Follow the example shown below, and change each repeating decimal in Exercises 3–8 to a fraction.

$$\begin{aligned} n &= 1.\overline{3} = 1.333\ldots \\ 10n &= 13.333\ldots \\ n &= \ \ 1.333\ldots \\ \hline 9n &= 12 \quad \text{Subtract} \\ n &= \frac{12}{9} \\ &= \frac{4}{3} \end{aligned}$$

3. $0.\overline{6}$
4. $2.\overline{1}$
5. $0.\overline{18}$
6. $3.\overline{45}$
7. $0.\overline{123}$
8. $1.\overline{9}$

In Exercises 9–11, change each fraction to a percent by making the denominator equal to 100. The numerator will then be the required percent.

9. $\frac{7}{20}$
10. $\frac{8}{25}$
11. $\frac{61}{25}$
12. In your own words, describe how to convert a percent to a decimal and a decimal to a percent.

CHAPTER 1 REVIEW

KEY WORDS

1.1 A **numeral** is the name or symbol for a number.

The **natural** or **counting numbers** are 1, 2, 3, 4, ...

The **whole numbers** are 0, 1, 2, 3, ...

Fractions that are names for the same number are called **equivalent fractions.**

A fraction is **reduced to lowest terms** when 1 is the only natural number that divides both numerator and denominator.

A **prime number** is a natural number greater than 1 whose only divisors are 1 and itself.

1.2 The **reciprocal** of a fraction is the fraction formed by interchanging its numerator and denominator.

The **least common denominator (LCD)** of two fractions is the smallest number that has both denominators as factors.

1.3 A **place-value system** is a number system in which a digit has a particular value determined by its place in the numeral.

The **digits** are 0, 1, 2, 3, 4, 5, 6, 7, 8, and 9.

1.4 A **rational number** has a decimal representation that terminates or repeats.

An **irrational number** has a decimal representation that neither terminates nor repeats.

The word **percent** means per hundred.

KEY CONCEPTS

1.1 **1.** When reducing fractions by canceling common factors, do not make the numerator 0 when it is actually 1. For example,

$$\frac{5}{5 \cdot 3} = \frac{\not{5}}{\not{5} \cdot 3} = \frac{1}{3}, \textit{ not } \frac{0}{3}.$$

2. Factors common to the numerator and denominator of a fraction may be divided or canceled. However, do not cancel numbers that are not factors. For example,

$$\frac{2 \cdot 3}{2} = \frac{\not{2} \cdot 3}{\not{2}} = 3, \text{ but } \frac{2+3}{2} \text{ is } \textit{not} \text{ equal to } \frac{\not{2}+3}{\not{2}}.$$

1.2 **1.** To add or subtract fractions with different denominators, find the LCD. However, *do not* find the LCD to multiply or divide fractions.

2. For any nonzero number a, $\frac{0}{a} = 0$, but $\frac{a}{0}$ is undefined.

1.4 **1.** To convert **a percent to a decimal,** remove the % symbol and multiply by 0.01 (move the decimal point two places to the *left*). For example,

$$48\% = 48(0.01) = 0.48.$$

2. To convert **a decimal to a percent,** multiply by 100 (move the decimal point two places to the *right*) and attach the % symbol. For example,

$$0.172 = 0.172(100\%) = 17.2\%.$$

CHAPTER 1 REVIEW EXERCISES

PART I

1.1 **1.** Express 490 as a product of primes.

2. Reduce $\frac{110}{385}$ to lowest terms.

3. Write an equivalent fraction for $\frac{3}{11}$ having 44 for the denominator.

4. Supply the missing numerator. $\frac{9}{13} = \frac{\quad}{39}$

1.2 *Perform the indicated operations in Exercises 5–8.*

5. $\frac{3}{14} \cdot \frac{21}{9}$

6. $3\frac{1}{3} \div \frac{20}{9}$

7. $\frac{5}{9} + \frac{7}{12}$

8. $\frac{17}{18} - \frac{2}{3}$

9. Change $\frac{219}{4}$ to a mixed number.

10. Change $5\frac{2}{7}$ to an improper fraction.

11. On a map, one inch represents $\frac{3}{4}$ mi. How many miles are represented by $2\frac{1}{3}$ in?

12. Gail Taggart bought two pieces of fabric, one $3\frac{1}{8}$ yd long and the other $4\frac{3}{4}$ yd long. How many yards of fabric did she purchase?

1.3 **13.** Express 29.34 in expanded notation.

14. Express $2000 + 4 + \frac{4}{10} + \frac{2}{1000}$ in decimal notation.

15. Add.

$$\begin{array}{r} 14.5 \\ 0.007 \\ +\ 325.16 \\ \hline \end{array}$$

16. Subtract.

$$\begin{array}{r} 307.2 \\ -\ 12.009 \\ \hline \end{array}$$

17. Multiply.

$$\begin{array}{r} 1.31 \\ \times\ 0.02 \\ \hline \end{array}$$

18. Divide.

$0.005\overline{)36.15}$

1.4 **19.** Convert $\frac{3}{8}$ to a decimal.

20. Convert 27.235 to a fraction.

21. Convert 35.2% to a decimal.

22. Convert $\frac{4}{3}$ to a percent.

23. Sherman's Shoes has an inventory consisting of 1980 pairs of men's and women's shoes. If 55% of the inventory consists of women's shoes, how many pairs of women's shoes are in stock?

PART II

24. In a test of 560 video games, 420 were working. What fractional part were working? Reduce the fraction.

25. Bill Ewing works in Perko's Delicatessen as a registered cheese cutter. If he is paid $9.85 per hr and worked a total of 35.6 hr last week, what did he earn?

Perform the indicated operations in Exercises 26–29.

26. $0 \div \frac{5}{4}$

27. $4.7 - 0.001$

28. $1\frac{1}{5} + \frac{9}{10} - \frac{1}{3}$

29. $(1.04)(1.04)(1.04)$

30. Convert $\frac{3}{11}$ to a decimal.

31. Convert 25 to a percent.

32. Change $\frac{31}{9}$ to a mixed number.

33. Convert 1.85 to a fraction.

34. Change $5\frac{23}{27}$ to an improper fraction.

35. There were 942 books in a shipment. If $\frac{1}{6}$ of these were science books, how many science books were in the shipment?

36. Kelly received 250 of the 600 votes cast for the two candidates in an election. What fractional part of the total number of votes did she receive?

CHAPTER 1 TEST

1. Reduce $\frac{322}{350}$ to lowest terms.

2. Write an equivalent fraction for $\frac{8}{25}$ with 75 as the denominator.

3. Supply the missing term. $\dfrac{4}{15} = \dfrac{\quad}{90}$

4. In a contest, Michelle received 385 of the 525 possible points. What fractional part of the points did Michelle get? Reduce the fraction.

Perform the indicated operation.

5. $\dfrac{2}{5} \cdot \dfrac{15}{22}$

6. $\dfrac{9}{14} \div \dfrac{2}{7}$

7. $\dfrac{5}{6} + \dfrac{7}{9}$

8. $\dfrac{17}{24} - \dfrac{2}{3}$

9. Change $\frac{28}{5}$ to a mixed number.

10. Change $2\frac{14}{15}$ to an improper fraction.

11. There were 720 tires in a shipment. If $\frac{3}{5}$ of these were whitewalls, how many whitewall tires were in the shipment?

12. A bottle contains $7\frac{2}{5}$ liters of solution. If $2\frac{7}{10}$ liters are used, how many liters are left in the bottle?

Perform the indicated operation.

13. $14.06 + 3.057$

14. $26.3 - 7.441$

15. $(0.42)(5.06)$

16. $46.2 \div 1.05$

17. Convert $\frac{1}{5}$ to a percent.

18. Convert 3.15 to a fraction.

19. Convert 2.35 to a percent.

20. The tax rate on purchases is 4%. What is the tax on a \$27 purchase?

21. In a shipment of 450 computer disks, 20 were found to be defective. What fraction of the disks were defective? What percent of the disks were defective?

22. When solving an applied problem suppose you obtain an answer of $\frac{78}{7}$ feet for the length of a rectangle. Explain why it might be better in this case to give the answer as a mixed number.

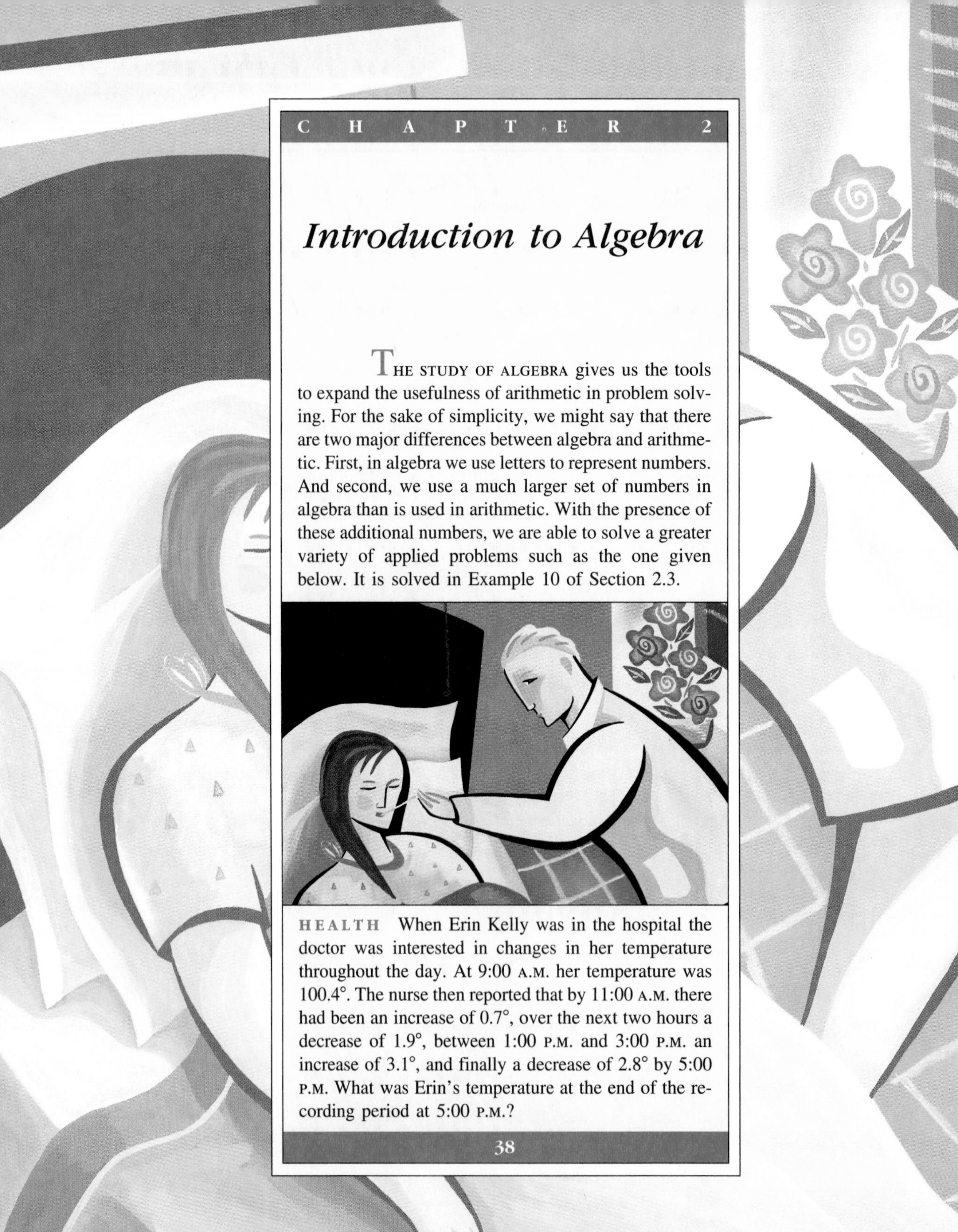

C H A P T E R 2

Introduction to Algebra

THE STUDY OF ALGEBRA gives us the tools to expand the usefulness of arithmetic in problem solving. For the sake of simplicity, we might say that there are two major differences between algebra and arithmetic. First, in algebra we use letters to represent numbers. And second, we use a much larger set of numbers in algebra than is used in arithmetic. With the presence of these additional numbers, we are able to solve a greater variety of applied problems such as the one given below. It is solved in Example 10 of Section 2.3.

HEALTH When Erin Kelly was in the hospital the doctor was interested in changes in her temperature throughout the day. At 9:00 A.M. her temperature was 100.4°. The nurse then reported that by 11:00 A.M. there had been an increase of 0.7°, over the next two hours a decrease of 1.9°, between 1:00 P.M. and 3:00 P.M. an increase of 3.1°, and finally a decrease of 2.8° by 5:00 P.M. What was Erin's temperature at the end of the recording period at 5:00 P.M.?

We begin our study of algebra by introducing *variables* and *exponents,* and agree to a precise order to be used when performing operations with numbers and variables. Next we expand our number system to include negative numbers and develop the arithmetic operations on such numbers. One of the most important properties of operations, the distributive law, is discussed next, with emphasis on simplifying *algebraic expressions.* We conclude the chapter by describing the *real number system,* the set of numbers that is used extensively in algebra.

SECTION 2.1 Variables, Exponents, and Order of Operations

Student guideposts

- ▶ *Variables*
- ▶ *Exponential notation*
- ▶ *Order of operations*
- ▶ *Symbols of grouping*
- ▶ *Evaluating algebraic expressions*
- ▶ *Formulas*

▶ ***Variables*** In algebra, we often use letters such as a, b, x, y, A, and B to represent numbers. A letter that can be replaced by various numbers is called a **variable.** In a sense, a variable acts as a placeholder in phrases or statements that are made algebraically. For example, lengthy verbal statements can often be translated and symbolized by brief algebraic expressions using variables, as in the following examples.

Three	times	a natural number	becomes $3 \cdot n$ or $3n$
↓	↓	↓	
3	$\cdot$	n	

Seven	plus	twice	a natural number	becomes $7 + 2 \cdot n$ or $7 + 2n$
↓	↓	↓	↓	
7	+	$2 \cdot$	n	

In each example, the variable n represents a natural number. Other notations for $3 \cdot n$ are $3(n)$, $(3)(n)$, and $3n$, with the last form preferred. The product of two natural numbers m and n would most likely be represented by mn, but could also be expressed by $m \cdot n$, $m(n)$, and $(m)(n)$. We usually avoid using the symbol $\times$ for multiplication since it can be confused with the letter x used as a variable.

When we translate a verbal phrase or statement into an algebraic expression, we need to be aware of some common terms and their translations. Several terms and their symbolic forms are presented in the table below.

Symbol	+	−	·	÷	=
Terms	sum	minus	times	divided by	equals
	sum of	less	of	quotient of	is
	plus	less than	product	ratio	is equal to
	and	diminished by	product of		is as much as
	added to	difference	multiplied by		is the same as
	increased by	difference between			the result is
	more than	subtracted from			yields
		decreased by			

Often we will use x as the variable in a translation. However, it is sometimes helpful to use another letter more indicative of the number or quantity that it represents. For example, we might use t for time, A for area, V for volume, or perhaps M for Mary's age.

EXAMPLE 1 **Translating Phrases into Symbols**

Select a variable to represent each quantity and translate the phrase into symbols.

Word phrase	*Symbolic translation*
(a) The time plus 4 hours	$t + 4$
(b) My wages less \$100 for taxes	$w - 100$
(c) One half of the area	$\frac{1}{2}A$
(d) Twice Mary's age in 3 years	$2(M + 3)$
(e) \$2000 less than the cost	$c - 2000$ ■

▶ *Exponential notation*

When a variable or number is multiplied by itself several times, as in

$$2 \cdot 2 \cdot 2 \cdot 2 \text{ or } x \cdot x \cdot x,$$

we can use **exponential notation** to avoid writing long strings of **factors** (the individual numbers in the expressed product). For example, we write $2 \cdot 2 \cdot 2 \cdot 2$ as 2^4,

$$\underbrace{2 \cdot 2 \cdot 2 \cdot 2}_{\text{4 factors}} = \underset{\uparrow \text{ Base}}{2}^{4 \leftarrow \text{Exponent}},$$

where 2 is called the **base,** 4 the **exponent,** and 2^4 the **exponential expression** (read 2 to the **fourth power**). Similarly, $x \cdot x \cdot x = x^3$ is called the **third power** or **cube** of x. The **square** or **second power** of a is a^2. The **first power** of a is a^1, which we write simply as a.

Exponential Notation

If a is any number and n is a natural number,

$$a^n = \underbrace{a \cdot a \cdot a \cdots a}_{n \text{ factors}}.$$

CAUTION The exponential expression a^n is not the same as na. For example, if a is 3 and n is 2,

$$a^n = 3^2 = 3 \cdot 3 = 9 \quad \text{but} \quad na = (2)(3) = 6.$$

EXAMPLE 2 **Using Exponents**

Write in exponential notation.

(a) $\underbrace{7 \cdot 7 \cdot 7}_{\text{3 factors}} = 7^3$

(b) $\underbrace{a \cdot a \cdot a \cdot a \cdot a \cdot a}_{\text{6 factors}} = a^6$

(c) $\underbrace{3 \cdot 3}_{\text{2 factors}} \cdot \underbrace{x \cdot x \cdot x \cdot x \cdot x}_{\text{5 factors}} = 3^2x^5$ ■

▶ *Order of operations* When exponents or powers are used together with the operations of addition, subtraction, multiplication, and division, the resulting numerical expressions can be confusing unless we agree to an order of operations. For example,

$2 \cdot 5^2$ *could* equal 10^2 or 100, — If we first multiply then square

or **$2 \cdot 5^2$ *could* equal $2 \cdot 25$ or 50.** — If we first square then multiply

Similarly,

$2 \cdot 3 + 4$ *could* equal $2 \cdot 7$ or 14, — If we first add then multiply

or **$2 \cdot 3 + 4$ *could* equal $6 + 4$ or 10.** — If we first multiply then add

To prevent problems with different interpretations such as these, we will agree to follow the steps given below when evaluating numerical expressions.

Step 1: Evaluate all powers, in any order, first.
Step 2: Do all multiplications and divisions in order from left to right.
Step 3: Do all additions and subtractions in order from left to right.

In view of this agreement, we can see that the second procedure, highlighted in the examples above, is the correct one to use.

EXAMPLE 3 **Evaluating Numerical Expressions**

Evaluate each numerical expression.

(a) $2 + 3 \cdot 4 = 2 + 12 = 14$ — Multiply first, then add

(b) $20 - 3^2 = 20 - 9 = 11$ — Square first, then subtract

(c) $5 \cdot 6 - 12 \div 3 = 30 - 4 = 26$ — Multiply and divide first, then subtract

(d) $25 \div 5 + 3 \cdot 2^3 = 25 \div 5 + 3 \cdot 8$ — Cube first

$= 5 + 24$ — Divide and multiply second

$= 29$ — Add last ■

▶ *Symbols of grouping*

Suppose that we want to evaluate three times the sum of 2 and 5. If we write $3 \cdot 2 + 5$ and use the above rule, we will obtain $6 + 5$ or 11. However, it is clear from the first sentence, that we want 3 times 7 or 21 for the result. **Symbols of grouping,** such as parentheses ( ), square brackets [ ], or braces { }, can help us symbolize the problem correctly as $3 \cdot (2 + 5)$. The grouping symbols contain the expression that must be evaluated first. In this case, we must add before multiplying.

$$3 \cdot (2 + 5) = 3 \cdot (7) = 21$$

Generally, we omit the dot and write $3(2 + 5)$ for $3 \cdot (2 + 5)$. Also, instead of writing $3 \cdot (7)$, we will write $(3)(7)$.

One other method of grouping is to use a fraction bar. For example, in

$$\frac{4 \cdot 5}{7 + 3},$$

the fraction bar acts like parentheses since the expression is the same as

$$(4 \cdot 5) \div (7 + 3).$$

We first multiply 4 and 5, then add 7 and 3, and finally we divide the results. Thus,

$$\frac{4 \cdot 5}{7 + 3} = \frac{20}{10} = 2.$$

With this in mind, when evaluating a numerical expression, we will agree to evaluate all expressions within grouping symbols first, beginning with innermost symbols of grouping, if more than one set of symbols is present. This is illustrated in the next example.

EXAMPLE 4

Evaluating Numerical Expressions

Evaluate each numerical expression.

(a) $3 + (2 \cdot 5) = 3 + 10 = 13$ — Evaluate inside the parentheses first

(b) $(4 + 5)2 + 3 = (9)2 + 3$ — Work inside the parentheses first

$= 18 + 3$ — Multiply before adding

$= 21$

(c) $[3(8 + 2) + 1]4 = [3(10) + 1]4$ — Innermost grouping symbol first

$= [30 + 1]4$ — Multiply before adding inside brackets

$= [31]4$ — Add numbers inside brackets before multiplying

$= 124$ ■

We now summarize the order to follow when evaluating a numerical expression.

Order of Operations

1. Evaluate within grouping symbols first, beginning with the innermost set if more than one set is used.
2. Evaluate all powers.
3. Perform all multiplications and divisions in order from left to right.
4. Perform all additions and subtractions in order from left to right.

EXAMPLE 5 **Evaluating Using All Rules**

Evaluate each expression.

(a) $2^3 + 4^3 = 8 + 64 = 72$ Cube first, then add

(b) $(2 + 4)^3 = 6^3 = 216$ Add first inside parentheses, then cube

(c) $(3 \cdot 5)^2 = 15^2 = 225$ Multiply first, then square

(d) $3 \cdot 5^2 = 3 \cdot 25 = 75$ Square first, then multiply

(e) $5^2 - 4^2 = 25 - 16 = 9$ Square first, then subtract

(f) $(5 - 4)^2 = 1^2 = 1$ Subtract first, then square

(g) $3^2 - 15 \div 5 + 5 \cdot 2 = 9 - 15 \div 5 + 5 \cdot 2$ Square first

$= 9 - 3 + 10$ Divide and multiply in order

$= 16$ Subtract and add in order

(h) The square of the difference seven minus three
$(7 - 3)^2 = 4^2 = 16$ Subtract first, then square

(i) Seven squared minus three squared
$7^2 - 3^2 = 49 - 9 = 40$ Square first, then subtract ■

CAUTION Example 5 points out common errors to avoid when working with exponents. For example,

$$2^3 + 4^3 \neq (2 + 4)^3, \quad (3 \cdot 5)^2 \neq 3 \cdot 5^2, \quad 5^2 - 4^2 \neq (5 - 4)^2.$$

The symbol $\neq$ means "is *not* equal to." In general, if a, b, and n are variables representing numbers,

$$a^n + b^n \neq (a + b)^n, \ (ab)^n \neq ab^n, \ a^n - b^n \neq (a - b)^n.$$

▶ *Evaluating algebraic expressions*

An **algebraic expression** contains variables as well as numbers. We can use the order of operations for evaluating numerical expressions to evaluate algebraic expressions when specific values for the variables are given.

To Evaluate an Algebraic Expression

1. Replace each variable (letter) with the specified value.
2. Proceed as in evaluating numerical expressions.

EXAMPLE 6 **Evaluating an Algebraic Expression**

(a) Evaluate $2(a + b) - c$ when $a = 3$, $b = 4$, and $c = 5$.

$$2(a + b) - c = 2(3 + 4) - 5 \quad \text{Replace each letter with given value}$$
$$= 2(7) - 5 \quad \text{Evaluate inside parentheses first}$$
$$= 14 - 5 = 9$$

(b) Evaluate $5[12 - 3(a + 1) + b] - c$ when $a = 2$, $b = 7$, and $c = 4$.

$$5[12 - 3(a + 1) + b] - c = 5[12 - 3(2 + 1) + 7] - 4 \quad \text{Replace variables with numbers}$$
$$= 5[12 - 3(3) + 7] - 4$$
$$= 5[12 - 9 + 7] - 4 \quad \text{Multiply before adding or subtracting}$$
$$= 5[10] - 4 = 50 - 4 = 46 \quad ■$$

EXAMPLE 7 **Evaluating an Algebraic Expression**

Evaluate $\dfrac{ab - 1}{c}$ for the given values.

(a) $a = 2$, $b = 3$, and $c = 0$

$$\frac{ab - 1}{c} = \frac{(2)(3) - 1}{0} \quad \text{Division by zero undefined}$$

That is, this expression is undefined when $c = 0$.

(b) $a = 3$, $b = \frac{1}{3}$, and $c = 5$

$$\frac{ab - 1}{c} = \frac{(3)\left(\frac{1}{3}\right) - 1}{5} = \frac{1 - 1}{5} = \frac{0}{5} = 0 \quad \frac{0}{5} = 0 \quad ■$$

EXAMPLE 8 **Evaluating an Algebraic Expression**

Evaluate the following when $a = 2$, $b = 1$, $c = 3$.

(a) $3a^2 = 3(2)^2$ Not $(3 \cdot 2)^2 = 6^2 = 36$
$= 3 \cdot 4 = 12$

(b) $2ab^2c^3 = 2(2)(1)^2(3)^3$
$= 2(2)(1)(27) = 4 \cdot 27 = 108$

(c) $(2c)^2 - 2c^2 = (2 \cdot 3)^2 - 2(3)^2$ Watch the substitution
$= 6^2 - 2 \cdot 9$
$= 36 - 18 = 18$

(d) $a^a + c^c = 2^2 + 3^3$
$= 4 + 27 = 31$ ■

CAUTION Notice the difference between $(2c)^2$ and $2c^2$ in Example 8 (c). Following our order of operations, we first work inside parentheses so that $(2c)^2$ becomes $(2 \cdot 3)^2 = 6^2 = 36$, but $2c^2$ becomes $2 \cdot 3^2 = 2 \cdot 9 = 18$ since we evaluate the exponent before evaluating the product. Remember in an expression such as $2c^2$ the exponent only applies to the base right next to it, c in this case, and does not extend to any other numbers or variables multiplied times c unless parentheses are used as in $(2c)^2$. In other words,

$$(2c)^2 \neq 2c^2.$$

Formulas

A **formula** is an algebraic statement that relates two or more variables. For example, the formula

$$d = rt$$

relates the distance, d, traveled by an object moving at an average rate, r, for a period of time, t. Other familiar formulas related to geometric figures, such as

$A = lw$ Area of a rectangle in terms of its length and width

and $P = 2l + 2w$ Perimeter of a rectangle in terms of its length and width

are summarized on the inside back cover of the text. To use a particular formula in an applied problem, we must first understand the meaning of the variables, and next, evaluate the algebraic expression (formula) for the given values.

EXAMPLE 9

Calculating Investment Returns

If we invest P dollars (called the principal) at an interest rate, r, compounded annually for a period of t years, it will grow to an amount, A, given by

$$A = P(1 + r)^t.$$

If a principal of \$1000 is invested at 12% interest, compounded annually, how much will be in the account at the end of two years?

$$\begin{aligned} A &= P(1 + r)^t && \text{Start with the formula} \\ &= \mathbf{1000}(1 + \mathbf{0.12})^2 && \text{Substitute 1000 for } P\text{, 0.12 for } r\text{, and 2 for } t \\ &= 1000(1.12)^2 \\ &= 1000(1.2544) \\ &= 1254.4 \end{aligned}$$

Thus, there will be \$1254.40 in the account. ■

NOTE In Example 9, 12% was converted to the decimal 0.12 in order to solve the problem. This is often the case when we are working with percents.

EXAMPLE 10 **Solving a Construction Problem**

The perimeter of a rectangle P is given by $P = 2l + 2w$, where l is its length and w is its width. If a play area is a rectangle of length 15 yards and width 8 yards, how many yards of fencing are required to enclose the area?

$$\begin{aligned} P &= 2l + 2w && \text{Start with the given formula} \\ &= 2(15) + 2(8) && \text{Replace variables with given values} \\ &= 30 + 16 \\ &= 46 \end{aligned}$$

The perimeter is 46 yards, and this is the length of fencing required. ∎

2.1 EXERCISES

1. What is a letter used to represent a number called?

Select a variable to represent each quantity in Exercises 2–15 and translate the phrase into symbols.

2. The sum of a number and 7
3. A number subtracted from 10
4. The product of a number and 3
5. A number divided by 13
6. The time 6 hours ago
7. His salary plus $200
8. Twice the volume
9. $3000 less the cost
10. A number added to its reciprocal
11. Her score less 20 points
12. 300 more than twice the number of votes
13. 300 more than the number of votes, doubled
14. 4% of the selling price
15. Cost plus 8% of the cost
16. Given the exponential expression x^7, **(a)** what is the base? **(b)** what is the exponent?
17. In the expression $3x$, what is the exponent on x?

Write in exponential notation in Exercises 18–20.

18. $(2x)(2x)$
19. $2 \cdot x \cdot x$
20. $6 \cdot 6 \cdot 6 \cdot y \cdot y \cdot z \cdot z \cdot z \cdot z$

Write without using exponents in Exercises 21–23.

21. $3y^3$
22. $(3y)^3$
23. 1^{51}

Evaluate each expression in Exercises 24–35.

24. $3 \cdot 2^2$
25. $(3 \cdot 2)^2$
26. $(5 - 2)^3$
27. $5^3 - 2^3$
28. $8 - 2^3$
29. $(8 - 2)^3$
30. $(9 - 2) \cdot 3 + 4 \cdot 0$
31. $\dfrac{2(3 - 1) - 4}{5}$
32. $\dfrac{4(3 + 5) - 10}{0}$
33. $2[8 - 2(4 - 1) + 5]$
34. $15 - 3\{2(5 - 4) + 3\}$
35. $16 \div 4 \cdot 2 \div 4 - 2$
36. The cube of the difference five minus two
37. Five cubed minus two cubed
38. Ten minus three squared
39. The square of the difference ten minus three

Evaluate each expression in Exercises 40–51 when $a = 2$, $b = 3$, $c = 5$, $d = 0$, and $x = 12$.

40. $6a + b$
41. $6(a + b)$
42. $2b^2$
43. $(2b)^2$
44. $(c - b)^2$
45. $c^2 - b^2$
46. $(a + b)^3$
47. $a^3 + b^3$
48. $3a^3 + 2$
49. $(3a)^3 + 2$
50. $x - [a(b + 1) - c]$
51. $5a + 2[c + x \div b]$

52. GEOMETRY The perimeter of a rectangle, P, is given by $P = 2l + 2w$, where l is its length and w is its width. What is the perimeter of a rectangle of length 20 ft and width 13 ft?

53. TRAVEL The distance an automobile travels, d, at an average rate of speed, r, for a period of time, t, is given by $d = rt$. How far does a car travel in 11 hr at an average speed of 55 mph?

54. INVESTMENT Use $A = P(1 + r)^t$ to find the amount of money in an account at the end of two years if a principal of \$500 is invested at 14% interest, compounded annually.

55. GEOMETRY The area of a square, A, is given by $A = s^2$, where s is the length of a side. What is the area of a square with side 3.5 cm?

56. GEOMETRY The area of a triangle, A, is given by $A = \frac{1}{2}bh$, where b is the length of its base and h is its height. Find the area of a triangle with height 15 m and base 8 m.

57. TEMPERATURE The temperature measured in degrees Celsius, °C, can be obtained from degrees Fahrenheit, °F, by using $C = \frac{5}{9}(F - 32)$. Find C when F is 200°.

58. GEOMETRY The surface area of a cube, A, is given by $A = 6e^2$ where e is the length of an edge. Find the surface area of a cube with an edge of $2\frac{1}{2}$ in.

59. GEOMETRY The surface area of a cylinder, A, with height, h, and base radius, r, is given by $A = 2\pi rh + 2\pi r^2$. Use 3.14 for π and find the surface area of a cylinder with a radius of 2 cm and a height of 10 cm.

FOR REVIEW

60. Convert $\frac{5}{11}$ to a percent.

61. Convert $7\frac{3}{4}\%$ to a decimal.

62. A chemist has a solution that is 0.6% salt. If the solution weighs 650 g, what is the weight of the salt?

2.1 PARALLEL EXERCISES

1. When evaluating a numerical expression with more than one set of grouping symbols, always evaluate within which set of symbols first?

Select a variable to represent each quantity in Exercises 2–15 and translate the phrase into symbols.

2. The sum of a number and 12
3. A number subtracted from 33
4. The product of a number and 5
5. A number divided by 7
6. The time plus 3 hours
7. My wages less \$75
8. Three times the volume
9. \$5000 less the cost
10. A number less its reciprocal
11. His score less 28 points
12. 100 more than triple the number of votes
13. 100 more than the number of votes, tripled
14. 24% of a number
15. Cost plus 10% of the cost

16. In the exponential expression a^6, **(a)** what is the base? **(b)** what is the exponent?

17. In the expression $8y$, what is the exponent on y?

Write in exponential notation in Exercises 18–20.

18. $(3a)(3a)$

19. $3 \cdot a \cdot a$

20. $5 \cdot 5 \cdot 5 \cdot a \cdot a \cdot c \cdot c \cdot c$

Write without using exponents in Exercises 21–23.

21. $2z^3$

22. $(2z)^3$

23. $x^2 - y^2$

Evaluate each expression in Exercises 24–35.

24. $2 \cdot 7^2$

25. $(2 \cdot 7)^2$

26. $(2 + 7)^2$

27. $2^2 + 7^2$

28. $4 - 2^2$

29. $(4 - 2)^2$

30. $0 \cdot (5 - 2) + 0$

31. $\dfrac{2(5 + 1) - 3}{3}$

32. $\dfrac{5(2 + 8) - 19}{0}$

33. $25 \div 5 + 2 \cdot 4 - 1$

34. $30 - 5[7 - 2(6 - 3)]$

35. $20 \div 5 \cdot 2 \div 4 - 2$

36. The square of the sum of eleven and three

37. Eleven squared plus three squared

38. Twelve minus two cubed

39. The cube of the difference twelve minus two

Evaluate each expression in Exercises 40–51 when $x = 3$, $y = 2$, $z = 4$, $w = 0$, and $a = 24$.

40. $5x + y$

41. $5(x + y)$

42. $3y^2$

43. $(3y)^2$

44. $(z - y)^2$

45. $z^2 - y^2$

46. $(x + z)^3$

47. $x^3 + z^3$

48. $2z^3 + 1$

49. $(2z)^3 + 1$

50. $a - [x(y + 3) - z]$

51. $3x + 4[x + z \div y]$

---

52. **GEOMETRY** The perimeter of a square, P, with side of length s is given by $P = 4s$. What is the perimeter of a square with side of length 15 ft?

53. **GEOMETRY** The area of a rectangle, A, is given by $A = lw$, where l is its length and w its width. If a rectangle is 2 cm wide and 7 cm long, what is its area?

54. **INVESTMENT** Use the formula $A = P(1 + r)^t$ to find the amount of money in an account at the end of two years if a principal of \$2000 is invested at 8% interest, compounded annually.

55. **GEOMETRY** The area of a circle, A, with radius r, is given by $A = \pi r^2$. Use 3.14 for π and find the area of a circle with radius 20 m.

56. **GEOMETRY** The volume, V, of a box with length l, width w, and height h, is given by $V = lwh$. If the box is 9 in long, 6 in wide, and 11 in high, what is its volume?

57. **TEMPERATURE** The temperature measured in degrees Fahrenheit, °F, can be obtained from degrees Celsius, °C, by using $F = \frac{9}{5}C + 32$. Find F when C is 20°.

58. **GEOMETRY** The surface area of a sphere, A, with radius r, is given by $A = 4\pi r^2$. Use 3.14 for π and find the surface area of a sphere with radius 50 cm.

59. **GEOMETRY** The surface area of a cylinder, A, is given by $A = 2\pi rh + 2\pi r^2$, where r is the radius of its base and h is its height. Find A if $r = 10$ in, $h = 8$ in, and $\pi = 3.14$.

FOR REVIEW

60. Convert $\frac{8}{9}$ to a percent.

61. Convert $10\frac{1}{4}$% to a decimal.

62. It has been estimated that 32% of the population of Northern, Minnesota is of Danish ancestry. If 19,270 people live in Northern, approximately how many of them are of Danish background?

2.1 ENRICHMENT EXERCISES

Evaluate each expression in Exercises 1–3.

1. $2(5-3)^3 - [7-(8-6)^2]$ **2.** $13 - [11 - (7-4)^2]^3$ **3.** $[(6 \div 3)^2 + 9 \cdot (3-1)^2]^2$

Evaluate each expression in Exercises 4–6 when $a = 1.35$, $b = 2.75$, and $c = 6.2$. A calculator would be helpful for these problems.

4. $abc + b^2$ **5.** $c^2 - a^2 + b^2$ **6.** $2c^2 - (a+b)$

In Exercises 7–12, write each expression in words.

7. $3(a+b)$ **8.** $2a + x$ **9.** $4y^2$

10. $(4y)^2$ **11.** $(3+z) \div 2$ **12.** $6 \div (5-t)$

13. Evaluate $(a+b)^2$ and $a^2 + b^2$ when $a = 2$ and $b = 5$. What can you conclude about these two expressions?

14. In your own words, describe the order of operations that we use to evaluate expressions.

15. Describe the difference between the two expressions $2x^3$ and $(2x)^3$. There is only one value for x for which these two expressions will be equal. What is that value?

SECTION 2.2 Integers, Rational Numbers, and the Number Line

Student guideposts

- *Number line*
- *Less than and greater than*
- *Integers*
- *Equal and unequal numbers*
- *Rational numbers*
- *Absolute value*

Number line

Many ideas in algebra can be better understood if we "picture" them in some way. Numbers are often pictured using a *number line*. Consider the set of whole numbers. We draw a line like the one in Figure 2.1, and select some unit of length. Then, starting at an arbitrary point that we label 0 and call the **origin,** we mark off unit lengths to the right, labeling the points 1, 2, 3, ... The result is a **number line** displaying the whole numbers, shown in Figure 2.1. Every whole number is paired with a point on this line. The arrowhead points to the direction in which the whole numbers continue.

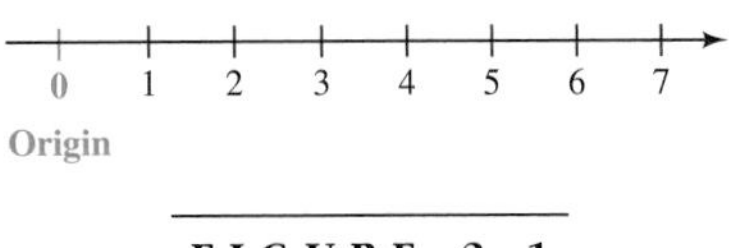

FIGURE 2.1

EXAMPLE 1

Pairing Numbers with Points

What whole numbers are paired with a, b, and c on the number line in Figure 2.2?

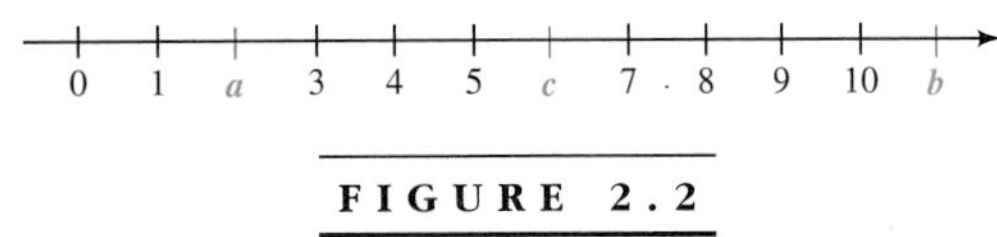

FIGURE 2.2

Point a is paired with 2, point b with 11, and point c with 6. ∎

Less than and greater than

The whole numbers occur in a natural order. For example, we know that 3 is less than (has a smaller value than) 8, and that 8 is greater than (has a larger value than) 3. Note on the number line in Figure 2.2, that 3 is to the left of 8, while 8 is to the right of 3. The symbol $<$ means **"is less than."** We write "3 is less than 8" as

$$3 < 8.$$

Similarly, the symbol $>$ means **"is greater than."** We write "8 is greater than 3" as

$$8 > 3.$$

> NOTE Observe that $3 < 8$ and $8 > 3$ have the same meaning even though they are read differently.

Order of Whole Numbers

Suppose a and b are any two whole numbers.

1. If a is to the left of b on a number line, then $a < b$.
2. If a is to the right of b on a number line, then $a > b$.

EXAMPLE 2

Ordering Whole Numbers

Place the correct symbol ($<$ or $>$) between the numbers in the given pairs. Use part of a number line if necessary.

(a) 2 7

$2 < 7$. Notice that 2 is to the left of 7 on the number line in Figure 2.3.

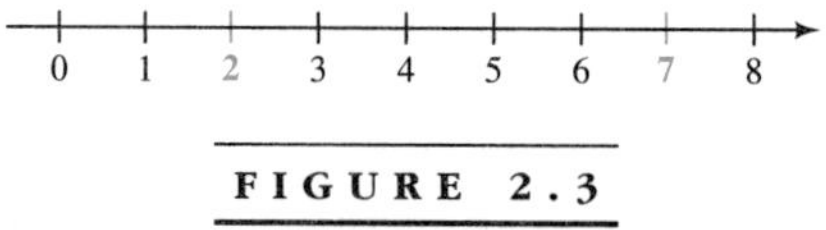

FIGURE 2.3

(b) 12 9

$12 > 9$. Notice that 12 is to the right of 9 on the number line in Figure 2.4. ■

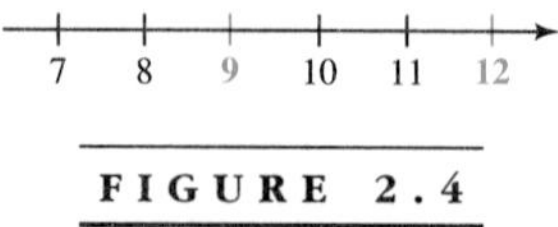

FIGURE 2.4

> NOTE In Example 2, when $<$ and $>$ are used, notice that the symbol *always points to the smaller of the two numbers.*

The number lines we have looked at so far display no numbers to the left of 0. What meaning could we give to a number to the left of 0? One example of such a number is a temperature of 5° below zero on a cold day, which is sometimes represented as $-5°$ (read "negative 5°"). Others are shown in the following table.

Measurement	*Number*
5° above zero	5° (or +5°)
5° below zero	−5°
100 ft above sea level	100 ft (or +100 ft)
100 ft below sea level	−100 ft
\$16 deposit into an account	\$16 (or +\$16)
\$16 check written on an account	−\$16

▶ *Integers*

When we put a negative sign in front of each of the counting numbers, we obtain the **negative integers.** The collection of negative integers together with the counting numbers (sometimes called **positive integers**) and zero is called the set of **integers.**

$$I = \{\ldots, -3, -2, -1, 0, 1, 2, 3, \ldots\} \qquad \text{Integers}$$

The whole numbers are often called **nonnegative integers.** The number line in Figure 2.5 shows negative integers, positive integers, and zero. Note that we can write 1 as +1, 2 as +2, and so on. Also, we read −1 as "negative 1," for example.

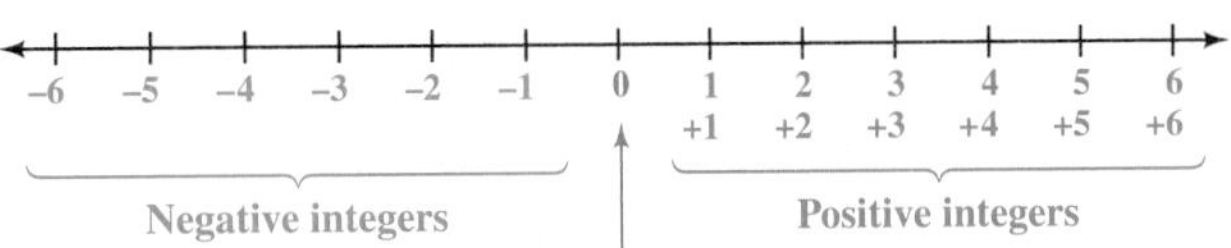

FIGURE 2.5

▶ *Equal and unequal numbers*

We say that two numbers are **equal** (for example, $3^2 = 9$) if they correspond to the same point on a number line. If two numbers correspond to different points on a number line, they are **unequal.** We use ≠ to represent "is not equal to." We can expand our definitions of *less than* and *greater than* for whole numbers to include the integers. That is, one integer is **less than** a second if it is to the left of the second on a number line, and one integer is **greater than** a second if it is to the right of the second on a number line. If one number is **less than or equal to** another number, we use the symbol ≤ (similarly ≥ represents **greater than or equal to**). For example,

$$-4 \leq 4, \quad -2 \leq 0, \quad 0 \leq 3, \quad 2 \leq 2, \quad \text{and} \quad -1 \leq 1.$$

> NOTE All negative integers are less than zero ($n < 0$), all positive integers are greater than zero ($n > 0$), and any positive integer is greater than any negative integer.

EXAMPLE 3 **Determining Order Relations Between Numbers**

Some relationships between numbers on the number line in Figure 2.6 follow.

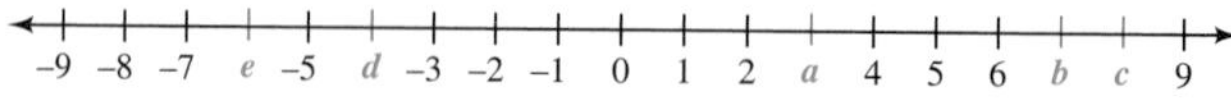

FIGURE 2.6

In Words	*In Symbols*
(a) 1 is less than a	$1 < a$
(b) c is greater than d	$c > d$
(c) e is unequal to -5	$e \neq -5$
(d) d is equal to -4	$d = -4$
(e) b is less than or equal to b	$b \leq b$
(f) a is greater than or equal to 2	$a \geq 2$ ■

▶ *Rational numbers*

In addition to the integers, the fractions we studied in Chapter 1, together with their negatives, can be shown or **plotted** on a number line. All of the fractions to the right of zero are called **positive rational numbers.** Those to the left of zero are **negative rational numbers,** and together, along with zero, they form the set of **rational numbers.** We can think of the rational numbers as

Q = {all numbers that can be written as a quotient of two integers}.

An alternative way to consider the rational numbers is by using decimal notation. Consider the following rational numbers and their decimal form.

$$\frac{1}{2} = 0.5, \quad \frac{3}{4} = 0.75, \quad \frac{1}{3} = 0.\overline{3}, \quad \textit{and} \quad \frac{2}{11} = 0.\overline{18}.$$

In all cases the decimal form either terminates or has a repeating block of digits. This is true in general, so we have

Q = {all numbers whose decimal form terminates or repeats a block of digits}.

NOTE Since any integer can be expressed as a quotient of two integers, for example,

$$2 = \frac{2}{1}, \quad 17 = \frac{17}{1}, \quad \textit{and} \quad -8 = \frac{-8}{1}$$

we see that the integers are also rational numbers.

Some examples of rational numbers are plotted in Figure 2.7.

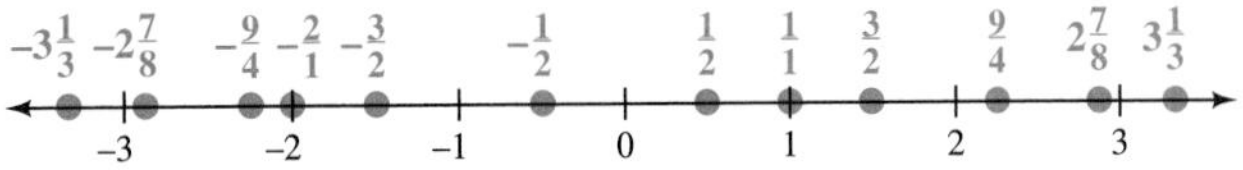

$-3\frac{1}{3}$ $-2\frac{7}{8}$ $-\frac{9}{4}$ $-\frac{2}{1}$ $-\frac{3}{2}$ $-\frac{1}{2}$ $\frac{1}{2}$ $\frac{1}{1}$ $\frac{3}{2}$ $\frac{9}{4}$ $2\frac{7}{8}$ $3\frac{1}{3}$

−3 −2 −1 0 1 2 3

FIGURE 2.7

Just as with integers, we can define the order relationships of *less than* and *greater than* for rational numbers and mixed numbers. For example, we see that

$$-\frac{1}{2} < \frac{1}{2}, \quad \frac{3}{2} < \frac{9}{4}, \quad 2\frac{7}{8} > -\frac{3}{2}, \quad \text{and} \quad -\frac{9}{4} > -3\frac{1}{3}$$

by looking at the number line in Figure 2.7.

A very important property of our number system states that if two numbers are unequal, then one of them must be less than the other. With two integers, it is easy to see if they are equal and, if not, which is less than the other. For two rational numbers we find a common denominator and compare the integers in the numerator.

Ordering Rational Numbers

To order two rational numbers, write each as an equivalent fraction with the same denominator.

1. If the numerators are equal, the fractions are equal.
2. If the numerators are different, the order of the fractions is the same as the order of the numerators.

EXAMPLE 4

Ordering Rational Numbers

Place the correct symbol, =, <, or >, between the given pair of fractions.

(a) $\frac{4}{6} \quad \frac{28}{42}$

If we multiply numerator and denominator of $\frac{4}{6}$ by 7, the denominator becomes 42.

$$\frac{4 \cdot 7}{6 \cdot 7} = \frac{28}{42}$$

Since the fractions now have the same denominator and the numerators are equal, the fractions are equal.

$$\frac{4}{6} = \frac{28}{42}$$

(b) $\frac{24}{7} \quad \frac{39}{11}$

Multiplying numerator and denominator of $\frac{24}{7}$ by 11 and of $\frac{39}{11}$ by 7 gives a common denominator of 77.

$$\frac{24 \cdot 11}{7 \cdot 11} = \frac{264}{77} \quad \text{and} \quad \frac{39 \cdot 7}{11 \cdot 7} = \frac{273}{77}.$$

Since 264 < 273, $\dfrac{24}{7} < \dfrac{39}{11}$.

(c) $\dfrac{15}{9}$ $\dfrac{31}{20}$

We get a common denominator of 180 by multiplying numerator and denominator of the first fraction by 20 and the second fraction by 9.

$$\frac{15 \cdot 20}{9 \cdot 20} = \frac{300}{180} \quad \text{and} \quad \frac{31 \cdot 9}{20 \cdot 9} = \frac{279}{180}.$$

Since 300 > 279, $\dfrac{15}{9} > \dfrac{31}{20}$. ■

Absolute value

In Chapter 1 we reviewed the four basic operations of addition, subtraction, multiplication, and division on the nonnegative rational numbers. When operating on *all* rational numbers we will use the idea of *absolute value.*

Absolute Value of a Number

The **absolute value** of a number x is the distance from zero to x on a number line. We symbolize the absolute value of x by $|x|$.

EXAMPLE 5

Absolute Value Using a Number Line

Use Figure 2.8 to find the absolute values of the following numbers.

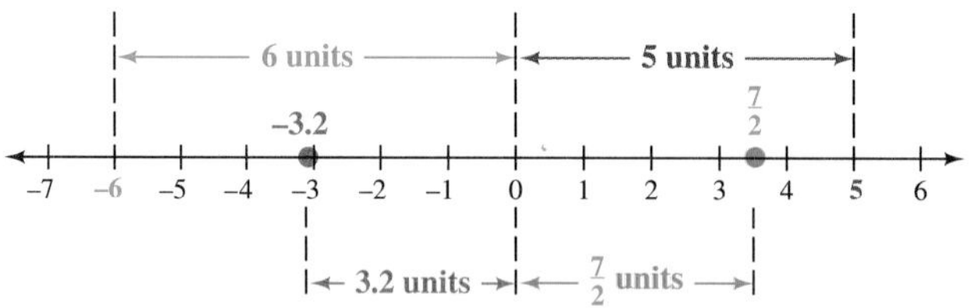

FIGURE 2.8
Absolute Value Using a Number Line

(a) 5 is 5 units from 0. Thus, $|5| = 5$.

(b) $\dfrac{7}{2}$ is $\dfrac{7}{2}$ units from 0. Thus, $\left|\dfrac{7}{2}\right| = \dfrac{7}{2}$.

(c) 0 is 0 units from 0. Thus, $|0| = 0$.

(d) -6 is 6 units from 0. Thus, $|-6| = 6$.

(e) -3.2 is 3.2 units from 0. Thus, $|-3.2| = 3.2$. ■

NOTE Remember that the absolute value of a positive number or zero is the number itself. The absolute value of a negative number is the positive number formed by removing the minus sign. Thus, *the absolute value of a number is always greater than or equal to zero, never negative.*

2.2 EXERCISES

Answer true *or* false *in Exercises 1–5. If the statement is false, tell why.*

1. $\{0, 1, 2, 3, \ldots\}$ is the set of nonnegative integers.
2. If a number x is located to the left of a number y on a number line, then $x > y$.
3. The distance from zero to a number y on a number line is called the absolute value of y.
4. An elevation of 4500 feet above sea level would be denoted by -4500.
5. A withdrawal of \$200 from a savings account could be denoted by $-\$200$.

Place the correct symbol, =, >, or <, between the given pairs of numbers in Exercises 6–9.

6. $-2 \quad 0$
7. $2 \quad 9$
8. $-\frac{3}{4} \quad \frac{1}{4}$
9. $-5 \quad -5$

Is each statement given in Exercises 10–13 true *or* false? *If the statement is false, tell why.*

10. $-12 \le 0$
11. $0 \le -3$
12. $-2 \le -7$
13. $-0.5 \le -\frac{1}{2}$

14. Plot the numbers $\frac{2}{3}$, $-\frac{7}{8}$, $\frac{5}{4}$, $-\frac{7}{4}$, $\frac{5}{2}$, and $-\frac{10}{3}$ on a number line.

Place the correct symbol, =, >, or <, between the given pairs of fractions in Exercises 15–18.

15. $\frac{17}{43} \quad \frac{28}{79}$
16. $\frac{4}{11} \quad \frac{7}{19}$
17. $\frac{13}{50} \quad \frac{39}{150}$
18. $\frac{2}{9} \quad \frac{21}{91}$

Evaluate each absolute value in Exercises 19–22.

19. $|-1|$
20. $|0|$
21. $\left|-\frac{3}{4}\right|$
22. $|3.1|$

FOR REVIEW

Select a variable to represent each quantity in Exercises 23–24 and translate the phrase into symbols.

23. \$200 more than triple his salary
24. the price decreased by 20% of the price

Evaluate each expression in Exercises 25–27 when $x = 5$.

25. $3x^2$
26. $(3x)^2$
27. $30 - x^2$

28. The area of a circle is given by $A = \pi r^2$ where r is the radius of the circle. Find the area of a circle with radius 6.2 centimeters. Use 3.14 for π and round to the nearest tenth.

2.2 PARALLEL EXERCISES

Answer true *or* false *in Exercises 1–5. If the statement is false, tell why.*

1. $\{\ldots, -3, -2, -1\}$ is called the set of negative integers.
2. If a number w is located to the right of a number v on a number line, then $w < v$.
3. The numeral -11 is read "negative eleven."
4. The absolute value of z, denoted by $|z|$, is the distance from zero to z on a number line.
5. An airplane flying at an altitude of 25,000 feet could be described as flying at an altitude of $-25{,}000$ feet.

Place the correct symbol, =, >, or <, between the given pairs of numbers in Exercises 6–9.

6. $0 \quad -7$ **7.** $3 \quad 12$ **8.** $\frac{2}{3} \quad -\frac{2}{3}$ **9.** $-6 \quad -6$

Is each statement given in Exercises 10–13 true *or* false? *If the statement is false, tell why.*

10. $-3 \geq -4$ **11.** $-1 \geq -1$ **12.** $-5 \leq -40$ **13.** $-0.1 \leq -\frac{1}{10}$

14. Plot the numbers $\frac{1}{3}$, $-\frac{3}{4}$, $\frac{7}{4}$, $-\frac{9}{4}$, $\frac{7}{2}$, and $-\frac{11}{3}$ on a number line.

Place the correct symbol, =, >, or <, between the given pairs of fractions in Exercises 15–18.

15. $\frac{3}{5} \quad \frac{7}{10}$ **16.** $\frac{36}{11} \quad \frac{77}{20}$ **17.** $\frac{19}{43} \quad \frac{57}{129}$ **18.** $\frac{27}{201} \quad \frac{13}{121}$

Evaluate each absolute value in Exercises 19–22.

19. $|-2|$ **20.** $|-0|$ **21.** $|8.7|$ **22.** $|-0.03|$

FOR REVIEW

Select a variable to represent each quantity in Exercises 23–24 and translate the phrase into symbols.

23. twice the sum of my age and 10 **24.** the cost increased by 35%

Evaluate each expression in Exercises 25–27 when $x = 3$.

25. $7x^2$ **26.** $(7x)^2$ **27.** $15 - x^2$

28. The surface area of a sphere is given by $A = 4\pi r^2$ where r is the radius of the sphere. Find the surface area of a sphere with radius 3.5 inches. Use 3.14 for π and round to the nearest tenth.

2.2 ENRICHMENT EXERCISES

Place the correct symbol, =, >, or <, between the pairs of fractions.

1. $-\frac{14}{19} \quad -\frac{2}{3}$ **2.** $-\frac{21}{8} \quad -\frac{31}{11}$ **3.** $-\frac{77}{14} \quad -\frac{11}{2}$

Answer true *or* false *in Exercises 4–13. If the answer is false, explain why.*

4. Zero is a rational number.
5. Every integer is a rational number.
6. Some rational numbers are integers.

7. Negative 5 is greater than negative 3.
8. The absolute value of 7 is −7.
9. The absolute value of −5 is greater than the absolute value of 2.
10. The absolute value of any negative rational number is always greater than 0.
11. Every whole number is an integer.
12. $0.\overline{31}$ is a rational number.
13. −13 is greater than −4.
14. Is 0.01001000100001000001 . . . a rational number? Explain why or why not.
15. Using complete sentences, give two descriptions of the set of rational numbers. Can you find a number that is not rational?

SECTION 2.3 Addition and Subtraction of Rational Numbers

Student guideposts

- *Adding numbers with like signs*
- *Adding numbers with unlike signs*
- *Additive identity*
- *Additive inverse (opposite)*
- *Commutative law of addition*
- *Associative law of addition*
- *Adding more than two numbers*
- *Subtracting numbers*

In Chapter 1 we reviewed the four basic operations on the nonnegative rational numbers. Now we extend our treatment to addition and subtraction of all rational numbers. Consider the addition problem 3 + 2 on the number line in Figure 2.9.

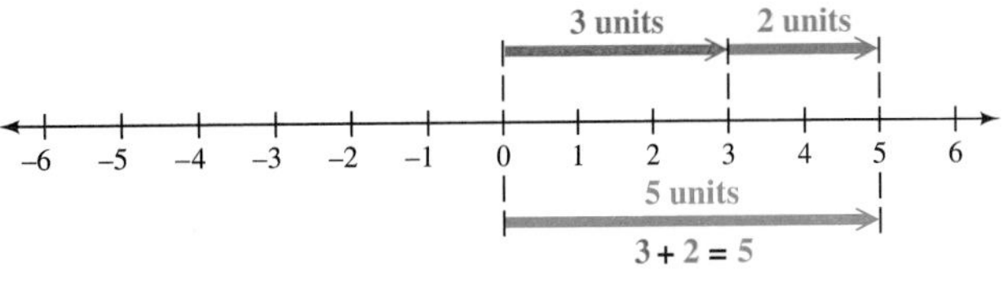

FIGURE 2.9

To find 3 + 2, we start at 0, move 3 units to the *right,* and then move 2 more units to the *right.* We are then 5 units to the *right* of zero. Thus, 3 + 2 = 5.

We can also find 3 + (−2) on a number line. We first move 3 units to the *right* and then 2 units to the *left.* This puts us 1 unit to the *right* of 0, as shown in Figure 2.10. Thus, 3 + (−2) = 1.

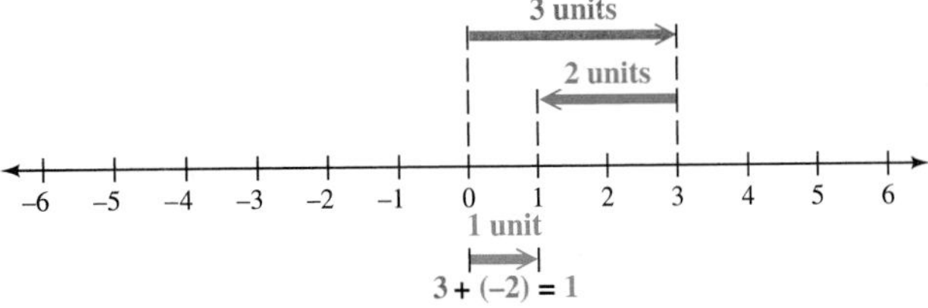

FIGURE 2.10

NOTE If we think of numbers as temperatures, an increase of 3° (+3) followed by a second increase of 2° (+2) results in a total increase of 5° (+5). Similarly, an increase of 3° (+3) followed by a decrease of 2° (−2) results in a net increase of 1° (+1).

When adding numbers using a number line, remember to move to the *right when a number is positive* and to the *left when it is negative.*

EXAMPLE 1

Adding Numbers with Like Signs

Find $(-3) + (-2)$.

Draw a number line. Move 3 units to the left for -3 and then 2 more units to the left for -2. As seen in Figure 2.11, we end up 5 units to the left of 0, at -5. Thus, $(-3) + (-2) = -5$. ■

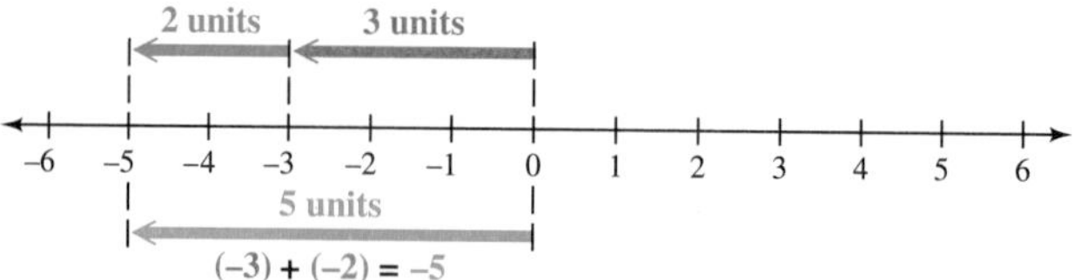

FIGURE 2.11

EXAMPLE 2

Adding Numbers with Unlike Signs

Find $(-3) + 2$.

Draw a number line. Move 3 units to the left and then 2 units to the right. As Figure 2.12 shows, we are then at -1. Thus, $(-3) + 2 = -1$. ■

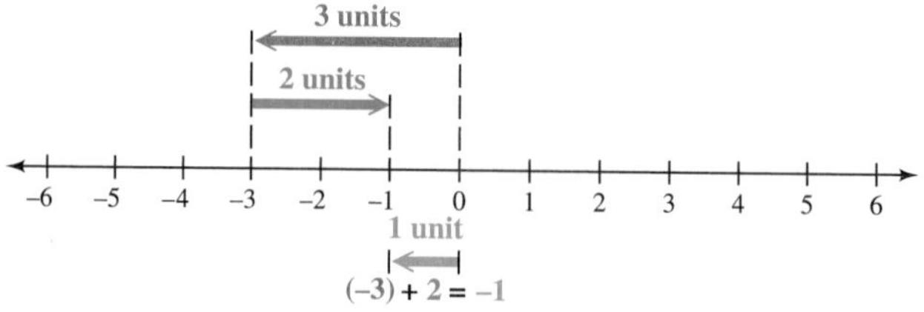

FIGURE 2.12

EXAMPLE 3

Adding Numbers with Unlike Signs

Find $2 + (-3)$.

Draw a number line. Move 2 units to the right and then 3 units to the left. (See Figure 2.13.) This puts us at -1. Thus, $2 + (-3) = -1$. ■

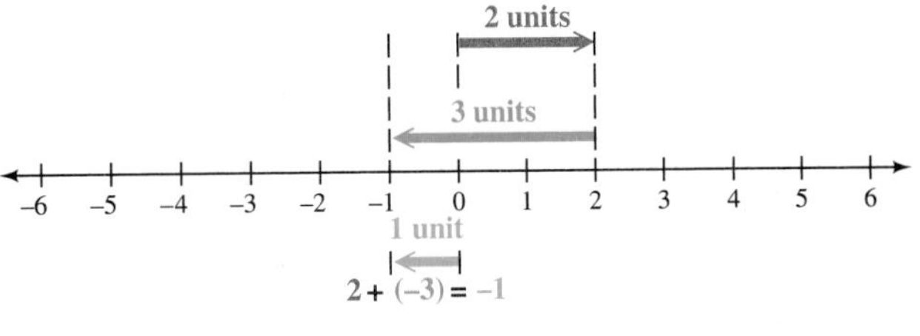

FIGURE 2.13

▶ *Adding numbers with like signs*

The number-line method of adding numbers shows us what addition means, but it takes too much time. For example, we found $(-3) + (-2)$ to be -5 using a number line (Figure 2.11). However, we could have added $3 + 2$ and attached a minus sign:

$$(-3) + (-2) = -(3 + 2) = -5.$$

This is an example of the following rule.

Adding Numbers Having Like Signs

To add two numbers having **like signs,** add their absolute values (numbers that are greater than or equal to zero). The sum has the same sign as the numbers being added.

▶ *Adding numbers with unlike signs*

When the signs of the numbers being added are not the same, we need another rule. For $3 + (-2) = 1$ (Figure 2.10), we could have found the difference between 3 and 2 and attached a plus sign:

$$3 + (-2) = +(3 - 2) = +1 = 1.$$

Also, for $(-3) + 2 = 2 + (-3) = -1$ (Figures 2.12 and 2.13), we could have subtracted 2 from 3 and attached a minus sign:

$$(-3) + 2 = 2 + (-3) = -(3 - 2) = -1.$$

These are examples of the following rule.

Adding Numbers Having Unlike Signs

To add two numbers having **unlike signs,** subtract the smaller absolute value from the larger absolute value. The result has the same sign as the number with the larger absolute value. If the absolute values are the same, the sum is zero.

NOTE Remember that if a number (other than zero) has no sign, this is the same as having a plus sign attached. For example, 5 and +5 are the same.

EXAMPLE 4 **Adding Rational Numbers**

Add using the preceding rules.

(a) $6 + 7 = 13$

(b) $(-6) + (-7) = -(6 + 7) = -13$ $|-6| = 6, |-7| = 7$

(c) $6 + (-7) = -(7 - 6) = -1$ $|-7| = 7 > 6 = |6|$

(d) $(-6) + 7 = +(7 - 6) = +1 = 1$ $|-6| = 6 < 7 = |7|$

(e) $12 + (-12) = 0$ $|12| = 12 = |-12|$

(f) $(-2.3) + (-4.1) = -(2.3 + 4.1) = -6.4$

(g) $(-3.5) + 1.7 = -(3.5 - 1.7) = -1.8$

(h) $\frac{1}{2} + \left(-\frac{3}{4}\right) = -\left(\frac{3}{4} - \frac{1}{2}\right) = -\left(\frac{3}{4} - \frac{2}{4}\right) = -\frac{1}{4}$ ■

▶ *Additive identity*

The number 0 plays a special role in our number system since for any number a,

$$a + 0 = 0 + a = a.$$

Intuitively, we see any number a remains identically the same when added to 0. For this reason, 0 is called the **additive identity.**

▶ *Additive inverse (opposite)*

Example 4(e) illustrates another property of our number system. If a is any number, we call $-a$ the **additive inverse,** or **opposite** of a, which means

$$a + (-a) = (-a) + a = 0.$$

NOTE We use the term *opposite* since a and $-a$ are the same distance from but on opposite sides of 0 on a number line. The term **negative** a is also used for the additive inverse of a.

EXAMPLE 5 **Additive Identity and Inverses**

Add.

(a) $0 + 7 = 7 + 0 = 7$ 0 is the additive identity

(b) $0 + (-7) = (-7) + 0 = -7$ 0 is the additive identity

(c) $6.1 + (-6.1) = 0$ Additive inverse

(d) $-\frac{3}{4} + \frac{3}{4} = 0$ Additive inverse ■

▶ *Commutative law of addition*

With two more properties of addition, we can change the order of addition, and rearrange grouping symbols in sums of three (or more) numbers. If a and b are two numbers, the **commutative law of addition** states that

$$a + b = b + a.$$

That is, the order of addition can be changed by the commutative law. For example, $16 + 5 = 5 + 16$.

▶ *Associative law of addition*

Given another number c, the **associative law of addition** states that

$$(a + b) + c = a + (b + c).$$

That is, the grouping symbols can be rearranged by the associative law. For example, $(5 + 2) + 3 = 5 + (2 + 3)$.

EXAMPLE 6

Commutative and Associative Laws

(a) Use the commutative law to complete the statement: $5 + \frac{1}{4} =$ _____. The commutative law says the order of addition can be changed, so

$$5 + \frac{1}{4} = \frac{1}{4} + 5.$$

(b) Use the associative law to complete the statement: $(7 + \frac{1}{2}) + (-2) =$ _____. The associative law says the grouping symbols can be rearranged, so

$$\left(7 + \frac{1}{2}\right) + (-2) = 7 + \left[\frac{1}{2} + (-2)\right]. \quad ■$$

▶ *Adding more than two numbers*

Taken together, the commutative and associative laws of addition allow us to add several signed numbers by reordering and regrouping the numbers to obtain the sum in the most convenient manner.

Adding More Than Two Numbers

1. Add all positive numbers.
2. Add all negative numbers.
3. Now use the rule for adding numbers with unlike signs.

EXAMPLE 7

Adding Several Numbers

Add.

$$\begin{aligned}(-2) + (-3) + 2 + 7 + (-5) + 6 + 9 + (-1)& \\ &= [2 + 7 + 6 + 9] + [(-2) + (-3) + (-5) + (-1)] \\ &= [2 + 7 + 6 + 9] + [-(2 + 3 + 5 + 1)] \\ &= [24] + [-11] = +[24 - 11] = 13 \quad ■\end{aligned}$$

NOTE With practice we should be able to skip many of the intermediate steps in the preceding examples and make computations mentally.

▶ *Subtracting numbers*

Subtraction of numbers can be defined as addition of an additive inverse. For example, we can think of $5 - 3 = 2$ as $5 + (-3) = 2$.

Subtracting Numbers

To subtract one number from another, change the sign of the number being subtracted and use the rule for adding numbers. Thus, for rational numbers a and b,

$$a - b = a + (-b).$$

EXAMPLE 8 **Subtracting Numbers**

Subtract.

(a) $5 - (+3) = 5 + (-3)$ Change sign and add
$= 5 - 3 = 2$

(b) $5 - (-3) = 5 + 3 = 8$ Change sign and add

(c) $(-5) - 3 = (-5) + (-3)$ Change sign and add
$= -(5 + 3) = -8$

(d) $(-5) - (-3) = (-5) + 3$ Change sign and add
$= -(5 - 3) = -2$

(e) $(-5) - 0 = (-5) + (-0)$ Change sign and add
$= (-5) + 0$ The negative of zero is zero: $-0 = 0$
$= -5$ ■

EXAMPLE 9 **Subtracting Numbers**

Subtract.

(a) $5 - (+5) = 5 + (-5) = 0$

(b) $5 - (-5) = 5 + 5 = 10$

(c) $(-5) - 5 = (-5) + (-5) = -(5 + 5) = -10$

(d) $(-5) - (-5) = (-5) + 5 = 0$

(e) $(-5.8) - (-3.2) = (-5.8) + 3.2 = -(5.8 - 3.2) = -2.6$

(f) $\left(-\frac{2}{3}\right) - \frac{1}{6} = \left(-\frac{2}{3}\right) + \left(-\frac{1}{6}\right) = \left(-\frac{4}{6}\right) + \left(-\frac{1}{6}\right) = -\frac{5}{6}$ ■

CAUTION Although addition satisfies both the commutative and associative laws, subtraction does not. For example,

$$3 = 5 - 2 \neq 2 - 5 = -3.$$ Subtraction is *not* commutative

Likewise, $(8 - 4) - 3 = 4 - 3 = 1$,
but $8 - (4 - 3) = 8 - 1 = 7$. Subtraction is *not* associative

We now solve the applied problem presented in the chapter introduction.

EXAMPLE 10

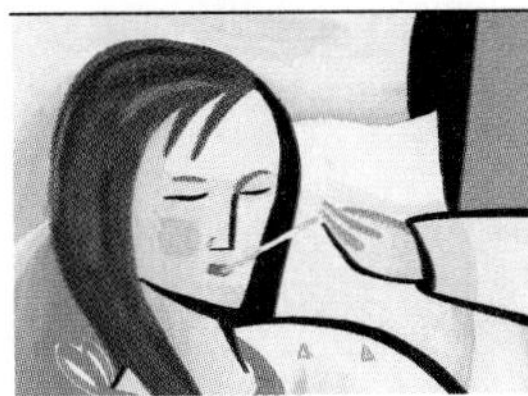

Application to Health

When Erin Kelly was in the hospital the doctor was interested in changes in her temperature throughout the day. At 9:00 A.M. her temperature was 100.4°. The nurse then reported that by 11:00 A.M. there had been an increase of 0.7°, over the next two hours a decrease of 1.9°, between 1:00 P.M. and 3:00 P.M. an increase of 3.1°, and finally a decrease of 2.8° by 5:00 P.M. What was Erin's temperature at the end of the recording period at 5:00 P.M.?

We consider the increases in Erin's temperature as positive numbers and the decreases as negative numbers. Thus, we must add 0.7, −1.9, 3.1, and −2.8 to find the total change from the original temperature of 100.4°.

$$\begin{aligned} 0.7 + (-1.9) + 3.1 + (-2.8) &= 0.7 + 3.1 + (-1.9) + (-2.8) \\ &= 0.7 + 3.1 - (1.9 + 2.8) \\ &= 3.8 - 4.7 \\ &= -0.9 \end{aligned}$$

Now add 100.4 and −0.9 to find her temperature at the end of the recording period.

$$\begin{aligned} 100.4 + (-0.9) &= 100.4 - 0.9 \\ &= 99.5 \end{aligned}$$

Erin's temperature was 99.5° at 5:00 P.M. ■

2.3 EXERCISES

Perform the indicated operation in Exercises 1–28.

1. $4 + 3$ **2.** $(-4) + (-3)$ **3.** $4 + (-3)$

4. $(-4) + 3$ **5.** $4 + 0$ **6.** $0 + (-4)$

7. $7 + (-7)$ **8.** $(-7) + (-7)$ **9.** $(-8) + (-5)$

10. $9 + (-1)$ **11.** $19 + (-25)$ **12.** $(-4) - (-3)$

13. $4 - (-3)$ **14.** $(-4) - 3$ **15.** $(-7) - (-7)$

16. $9 - (-1)$ **17.** $(-1) - 9$ **18.** $(-16) - 14$

19. $1.3 + (-2.5)$ **20.** $(-1.3) + 2.5$ **21.** $(-1.3) - (-2.5)$

22. $\left(-\frac{1}{2}\right) + \left(-\frac{2}{5}\right)$ **23.** $\frac{1}{2} - \left(-\frac{2}{5}\right)$ **24.** $\left(-\frac{1}{2}\right) - \frac{2}{5}$

25. $(-3) + 2 + (-7) + (-8) + 9$ **26.** $5 + 8 + 9 + (-3) + (-7)$

27. $(-8) + (-6) + 9 + (-3) + 5 + (-6)$ **28.** $(-4) + (-2) + 6 + 7 + (-1)$

29. Show by example that subtraction does not satisfy the commutative law. Can you find numbers a and b for which $a - b$ does equal $b - a$?

Add in Exercises 30–32.

30.
$$\begin{array}{r} 23 \\ -16 \\ -36 \\ 5 \\ \underline{81} \end{array}$$

31.
$$\begin{array}{r} -16 \\ -81 \\ -14 \\ -70 \\ \underline{-93} \end{array}$$

32.
$$\begin{array}{r} -64 \\ 25 \\ 38 \\ -17 \\ \underline{-83} \end{array}$$

33. TEMPERATURE When a cold front came through Cut Bank, Montana, the temperature dropped from 35° above zero to 13° below zero (−13°). What was the total change in temperature?

34. BANKING On March 1, Allen had \$64 in his bank account. During the month, he wrote checks for \$81, \$108, and \$192 and made deposits of \$123 and \$140. What was the value of his account at the end of the month?

35. MILITARY A helicopter is 600 feet above sea level and a submarine directly below it is 250 feet below sea level (−250 ft). How far apart are they?

36. TEMPERATURE At 5:30 A.M., it was −42°F. By 2:00 P.M. the same day, the temperature had risen 57° to the recorded high temperature. Shortly thereafter, a cold front passed through dropping the temperature 41° by 5:00 P.M. What was the temperature at 5:00 P.M.?

FOR REVIEW

Place the correct symbol, =, <, or >, between the given pairs of numbers in Exercises 37–40.

37. $-5 \quad -4$ **38.** $\frac{2}{3} \quad \frac{77}{110}$ **39.** $\frac{5}{12} \quad \frac{30}{72}$ **40.** $-4.7 \quad -1.2$

Evaluate each absolute value in Exercises 41–44.

41. $|-81|$ **42.** $\left|-\frac{5}{4}\right|$ **43.** $|17|$ **44.** $|-7.25|$

2.3 PARALLEL EXERCISES

Perform the indicated operations in Exercises 1–28.

1. $5 + 2$ **2.** $(-5) + (-2)$ **3.** $5 + (-2)$
4. $(-5) + 2$ **5.** $0 + 5$ **6.** $(-5) + 0$
7. $(-5) + 5$ **8.** $(-5) + (-5)$ **9.** $18 + (-23)$
10. $(-15) + 19$ **11.** $8 - 7$ **12.** $(-8) - (-7)$
13. $8 - (-7)$ **14.** $0 - (-10)$ **15.** $6 - (-6)$
16. $(-11) - (-4)$ **17.** $(-12) - 24$ **18.** $18 - (-27)$
19. $(-1.5) + (-3.8)$ **20.** $1.5 - (-3.8)$ **21.** $(-1.5) - 3.8$
22. $\frac{1}{4} + \left(-\frac{3}{8}\right)$ **23.** $\left(-\frac{1}{4}\right) + \frac{3}{8}$ **24.** $\left(-\frac{1}{4}\right) - \left(-\frac{3}{8}\right)$
25. $(-5) + 4 + (-9) + (-10) + 6$ **26.** $5 + 9 + (-3) + 1 + (-10)$
27. $(-5) + (-7) + 10 + (-3) + 4 + (-7)$ **28.** $(-6) + (-3) + 6 + 10 + (-2)$

29. Show by example that subtraction does not satisfy the associative law. Can you find numbers, a, b, and c for which $(a - b) - c$ does equal $a - (b - c)$?

Add in Exercises 30–32.

30. $\begin{array}{r} 26 \\ -14 \\ -51 \\ 3 \\ \underline{92} \end{array}$

31. $\begin{array}{r} -17 \\ -20 \\ -43 \\ -5 \\ \underline{-110} \end{array}$

32. $\begin{array}{r} -78 \\ 32 \\ 51 \\ -60 \\ \underline{-92} \end{array}$

---

33. TEMPERATURE In a five-hour period of time, the temperature in Empire, NY dropped from 41° to 12° below zero. What was the total temperature change?

34. BANKING On July 4, Uncle Sam had \$97 in his checking account. During the next week he wrote checks for \$15, \$102, and \$312, and made deposits of \$145 and \$170. What was the value of his account at the end of the week?

35. METEOROLOGY A weather balloon is 1200 feet above sea level, and a diving bell directly below it is 340 feet beneath the surface of the water. How far apart are the two?

36. HEALTH At 8:00 A.M., Leah Johnson had a temperature of 99.8°. It rose another 3.1° before falling 4.3° by noon. What was her temperature at noon?

FOR REVIEW

Place the correct symbol, =, <, or >, between the given pairs of numbers in Exercises 37–40.

37. $-6 \quad -7$ **38.** $\frac{3}{4} \quad \frac{96}{120}$ **39.** $\frac{7}{8} \quad \frac{77}{88}$ **40.** $0 \quad -11.5$

Evaluate each absolute value in Exercises 41–44.

41. $\left|-\frac{9}{10}\right|$ **42.** $|-210|$ **43.** $|42|$ **44.** $|-0.01|$

2.3 ENRICHMENT EXERCISES

Perform the indicated operations in Exercises 1–3.

1. $(-962) - (-508)$ **2.** $-48.62 - 40.002$ △ **3.** $64\frac{7}{24} - 98\frac{13}{16}$

In Exercises 4–9, give the name of the property that is being illustrated.

4. $7 + (-7) = 0$ **5.** $x + 3 = 3 + x$

6. $4 + (a + 8) = (4 + a) + 8$ **7.** $2.5 + 0 = 2.5$

8. $(2 + y) + z = z + (2 + y)$ **9.** $24 + (x + 3) = 24 + (3 + x)$

In Exercises 10–13, answer true *or* false. *If the answer is false, explain why.*

10. The sum of any two negative numbers is always a negative number.

11. The sum of a negative number and a positive number is always a negative number.

12. If x is subtracted from y, we find the result by adding the opposite of x to y.

13. If a is a positive number and b is a negative number, then $a - b$ is positive.

In Exercises 14–17, write a complete sentence describing the given property.

14. additive inverse property

15. additive identity property

16. commutative law of addition

17. associative law of addition

18. In your own words, describe the method used to add two numbers with like signs.

19. In your own words, describe the method used to add two numbers with unlike signs.

20. In your own words, describe the method used to subtract one number from another.

SECTION 2.4 Multiplication and Division of Rational Numbers

Student guideposts

- *Multiplying numbers*
- *Multiplicative identity*
- *Multiplicative inverse (reciprocal)*
- *Commutative law of multiplication*
- *Associative law of multiplication*
- *Dividing numbers*
- *Sign properties*

Multiplying numbers

In multiplying and dividing numbers, we need to decide what sign to give the product or quotient. To help us, we look for patterns in several products.

Decreases by 1 each time → first factor; Decreases by 2 each time → product

$$
\begin{aligned}
4 \cdot 2 &= 8 \\
3 \cdot 2 &= 6 \quad \text{6 is 2 less than 8} \\
2 \cdot 2 &= 4 \\
1 \cdot 2 &= 2 \\
0 \cdot 2 &= 0 \\
(-1) \cdot 2 &= -2 \quad \text{-2 is 2 less than 0} \\
(-2) \cdot 2 &= -4 \quad \text{-4 is 2 less than -2} \\
(-3) \cdot 2 &= -6 \\
(-4) \cdot 2 &= -8
\end{aligned}
$$

We know the products $4 \cdot 2$, $3 \cdot 2$, $2 \cdot 2$, $1 \cdot 2$, and $0 \cdot 2$, and we can see that these products decrease by 2 each time. For this pattern to continue, a negative number times a positive number must be negative. For example,

$$(-1) \cdot 2 = -2, \quad (-2) \cdot 2 = -4, \quad (-3) \cdot 2 = -6, \quad (-4) \cdot 2 = -8.$$

Similarly, any positive number times any negative number must be negative. We use this to find a pattern in the following products.

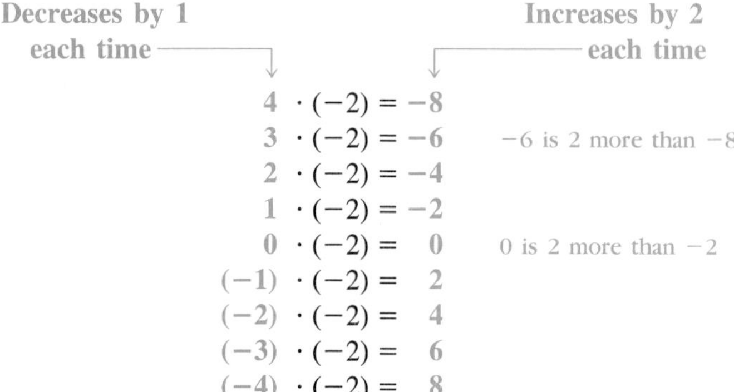

For this pattern to continue, a negative number times a negative number must be a positive number. For example,

$$(-1) \cdot (-2) = 2, \quad (-2) \cdot (-2) = 4, \quad (-3) \cdot (-2) = 6, \quad (-4) \cdot (-2) = 8.$$

Our results are summarized in the following rule.

Multiplying Numbers

1. Multiply the absolute values of the numbers.
2. If both signs are positive or both negative, the product is positive.
3. If one sign is positive and one is negative, the product is negative.
4. If one number (or both numbers) is zero, the product is zero.

NOTE When multiplying numbers, remember that *like signs have a positive product and unlike signs have a negative product.*

EXAMPLE 1

Multiplying Numbers

Multiply.

(a) $5 \cdot 2 = 10$ Like signs

(b) $(-5)(-2) = (5 \cdot 2) = 10$ Like signs

(c) $5 \cdot (-2) = -(5 \cdot 2) = -10$ Unlike signs

(d) $(-5) \cdot 2 = -(5 \cdot 2) = -10$ Unlike signs

(e) $0 \cdot (-8) = 0$

(f) $0 \cdot 0 = 0$

(g) $(3)\left(\frac{1}{3}\right) = 1$

(h) $(-2.1) \cdot (-3.5) = (2.1)(3.5) = 7.35$

(i) $\left(\frac{1}{4}\right)\left(-\frac{3}{5}\right) = -\left(\frac{1}{4}\right)\left(\frac{3}{5}\right) = -\frac{3}{20}$ ■

▶ *Multiplicative identity*

The number 1 plays a role in multiplication similar to the one 0 plays in addition. Since for any number a,

$$a \cdot 1 = 1 \cdot a = a,$$

we see that a number remains identically the same when multiplied by 1. For this reason, 1 is called the **multiplicative identity.**

▶ *Multiplicative inverse (reciprocal)*

Example 1(g) illustrates a property of reciprocals that we have seen before. If a is any number except 0, we call $\frac{1}{a}$ the **multiplicative inverse** (or **reciprocal**) of a, which means that

$$a \cdot \frac{1}{a} = \frac{1}{a} \cdot a = 1.$$

EXAMPLE 2

Using the Multiplicative Identity and Inverses

Multiply.

(a) $(-5)\left(-\frac{1}{5}\right) = 1$ -5 and $-\frac{1}{5}$ are reciprocals or multiplicative inverses

(b) $1 \cdot (-7) = (-7) \cdot 1 = -7$ 1 is the multiplicative identity ■

▶ *Commutative law of multiplication*

With two more properties of multiplication, like the ones for addition, we can change the order of multiplication and rearrange grouping symbols in products of three (or more) numbers. If a and b are two numbers, the **commutative law of multiplication** states that

$$ab = ba.$$

That is, the order of multiplication can be changed by the commutative law. For example, $4 \cdot 7 = 7 \cdot 4$.

▶ *Associative law of multiplication*

Given another number c, the **associative law of multiplication** states that

$$(ab)c = a(bc).$$

That is, the grouping symbols can be rearranged by the associative law. For example, $(2 \cdot 5) \cdot 3 = 2 \cdot (5 \cdot 3)$.

EXAMPLE 3

Using the Commutative and Associative Laws

(a) Use the commutative law to complete the statement: $7 \cdot \frac{3}{4} =$ ______. The commutative law says the order of multiplication can be changed, so

$$7 \cdot \frac{3}{4} = \frac{3}{4} \cdot 7.$$

(b) Use the associative law to complete the statement: $\left(3 \cdot \frac{1}{5}\right) \cdot (-5) =$ _____. The associative law says the grouping symbols can be rearranged, so

$$\left(3 \cdot \frac{1}{5}\right) \cdot (-5) = 3 \cdot \left(\frac{1}{5} \cdot (-5)\right). \quad \blacksquare$$

Often we will need to multiply more than two numbers. To do this, multiply in pairs and keep track of the sign.

EXAMPLE 4

Multiplying More Than Two Numbers

Multiply.

(a) $(3)(-2)(-4) = (-6)(-4) = 24$ Multiply 3 times -2 first

(b) $(-1)(-1)(-2)(-3)(-4) = (1)(-2)(-3)(-4)$ $(-1)(-1) = 1$

$= (-2)(-3)(-4)$ $(1)(-2) = -2$

$= (6)(-4)$ $(-2)(-3) = 6$

$= -24$

(c) $(-2)^3 = (-2)(-2)(-2) = (4)(-2)$ $(-2)(-2) = 4$

$= -8$ ■

NOTE We can see from Example 4 that *products involving an odd number of minus signs are negative and those with an even number of minus signs are positive.* For example, in part (a), there were two minus signs and the product was positive, while in part (b), there were five minus signs and the product was negative. We can take advantage of this observation and multiply the absolute values of the numbers and attach the appropriate sign when we are through.

▶ *Dividing numbers*

We have seen that the only difference between multiplying positive numbers and multiplying rational numbers is finding the sign of the product. Recall that division can be thought of as multiplication by a reciprocal. For example,

$$15 \div 3 \text{ or } \frac{15}{3} \quad \text{is the same as} \quad 15 \cdot \frac{1}{3}.$$

In general, we have the following definition.

Dividing Numbers

If a and b are numbers, $b \neq 0$, then division is defined by

$$a \div b = \frac{a}{b} = a \cdot \frac{1}{b}.$$

Thus, we can use the same rules for signs in division that we used for multiplication.

Dividing Numbers

1. Divide the absolute values of the numbers.
2. If both signs are positive or both negative, the quotient is positive.
3. If one sign is positive and one negative, the quotient is negative.
4. Zero divided by any number (except zero) is zero, and division of any number by 0 is undefined.

NOTE Simply remember that the rule of signs for division is exactly the same as for multiplication: *like signs have a positive quotient and unlike signs have a negative quotient.*

EXAMPLE 5 **Dividing Numbers**

Divide.

(a) $6 \div 3 = 2$ Like signs

(b) $(-6) \div (-3) = 6 \div 3 = 2$ Like signs

(c) $6 \div (-3) = -(6 \div 3) = -2$ Unlike signs

(d) $(-6) \div 3 = -(6 \div 3) = -2$ Unlike signs

(e) $0 \div (-3) = 0$

(f) $(-3) \div 0$ is undefined

(g) $\frac{1}{2} \div \left(-\frac{3}{5}\right) = \frac{1}{2} \cdot \left(-\frac{5}{3}\right) = -\left(\frac{1}{2} \cdot \frac{5}{3}\right) = -\frac{5}{6}$ ■

CAUTION Although multiplication satisfies both the commutative and associative laws, division does not. For example,

$$3 = 6 \div 2 \neq 2 \div 6 = \frac{2}{6} = \frac{1}{3}. \quad \text{Division is } \textit{not} \text{ commutative}$$

Likewise, $(8 \div 4) \div 2 = 2 \div 2 = 1$
but $8 \div (4 \div 2) = 8 \div 2 = 4.$ Division is *not* associative

EXAMPLE 6 **Applying Signed Numbers to Personal Banking**

Willie wrote 3 checks for \$75 each and 4 checks for \$105 each. By how much did this change his bank balance?

The 3 checks for \$75 could be calculated as follows:

$$(3)(-75) = -225.$$

There are 4 checks for \$105, so

$$(4)(-105) = -420.$$

Thus, his account is changed by

$$-225 + (-420) = -225 - 420 = -645 \text{ dollars.}$$

His balance is \$645 less. ■

EXAMPLE 7

Applying Signed Numbers to Personal Finance

Mary, Sue, and Eve share an apartment with total rent of \$720. How much is each woman's bank account changed if they each write a check for an equal share of the rent?

Since the rent is a decrease in their accounts, we use -720. To find the shares, we divide -720 by 3:

$$-720 \div 3 = -240.$$

Thus, each woman's account is decreased by \$240. ■

When evaluating numerical expressions involving rational numbers, follow the order of operations and rules of grouping given in Section 2.1. That is, evaluate within grouping symbols first, beginning with the innermost, evaluate powers next, and then perform multiplication and division left to right followed by addition and subtraction.

EXAMPLE 8

Using the Order of Operations

Evaluate each numerical expression.

(a) $(-3) + 5 \cdot (-1) - (-4)$

$= (-3) + (-5) - (-4)$ Multiply first

$= (-8) - (-4)$ Add first from left

$= (-8) + 4$ Then subtract

$= -4$

(b) $(-2)^3 + 1 = (-2)(-2)(-2) + 1$ $a^3 = aaa$

$= (4)(-2) + 1$ $(-2)(-2) = 4$

$= (-8) + 1$ Multiply first

$= -7$ Then add

(c) $\frac{1}{2} - \left\{\frac{1}{4} - \left[\left(-\frac{3}{4}\right) - \left(-\frac{1}{4}\right)\right]\right\}$

$= \frac{1}{2} - \left\{\frac{1}{4} - \left[\left(-\frac{3}{4}\right) + \frac{1}{4}\right]\right\}$

$= \frac{1}{2} - \left\{\frac{1}{4} - \left[-\frac{2}{4}\right]\right\}$ Innermost parentheses first

$= \frac{1}{2} - \left\{\frac{1}{4} + \frac{2}{4}\right\}$

$= \frac{1}{2} - \left(\frac{3}{4}\right)$

$= \frac{2}{4} - \frac{3}{4} = -\frac{1}{4}$ ■

Sign properties

Notice in Example 8 that we use parentheses to avoid writing plus and minus signs right next to each other. The parentheses may be removed and the two signs replaced by one according to the following rule, part 4 of which is called the **double negative property.**

Sign Properties

If a is any number,

1. $+(+a) = +a$
2. $+(-a) = -a$
3. $-(+a) = -a$
4. $-(-a) = +a.$

NOTE When a plus sign is before parentheses, we *do not* change the sign inside when the parentheses and plus sign are removed. However, when a minus sign is before parentheses, we *do* change the sign inside when the parentheses and minus sign are removed.

EXAMPLE 9

Using Sign Properties

Write without parentheses.

(a) $+(+6) = +6 = 6$

(b) $+(-8) = -8$

(c) $-(+7) = -7$

(d) $-(-5) = +5 = 5$

(e) $-[-(-2)] = -[+2] = -2$ Remove innermost parentheses first ∎

Another important property of signs involves fractions. Consider the following:

$\frac{-8}{4} = -2$ A negative number divided by a positive number is negative

$\frac{8}{-4} = -2$ A positive number divided by a negative number is negative

$-\frac{8}{4} = -2$ The additive inverse of a number a is $-a$

Thus, using the rules of signs for division along with the property of additive inverses, we can see that

$$\frac{-8}{4} = \frac{8}{-4} = -\frac{8}{4}.$$

The same is true in general.

Negative Fraction Property

If a and b are any two integers with $b \neq 0$, then

$$\frac{-a}{b} = \frac{a}{-b} = -\frac{a}{b}.$$

NOTE Simply stated, the negative fraction property says that we can negate a fraction by writing a minus sign in the numerator, or in the denominator, or in front of the fraction.

When we evaluate expressions for values of the variable(s) that are negative, we can follow the same procedures that we used in Section 2.1. The only difference involves placing parentheses around the negative numbers at the substitution step. Doing so will help us avoid the problem of writing two signs next to each other and lessen the chance of making sign errors. This is illustrated in the next two examples.

EXAMPLE 10 **Evaluating Expressions**

Evaluate when $a = -3$ and $b = -2$.

(a) $a - b = (-3) - (-2) = (-3) + 2 = -1$ Use parentheses to substitute

(b) $b - [-a] = (-2) - [-(-3)] = (-2) - [3]$
$= -2 - 3 = -5$

(c) $2a - 3b = 2(-3) - 3(-2) = -6 - (-6) = -6 + 6 = 0$

(d) $|a - 2b| = |(-3) - 2(-2)| = |(-3) - (-4)|$
$= |(-3) + 4| = |1| = 1$ ∎

EXAMPLE 11 **Evaluating Expressions**

Evaluate $3[2(a + 2) - 3(b + c)]$ when $a = -2$, $b = 4$, and $c = -8$.

$3[2(a + 2) - 3(b + c)] = 3[2(-2 + 2) - 3(4 + (-8))]$ Replace variables with numbers
$= 3[2(0) - 3(-4)]$ Add inside parentheses first
$= 3[0 + 12]$
$= 3[12]$
$= 36$ ∎

CAUTION Always place parentheses around negative numbers when evaluating expressions to avoid making sign errors.

2.4 EXERCISES

Perform the indicated operations in Exercises 1–28.

1. $(2)(6)$
2. $(-2)(-6)$
3. $(2)(-6)$
4. $(-2)(6)$
5. $0 \cdot (-6)$
6. $(-3)(-9)$
7. $(-10)(8)$
8. $(-15) \cdot 20$
9. $(-6) \div (-2)$
10. $6 \div (-2)$
11. $0 \div (-6)$
12. $(-6) \div 0$
13. $\dfrac{-99}{|-11|}$
14. $\dfrac{|-36|}{|-4|}$
15. $\dfrac{-|-12|}{12}$
16. $\dfrac{|-48|}{|-16|}$
17. $(-1.2)(2.3)$
18. $\left(\frac{2}{5}\right)\left(-\frac{15}{4}\right)$
19. $\left(-\frac{2}{5}\right)\left(-\frac{15}{4}\right)$
20. $(-6.4) \div (-0.8)$
21. $\dfrac{-6.4}{0.8}$
22. $\frac{3}{5} \div \left(-\frac{9}{15}\right)$
23. $\left(-\frac{3}{5}\right) \div \left(-\frac{9}{15}\right)$
24. $\dfrac{-\frac{3}{5}}{\frac{9}{15}}$
25. $(-1)(-1)(-1)$
26. $(-1)(2)(-3)$
27. $(-1)(-2)(-3)(-4)$
28. $(-1)(-2)(-3)(4)(-5)(6)(-1)$
29. Show by example that division does not satisfy the associative law. Can you find numbers a, b, and c for which $(a \div b) \div c$ does not equal $a \div (b \div c)$?

30. **BANKING** Tony had to write four \$12 checks during the month of June. By how much did this change his bank balance?

31. **SPORTS** Martha had 423 points in an athletic contest, but then she received 20 penalty points 3 times. What was her total after the 3 penalties?

Evaluate each numerical expression in Exercises 32–34.

32. $(-1)^5 + (-1)^3$
33. $4 + 2[(-1) - (-5)]$
34. $3 - \dfrac{2 + (-4)}{1 - 5}$

Write each expression in Exercises 35–38 without parentheses using only one sign (or no sign).

35. $-(+4)$
36. $-(-x)$
37. $-[-(+3)]$
38. $-[-(-4)]$

Evaluate each expression in Exercises 39–44 when $a = -1$, $b = 2$, and $c = -4$.

39. $a^2 - 1$
40. $abc + b^2$
41. $3(a + b) + c$
42. $2(b - a) - c$
43. $2[3(a + 1) + 2(4 + c)]$
44. $a^2 + b^2 + c$

FOR REVIEW

Perform the indicated operations in Exercises 45–47.

45. $(-12) + 9$
46. $(-12) - (-9)$
47. $15 - (-8)$

Add in Exercises 48–51.

48.	49.	50.	51.
−13	−28	−92	−102
12	−29	81	321
26	−42	27	−421
−18	−36	−61	−60

52. FINANCE The Brisebois family owed the credit union \$3000. They repaid \$1200 and later borrowed \$650. What number represents the status of their account?

2.4 PARALLEL EXERCISES

Perform the indicated operations in Exercises 1–28.

1. $(5)(9)$ **2.** $(-5)(-9)$ **3.** $(5)(-9)$

4. $(-5)(9)$ **5.** $(-7)(0)$ **6.** $(-12)(2)$

7. $(-6)(-13)$ **8.** $(-15)(30)$ **9.** $(-9) \div (-3)$

10. $(-9) \div 3$ **11.** $0 \div (-5)$ **12.** $(-5) \div 0$

13. $\dfrac{-88}{|-11|}$ **14.** $\dfrac{|-24|}{|-8|}$ **15.** $\dfrac{-|-15|}{-15}$

16. $\dfrac{0}{|-25|}$ **17.** $(-1.5)(-2.2)$ **18.** $\left(\dfrac{3}{5}\right)\left(-\dfrac{10}{9}\right)$

19. $\left(-\dfrac{3}{5}\right)\left(\dfrac{10}{9}\right)$ **20.** $4.8 \div (-0.6)$ **21.** $\dfrac{-4.8}{-0.6}$

22. $\dfrac{2}{5} \div \left(-\dfrac{6}{15}\right)$ **23.** $\left(-\dfrac{2}{5}\right) \div \left(-\dfrac{6}{15}\right)$ **24.** $\dfrac{-\frac{2}{5}}{\frac{6}{15}}$

25. $(-1)(-1)(-1)(-1)$ **26.** $(-1)(-2)(-3)$ **27.** $(-1)(2)(-3)(4)$

28. $(-1)(-2)(3)(-1)(5)(-4)$

29. Show by example that division does not satisfy the commutative law. Can you find numbers a and b for which $a \div b$ does equal $b \div a$?

---

30. TEMPERATURE During each of 5 consecutive hours, the temperature dropped 7°. By how much did this change the temperature?

31. RECREATION Hank Anderson received 330 points for a performance, but then was penalized 25 points each for four rule infractions. What was his point total after the penalties were imposed?

Evaluate each numerical expression in Exercises 32–34.

32. $(-2)^2 + 3$ **33.** $(4 - 7) \cdot 5 + 2$ **34.** $2 - \dfrac{4 + (-5)}{3 - 5}$

Write each expression in Exercises 35–38 without parentheses using only one sign (or no sign).

35. $-(-5)$ **36.** $-(+a)$ **37.** $-[+(-3)]$ **38.** $-[-(-7)]$

Evaluate each expression in Exercises 39–44 when $x = -2$, $y = 1$, and $z = -3$.

39. $3xy + z$ **40.** $xyz + z^2$ **41.** $3(y - x) - z$

42. $x + \dfrac{y}{z}$ **43.** $2[4(x + 2) + 7(z + 3)]$ **44.** $x^2 + y^2 + z$

FOR REVIEW

Perform the indicated operations in Exercises 45–47.

45. $(-17) + (-6)$ **46.** $(-17) - 6$ **47.** $(-17) - (-6)$

Add in Exercises 48–51.

48.	**49.**	**50.**	**51.**
−16	−40	−97	−205
15	−27	27	420
3	−19	13	−318
−27	−52	−47	− 65

52. **SPORTS** A football team lost 6 yards on first down, gained 11 yards on second down, and lost 4 yards on third down. If the series started on their 25 yard line, where was the ball placed on fourth down?

2.4 ENRICHMENT EXERCISES

Evaluate each numerical expression in Exercises 1–4.

1. $-2 - [3 - (4 - 2)^2]^2$

2. $[17 - (-5 + 8)^2 - 6 \div 2]^2$

3. $-[2^3 - (2 - 4)]^2 - \dfrac{16 - (-6)}{15 - 4}$

4. $\dfrac{|(-3)^2 - (-5)|}{(-2)^3 - (-1)^3} - (-4)^2$

A calculator would be helpful when evaluating each expression in Exercises 5–8.

5. $(3.65)^2 - (2.57 - 1.22)^2$

6. $0.0123[7.2 - (5.5 - 4.6)]$

7. $\dfrac{1.63 - 0.7}{4.8} + \dfrac{(0.76)^2}{1 - (2.71 - 2.11)}$

8. $3.5 - (-5.1) + \dfrac{|(-1.1)^2 - (-2.3)^2|}{|-6.5 - (-4.5)|}$

In Exercises 9–14, give the name of the property that is being illustrated.

9. $4(x + 1) = (x + 1)4$

10. $\left(\dfrac{1}{3}\right)3 = 1$

11. $-\dfrac{1}{a} = \dfrac{-1}{a}$

12. $\dfrac{1}{2}\left(10 \cdot \dfrac{2}{3}\right) = \left(\dfrac{1}{2} \cdot 10\right)\dfrac{2}{3}$

13. $-[-(a + 5)] = a + 5$

14. $1 \cdot (a^2 + 3) = a^2 + 3$

In Exercises 15–18, answer true *or* false. *If the answer is false, explain why.*

15. The product of any two negative numbers is always a negative number.

16. The quotient of two numbers with opposite signs is always a negative number.

17. If x is divided by y, we can find the result by multiplying x by the multiplicative inverse of y.

18. If a is a positive number, then a divided by 0 is also positive.

In Exercises 19–24, write a complete sentence describing the given property.

19. multiplicative inverse property

20. multiplicative identity property

21. associative law of multiplication

22. commutative law of multiplication

23. double negative property

24. negative fraction property

25. In your own words, state the rules that determine the signs when multiplying and dividing numbers.

SECTION 2.5 The Distributive Laws and Simplifying Expressions

Student guideposts

- ▶ *Distributive laws*
- ▶ *Terms, factors, and coefficients*
- ▶ *Collecting like terms*
- ▶ *Simplified expressions*

▶ *Distributive laws*

The operations of addition (or subtraction) and multiplication are related by two important properties called the **distributive laws.** Consider the numerical expression $2(3 + 5)$. Since the order of operations tells us to work within the parentheses first, we evaluate it as follows:

$$2(3 + 5) = 2(8) = 16.$$

However, in this case if we were to "distribute" the product of 2 over the sum of $3 + 5$,

$$2(3 + 5) = 2 \cdot 3 + 2 \cdot 5 = 6 + 10 = 16,$$

we obtain the same result. Similarly,

$$4(8 - 3) = 4(5) = 20,$$

$$\text{and} \quad 4(8 - 3) = 4 \cdot 8 - 4 \cdot 3 = 32 - 12 = 20.$$

Thus multiplication can be "distributed over" addition and subtraction. These examples illustrate the following laws.

Distributive Laws of Multiplication over Addition and Subtraction

If a, b and c are numbers,

1. $a(b + c) = ab + ac$ 2. $a(b - c) = ab - ac$

Since multiplication is commutative, products are not affected by changing the order of multiplication. Thus we also have

$$(b + c)a = ba + ca \quad \text{and} \quad (b - c)a = ba - ca.$$

Also, multiplication distributes over sums with more than two terms.

$$a(b + c + d) = ab + ac + ad$$

EXAMPLE 1 Evaluating Using the Distributive Law

Evaluate each numerical expression in two ways.

(a) $7(3 + 2) = 7 \cdot 3 + 7 \cdot 2 = 21 + 14 = 35.$

Also, $7(3 + 2) = 7(5) = 35.$

(b) $5(8 - 3) = 5 \cdot 8 - 5 \cdot 3 = 40 - 15 = 25.$

Also, $5(8 - 3) = 5(5) = 25.$

(c) $6(7 + 3 - 5) = 6 \cdot 7 + 6 \cdot 3 - 6 \cdot 5 = 42 + 18 - 30 = 30.$

Also, $6(7 + 3 - 5) = 6(5) = 30.$

(d) $-7(3 + 2) = (-7)(3) + (-7)(2) = (-21) + (-14) = -35.$
Also, $-7(3 + 2) = (-7)(5) = -35.$

(e) $-2(-3 - 6) = (-2)(-3) - (-2)(6) = 6 - (-12) = 6 + 12 = 18.$
Also, $-2(-3 - 6) = -2(-9) = (2)(9) = 18.$ ■

The distributive laws are useful in computation, but they are more useful when we work with algebraic expressions. In Section 2.1, we introduced algebraic expressions involving sums, differences, products, or quotients of numbers and variables.

▶ *Terms, factors, and coefficients*

A **term** is a part of an expression that is a product of numbers and variables and that is separated from the rest of the expression by plus or minus signs. The numbers and letters that are multiplied in a term are **factors** of the term. The numerical factor is the **(numerical) coefficient** of the term. For example,

$$3x, \quad 4a + 7, \quad 3x + 7y - z, \quad 4x + 5a + 3 - 8x$$

are algebraic expressions with one, two, three, and four terms, respectively. In $4a + 7$, the term $4a$ has factors 4 and a, and 4 is the coefficient of the term.

Two terms are **like** or **similar terms** if they contrain the same variables to the same powers. In $4x + 5a + 3 - 8x$, the terms $4x$ and $-8x$ are like terms.

NOTE When considering terms of an algebraic expression, remember that a minus sign goes with the term. For example, in $2x - 3a + 7$, one term is $-3a$ with the coefficient of the term -3.

If the terms of an expression have a common factor, the distributive laws can be used in reverse to **remove the common factor** by a process called **factoring.** We use the distributive law in the following way.

$$ab + ac = a(b + c)$$

EXAMPLE 2

Factoring Using the Distributive Law

Use the distributive laws to factor.

(a) $3x + 3y = 3(x + y)$ — The distributive law in reverse order

(b) $4a - 4b = 4(a - b)$ — 4 and $(a - b)$ are factors of $4a - 4b$

(c) $5u + 5v - 5w = 5(u + v - w)$

(d) $3x + 6 = 3 \cdot x + 3 \cdot 2$ — 6 is $3 \cdot 2$
$= 3(x + 2)$ — Factor out 3

(e) $8a - 8 = 8 \cdot a - 8 \cdot 1$ Express 8 as $8 \cdot 1$

$= 8(a - 1)$ Factor out 8

(f) $-3x - 3y = (-3)x + (-3)y$ Factor out -3

$= (-3)(x + y)$

Notice that $-3x - 3y$ is not $-3(x - y)$ since $-3(x - y) = -3x + 3y$. ■

NOTE In any factoring problem, we check by multiplying. For example, since

$$3(x + y) = 3x + 3y \quad \text{and} \quad 4(a - b) = 4a - 4b,$$

our factoring in the first two parts of Example 2 is correct.

▶ *Collecting like terms*

When an expression contains like terms, it can be simplified by **collecting like terms.** This process is illustrated in the next example.

EXAMPLE 3

Collecting Like Terms

Use the distributive laws to collect like terms.

(a) $5x + 7x = (5 + 7)x = 12x$ Factor out x

(b) $-8x + 2x = (-8 + 2)x = -6x$ Factor out x

(c) $-2a + 7a - 9a = (-2 + 7 - 9)a = -4a$ Factor out a

(d) $6y + 2y - y + 5 = 6 \cdot y + 2 \cdot y - 1 \cdot y + 5$ $-y = -1 \cdot y$

$= (6 + 2 - 1)y + 5$ Factor y out of first three terms

$= 7y + 5$

The terms $7y$ and 5 *cannot* be collected since they are not like terms. Thus, $7y + 5$ *is not* $12y$. You can see this more easily if you replace y by some number. For example, when $y = 2$,

$$7y + 5 = 7(2) + 5 = 14 + 5 = 19, \quad \text{but} \quad 12y = 12(2) = 24.$$

(e) $4a + 7b - a + 6b = 4a - a + 7b + 6b$ Commutative law

$= 4 \cdot a - 1 \cdot a + 7 \cdot b + 6 \cdot b$ $-a = -1 \cdot a$

$= (4 - 1)a + (7 + 6)b$ Distributive law

$= 3a + 13b$

With practice some steps can be left out. We should be able to see, for example, that $4a - a = 3a$ and $7b + 6b = 13b$.

(f) $0.07x + x = (0.07)x + 1 \cdot x$ $x = 1 \cdot x$

$= (0.07 + 1)x$ Distributive law

$= 1.07x$ ■

Simplified expressions When all like terms of an expression have been collected, we say that the expression has been **simplified.**

Using the distributive law and the fact that $-x = (-1) \cdot x$, we get

$$-(a + b) = (-1)(a + b) = (-1)(a) + (-1)(b) = -a - b,$$
$$-(a - b) = (-1)(a - b) = (-1)(a) - (-1)(b) = -a + b,$$
$$-(-a - b) = (-1)(-a - b) = (-1)(-a) - (-1)(b) = a + b.$$

These observations lead us to the next rule.

To Simplify an Expression by Removing Parentheses

1. When a negative sign is before parentheses, remove the parentheses (and the negative sign in front of the parentheses) by changing the sign of every term within the parentheses.
2. When a plus sign is before parentheses, remove the parentheses without changing any of the signs of the terms.

EXAMPLE 4 **Removing Parentheses**

Simplify by removing parentheses.

(a) $-(x + 1) = -x - 1$ Change all signs

(b) $-(x - 1) = -x + 1$ Change all signs

(c) $-(-x + y + 5) = +x - y - 5$
$= x - y - 5$ Change all signs

(d) $+(-x + y + 5) = -x + y + 5$ Change *no* signs

(e) $x - (y - 3) = x - y + 3$ Change all signs within parentheses ■

The process of removing parentheses can be called **clearing parentheses.**

EXAMPLE 5 **Clearing Parentheses and Collecting Like Terms**

Clear parentheses and collect like terms.

(a) $3x + (2x - 7) = 3x + 2x - 7$ Do not change signs
$= (3 + 2)x - 7$ Collect like terms
$= 5x - 7$

(b) $y - (4y - 4) = y - 4y + 4$ Change all signs within parentheses
$= (1 - 4)y + 4$ Collect like terms
$= -3y + 4$

(c) $3 - (5a + 2) + 7a = 3 - 5a - 2 + 7a$ Change all signs within parentheses
$= 7a - 5a + 3 - 2$ Commutative law
$= 2a + 1$ Collect like terms

(d) $3x - (-2x - 7) + 5 = 3x + 2x + 7 + 5$ Change all signs within parentheses
$= (3 + 2)x + 7 + 5$
$= 5x + 12$ ■

CAUTION Change *all* signs within the parentheses.

$$-(-2x - 7) = 2x + 7, \quad \textit{not} \quad 2x - 7.$$

EXAMPLE 6

Evaluating Expressions

Evaluate the expressions when $a = -2$ and $b = -1$.

(a) $3a + 7 = 3(-2) + 7 = -6 + 7 = 1.$

Note how using parentheses at the substitution step helps us avoid ambiguous statements. Without parentheses we would have $3 \cdot -2 + 7$, which is confusing.

(b) $4a^2 = 4(-2)^2 = 4 \cdot 4 = 16$ Only -2 is squared. Compare this example with the next one

(c) $(4a)^2 = (4 \cdot (-2))^2 = (-8)^2 = 64$ From (b) and (c) we see that $4a^2 \neq (4a)^2$

(d) $-a^2 = -(-2)^2 = -(4) = -4$ Compare this with the next example

(e) $(-a)^2 = (-(-2))^2 = (2)^2 = 4$ From (d) and (e) we see that $-a^2 \neq (-a)^2$

(f) $-a - b = -(-2) - (-1) = 2 + 1 = 3$

(g) $-a^3 = -(-2)^3 = -(-8) = +8 = 8$ ■

CAUTION Two common mistakes: (1) Don't forget to change *all* signs when a minus sign appears in front of a set of parentheses. For example, $-(x - 2)$ is $-x + 2$ not $-x - 2$. (2) Don't make sign errors when evaluating expressions such as $-a^2$. For example, $-a^2$ is not the same as $(-a)^2$.

2.5 EXERCISES

1. **(a)** Compute $-2(3 - 8)$ **(b)** Compute $(-2)(3) - (-2)(8)$ **(c)** Why are these two equal?
2. **(a)** Compute $-3(4 + 2)$ **(b)** Compute $(-3)(4) + (-3)(2)$ **(c)** Why are these two equal?
3. In $2x - 3y + 7 - 9x$ the terms $2x$ and $-9x$ are called similar or ____ terms.

How many terms does each expression in Exercises 4–6 have?

4. $2a + b - 3$
5. $-2x - 3y + 4 - z$
6. $3w$

Multiply in Exercises 7–12.

7. $4(x + y)$
8. $5(x - y)$
9. $10(x + 2y)$
10. $10(x + 2y + 3z)$
11. $2(2a + 1 + 6b)$
12. $-5(x + y)$

Use the distributive laws to factor in Exercises 13–18.

13. $4x + 4y$
14. $5x - 5y$
15. $10x + 20y$
16. $10x + 20y + 30z$
17. $4a + 2 + 12b$
18. $-5x - 5y$

Simplify by removing parentheses in Exercises 19–24.

19. $-(-a - b)$
20. $-(2y - 2)$
21. $x - (3 - b)$
22. $-(x - y - 4)$
23. $-(1 + x) + (a - b)$
24. $+(u - v) - (w - 3)$

Use the distributive laws and collect like terms in Exercises 25–42.

25. $3x - 8x$
26. $1 - 2x + x$
27. $2x - y - 5x + y$
28. $a - b + a - b$
29. $-a + 3 + b - 2a + b$
30. $u - 3 + 3v - 2u + 1$
31. $\frac{1}{2}x - \frac{2}{3}y - \frac{5}{2}x - \frac{1}{3}y$
32. $-\frac{3}{4}a + \frac{1}{4} + \frac{3}{4}a - \frac{1}{4}b$
33. $2.1u - 3 - 5.8u$
34. $2a - (1 - 3a)$
35. $2x - (-x + 1) + 3$
36. $7u - (-3u - 1) + 5$
37. $-2[x - 3(x + 1)]$
38. $a - [3a - (1 - 2a)]$
39. $2 - [3u - (-2 + 3u)]$
40. $3(x - 2) - 2[5y - (2x - y)]$
41. $2(3a - 4b) - (-4a + b) - (-4b - 5a)$
42. $-[2u - (u - v)] - 3[(u - 2v) - 3v]$

Evaluate each expression in Exercises 43–54 when $x = -3$, $y = -1$ and $z = 2$.

43. $-2x - y$
44. $-2x^2$
45. $(-2x)^2$
46. $-x - y + z$
47. $x^2 - y^2 - z^2$
48. $-3y^2 - (x + z)$
49. $x^2 - 4yz$
50. $(x - y)^3$
51. $x^3 - y^3$
52. $2x + 3z + y + 1$
53. $|x + y|$
54. $|x - y|$

FOR REVIEW

Perform the indicated operations in Exercises 55–60.

55. $(3)(-11)$
56. $(-3)(-11)$
57. $(-12) \div 6$
58. $(-12) \div (-6)$
59. $\left(-\frac{1}{3}\right)\left(-\frac{3}{4}\right)$
60. $(-6.3) \div (-0.9)$

2.5 PARALLEL EXERCISES

1. (a) Compute $-3(5 - 2)$. **(b)** Compute $(-3)(5) - (-3)(2)$. **(c)** Why are these two equal?
2. (a) Compute $-4(6 + 2)$. **(b)** Compute $(-4)(6) + (-4)(2)$. **(c)** Why are these two equal?
3. In $2a + b + 8 - 10a$ the terms $2a$ and $-10a$ are called like or ______ terms.

How many terms does each expression have?

4. $2a + 7 + 6w - 3$
5. $4a + 8b$
6. $2w - 3 + 7b + a + c$

Multiply in Exercises 7–12.

7. $4(x - y)$
8. $a(x + y)$
9. $10(a + 4b)$
10. $11(x + 2y + 3z)$
11. $2(3x + 1 + 4y)$
12. $-6(a + w)$

Use the distributive laws to factor in Exercises 13–18.

13. $4x - 4y$ **14.** $ax + ay$ **15.** $10a + 40b$

16. $11x + 22y + 33z$ **17.** $6x + 2 + 8y$ **18.** $-6a - 6w$

Simplify by removing parentheses in Exercises 19–24.

19. $-(x + 3)$ **20.** $-(-w + 5)$ **21.** $a - (2 - y)$

22. $-(a - b - 9)$ **23.** $-(1 + a) + (w - c)$ **24.** $+(x - y) - (a - 8)$

Use the distributive laws and collect like terms in Exercises 25–42.

25. $-3w - 10w$ **26.** $5y + 2 - 3y$ **27.** $x + y - x - y$

28. $2y - u + y - 3u$ **29.** $1 - 2a + b - a - 3b$ **30.** $z - 4 + 3z - a + 2$

31. $\frac{1}{4}a - \frac{1}{5}w + \frac{3}{4}a + \frac{2}{5}w$ **32.** $-\frac{1}{3}x + \frac{1}{2} - \frac{2}{3}x + \frac{1}{3}y$ **33.** $2.5w - 3 + 4.1w$

34. $a - 2(a + 5)$ **35.** $2b - (-b + 2) + 5$ **36.** $2y - (-5y - 2) + 7$

37. $-3[a - 2(a + 2)]$ **38.** $x - [4x - (3 - 4x)]$ **39.** $4 - [2w - (-3 - 2w)]$

40. $-6(x + 2y) - 5[8x - (-2x + y)]$ **41.** $-3(-a + 3b) + 5(-2a - 2b) - 2(3a - b)$

42. $-[(6u - v) - 5v] - 4[-u - (2u - v)]$

Evaluate each expression in Exercises 43–54 when $a = -2$, $b = -1$, and $c = 3$.

43. $-3a - b$ **44.** $-3a^2$ **45.** $(-3a)^2$ **46.** $-a - b + c$

47. $a^2 - b^2 - c^2$ **48.** $-2b^2 - (a + c)$ **49.** $a^2 - 3bc$ **50.** $(a - b)^3$

51. $a^3 - b^3$ **52.** $2a + b - 3c + 5$ **53.** $|a + c|$ **54.** $|a - c|$

FOR REVIEW

Perform the indicated operations in Exercises 55–60.

55. $(4)(-10)$ **56.** $(-4)(-10)$ **57.** $(-18) \div 9$

58. $(-18) \div (-9)$ **59.** $\left(-\frac{1}{5}\right)\left(-\frac{5}{6}\right)$ **60.** $(-5.4) \div (-0.9)$

2.5 ENRICHMENT EXERCISES

Use the distributive laws and collect like terms in Exercises 1–4.

1. $3\{x - 2[x - (y - x)] - (2x - y)\}$ △ **2.** $4\{[5(a - 2b) - 3b] - 2[6a - (3b - a)]\}$

3. $7x - \{[6x - 2y - 3(2x - y)] - 3[-x - (3y - x)]\}$ △ **4.** $-5\{[-4(a + 5b) - 2b] - 7[a - (-a - b)]\}$

Find the error in Burford's work simplifying expressions in Exercises 5–6. What is the correct simplification?

5.
$$\begin{aligned} 2x - (3 - 5x) &= 2x - 3 - 5x \\ &= 2x - 5x - 3 \\ &= (2 - 5)x - 3 \\ &= -3x - 3 \\ &= -3(x - 3) \end{aligned}$$

△ **6.**
$$\begin{aligned} 5y - (2x - y) + 4x &= 5y - 2x + y + 4x \\ &= 5y + y - 2x + 4x \\ &= 6y + 2x \\ &= 8yx \end{aligned}$$

In Exercises 7–12, answer true *or* false. *If the answer is false, change the right side to make it true.*

7. $-(x - 5) = -x - 5$ **8.** $3y - 4y = -y$ **9.** $a + 2a = 3a^2$

10. $5(xy) = (5x)(5y)$ **11.** $6 + 2z = 8z$ **12.** $-2a + 6b = -2(a + 3b)$

13. How many terms does the expression $2x + 4y$ have? How many terms does the expression $2(x + 2y)$ have? What conclusion can be reached comparing these two expressions?

14. Explain why you should never give an incorrect answer to a factoring problem.

15. Give the rule for removing parentheses preceded by a plus or a minus sign.

SECTION 2.6 Irrational and Real Numbers

Student guideposts

- ▶ *Irrational and real numbers*
- ▶ *Perfect squares and square roots*
- ▶ *Principal square roots, radicals, and radicands*

So far we have concentrated on working with the rational numbers. Remember that a **ratio**nal number is the quotient or **ratio** of two integers. Equivalently a rational number is a number with a decimal form that either terminates or repeats a block of digits.

▶ *Irrational and real numbers*

There are many numbers that cannot be expressed this way. One of the most familiar of these is π, the number equal to the ratio of the circumference of any circle to its diameter. Such numbers are called *irrational numbers.* In decimal notation **irrational numbers** do not terminate nor do they have a repeating block of digits. The set of **real numbers** includes both the rational numbers and the irrational numbers.

▶ *Perfect squares and square roots*

Before identifying some of the more familiar irrational numbers, we look at the idea of perfect squares and their *square roots.*

Perfect Square and Square Root

When an integer is squared, the result is called a **perfect square.** Either of the identical factors of a perfect square number is called a **square root** of the number.

EXAMPLE 1 Calculating Square Roots

(a) 4 is a perfect square since $4 = 2^2$. We call 2 a square root of 4. Since $4 = (-2)^2$, -2 is also a square root of 4.

(b) 25 is a perfect square since $25 = 5^2$. The two square roots of 25 are 5 and -5.

(c) 0 is a perfect square since $0 = 0^2$. Unlike other perfect squares, 0 has only one square root, namely itself, 0. ■

CAUTION Do not confuse the terms *square* and *square root!*

5 is a square root of 25 ↴ 25 is the square of 5 ↴

$$5^2 = 5 \cdot 5 = 25$$

▶ *Principal square roots, radicals, and radicands*

All perfect squares other than 0 have two square roots, one positive and one negative. When we refer to the square root of a number, do we mean the positive root or the negative root? To avoid confusion, we refer to the positive root as the **principal square root** and we use the symbol $\sqrt{}$, called a **radical,** to represent it. The principal or positive square root of 4 is $\sqrt{4}$, or 2. The number under the radical (4 in this case) is the **radicand.** Since the radical symbol only designates the principal or positive (possibly zero) square root of a number, we designate the negative square root by $-\sqrt{}$. For example, $-\sqrt{4} = -2$.

The first sixteen perfect squares and their square roots are listed in the following table.

Perfect Square	*Positive Square Root of N*	*Negative Square Root of N*
N	$\sqrt{N}$	$-\sqrt{N}$
0	0	$-0 = 0$
1	1	-1
4	2	-2
9	3	-3
16	4	-4
25	5	-5
36	6	-6
49	7	-7
64	8	-8
81	9	-9
100	10	-10
121	11	-11
144	12	-12
169	13	-13
196	14	-14
225	15	-15

In addition to whole number perfect squares, there are also fractional perfect squares. A fraction that can be factored into the product of two identical fractional factors is called a **perfect square,** and each factor is called a **square root** of the fraction.

EXAMPLE 2

Identifying Fractional Perfect Squares

(a) $\frac{4}{9}$ is a perfect square, with $\sqrt{\frac{4}{9}} = \frac{2}{3}$ and $-\sqrt{\frac{4}{9}} = -\frac{2}{3}$.

(b) $\frac{25}{81}$ is a perfect square, with $\sqrt{\frac{25}{81}} = \frac{5}{9}$ and $-\sqrt{\frac{25}{81}} = -\frac{5}{9}$. ■

Example 2 shows that a fraction is a perfect square if its numerator and denominator are whole number perfect squares. However, a fraction can be a perfect square without this feature. For example, if we reduce $\frac{8}{18}$ to lowest terms, we change it to a ratio of whole number perfect squares:

$$\sqrt{\frac{8}{18}} = \sqrt{\frac{\not{2} \cdot 4}{\not{2} \cdot 9}} = \sqrt{\frac{4}{9}} = \frac{2}{3}.$$

Thus far we have discussed only square roots of perfect squares. What about square roots of other numbers? This problem can be divided into two parts, square roots of negative numbers and square roots of positive numbers. The square root of a negative number is not a real number. For example, consider the square root of -4, $\sqrt{-4}$. Suppose that $\sqrt{-4}$ is the real number a. Then $a^2 = -4$. There are three possibilities for a:

1. If $a = 0$, then $a^2 = 0^2 = 0$, and $a^2 \neq -4$.
2. If $a > 0$, then $a^2 = (a)(a)$. Since this is the product of two positive numbers $(a > 0)$, a^2 must be positive. With $a^2 > 0$, we know that $a^2 \neq -4$.
3. If $a < 0$, then $a^2 = (a)(a)$. Since this is the product of two negative numbers $(a < 0)$, a^2 must be positive. With $a^2 > 0$, we know that $a^2 \neq -4$.

Since we have exhausted all the possibilities for a, we must conclude that there is no real number a such that $a = \sqrt{-4}$ or $a^2 = -4$. In Chapter 10 we will briefly consider the problem of square roots of negative numbers in a bit more detail.

Square roots of positive numbers that are not perfect squares supply us with many examples of irrational numbers. These include $\sqrt{2}$, $\sqrt{3}$, $\sqrt{5}$, $\sqrt{6}$, and $\sqrt{7}$ among many, many more. Suppose we consider $\sqrt{2}$, the number which when squared is 2. We know that

$$\sqrt{1} = 1 \quad \text{and} \quad \sqrt{4} = 2.$$

With $1 < 2 < 4$, we would expect $\sqrt{1} < \sqrt{2} < \sqrt{4}$ so that

$$1 < \sqrt{2} < 2.$$

Since there is no integer between 1 and 2, $\sqrt{2}$ cannot be an integer. In more advanced work it can be shown that $\sqrt{2}$ is not a rational number either. That is, $\sqrt{2}$ cannot be expressed as a quotient of two integers. This means that $\sqrt{2}$ is irrational.

Most of our work in this text will be with rational numbers until Chapter 9, when we consider operations with radicals.

EXAMPLE 3 **Identifying Number Systems**

Find the numbers in the set $\left\{-5, 0, 4, \sqrt{7}, 5, -\pi, \frac{3}{2}, -1.8\right\}$ that belong to the specified set.

(a) Natural numbers: 4 and 5

(b) Whole numbers: 0, 4, and 5

(c) Integers: 0, 4, 5, and -5

(d) Rational numbers: 0, 4, 5, -5, $\frac{3}{2}$, and -1.8

(e) Irrational numbers: $\sqrt{7}$, $-\pi$

(f) Real numbers: all the numbers in the set are real numbers ∎

We conclude with the diagram in Figure 2.14 that shows the relationships among the number systems we have discussed.

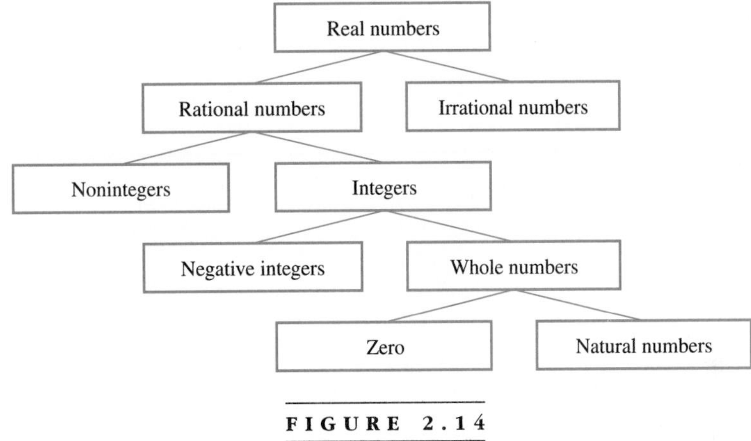

FIGURE 2.14

2.6 EXERCISES

Evaluate each square root in Exercises 1–12.

1. $\sqrt{225}$ **2.** $-\sqrt{196}$ **3.** $\sqrt{0}$ **4.** $-\sqrt{1}$

5. $\sqrt{\frac{9}{25}}$ **6.** $-\sqrt{\frac{36}{225}}$ **7.** $\sqrt{\frac{4}{169}}$ **8.** $\sqrt{\frac{9}{81}}$

9. $\sqrt{\frac{8}{18}}$ **10.** $-\sqrt{\frac{2}{50}}$ **11.** $\sqrt{\frac{12}{48}}$ **12.** $\sqrt{\frac{75}{363}}$

13. **(a)** Compute $(16)^2$ **(b)** $\sqrt{256} =$

14. **(a)** Compute $(17)^2$ **(b)** $\sqrt{289} =$

15. **(a)** Compute $(18)^2$ **(b)** $\sqrt{324} =$

16. **(a)** Compute $(19)^2$ **(b)** $\sqrt{361} =$

17. If x is any whole number, what is $\sqrt{x^2}$?

18. If x is any natural number, what is $-\sqrt{x^2}$?

19. **(a)** What is the square of 9? **(b)** What is the principal square root of 9?

20. **(a)** What is the square of $\frac{1}{4}$? **(b)** What is the principal square root of $\frac{1}{4}$?

21. Between what two positive integers is $\sqrt{15}$ located?

22. Between what two positive integers is $\sqrt{150}$ located?

In Exercises 23–28, list the numbers in the set $\left\{-\frac{7}{2}, -1, 0, -\sqrt{11}, -3, 2.66, 2\pi, \frac{\sqrt{2}}{2}\right\}$ *that belong to the specified set.*

23. Natural numbers **24.** Whole numbers **25.** Integers

26. Rational numbers **27.** Irrational numbers **28.** Real numbers

Of the natural numbers, the whole numbers, the integers, the rational numbers, and the real numbers, which is the smallest set that contains each of the numbers in Exercises 29–32?

29. -3 **30.** 0 **31.** -1.326 **32.** $3\sqrt{3}$

FOR REVIEW

Remove parentheses and collect like terms in Exercises 33–35.

33. $-(1-a)+(a+1)$ **34.** $2[y-(3y-2)]$ **35.** $-[-(-y)]+y$

2.6 PARALLEL EXERCISES

Evaluate each square root in Exercises 1–12.

1. $\sqrt{49}$ **2.** $-\sqrt{121}$ **3.** $\sqrt{144}$ **4.** $-\sqrt{64}$

5. $\sqrt{\frac{4}{9}}$ **6.** $-\sqrt{\frac{81}{121}}$ **7.** $\sqrt{\frac{4}{36}}$ **8.** $\sqrt{\frac{49}{121}}$

9. $\sqrt{\frac{8}{32}}$ **10.** $-\sqrt{\frac{50}{98}}$ **11.** $\sqrt{\frac{12}{75}}$ **12.** $\sqrt{\frac{147}{363}}$

13. **(a)** Compute $(20)^2$ **(b)** $\sqrt{400}=$

14. **(a)** Compute $(21)^2$ **(b)** $\sqrt{441}=$

15. **(a)** Compute $(24)^2$ **(b)** $\sqrt{576}=$

16. **(a)** Compute $(25)^2$ **(b)** $\sqrt{625}=$

17. If a is any whole number, what is $\sqrt{a^2}$?

18. If a is any natural number, what is $-\sqrt{a^2}$?

19. **(a)** What is the square of 16? **(b)** What is the principal square root of 16?

20. **(a)** What is the square of $\frac{1}{9}$? **(b)** What is the principal square root of $\frac{1}{9}$?

21. Between what two positive integers is $\sqrt{30}$ located?

22. Between what two positive integers is $\sqrt{200}$ located?

In Exercises 23–28, list the numbers in the set $\left\{6, \frac{5}{4}, -0.235, 0, \sqrt{22}, -4, \frac{\pi}{2}\right\}$ *that belong to the specified set.*

23. Natural numbers **24.** Whole numbers **25.** Integers

26. Rational numbers **27.** Irrational numbers **28.** Real numbers

Of the natural numbers, the whole numbers, the integers, the rational numbers, and the real numbers, which is the smallest set that contains each of the numbers in Exercises 29–32?

29. -16 **30.** 45 **31.** 4π **32.** $-\frac{21}{5}$

FOR REVIEW

Remove parentheses and collect like terms in Exercises 33–35.

33. $4y-(6y-3)$ **34.** $-4[-w+(2-w)]$ **35.** $-[-(-w)]-w$

2.6 ENRICHMENT EXERCISES

In Exercises 1–4, evaluate the square roots where a is a natural number.

1. $\sqrt{25a^2}$ **2.** $\sqrt{\frac{16}{a^4}}$ **3.** $-\sqrt{\frac{625}{576}}$ △ **4.** $-\sqrt{\frac{847}{1008}}$

In Exercises 5–8, use a calculator to find the square root of each number to two decimal places.

5. $\sqrt{2}$ **6.** $\sqrt{7}$ **7.** $\sqrt{26}$ **8.** $\sqrt{191}$

9. If a is any integer, is $\sqrt{a}$ a real number?

10. If a is an integer and $a > 0$, is $\sqrt{a}$ a rational number?

11. If a is an integer and $a > 0$, is $\sqrt{a}$ a real number?

12. If a is an integer and $a < 0$, is $\sqrt{-a}$ a real number?

13. Is $\sqrt{9}$ positive or negative?

14. Is $-\sqrt{9}$ positive or negative?

15. Explain the difference between the terms *square, square root,* and *principal square root.*

16. Discuss the decimal form of any irrational number.

CHAPTER 2 REVIEW

KEY WORDS

2.1 A **variable** is a letter that can be replaced by various numbers.

An **exponent** is a power on a number or variable indicating how many times the number or variable is used as a factor.

The **base** of an exponential expression is the number or variable that is raised to a power.

2.2 The **integers** are . . . , $-3, -2, -1, 0, 1, 2, 3, \ldots$.

The **rational numbers** are the numbers that can be written as the ratio of two integers.

2.3 The **additive identity** is 0.

The **additive inverse** or **opposite** of a is $-a$.

2.4 The **multiplicative identity** is 1.

The **multiplicative inverse** or **reciprocal** of a $(a \neq 0)$ is $\frac{1}{a}$.

2.5 A **term** is part of an expression that is a product of numbers and variables and that is separated from the rest of the expression by plus or minus signs.

The **factors** of a term are numbers or letters that are multiplied in the term.

The **coefficient** of a term is the numerical factor.

2.6 An **irrational number** is a number that is not rational and has a decimal representation that does not terminate or repeat.

The **real numbers** are the rational numbers together with the irrational numbers.

A **perfect square** results when an integer or a rational number is squared.

Either of the identical factors of a perfect square number is a **square root** of the number.

The positive square root of a number is called the **principal square root.**

The symbol $\sqrt{}$ is called a **radical,** and the number under a radical is the **radicand.**

KEY CONCEPTS

2.1

1. In an expression such as $2y^3$, only y is cubed—not $2y$. That is, $2y^3$ is not the same as $(2y)^3$.
2. When simplifying a numerical expression,
   First, evaluate within grouping symbols.
   Second, evaluate all powers.
   Third, perform all multiplications and divisions in order from left to right.
   Fourth, perform all additions and subtractions in order from left to right.

2.2

1. If a and b are any numbers such that a is to the left of b on a number line, then $a < b$ and $b > a$.
2. The absolute value of a number x, denoted by $|x|$, is the distance from x to zero on a number line and as a result, is never negative.

2.3 If a, b, and c are any numbers.

(a) $a + 0 = 0 + a = a$, Additive identity

(b) $a + (-a) = (-a) + a = 0$, Additive inverses (opposites)

(c) $a + b = b + a$, Commutative law of addition

(d) $(a + b) + c = a + (b + c)$, Associative law of addition

2.4 If a, b, and c are any numbers,

(a) $a \cdot 1 = 1 \cdot a = a$, Multiplicative identity

(b) $a \cdot \frac{1}{a} = \frac{1}{a} \cdot a = 1 \quad (a \neq 0)$, Multiplicative inverses (reciprocals)

(c) $ab = ba$, Commutative law of multiplication

(d) $(ab)c = a(bc)$. Associative law of multiplication

2.5

1. The distributive laws, $a(b + c) = ab + ac$ and $a(b - c) = ab - ac$, are used to factor and to collect like terms in algebraic expressions.
2. Only like terms can be combined. For example, $4y + 5 \neq 9y$ since $4y$ and 5 are *not* like terms.
3. A minus sign before a set of parentheses changes the sign of *every* term inside when the parentheses are removed. For example, $-(2 - a) = -2 + a$, *not* $-2 - a$.

2.6 The radical symbol by itself only designates the principal (positive or zero) square root of a number. For example, $\sqrt{9} = 3$, not -3. We must write $-\sqrt{9}$ to represent -3.

CHAPTER 2 REVIEW EXERCISES

PART I

2.1 *Select a variable to represent each quantity in Exercises 1–4 and translate the phrase into symbols.*

1. a number less 5
2. four times the area
3. the cost increased by 25% of the cost
4. 3 more than the reciprocal of a number

Write in exponential notation in Exercises 5–7.

5. $aaaaa$

6. $(3z)(3z)(3z)$

7. $(a + w)(a + w)$

Write without using exponents in Exercises 8–10.

8. b^7

9. $2x^3$

10. $(2x)^3$

Evaluate each expression in Exercises 11–12.

11. $2 \cdot 5 - 9 \div 3 + 1$

12. $2 \cdot 3^3 - 3 \cdot 2^3$

Evaluate each expression in Exercises 13–15 when $a = 2$, $b = 5$, and $x = 4$.

13. $3a^2$

14. $(3a)^2$

15. $2a + 3[x \div a \cdot b - 4]$

2.2 *Find each absolute value in Exercises 16–18.*

16. $|12|$

17. $|-7|$

18. $|-2.51|$

Answer true *or* false *in Exercises 19–21. If the statement is false, tell why.*

19. $-11 < -1$

20. $0 \le -4$

21. $5 \le 5$

Place the correct symbol, =, >, or <, between each pair of fractions in Exercises 22–24.

22. $\frac{2}{17} \quad \frac{10}{85}$

23. $\frac{13}{5} \quad \frac{28}{11}$

24. $\frac{6}{7} \quad \frac{11}{12}$

25. **TEMPERATURE** The lowest temperature ever recorded in Hawley Lake, Arizona was 41° below zero. How could this be written?

2.3 *Perform the indicated operations in Exercises 26–31.*

26. $(-2) + (-5)$

27. $2 + (-5)$

28. $2 - (-5)$

29. $0 - (-2)$

30. $(-2.3) + (-1.5)$

31. $\left(-\frac{1}{5}\right) - \left(-\frac{3}{10}\right)$

32. $(-5) + (-3) + 5 + (-8) + (-4) + (-6)$

33. **SPORTS** On first down the LSU football team made 7 yards. It lost 9 yards on second down, then picked up 11 yards on third down. If the series started at the LSU 30-yard line, where was the ball spotted on fourth down?

2.4 *Perform the indicated operations in Exercises 34–37.*

34. $(-4)(2)$

35. $(-14) \div (-7)$

36. $\left(-\frac{1}{3}\right)\left(\frac{15}{8}\right)$

37. $(-2)(-2)(-1)(2)(-3)(-1)(-1)(-1)$

38. **NUTRITION** When Bertha was on a crash diet, she lost 7 pounds in each of 6 consecutive weeks. Use a number to express her total weight loss.

Evaluate each expression in Exercises 39–41.

39. $(-2) + (-8) \div (-4)$

40. $(-1)^3 + 5$

41. $(6 - 8) \cdot 2 - (-4)$

Write without parentheses using only one sign (or no sign) in Exercises 42–44.

42. $-(-9)$

43. $-[-(-8)]$

44. $-[+(-x)]$

2.5 *Factor each expression in Exercises 45–47.*

45. $-4x + 12$

46. $-2 - 6x - 10y$

47. $-5x - 25y$

Collect like terms in Exercises 48–49.

48. $3a - 2 - 7a + 4 - a$

49. $-x + 2 - 3y + 4x + y$

Clear parentheses and collect like terms in Exercises 50–51.

50. $y - (2y - 3) + y - (-y + 2)$

51. $-3[2a - (4 - a)] - (-a - 3)$

Evaluate each expression in Exercises 52–54 when $b = -2$ and $c = 4$.

52. $-7b^2$

53. $(-7b)^2$

54. $|b^2 - c|$

Evaluate the square roots in Exercises 55–57.

55. $-\sqrt{169}$

56. $\sqrt{\frac{48}{75}}$

57. $-\sqrt{\frac{27}{3}}$

58. **(a)** What is the square of 25? **(b)** What is the principal square root of 25?

Of the natural numbers, the whole numbers, the integers, the rational numbers, and the real numbers, which is the smallest set that contains each in Exercises 59–64?

59. 11

60. -13

61. $\frac{4}{5}$

62. $-\sqrt{17}$

63. -3.2

64. 0

PART II

Perform the indicated operations in Exercises 65–67.

65. $\left(\frac{3}{4}\right) \div \left(-\frac{15}{8}\right)$

66. $(-1)(-2)(-4)(-6)$

67. $\left(-\frac{2}{7}\right) - \left(-\frac{3}{14}\right)$

Evaluate each expression in Exercises 68–73.

68. $(2 - 8) \cdot 5 + 4 \div 2$

69. $|6 - 8|$

70. $2^3 - (6 - 3) \cdot 5$

71. $-[-(-8)]$

72. $\sqrt{\frac{32}{50}}$

73. $-\sqrt{\frac{169}{144}}$

In Exercises 74–76, evaluate when $x = -2$ and $y = -5$.

74. $-y^3$

75. $|x - y^2|$

76. $-x^2$

Clear parentheses and collect like terms in Exercises 77–78.

77. $x + (x - 3) - (2x + 1)$

78. $-2[5 - (y - 2)] - 3(y + 1)$

79. **INVESTMENT** Use $A = P(1 + r)^t$ to find the amount of money in an account at the end of two years if a principle of \$5000 is invested at 15% interest, compounded annually.

Select a variable to represent each quantity in Exercises 80–81 and translate each phrase into symbols.

80. 10 increased by twice the number of cars

81. the time 20 minutes ago

Answer true *or* false *in Exercises 82–92. If the answer is false, write a complete sentence explaining why.*

82. When evaluating expressions, we always add and subtract in order from left to right before multiplying and dividing.

83. The expression $3x^2$ means "multiply x by 3 and square the result."

84. Every irrational number is also a real number.

85. The absolute value of any real number is always greater than or equal to zero.

86. Some rational numbers are whole numbers.

87. By the commutative law of addition, we know that $(x + 3) + y = y + (x + 3)$.

88. The product of a positive number and a negative number is always a positive number.

89. When a minus sign precedes a set of parentheses, we remove the parentheses and change the sign of the first term only.

90. When we collect like terms in the expression $2x + 3$, we obtain $5x$.

91. The principal square root of 16 is -4.

92. If a is any positive integer, $\sqrt{a}$ is an irrational number.

CHAPTER 2 TEST

1. Write $a \cdot a \cdot a$ in exponential notation.

2. Evaluate. $42 \div 6 - (4 - 2) \cdot 3$

Evaluate when $x = -3$, $y = 2$, and $z = -5$.

3. $3z^2$

4. $(3z)^2$

5. $-x^2$

6. $(x + y)^3$

7. $x^3 + y^3$

8. $z + 2[(x + y) - z]$

9. Use $A = P(1 + r)^t$ to find the amount of money in an account at the end of two years if a principal of \$500 is invested at 9% interest, compounded annually.

10. Find the absolute value. $|-13|$

11. Place the correct symbol, $=$, $<$, or $>$, between the pair of fractions. $\frac{6}{13}$ $\frac{3}{5}$

12. The lowest temperature recorded in Polar, Idaho was 49° below zero. If the highest temperature was 92°, what is the difference between these extremes?

13. Select a variable and translate the phrase into symbols: 100 pounds more than twice my weight.

Perform the indicated operations.

14. $(-8) + (-14)$

15. $5 - (-3)$

16. $\left(\frac{1}{3}\right)\left(-\frac{3}{8}\right)$

17. $(-4.5) \div (-1.5)$

18. $(-3) + 8 - (-7) - 9 - (-2)$

19. $(-2)(-1)(-1)(-1)(3)(-3)$

20. Write $-[-(-6)]$ without parentheses using only one sign (or no sign).

21. Factor. $-3y + 15$

22. Collect like terms. $3y - 2b + 5 + b - 5y$

23. Clear parentheses and collect like terms. $y - (2y - 3) + y$

24. Evaluate $x^2 - y^2$ when $x = 4$ and $y = -1$.

25. Multiply. $-3(4y - 2)$

26. Evaluate. $\sqrt{121}$

27. Evaluate. $-\sqrt{\frac{50}{32}}$

Are the following true or false?

28. $\sqrt{81}$ is an integer.

29. 4π is a rational number.

30. The number $\frac{2}{7}$ is the opposite of $\frac{7}{2}$.

31. For what values of a is $\sqrt{-a}$ a real number?

32. Give a definition of $|a|$.

Linear Equations and Inequalities

UP TO THIS POINT, we have discussed algebraic expressions and learned how to evaluate and simplify them. In this chapter we will see that algebraic expressions are used to form linear equations and inequalities. The properties of the real number system allow us to solve equations and applied problems that can be translated into equations. One application we will consider in this chapter is presented below and solved in Example 9 of Section 3.7.

EDUCATION For Kevin Connors to get an A in his Spanish course, he must earn a total of 360 points on four tests each worth 100 points. If he got scores of 87, 96, and 91 on the first three tests, find (using an inequality) the range of scores he could make on the fourth test to get an A.

We begin by defining a linear equation and giving the two major equation-solving rules, the addition-subtraction rule and the multiplication-division rule. Next we solve formulas and literal equations for a specified variable. We then present a strategy to be used for solving applied problems, and illustrate the technique with a variety of problems involving percent, consumer, geometry, and motion applications. We conclude the chapter by solving and graphing linear inequalities and compound inequalities, and presenting applications involving inequalities.

SECTION 3.1 Linear Equations and the Addition-Subtraction Rule

Student guideposts

- *Equations*
- *Linear equations*
- *Equivalent equations*
- *Addition-subtraction rule*

Equations

An **equation** is a statement that two quantities are equal. The two quantities are written with an equal sign (=) between them. Some equations are true, some are false, and for some the truth value cannot be determined. For example,

$1 + 2 = 3$ is true,
$2 + 5 = 3 - 7$ is false, and
$x + 2 = 9$ is neither true nor false since the value of x is not known.

Equations such as $x + 2 = 9$, which involve variables, are our primary concern in this chapter. If the variable can be replaced by a number that makes the resulting equation true, that number is called a **solution** of the equation. The process of finding all solutions is called **solving the equation.**

Linear equations

In this chapter we concentrate on **linear equations** in one variable in which the exponent on the variable is 1. For this reason, a linear equation is often called a **first-degree equation.** Every linear equation in one variable x can be written in the form

$$ax + b = 0$$

where a and b are known real numbers and $a \neq 0$. Some simple linear equations can be solved directly by inspection or observation. Others require more sophisticated techniques which are discussed in the material that follows. For example, it is easy to see that 5 is a solution to the equation $x = 5$, whereas finding the solution of $2x + 3 = 8 - x$ is not so obvious and will require something beyond simple inspection. The equation

$$x + 2 = 9$$

has 7 as a solution because when x is replaced by 7,

$$7 + 2 = 9 \quad \text{True}$$

is a true equation. Note that 3 is not a solution since

$$3 + 2 = 9 \qquad \text{False}$$

is false. An equation such as this, which is true for some replacements of the variable and false for others, is a **conditional equation.** The equation

$$x + 1 = 1 + x$$

has many solutions. In fact every number is a solution of this equation. An equation like this, called an **identity,** has the entire set of real numbers for its solution set. The equation

$$x + 1 = x$$

has no solutions. An equation like this is called a **contradiction.**

▶ *Equivalent equations*

Consider the two equations

$$x + 1 = 3 \quad \text{and} \quad x = 2.$$

Both equations have 2 as a solution. Although it is easier to see that 2 is a solution to the second, both can be solved by inspection. When two equations have exactly the same solutions, they are called **equivalent equations.** To solve an equation, we try to change it into an equivalent equation that can be solved by direct inspection. This usually means that the variable is isolated on one side, as in $x = 2$.

▶ *Addition-subtraction rule*

Following is the first rule for solving equations.

Addition-Subtraction Rule

An equivalent equation is obtained if the same quantity is added to or subtracted from both sides of an equation.

Suppose a, b, and c are real numbers.

If $a = b$, then $a + c = b + c$ and $a - c = b - c$.

For example, if we start with the true equation $5 = 5$ and then add 2 to both sides or subtract 3 from both sides,

$$5 + 2 = 5 + 2 \quad \text{and} \quad 5 - 3 = 5 - 3,$$

the resulting equations are also true since $7 = 7$ and $2 = 2$.

EXAMPLE 1

Using the Addition-Subtraction Rule

Solve. $x - 2 = 7$

$$3x - 2 + 2 = 7 + 2 \qquad \text{Add 2 to both sides to isolate } x \text{ on the left side}$$

$$x + 0 = 9$$

$$x = 9$$

The solution is 9. ■

EXAMPLE 2 **Using the Addition-Subtraction Rule**

Solve. $y + 3 = 17$

$$y + 3 - 3 = 17 - 3 \quad \text{Subtract 3 from both sides to isolate } y \text{ on the left side}$$
$$y + 0 = 14$$
$$y = 14$$

The solution is 14. ∎

> NOTE Get in the habit of checking all indicated solutions to an equation. To do this, replace the variable throughout the original equation with the indicated solution to see whether the resulting equation is true.

It is easy to see that the solutions we obtained in Examples 1 and 2 do indeed check. For example, 9 is a solution to the equation in Example 1 since:

$$x - 2 = 7 \quad \text{Original equation}$$
$$9 - 2 = 7 \quad \text{Substitute 9 for } x$$
$$7 = 7 \quad \text{This is an identity}$$

Similarly, since $14 + 3 = 17$, 14 checks as the solution to $y + 3 = 17$.

EXAMPLE 3 **Using the Addition-Subtraction Rule**

Solve. $3 = x + 5$

$$3 - 5 = x + 5 - 5 \quad \text{Subtract 5 from both sides to isolate } x \text{ on the right side}$$
$$-2 = x + 0$$
$$-2 = x \quad \text{or} \quad x = -2$$

The solution is -2.

Check: $3 \stackrel{?}{=} -2 + 5$ Replace x with -2 in the original equation

$3 = 3$

The solution -2 does check. ∎

> NOTE In Example 3, we isolated the variable on the right side of the equation instead of the left side as in the first two examples. Since $-2 = x$ and $x = -2$ are equivalent, we see that it makes no difference whether the isolated variable is on the left or on the right.

Equations involving fractions or decimals are solved in the same manner.

EXAMPLE 4 **Solving an Equation with Fractions**

Solve. $\frac{1}{2} + y = -3$

$$\frac{1}{2} - \frac{1}{2} + y = -3 - \frac{1}{2} \qquad \text{Subtract } \tfrac{1}{2} \text{ from both sides}$$

$$0 + y = -\frac{6}{2} - \frac{1}{2} \qquad \text{The LCD of } -3 \text{ and } -\tfrac{1}{2} \text{ is 2}$$

$$y = \frac{-6 - 1}{2}$$

$$y = -\frac{7}{2} \qquad \text{Subtract fractions}$$

The solution is $-\frac{7}{2}$. To check this, substitute $-\frac{7}{2}$ for y in $\frac{1}{2} + y = -3$.

$$\frac{1}{2} + \left(-\frac{7}{2}\right) \stackrel{?}{=} -3$$

$$\frac{1}{2} - \frac{7}{2} \stackrel{?}{=} -3$$

$$\frac{1 - 7}{2} \stackrel{?}{=} -3$$

$$-\frac{6}{2} \stackrel{?}{=} -3$$

$$-3 = -3 \quad ■$$

> **NOTE** We can remember the addition-subtraction rule with the statement, "Add or subtract the same quantity on both sides of the equation."

3.1 EXERCISES

Give an example of each equation in Exercises 1–3.

1. A true equation

2. A contradiction

3. A linear equation

Solve each equation in Exercises 4–9 by direct observation or inspection.

4. $x + 3 = 5$

5. $2y = 8$

6. $2 + z = 2 - z$

7. $2 + x = 2 + x$

8. $y + 5 = y + 1$

9. $2z = 5z$

Use the equation $y - 1 = 5$ to answer Exercises 10–12.

10. What is the variable?

11. What is the left side of the equation?

12. Is it an identity?

Use the addition-subtraction rule to solve each equation in Exercises 13–24. Check all solutions.

13. $x + 3 = 7$ **14.** $y - 4 = 9$ **15.** $z + 12 = -4$ **16.** $x - 9 = -6$

17. $4 = x + 1$ **18.** $-3 = z + 2$ **19.** $x - 2.1 = 3.4$ **20.** $-4.2 = y + 1.7$

21. $-2.6 = z - 3.9$ **22.** $x + 2\frac{1}{2} = 5$ **23.** $y - 3\frac{2}{3} = 4$ **24.** $1\frac{3}{8} + z = \frac{1}{4}$

In Exercises 25–28, is the statement true *or* false? *If the statement is false, tell why.*

25. -2 is a solution to $x + 2 = 0$.

26. $y + 3 = 5$ is a linear equation.

27. Zero is a solution of $x = 2x$.

28. $x + 2 = x$ is an identity.

FOR REVIEW

Exercises 29–32 review material from Chapters 1 and 2 to help prepare for the next section. Simplify each expression.

29. $2(5x)$ **30.** $(-1)(-z)$ **31.** $(-4)\left(-\frac{1}{4}y\right)$ **32.** $\left(-\frac{2}{5}\right)\left(-\frac{5}{2}x\right)$

3.1 PARALLEL EXERCISES

Give an example of each equation in Exercises 1–3.

1. A false equation

2. An identity

3. An equation that is neither true nor false

Solve each equation in Exercises 4–9 by direct observation or inspection.

4. $x + 5 = 12$ **5.** $3y = 15$ **6.** $4 + z = 4 - z$

7. $1 + x = 1 + x$ **8.** $y + 2 = y + 8$ **9.** $8z = 3z$

Use the equation $x + 3 = 19$ to answer Exercises 10–12.

10. What is the right side of the equation?

11. What is the solution?

12. Is this a contradiction?

Use the addition-subtraction rule to solve each equation in Exercises 13–24. Check all solutions.

13. $x + 2 = 12$ **14.** $y - 3 = 10$ **15.** $z + 13 = -2$ **16.** $x - 11 = -9$

17. $5 = x + 7$ **18.** $-3 = y - 3$ **19.** $x - 2.3 = 5.7$ **20.** $-5.7 = y - 2.3$

21. $-3.8 = z - 1.2$ **22.** $x + 1\frac{3}{4} = 3$ **23.** $y - 2\frac{1}{5} = 7$ **24.** $3\frac{2}{3} + z = \frac{1}{9}$

In Exercises 25–28, is the statement true *or* false? *If the statement is false, tell why.*

25. -4 is a solution to $4 + x = 0$.

26. $z + 2 = 8$ is a linear equation.

27. A solution of $3y = y$ is 0.

28. $y + 1 = 1 - y$ is a contradiction.

FOR REVIEW

Exercises 29–32 review material from Chapters 1 and 2 to help prepare for the next section. Simplify each expression.

29. $8(4x)$ **30.** $\frac{1}{3}(3y)$ **31.** $\left(-\frac{1}{2}\right)(-2x)$ **32.** $\left(-\frac{2}{3}\right)\left(-\frac{3}{2}z\right)$

3.1 ENRICHMENT EXERCISES

 *Solve each equation in Exercises 1–3. A calculator would be helpful for these exercises.*

1. $3.75 - x = 7\frac{2}{5}$ **2.** $0.00125 + y = \frac{1}{1000}$ **3.** $125\frac{7}{8} = 95.2 - z$

4. Suppose $x = 6$ is a solution to the equation $x + a = 8$. Find the value of a.

5. Suppose $x = -8$ is a solution to the equation $x - a = -13$. Find the value of a.

6. The definition of a linear equation $ax + b = 0$ states that a and b are real numbers with $a \neq 0$. Explain what happens if $a = 0$. What types of equations will result?

7. Which of the following equations are equivalent to $3x + 9 = 12$?
(a) $3x = 3$ **(b)** $3x = 21$ **(c)** $x = 1$ **(d)** $1 = x$

In Exercises 8–9, select a variable and write an equation that symbolizes the given sentence.

8. A number increased by 5 is the same as 2.

9. My age 3 years ago was 19.

10. Write a short paragraph explaining the difference between the terms *conditional equation, identity,* and *contradiction.*

11. In your own words, explain the *addition-subtraction rule* and how it is used to solve an equation.

12. Find three different equations that are equivalent to $x = 5$, and explain why the equations are all equivalent.

SECTION 3.2 The Multiplication-Division Rule

In Section 3.1 we were careful to choose equations for which the coefficient of the variable was 1. When the coefficient of the variable is a number other than 1, we need to carry out an additional step using the following rule.

Multiplication-Division Rule

An equivalent equation is obtained if both sides of an equation are multiplied or divided by the same nonzero quantity.

Suppose a, b, and c are real numbers with $c \neq 0$.

$$\text{If } a = b, \text{ then } ac = bc \text{ and } \frac{a}{c} = \frac{b}{c}.$$

For example, if we start with the true equation $6 = 6$ and then multiply both sides by 2 or divide both sides by 2,

$$6 \cdot 2 = 6 \cdot 2 \quad \text{and} \quad \frac{6}{2} = \frac{6}{2},$$

the resulting equations are also true since $12 = 12$ and $3 = 3$.

EXAMPLE 1 **Using the Multiplication-Division Rule**

Solve. $2x = 10$

$$\frac{1}{2} \cdot 2x = \frac{1}{2} \cdot 10 \qquad \text{Multiply both sides by the reciprocal of 2, which is } \tfrac{1}{2}$$

$$1 \cdot x = 5 \qquad \tfrac{1}{2} \cdot 2 = 1\text{, the multiplicative identity}$$

$$x = 5$$

The solution is 5.

Check: $2 \cdot 5 \stackrel{?}{=} 10$ Replace x with 5 in the original equation

$10 = 10$ ■

NOTE Equivalently, in Example 1 we could divide both sides of the equation by 2.

$$2x = 10$$

$$\frac{2x}{2} = \frac{10}{2} \qquad \text{Divide both sides by 2}$$

$$\frac{2}{2} \cdot x = 5$$

$$1 \cdot x = 5$$

$$x = 5$$

EXAMPLE 2 **Using the Multiplication-Division Rule**

Solve. $\frac{1}{3}x = 18$

$$3 \cdot \frac{1}{3}x = 3 \cdot 18 \qquad \text{Multiply both sides by the reciprocal of } \tfrac{1}{3}\text{, which is 3}$$

$$1 \cdot x = 54$$

$$x = 54$$

The solution is 54. Check. ■

NOTE In Examples 1 and 2, observe that we used the multiplication-division rule to make the coefficient of the variable equal to 1. This is the necessary final step in solving an equation. With practice, many of the steps may be performed mentally.

EXAMPLE 3 **Using the Multiplication-Division Rule**

Solve. $\dfrac{x}{\frac{4}{5}} = 20$

In an equation of this type, simplify the left side first.

$$\frac{x}{\frac{4}{5}} = \frac{\frac{x}{1}}{\frac{4}{5}} = \frac{x}{1} \div \frac{4}{5} = \frac{x}{1} \cdot \frac{5}{4} = \frac{5}{4} \cdot x$$

Thus we are actually solving

$$\frac{5}{4} \cdot x = 20$$

$$\frac{4}{5} \cdot \frac{5}{4} \cdot x = \frac{4}{5} \cdot 20 \qquad \text{Multiply both sides by } \frac{4}{5}$$

$$1 \cdot x = 16 \qquad \frac{4}{5} \cdot 20 = \frac{4 \cdot 20}{5} = \frac{4 \cdot 4}{1} = 16$$

$$x = 16$$

The solution is 16.

Check: $\dfrac{16}{\frac{4}{5}} \stackrel{?}{=} 20$

$$\frac{5}{4} \cdot 16 \stackrel{?}{=} 20$$

$$20 = 20 \quad \blacksquare$$

CAUTION A common error made when solving equations like the one in Example 3 is to multiply both sides of the equation by the reciprocal of $\frac{4}{5}$, which is $\frac{5}{4}$. Doing this will give the incorrect answer $x = \frac{5}{4}(20) = 25$. This is why it is better to simplify the left side of the equation first, as shown in the example.

EXAMPLE 4 **Solving an Equation with Decimals**

Solve. $-2.7x = 54$

$$\frac{-2.7x}{-2.7} = \frac{54}{-2.7} \qquad \text{Divide both sides by } -2.7$$

$$\frac{-2.7}{-2.7} \cdot x = \frac{54}{-2.7}$$

$$1 \cdot x = -20$$

$$x = -20$$

The solution is -20.

Check: $-2.7(-20) \stackrel{?}{=} 54$

$54 = 54$ ■

> NOTE We can remember the multiplication-division rule with the statement, "Multiply or divide both sides of the equation by the same quantity."

3.2 EXERCISES

Use the multiplication-division rule to solve each equation in Exercises 1–18. Check all solutions.

1. $5x = 25$ **2.** $56 = 8y$ **3.** $-11z = 77$ **4.** $-72 = -y$

5. $-2z = 2$ **6.** $-60y = 360$ **7.** $\frac{y}{4} = -3$ **8.** $-\frac{2}{5}z = 8$

9. $\frac{y}{\frac{7}{2}} = -6$ **10.** $\frac{z}{-\frac{1}{8}} = 16$ **11.** $\frac{3y}{2} = -6$ **12.** $\frac{4z}{-3} = -8$

13. $4x = -24.8$ **14.** $1.2y = 7.2$ **15.** $-0.8z = -6.4$

16. $2\frac{1}{2}x = 10$ **17.** $-3\frac{1}{3}y = 20$ **18.** $-4\frac{1}{5}z = -63$

FOR REVIEW

Solve each equation in Exercises 19–21.

19. $-8 + x = -12$ **20.** $-\frac{3}{4} + y = -\frac{7}{4}$ **21.** $7.4 + z = -3.2$

22. Is $2 + x = x + 2$ an identity? **23.** Is 0 a solution of $x - 3 = -3 - x$?

3.2 PARALLEL EXERCISES

Use the multiplication-division rule to solve each equation in Exercises 1–18. Check all solutions.

1. $7x = 49$ **2.** $72 = 6y$ **3.** $12x = -96$ **4.** $-63 = -y$

5. $-20x = -300$ **6.** $30y = -240$ **7.** $\frac{y}{5} = -3$ **8.** $-\frac{2}{7}z = 8$

9. $\frac{x}{\frac{1}{2}} = 10$ **10.** $\frac{z}{-\frac{2}{3}} = 12$ **11.** $\frac{4y}{3} = -2$ **12.** $\frac{8z}{-5} = -16$

13. $3x = -25.5$ **14.** $1.2y = 8.4$ **15.** $-1.2z = -4.8$

16. $3\frac{2}{3}x = 22$ **17.** $-4\frac{1}{4}y = 17$ **18.** $-1\frac{3}{5}z = -32$

FOR REVIEW

Solve each equation in Exercises 19–21.

19. $-21 + x = -25$ **20.** $-\frac{5}{6} + y = \frac{7}{12}$ **21.** $1.9 + z = -6.7$

22. Is $x + 1 = x - 1$ a contradiction? **23.** Is -6 a solution of $x - 6 = 0$?

3.2 ENRICHMENT EXERCISES

 *Solve. A calculator might be helpful in these exercises.*

1. $0.0568x = 0.006816$ **2.** $9\frac{7}{12}y = -7\frac{3}{16}$ △ **3.** $-15\frac{3}{4}z = 0.525$

 **4.** Suppose $x = 5$ is a solution to the equation $ax = 15$. Find the value of a.

5. Suppose $x = -\frac{1}{3}$ is a solution to the equation $ax = 3$. Find the value of a.

6. Which of the following equations are equivalent to $\frac{1}{4}x = -2$?
(a) $x = -8$ **(b)** $x = -\frac{1}{2}$ **(c)** $x = 8$ **(d)** $\frac{1}{2}x = -4$

In Exercises 7–8, select a variable and write an equation that symbolizes the given sentence.

△ **7.** Twice a number is the same as 36.

8. Half my age is 11 years.

9. In your own words, explain the *multiplication-division rule* and how it is used to solve an equation.

10. Find three different equations that are equivalent to $2x = -12$, and explain why the equations are all equivalent.

11. In the multiplication-division rule, we state that $c \neq 0$. Discuss what happens if $c = 0$, and explain why we do not necessarily obtain an equivalent equation in this case.

SECTION 3.3 Solving Equations by Combining Rules

Student guideposts

- ▶ ***Equations with like terms***
- ▶ ***Equations with the variable on both sides***
- ▶ ***Equations with parentheses***
- ▶ ***Equations with fractional or decimal coefficients***
- ▶ ***Summary of methods***

When we solve an equation, we isolate the varible on one side so we can find the solution by inspection. If we need to use both rules to do this, we generally use the addition-subtraction rule before the multiplication-division rule, as in the following example.

EXAMPLE 1 **Using Both Rules**

Solve. $3x + 5 = 11$

$$3x + 5 - 5 = 11 - 5$$ Use addition-subtraction rule first to subtract 5 from both sides

$$3x + 0 = 6$$

$$3x = 6$$

$$\frac{1}{3} \cdot 3x = \frac{1}{3} \cdot 6$$ Now use multiplication-division rule to multiply both sides by $\frac{1}{3}$

$$1 \cdot x = 2$$

$$x = 2$$

The solution is 2.

Check: $3 \cdot 2 + 5 \stackrel{?}{=} 11$

$6 + 5 \stackrel{?}{=} 11$

$11 = 11$ ■

▶*Equations with like terms* Sometimes the sides of an equation have like terms. These terms should be combined before attempting to apply the rules.

EXAMPLE 2 **Solving an Equation with Like Terms**

Solve. $15 = 4y + 3y$

$$15 = 7y$$ Collect like terms

$$\frac{15}{7} = \frac{7y}{7}$$ Divide both sides by 7

$$\frac{15}{7} = 1 \cdot y$$

$$\frac{15}{7} = y$$

The solution is $\frac{15}{7}$. Check by substituting in the original equation. ■

▶*Equations with the variable on both sides* When an equation has terms involving the variable on both sides, we use the addition-subtraction rule to get them together on the same side so they can then be combined.

EXAMPLE 3 **Solving When the Variable Is on Both Sides**

Solve. $7x - 2 = 2x + 3$

$$7x - 2 + 2 = 2x + 3 + 2 \qquad \text{Add 2 to both sides}$$
$$7x + 0 = 2x + 5$$
$$7x = 2x + 5$$
$$7x - 2x = 2x - 2x + 5 \qquad \text{Subtract } 2x \text{ from both sides}$$
$$5x = 0 + 5$$
$$5x = 5$$
$$\frac{5x}{5} = \frac{5}{5} \qquad \text{Divide both sides by 5}$$
$$1 \cdot x = 1$$
$$x = 1$$

The solution is 1. Check. ∎

> NOTE To solve an equation, use the addition-subtraction rule to isolate all terms involving the variable on one side of the equation and then combine them. Next apply, if necessary, the multiplication-division rule. Always remember to combine like terms before applying the rules.

EXAMPLE 4 **Solving When the Variable Is in Several Terms**

Solve. $2 - x + 10 = 3x + 2x + 24$

$$-x + 12 = 5x + 24 \qquad \text{Combine like terms}$$
$$-x + 12 - 12 = 5x + 24 - 12 \qquad \text{Subtract 12 from both sides}$$
$$-x = 5x + 12$$
$$-x - 5x = 5x - 5x + 12 \qquad \text{Subtract } 5x \text{ from both sides}$$
$$-6x = 12$$
$$\left(-\frac{1}{6}\right)(-6x) = \left(-\frac{1}{6}\right)12 \qquad \text{Multiply both sides by } -\tfrac{1}{6}$$
$$1 \cdot x = -2$$
$$x = -2$$

The solution is -2.

Check: $2 - (-2) + 10 \stackrel{?}{=} 3(-2) + 2(-2) + 24$

$$2 + 2 + 10 \stackrel{?}{=} -6 - 4 + 24$$
$$14 = 14$$ ∎

▶ *Equations with parentheses* When solving an equation containing parentheses, remove the parentheses using the distributive property. The resulting equation can then be solved using previous methods.

EXAMPLE 5 **Solving an Equation with Parentheses**

Solve. $3(x + 6) = 21$

$$3 \cdot x + 3 \cdot 6 = 21 \quad \text{To remove parentheses, multiply both 6 and } x \text{ by 3}$$
$$3x + 18 = 21$$
$$3x + 18 - 18 = 21 - 18 \quad \text{Subtract 18}$$
$$3x = 3$$
$$\frac{3x}{3} = \frac{3}{3} \quad \text{Divide by 3}$$
$$x = 1$$

The solution is 1. Check. ∎

EXAMPLE 6 **Solving an Equation with Parentheses**

Solve. $6z - (3z - 4) = 14$

$$6z - 3z + 4 = 14 \quad \text{Remove parentheses by changing signs}$$
$$3z + 4 = 14$$
$$3z + 4 - 4 = 14 - 4 \quad \text{Subtract 4}$$
$$3z = 10$$
$$z = \frac{10}{3}$$

The solution is $\frac{10}{3}$.

Check: $6\left(\frac{10}{3}\right) - \left(3\left(\frac{10}{3}\right) - 4\right) \stackrel{?}{=} 14$

$$20 - (10 - 4) \stackrel{?}{=} 14$$
$$20 - 6 \stackrel{?}{=} 14$$
$$14 = 14$$ ∎

EXAMPLE 7 **Solving an Equation with Parentheses**

Solve. $2x - 4(2x - 4) = 22 - 3(x - 5)$

$$2x - 8x + 16 = 22 - 3x + 15 \quad \text{Remove parentheses}$$
$$-6x + 16 = 37 - 3x \quad \text{Combine like terms}$$
$$-6x + 16 - 16 = 37 - 3x - 16 \quad \text{Subtract 16}$$
$$-6x = 21 - 3x$$
$$-6x + 3x = 21 - 3x + 3x \quad \text{Add } 3x$$
$$-3x = 21$$
$$\left(-\frac{1}{3}\right)(-3x) = \left(-\frac{1}{3}\right)21 \quad \text{Multiply by } -\tfrac{1}{3}$$
$$1 \cdot x = -7$$
$$x = -7$$

The solution is -7. Check. ∎

Equations with fractional or decimal coefficients

If an equation has fractional coefficients, it helps to simplify first by multiplying both sides by the least common denominator (LCD) of all fractions. For example, to solve

$$\frac{1}{2}x + \frac{3}{4} = \frac{5}{6},$$

first multiply both sides by the least common denominator 12.

$$12\left(\frac{1}{2}x + \frac{3}{4}\right) = 12 \cdot \frac{5}{6}$$

$$12 \cdot \frac{1}{2}x + 12 \cdot \frac{3}{4} = 12 \cdot \frac{5}{6} \qquad \text{Use distributive law}$$

$$6x + 9 = 10$$

We have less chance of making an error solving this equation than the original. The same remarks can apply to equations with decimal coefficients. First eliminate the decimals by multiplying both sides by an appropriate power of 10. For example, to solve

$$1.5y + 3.25 = 6,$$

multiply both sides by 100 to clear all decimals.

$$100(1.5y + 3.25) = 100 \cdot 6$$

$$150y + 325 = 600$$

$$150y = 275$$

$$y = \frac{275}{150} = \frac{11}{6}$$

NOTE We combined several steps and performed some of the calculations mentally in the above examples. With practice, you should be able to do the same.

Summary of methods

We conclude this section by summarizing how to solve linear equations.

To Solve a Linear Equation

1. Simplify both sides by clearing parentheses, fractions, or decimals. Collect like terms.
2. Use the addition-subtraction rule to isolate all variable terms on one side and all constant terms on the other side. Collect like terms when possible.
3. Use the multiplication-division rule to obtain a variable with coefficient of 1.
4. Check the solution by substituting in the original equation.
5. If an identity results, the original equation has every real number as a solution. If a contradiction results, there is no solution.

3.3 EXERCISES

Solve each equation in Exercises 1–16. Check all solutions.

1. $2x + 1 = 5$

2. $-4z + 3 = 5$

3. $\frac{3}{4}x + \frac{1}{4} = 1$

4. $12 = -1.2z + 24$

5. $2x + 3x = 10$

6. $3y - y = 7$

7. $\frac{1}{4}z + \frac{1}{2}z = -9$

8. $9.2x - 3.1x = 12.2$

9. $3z = 5 - 7z$

10. $32 - 8x = 3 - 9x$

11. $-7 + 21y + 23 = 16$

12. $z + 3z = 8 - 2z + 10$

13. $x + 9 + 6x = 2 + x + 1$

14. $6y - 4y + 1 = 12 + 2y - 11$

15. $2.1x - 3.2 = -8.4x - 45.2$

16. $3y + \frac{5}{2}y + \frac{3}{2} = \frac{1}{2}y + \frac{5}{2}y$

Remove parentheses and solve each equation in Exercises 17–35.

17. $3(2x + 1) = 21$

18. $10 = 5(y - 20)$

19. $3x - 4(x + 2) = 5$

20. $2y - (13 - 2y) = 59$

21. $4(y - 3) - 6(y + 1) = 0$

22. $9z - (3z - 18) = 36$

23. $5(2 - 3x) = 15 - (x + 7)$

24. $8y - (2y + 5) = 6y$

25. $9z - (5z - 2) = 8$

26. $7(x - 5) = 10 - (x + 1)$

27. $(y - 9) - (y + 6) = 4y$

28. $8(2z + 1) = 4(7z + 7)$

29. $5 + 3(x + 2) = 3 - (x + 2)$

30. $\frac{1}{3}(6x - 9) = \frac{1}{2}(8x - 4)$

31. $5(x + 1) - 4x = x - 5$

32. $3(2 - 4x) = 4(2x - 1) - 2(1 + x)$

33. $2 + y = 3 - 2[1 - 2(y + 1)]$

34. $-2(z - 1) - 3(2z + 1) = -9$

35. $-4(-x + 1) + 3(2x + 3) - 7x = -10$

FOR REVIEW

Solve each equation in Exercises 36–41.

36. $\frac{x}{-\frac{1}{5}} = 20$

37. $\frac{y}{-5} = -2$

38. $\frac{3z}{7} = -6$

39. $-2\frac{3}{8}x = -19$

40. $y - \frac{2}{3} = \frac{1}{9}$

41. $3.6 - z = 7.2$

3.3 PARALLEL EXERCISES

Solve each equation in Exercises 1–16. Check all solutions.

1. $3x + 1 = 7$

2. $-2z + 5 = 9$

3. $\frac{3}{5} - y = \frac{7}{10}$

4. $10 = -0.5z + 5$

5. $3x + 7x = 40$

6. $4y - y = 27$

7. $1.3x + 2.7x = 4.4$

8. $-\frac{1}{5}y + y = 8$

9. $5z = 2 - 9z$

10. $25 - 7x = 4 - 10x$

11. $-2 + 8y + 27 = 1$

12. $z + 2z = 3 - 2z + 17$

13. $x + 3 + 4x = 2 + x + 1$

14. $3y - y + 10 = 14 + 2y - 4$

15. $6.4 - 4.2x = 16.8x + 90.4$

16. $2x - \frac{1}{3} + \frac{2}{3}x = \frac{4}{9} + \frac{1}{3}x$

Clear parentheses and solve each equation in Exercises 17–35.

17. $2(3x + 1) = 14$

18. $9 = 3(4y - 1)$

19. $4x - 2(x + 1) = -1$

20. $7y - (4 - 3y) = 11$

21. $4(2y - 1) - 7(y + 2) = 0$

22. $6z - (2z - 5) = 0$

23. $3(2 - 4x) = 13 - (x + 1)$

24. $7y - (2y + 15) = 5y$

25. $8z - (3z - 1) = 0$

26. $4(x - 2) = 12 - (x + 3)$

27. $(y - 2) - (y + 2) = 4y$

28. $9(2z - 1) = 3(z + 2)$

29. $7 + 3(x + 1) = 5 - (x + 1)$

30. $\frac{1}{2}(2y - 4) = \frac{2}{3}(9y + 3)$

31. $6(z - 1) - 3z = 3z + 8$

32. $2(1 - 3x) = 5(2x + 1) - 3(1 + x)$

33. $4 + y = 8 - 3[2 - (y + 2)]$

34. $-3(z - 4) - 2(3z + 1) = -8$

35. $-7(-x + 2) + 5(2x + 1) - 11x = 3$

FOR REVIEW

Solve each equation in Exercises 36–41.

36. $-\frac{3}{5}x = 6$

37. $\frac{y}{-\frac{1}{7}} = 14$

38. $\frac{2z}{9} = -12$

39. $-3\frac{1}{7}x = -88$

40. $\frac{3}{4} - y = \frac{1}{2}$

41. $8.4 + z = -9.2$

3.3 ENRICHMENT EXERCISES

Solve and check in Exercises 1–6.

1. $0.02x - (0.56x - 7.33) = 2.15 - (0.7x - 0.11)$

△ **2.** $3\frac{2}{3}x + 7\frac{1}{9} - \left(\frac{x}{6} - 4\frac{1}{9}\right) = -\left(2\frac{1}{6} - 6\frac{2}{9}x\right)$

3. $x(x - 3) - 3x[1 - (x - 1)] = 4x(x - 5) + 22$

△ **4.** $-3[1 - (x^2 - 2)] - 2x(1 - x) = -5[4 - x(x - 2)]$

5. $\frac{x + 2}{5} + \frac{x - 3}{2} = 2$

6. $\frac{2x - 1}{6} - \frac{3x + 2}{3} = \frac{1}{3}$

△ **7.** Suppose $x = 4$ is a solution to the equation $ax + 3 = 11$. Find the value of a.

8. Suppose $x = -15$ is a solution to the equation $3(x + a) = 2x$. Find the value of a.

In Exercises 9–10, select a variable and write an equation that symbolizes the given sentence.

9. Twice the sum of a number and 3 is the same as 15.

10. Three more than twice a number is the same as 15.

11. When solving an equation, explain how you will know that the equation is a contradiction and has no solution.

12. When solving an equation, explain how you will know that the equation is an identity and has every real number as a solution.

13. In your own words, outline the method to use for solving a linear equation.

SECTION 3.4 Solving Literal Equations and Formulas

Student guideposts ▶ *Literal equations* ▶ *Formulas*

▶ ***Literal equations*** Many equations involve more than one variable, such as

$$x + y = 5.$$

Equations that contain two or more variables are called **literal (letter) equations.** A literal equation can often be solved for any of its variables in terms of the others. For example, in the equation above, if we subtract y from both sides we obtain

$$x + y - y = 5 - y$$
$$x = 5 - y$$

and the equation is solved for x. On the other hand, if we subtract x from both sides,

$$x - x + y = 5 - x$$
$$y = 5 - x$$

we have solved the equation for y.

To solve a given literal equation for a particular variable, remember that the variables represent real numbers so we can operate on them just like we operate on known constant numbers. If you have trouble solving for a variable in a literal equation, it may help to make up a similar equation with numbers instead of variables and pattern your solution steps after the procedure you use to solve the new equation. We will demonstrate this technique in the examples.

EXAMPLE 1 Using the Addition-Subtraction Rule

Solve $a + x = b$ for x.

Literal equation		*Similar numerical equation*	
$a + x = b$		$3 + x = 7$	
$a - a + x = b - a$	Subtract a	$3 - 3 + x = 7 - 3$	Subtract 3
$0 + x = b - a$		$0 + x = 7 - 3$	
$x = b - a$		$x = 4$	

The solution is $x = b - a$. ■

Just as with equations we solved in the first three sections, solving a literal equation for a particular variable is merely a process of isolating that variable on one side of the equation.

EXAMPLE 2

Using the Multiplication-Division Rule

Solve $cx = d$ for x.

Literal equation		*Similar numerical equation*	
$cx = d$		$5x = 10$	
$\frac{1}{c} \cdot cx = \frac{1}{c} \cdot d$	Multiply by $\frac{1}{c}$	$\frac{1}{5} \cdot 5x = \frac{1}{5} \cdot 10$	Multiply by $\frac{1}{5}$
$1 \cdot x = \frac{d}{c}$		$1 \cdot x = \frac{10}{5}$	
$x = \frac{d}{c}$		$x = 2$	

The solution is $x = \dfrac{d}{c}$. ■

NOTE When solving numerical equations, the answer is usually simplified to a real number. For example, in the above numerical equation, we simplified $\frac{10}{5}$ to the number 2. However, in the literal equation, when we obtained $\frac{d}{c}$ we were finished since this expression cannot be simplified.

EXAMPLE 3

Dividing by Two Variables

Solve $a = bcx$ for x.

$$a = bcx$$

$$\frac{a}{bc} = \frac{bcx}{bc} \qquad \text{Divide by } bc\text{, the coefficient of } x$$

$$\frac{a}{bc} = 1 \cdot x$$

$$\frac{a}{bc} = x$$

The solution is $x = \dfrac{a}{bc}$. ■

Sometimes we need to use both equation solving rules, the addition-subtraction rule and the multiplication-division rule, to solve a literal equation.

EXAMPLE 4 **Using a Combination of Rules**

Solve $ax + b = c$ for x.

Literal equation		*Similar numerical equation*	
$ax + b = c$		$3x + 5 = 20$	
$ax + b - b = c - b$	Subtract b	$3x + 5 - 5 = 20 - 5$	Subtract 5
$ax = c - b$		$3x = 15$	
$\frac{1}{a} \cdot ax = \frac{1}{a}(c - b)$	Multiply by $\frac{1}{a}$	$\frac{1}{3} \cdot 3x = \frac{1}{3} \cdot 15$	Multiply by $\frac{1}{3}$
$x = \frac{c - b}{a}$		$x = \frac{15}{3} = 5$	

The solution is $x = \frac{c - b}{a}$. ■

Formulas Most familiar formulas from geometry, business, or other areas are really literal equations. Consider, for example, the following:

$A = lw$	Area of a rectangle
$P = 2l + 2w$	Perimeter of a rectangle
$A + B + C = 180°$	Sum of the angles of a triangle
$A = P(1 + r)^t$	Compound interest formula

Sometimes when working with a particular formula, it is necessary to solve for one of the variables in terms of the others. This means that we must solve a literal equation.

EXAMPLE 5 **Using a Temperature Formula**

The formula for degrees Celsius $C°$ is given in terms of degrees Fahrenheit $F°$ by the formula $C = \frac{5}{9}(F - 32)$. Find a formula for F in terms of C. Use the formula to find the Fahrenheit temperature when the Celsius temperature is 40°.

$$C = \frac{5}{9}(F - 32)$$

$$\frac{9}{5}C = \frac{9}{5} \cdot \frac{5}{9}(F - 32) \qquad \text{Multiply both sides by } \frac{9}{5}$$

$$\frac{9}{5}C = 1 \cdot (F - 32)$$

$$\frac{9}{5}C = F - 32$$

$$\frac{9}{5}C + 32 = F - 32 + 32 \qquad \text{Add 32 to both sides}$$

$$\frac{9}{5}C + 32 = F$$

We usually write the formula as $F = \frac{9}{5}C + 32$. Substitute 40 for C to find the value of F.

$$F = \frac{9}{5}C + 32$$

$$\begin{aligned} F &= \frac{9}{5}(40) + 32 \\ &= 9(8) + 32 \\ &= 72 + 32 \\ &= 104 \end{aligned}$$

Thus the Fahrenheit temperature is 104°. ■

> NOTE If all we want is one temperature in °F for one temperature in °C, we could substitute for C in the original formula and solve for F, thus avoiding solving a literal equation. However, there are often instances when several values might be desired, and then it is wiser to solve the literal equation once and substitute values into this new formula.

EXAMPLE 6 **Using the Formula for the Perimeter of a Triangle**

The perimeter P of a triangle is given in terms of the three sides a, b, and c by the formula $P = a + b + c$. Find a formula for side a in terms of P, b, and c, and use it to find the value of a when P is 19 feet, b is 6 feet, and c is 5 feet.

We start with the formula

$$P = a + b + c.$$

Subtracting b and c from both sides we have

$$a = P - b - c.$$

Substitute 19 for P, 6 for b, and 5 for c.

$$a = 19 - 6 - 5$$

$$a = 8$$

Thus, side a is 8 feet in length. ■

3.4 EXERCISES

Solve for the indicated variable in Exercises 1–21.

1. $g = x + h$ for x

2. $t - x = k$ for x

3. $bx + d = e$ for x

4. $g - ax = m$ for x

5. $d = rt$ for t

6. $E = IR$ for I

7. $I = Prt$ for r

8. $C = 20c + d$ for d

9. $A = \frac{1}{2}bh$ for b

10. $r = \frac{d}{t}$ for d

11. $E = mc^2$ for m

12. $F = \frac{9}{5}C + 32$ for C

13. $A = \frac{1}{2}(c + d)$ for c

14. $A = \frac{1}{2}h(a + b)$ for a

15. $A = P + Prt$ for r

16. $3x - y + 5 = 0$ for y

17. $3x + 2y = 12$ for y

18. $y - 3 = -\frac{1}{2}(x - 2)$ for y

19. $\frac{x}{a} + \frac{y}{b} = 1$ for y

20. $ax + by + c = 0$ for x

21. $y = mx + b$ for x

22. **GEOMETRY** The area A of a rectangle is given in terms of its length l and width w by the formula $A = lw$. Find a formula for w, and use it to calculate the value of w when A is 4 cm^2 and l is 2.5 cm.

23. **BANKING** The simple interest I earned when a principal P is invested at a rate r for a time t is given by the formula $I = Prt$. Find a formula for P, and use it to calculate the value of P when I is \$360, r is 12%, and t is 2 years.

24. **ELECTRICITY** The power P in watts lost when an electric current I in amperes passes through a resistance R in ohms is given by the formula $P = I^2R$. Find a formula for R and use it to calculate the value of R (to the nearest tenth) when $P = 2000$ watts and I is 12 amperes.

FOR REVIEW

Solve and check in Exercises 25–26.

25. $2(y - 3) = 2(4y + 1) - 3(y + 1)$

26. $2 + x = 4 - 2[1 - (x - 3)]$

3.4 PARALLEL EXERCISES

Solve for the indicated variable in Exercises 1–21.

1. $x + k = w$ for x

2. $t = m - x$ for x

3. $ax + w = m$ for x

4. $p - bx = w$ for x

5. $A = bh$ for b

6. $T = cn$ for n

7. $V = lwh$ for h

8. $C = 20c + d$ for c

9. $W = \frac{1}{3}pq$ for q

10. $a = \frac{b}{m}$ for b

11. $A + B + C = 180$ for B

12. $V = \pi r^2h$ for h

13. $A = \frac{1}{2}(c + d)$ for d

14. $A = \frac{1}{2}h(a + b)$ for b

15. $A = P + Prt$ for t

16. $4x - y + 7 = 0$ for y

17. $2x + 3y = 12$ for y

18. $y - 2 = -\frac{1}{2}(x - 3)$ for y

19. $\frac{x}{a} + \frac{y}{b} = 1$ for x

20. $ax + by + c = 0$ for y

21. $y = mx + b$ for m

22. **GEOMETRY** The perimeter P of a rectangle is given in terms of its length l and width w by the formula $P = 2l + 2w$. Find a formula for l, and use it to calculate the value of l when P is 17.8 ft and w is 2.4 ft.

23. **GEOMETRY** The volume V of a rectangular solid with edges l, w, and h is given by the formula $V = lwh$. Find a formula for l, and use it to calculate the value of l when V is 24.5 cm^3, w is 3.5 cm, and h is 1.4 cm.

24. **ELECTRICITY** The formula $E = IR$, where E is voltage in volts, I is current in amperes, and R is resistance in ohms, is called Ohm's Law in electronics. Find a formula for R, and use it to calculate the value of R (to the nearest tenth) when E is 110 volts and I is 7 amperes.

FOR REVIEW

Solve and check in Exercises 25–26.

25. $3(y - 4) = 2(3y + 1) - (y - 3)$

26. $1 + x = 3 - 2[2 - (x - 5)]$

3.4 ENRICHMENT EXERCISES

Exercises 1–2 show Burford's solution for x in two literal equations. What is wrong with his work? What is the correct answer?

1.
$$\begin{aligned} ax - b &= 0 \\ ax - b + b &= 0 + b \\ ax &= b \\ x &= b - a \end{aligned}$$

2.
$$\begin{aligned} a + x &= b \\ x &= \frac{b}{a} \end{aligned}$$

In Exercises 3–8, solve each literal equation for x.

3. $3x + a = x + b$

4. $2(a - x) + 3(a + x) = 0$

5. $7x - 3(a - 1) = 2x + a - 5$

6. $4x - 3ab = 2x + 7ab$

7. $ax = x + 1$
[*Hint:* Use the distributive law.]

8. $3 + x = 2 - ax$

9. Write a complete sentence defining a literal equation.

10. Explain why we can follow the exact same steps when solving a literal equation that we use when solving an equation in only one variable.

SECTION 3.5 Techniques of Problem Solving

Student guideposts

- ▶ *Translating verbal statements into equations*
- ▶ *A strategy for problem solving*
- ▶ *Percent translations*
- ▶ *Tax and commission problems*
- ▶ *Percent increase and decrease*
- ▶ *Interest problems*

▶ *Translating verbal statements into equations*

One of the important ways that we use algebra involves solving word problems or application problems. To solve an applied problem, we must understand what is being asked, and then translate the *words* of the problem into a mathematical model, usually an equation or formula. Finally, we solve the equation or substitute known values into the formula. In some cases, part of the statement of the problem can be translated directly into an equation involving a variable that represents the desired quantity as shown below.

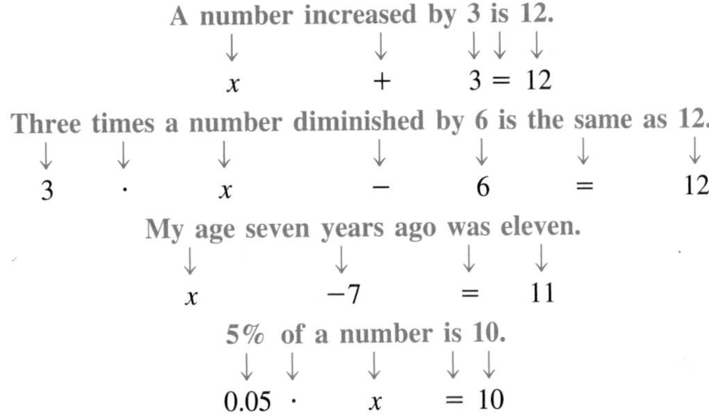

> **NOTE** You might want to review the table giving key terms and their symbolic translations presented in Section 2.1 before considering the next example.

EXAMPLE 1

Translating Sentences into Symbols

Use x for the variable and translate each word sentence into symbols.

Word expression	*Symbolic translation*
(a) Five times a number is 20.	$5x = 20$
(b) The product of a number and 7 is 35.	$7x = 35$
(c) Twice a number, increased by 3, is 11.	$2x + 3 = 11$
(d) Six is 4 less than twice a number.	$6 = 2x - 4$
(e) Six is 4 less twice a number. Notice the difference between (*d*) and (*e*).	$6 = 4 - 2x$
(f) One tenth of a number is 13.	$\frac{1}{10}x = 13$
(g) Five times a number, minus twice the number, equals 10.	$5x - 2x = 10$
(h) A number subtracted from 5 is 12.	$5 - x = 12$
(i) 5 subtracted from a number is 12. Notice the difference between (*h*) and (*i*).	$x - 5 = 12$
(j) A number divided by 9 is equivalent to $\frac{2}{3}$.	$\frac{x}{9} = \frac{2}{3}$ ■

We now expand our work with translating and solve a simple word problem.

EXAMPLE 2 **Solving a Number Problem**

Twice a number, increased by 13, is 71. What is the number?

Let x = the desired number.

The problem may be symbolized as follows.

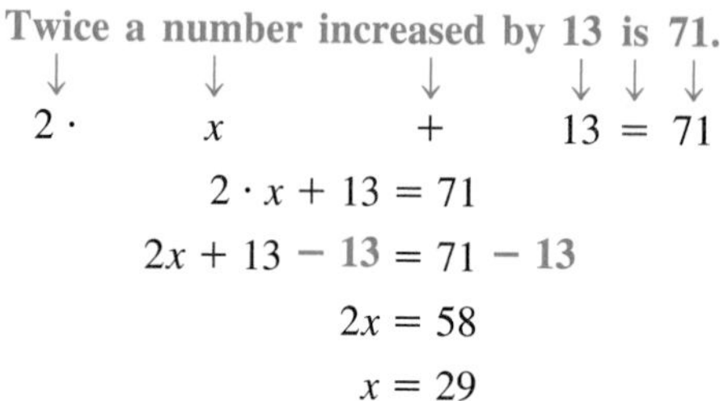

$$2 \cdot x + 13 = 71$$

$$2x + 13 - 13 = 71 - 13$$

$$2x = 58$$

$$x = 29$$

The number is 29.

Check: Twice 29 plus 13 is indeed 71. ∎

A strategy for problem solving

Many applied problems involve a bit more than simply translating a statement word-by-word into an equation. Often the techniques of translating will be used more indirectly. Consider the following example.

EXAMPLE 3 **Solving an Age Problem**

Bob is three times as old as Dick, and the sum of their ages is 48 years. How old is Dick?

Reading the problem we can see that the quantity we need to find is Dick's age. To do this, we identify his age with a variable, and then look for an equation involving that variable that is described in the words of the problem.

Let x = Dick's age.

Since we are told that Bob is three times as old as Dick, translating we have

$3x$ = Bob's age.

Since the sum of their ages is 48 years, we can form the equation

$$x + 3x = 48.$$

As you can see, the bulk of our work is now accomplished. We obtain a linear equation similar to the equations we learned to solve in the previous sections.

$$4x = 48 \quad \text{Collect like terms}$$

$$\frac{4x}{4} = \frac{48}{4} \quad \text{Divide both sides by 4}$$

$$x = 12$$

Remembering that x represents Dick's age, we now know that Dick is 12 years old. We can check our work by first observing that Bob must be $3(12) = 36$ years old. Then, $12 + 36 = 48$ shows that the sum of their ages is indeed 48. ∎

NOTE It is important when solving a word or applied problem to be neat and complete when writing your solution. Also, you should always write complete descriptions of the variable you use. Notice in the example above, that by identifying x as Dick's age, after we solved the equation, it was easy to see that the number we obtained was the answer to the question in the problem.

Unfortunately, there is no precise rule or method that we can use to solve all the different types of applied problems. However, we can describe a general strategy. "How do we *attack* an applied problem?" Every applied problem can be approached, or attacked, using the following:

A Strategy for Problem Solving

A—Analyze and familiarize: Try to understand the problem and what is being asked. Read it several times and try to determine what type of problem you have and whether some formula (perhaps from geometry such as $A = lw$, or relating to uniform motion such as $d = rt$, etc.) might be applicable.

T—Tabulate and sketch: Tabulate or list the known facts presented in the problem. Also list what you wish to find, that is, what is unknown. Use a variable to describe this unknown. A sketch might help picture what is stated, and a chart or table summarizing the information can also be useful.

T—Translate and solve: Translate the "words" and symbols into an equation, perhaps using the formulas identified as appropriate. The equation should then be solved using the techniques we have already learned.

A—Approximate and estimate: Ask yourself what type of answer is reasonable and appropriate. Does your answer fit this description? For example, if a problem was looking for the value of a new car, and you obtained an answer of $25, you would see that something is wrong, and you should look back to try to discover the error.

C—Check and verify: If your answer seems reasonable, check to see if it fits the original problem, that it satisfies the words of the problem (it doesn't just solve the equation which, of course, is something you came up with and may not be correct). Also, make sure that you have answered the question actually posed in the problem.

K—The **K**ey to problem solving is: ***Try something.*** What you try might not be correct, but at least you learn something from your mistakes and efforts. Don't be discouraged; if you need to, follow the steps again.

In a given problem, depending on the difficulty, you may use only some of these steps, and you may do many of them mentally. For example, as you analyze a problem, you probably won't write out your analysis. However, you should begin to write as you tabulate the known facts and identify the unknown quantity. Sometimes we will solve a problem in the text that uses all of these steps, and sometimes not. However, with practice, you will become more and more proficient at problem solving when you use these steps to **ATTACK** such problems.

Percent translations

Many applied problems involve the notion of percent. Before considering several more meaningful examples, we should point out that there are really three different types of percent problems. These are illustrated by the following:

What is 25% of 40?
What percent of 60 is 12?
8 is 40% of what number?

Letting x represent the unknown number in each statement and recalling that the word *of* translates to *times,* these three statements can be translated into equations. The first becomes

What is 25% of 40?

$$x = 0.25 \cdot 40.$$

Recall from Chapter 1 that 25% = 0.25

Solving, we have $x = (0.25)(40) = 10$. The second statement translates to

What percent of 60 is 12?

$$x \cdot 60 = 12.$$

Solving,

$$x = \frac{12}{60} = 0.2.$$

In percent notation, x becomes 20%.

Finally, the third statement becomes

8 is 40% of what number?

$$8 = 0.40 \cdot x.$$

Thus,

$$x = \frac{8}{0.40} = 20.$$

> **NOTE** When working with percent problems, since a percent is a decimal and we will be performing operations with decimals, a calculator can be helpful.

EXAMPLE 4

Solving Percent Problems

(a) 75% of 128 is what?
The equation to solve is $(0.75)(128) = x$.

$$96 = x$$

(b) 18 is what percent of 48?
The equation to solve is $18 = x \cdot 48$.

$$\frac{18}{48} = x \qquad \text{Divide by 48}$$

$$0.375 = x$$

In percent notation, $x = 37.5\%$. ■

In the next example we illustrate the **ATTACK** method by presenting all the steps in detail.

EXAMPLE 5

Solving an Application in Sports

Manny Black had a batting percentage (percent of hits in times at bat) of 40% in a series. If he had 12 hits, how many times was he at bat?

Analysis: We need to find the number of times Manny was at bat. Since we are given a percent in the problem, we should think of the three types of percent statements. In effect, we are asked: 12 is 40% of what?
Tabulation: Let x = the number of times Manny was at bat.
Translation: We can translate the above statement directly into the equation:

$$12 = (0.40)x$$

$$\frac{12}{0.40} = x \qquad \text{Divide both sides by 0.40}$$

$$30 = x \qquad \text{Use a calculator}$$

Approximation: Is 30 a reasonable number for the times a person would bat in a series? Yes, it is. Had we obtained a very large number, or perhaps a negative number or fraction, we would see that this answer is not reasonable. The *approximation* step can detect major errors in reasoning, and it should be performed mentally in most cases.
Check: If we take 40% of 30, we have $(0.40)(30) = 12$, so 30 does check—that is, 12 is indeed 40% of the number of times at bat.

Thus, Manny went to bat 30 times in the series. ■

▶ *Tax and commission problems*

Many types of tax problems involve percent. For example, in most states and in some cities there is a tax charged on purchases made in stores. The rate of this tax, called a *sales tax,* will vary from area to area. However, in general, we have:

sales tax = (tax rate) · (selling price)

and

total cost = (selling price) + (sales tax)

EXAMPLE 6

Solving a Sales Tax Application

If the sales tax on an item with a purchase price of \$125.00 amounts to \$7.50, what is the sales-tax rate?

Analysis: In effect we are asked: 7.50 is what percent of 125.00?
Tabulation: Let x = the sales-tax rate.
Translation: Then the above statement translates into the equation:

$$7.50 = x(125.00)$$

$$\frac{7.50}{125.00} = x \qquad \text{Divide by 125.00}$$

$$0.06 = x \qquad \text{Use a calculator}$$

Converting to percent notation, we obtain 6%.
Approximation: Notice that 6% is a reasonable rate for a sales tax. Had we obtained 150%, for example, we would recognize that something is wrong.
Check: If we take 6% of \$125.00, we have (0.06)(\$125.00) = \$7.50, so 6% does indeed check.

Thus, the sales-tax rate is 6%. ■

Some salespersons receive all or part of their income as a percent of their sales. This income is called a *commission.* The **commission rate** is the percent taken on the sales total that the person makes. Thus, we have:

commission = (commission rate) · (total sales)

For example, if a person works on a 25% commission and has total sales of \$6000, his commission is 25% of \$6000, which amounts to

$$(0.25)(\$6000) = \$1500.$$

EXAMPLE 7

Solving a Commission Application

Paul received a commission of \$720 on the sale of a machine. If his commission rate is 8% of the selling price, what was the selling price?

The problem can be written: 8% of what is \$720?
Let x = the selling price.

$$(0.08)x = 720$$

$$x = \frac{720}{0.08}$$

$$x = 9000$$

Thus, the machine sold for \$9000. ■

NOTE In Example 7 the solution more closely resembles the format you should try to achieve. Even though we did not specifically mention the steps in the problem-solving method, you should see that they were kept in mind as the solution was presented. Of course, you must always write out the description of the variable you are using because the equation really has no meaning without it.

▶ *Percent increase and decrease*

We are all familiar with statements such as:

Due to inflation, the price of an item rose 25% over its price the year before.

Due to declining enrollments, the revenue from tuition decreased 15% from last year.

These statements involve the notions of *percent increase* and *percent decrease.* If an amount changes by a percent to a new amount, the percent is always multiplied by the original amount, not the new amount. We can summarize percent increase and percent decrease problems as follows.

(original amount) + (% of original amount) = new amount **Percent Increase**

(original amount) − (% of original amount) = new amount **Percent Decrease**

EXAMPLE 8

Solving a Percent Increase Application in Economics

Due to inflation, the price of an item rose 25% over its price the year before. What was the price last year if the price this year is 60¢?

Analysis: We recognize this as a percent increase problem. It can be solved using

(price last year) + (increase in price) = (price this year)

where the increase in price is a percent of the price last year.

Tabulation: Let x = the price of the item last year,
$(0.25)x$ = the increase in price.

Translation: Then we must solve:

$$x + (0.25)x = 60$$

$$1.25x = 60 \qquad x + (0.25)x = 1 \cdot x + (0.25)x = (1 + 0.25)x = 1.25x$$

$$x = \frac{60}{1.25} \qquad \text{Divide by 1.25}$$

$$x = 48 \qquad \text{Use a calculator}$$

Thus, the price of the item was 48¢ last year. Is this a reasonable answer? Check. ∎

CAUTION Students will often try to solve a problem such as this by taking 25% of 60¢ and subtracting the result from 60¢. Notice that (0.25)(60¢) = 15¢, and 60¢ − 15¢ = 45¢, not 48¢, the correct answer. Remember that the percent is always taken on the *original amount* and added or subtracted to obtain the new amount in a percent increase or decrease problem.

EXAMPLE 9

Solving a Percent Decrease Application in Business

A jacket is put on sale at a 30% discount rate. If the sale price of the jacket is $98.00, what was the original price?

Let $x =$ the original price of the jacket,
$(0.30)x =$ the amount of the discount.

Then since

$$\text{(original price)} - \text{(discount)} = \text{(sale price)},$$

we must solve:

$$x - (0.30)x = 98.00$$
$$(0.70)x = 98.00 \qquad 1 - 0.30 = 0.70$$
$$x = \frac{98.00}{0.70} \qquad \text{Divide by } 0.70$$
$$x = 140$$

Thus, the original selling price was \$140. Is this a reasonable price? Check. ■

▶ *Interest problems*

Money that we pay to borrow money or the money earned on savings is called **interest.** The money borrowed or saved is the **principal,** and the interest is calculated as a percent of the principal. This percent is called the **interest rate.** For example, suppose you borrow \$500 for one year and the interest rate is 12% per year. The interest charged would be

$$(0.12)(\$500) = \$60.$$

If you needed the money for two years, the interest rate would be

$$2(0.12) = 0.24 = 24\%,$$

with the total interest for two years amounting to

$$(0.24)(\$500) = \$120.$$

This type of interest is called **simple interest** since interest is charged only on the principal and not on the interest itself. If we use I for interest, P for principal, r for the yearly interest rate, and t for time in years, then

$$I = Prt.$$

If A is the amount in the savings account or the amount to pay back on a loan, then

$$A = P + I = P + Prt.$$

EXAMPLE 10

Solving a Simple Interest Application

What sum of money invested at 4% simple interest will amount to \$988 in one year?

Let $P =$ the principal to invest.

In this case, as with many applied problems, the equation we must solve comes from substituting values into a known formula. We have that $A = 988$, $r = 0.04$, and $t = 1$, and we can substitute these values into

$$
\begin{aligned}
A &= P + Prt. \\
988 &= P + P(0.04)(1) \\
988 &= P + (0.04)P \\
988 &= (1.04)P \\
\frac{988}{1.04} &= P \\
950 &= P
\end{aligned}
$$

Thus, the principal to invest is \$950. ■

3.5 EXERCISES

Using x for the variable, translate each statement in Exercises 1–20 into an equation. Do not solve the equation.

1. 7 times a number is 25.
2. A number increased by 8 equals 12.
3. A number decreased by 15 is equal to 35.
4. The product of a number and 6 is 42.
5. Twice a number, increased by 3, is 27.
6. Three times a number, diminished by 8, equals 24.
7. A number less 5 is 12.
8. 8 is 4 less than three times a number.
9. A number diminished by 3 is 9.
10. Seven times a number, less 2, is 31.
11. The product of a number and 3, decreased by 5, equals 34.
12. When 10 is added to three times a number the result is the same as twice the number, plus 12.
13. 3% of a number is 12.
14. The sum of two numbers is 24 and one of them is three times the other.
15. Seven times 2 less than a number is 31. (Compare with Exercise 10.)
16. Twice the sum of a number and 5 is three times the number.
17. Seven more than a number is 13.
18. Four times my age in 3 years is 48.
19. When 4 is divided by some number the quotient is the same as $\frac{1}{2}$.
20. One half a number, less twice the reciprocal of the number is $\frac{3}{2}$.

A calculator may be helpful in some of the following exercises. Solve each problem in Exercises 21–52.

21. **NUMBER** If 14 is added to four times a number, the result is 38. Find the number.
22. **NUMBER** The sum of the two numbers is 180. The larger number is five times the smaller number. Find the two numbers.

23. **NUMBER** Two-thirds of a number is 124; what is the number?

24. **BIOLOGY** Two-thirds of the human body is water. If your body contains 124 pounds of water, how much do you weigh? [*Hint:* Compare with Exercise 23.]

25. **NUMBER** The first of two numbers is four times the second. If the first is 30,168, what is the second?

26. **GEOGRAPHY** The area of Lake Superior is four times the area of Lake Ontario. If the area of Lake Superior is 30,168 mi^2, what is the area of Lake Ontario? [*Hint:* Compare with Exercise 25.]

27. **NUMBER** The sum of two numbers is 9, and one is twice the other. What are the numbers?

28. **CONSTRUCTION** A board is 9 feet long. It is to be cut into two pieces in such a way that one piece is twice as long as the other. How long is each piece? [*Hint:* Compare with Exercise 27.]

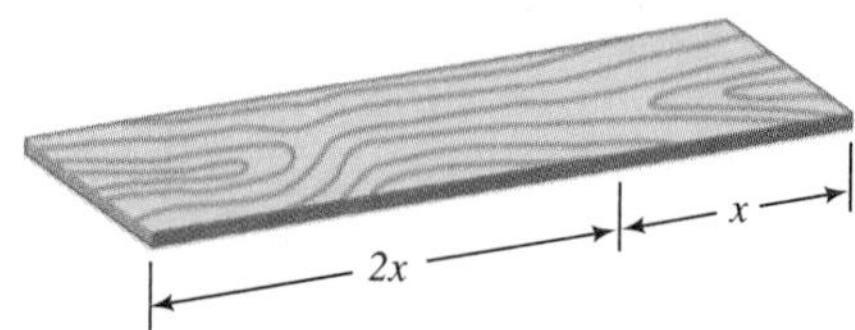

29. **CONSTRUCTION** A board is 17 ft long. It is to be cut into two pieces in such a way that one piece is 7 ft longer than the other. How long is each piece?

30. **AGE** Tony is four times as old as Angela and half as old as Theresa. The sum of the three ages is 39 years. How old is each?

---

31. 45 is 15% of what?

32. 25% of 164 is what?

33. What is 30% of 420?

34. What percent of 320 is 20?

35. 25 is what percent of 500?

36. 25 is 4% of what?

---

37. **CHEMISTRY** In 150-ml acid solution there are 45 ml of acid. What is the percent of acid in the solution?

38. **SPORTS** A basketball player hit 120 free throws in 150 attempts. What percent of her shots did she make?

39. **BUSINESS** Juan received a commission of \$104.50 on the sale of a typewriter. If his commission rate is 11% of the selling price, what was the selling price?

40. **INVESTMENT** Percy received \$31.50 interest on his savings last year. If he was paid 6% simple interest, what amount did he have invested?

41. **SPORTS** A baseball player got 42 hits one season. If his batting average was 28%, how many times was he up to bat?

42. **CONSUMER** A dress is discounted 30% and the sale price is \$51.45. What was the original price?

43. **CONSUMER** If the sales-tax rate is 5% and the marked price plus tax of a mixer is \$37.59, what is the marked price?

44. **CONSUMER** The price of a package of gum rose 20% last year. If the present price is 42¢, what was the price last year?

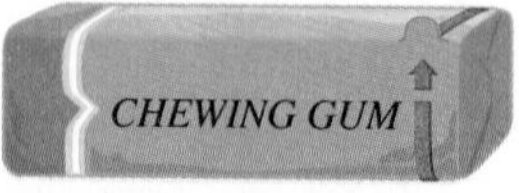

45. **BUSINESS** If the present retail price of an item is 65¢ and due to increased overhead the price will have to be raised 20%, what will be the new price?

46. **INTEREST** What sum invested at $4\frac{1}{2}\%$ simple interest will amount to \$1254 in one year?

47. **SPORTS** A baseball player got 21 hits in 70 times at bat. What was his batting average?

48. **CONSUMER** A family spent \$200 a month for food. This was 16% of their monthly income. What was their monthly income?

49. **TAX** The sales-tax rate in Murphyville is 4%. How much tax would be charged on a purchase of \$12.50?

50. INTEREST What sum at 4% simple interest will amount to \$1508 in 1 year?

51. GEOGRAPHY The area of Greenland is 25% of the area of the United States. What is the area of Greenland if the area of the U.S. is 3,615,000 mi^2?

52. BIOLOGY The human brain is $2\frac{1}{2}$% of the total body weight. If Nick's brain weighs 4 lb, how much does Nick weigh?

FOR REVIEW

Exercises 53–56 review formulas from geometry that will help you prepare for the next section. These formulas with figures are on the inside cover of this text and were reviewed in the Geometry Appendix. A calculator will be helpful in some exercises.

53. GEOMETRY A rectangle with length l and width w has area A given by $A = lw$. Find the area of a rectangle with length 4.5 ft and width 3.2 ft.

54. GEOMETRY A triangle with base b and altitude h has area A given by $A = \frac{1}{2}bh$. Find the area of a triangle with base $\frac{5}{4}$ in and altitude $\frac{8}{3}$ in.

55. GEOMETRY A circle with radius r has circumference C given by $C = 2\pi r$. Find the circumference of a circle with diameter 9.2 yd, correct to the nearest tenth of a yard.

56. GEOMETRY A trapezoid with bases b_1 and b_2 and altitude h has area A given by $A = \frac{1}{2}(b_1 + b_2)h$. Find the area, to the nearest tenth of a square centimeter, of a trapezoid with bases 8.6 cm and 12.3 cm and altitude 4.9 cm.

3.5 PARALLEL EXERCISES

Using x for the variable, translate each statement in Exercises 1–20 into an equation. Do not solve the equation.

1. 4 times a number is 32.

2. A number increased by 3 equals 14.

3. A number decreased by 13 is equal to 49.

4. The product of a number and 8 is 96.

5. Twice a number, increased by 4, is 86.

6. Three times a number, diminished by 17, equals 42.

7. A number less 4 is 21.

8. 9 is 3 less than five times a number.

9. A number diminished by 2 is 18.

10. Twelve times a number, less 17, is 39.

11. The product of a number and 7, decreased by 8, equals 29.

12. When 15 is added to three times a number the result is the same as twice the number, plus 40.

13. 9% of a number is 15.

14. The sum of two numbers is 86, and one of them is three times the other.

15. Eleven times 4 less than a number is 25.

16. Twice the sum of a number and 8 is four times the number.

17. Six more than a number is 29.

18. Five times my age in 2 years is 200.

19. When 7 is divided by some number the quotient is the same as $\frac{4}{9}$.

20. One third a number, less three times the reciprocal of the number is $\frac{4}{3}$.

A calculator may be helpful in some of the following exercises. Solve each problem in Exercises 21–52.

21. **NUMBER** If 9 is added to six times a number, the result is 39. Find the number.

22. **NUMBER** The sum of two numbers is 72. The larger number is five times the smaller number. Find the two numbers.

23. **NUMBER** Three-fourths of a number is 288; what is the number?

24. **CONSUMER** Three-fourths of the contents of a filled tank is water. If the tank is holding 288 gallons of water, how much fluid is in it? [*Hint:* Compare with Exercise 23.]

25. **NUMBER** The first of two numbers is five times the second. If the first is 1250, what is the second?

26. **AGRICULTURE** The number of acres in the Henderson farm is five times the number of acres in the Carlson farm. If the Henderson farm has 1250 acres, how many acres are there in the Carlson farm? [*Hint:* Compare with Exercise 25.]

27. **NUMBER** The sum of two numbers is 168, and one is three times the other. What are the numbers?

28. **CONSTRUCTION** A rope is 168 feet long. It is to be cut into two pieces in such a way that one piece is three times as long as the other. How long is each piece? [*Hint:* Compare with Exercise 27.]

29. **CONSTRUCTION** A steel rod is 22 m long. It is cut into two pieces in such a way that one piece is 6 m longer than the other. How long is each piece?

30. **AGE** Hortense is five times as old as Wally and half as old as Lew. The sum of their ages is 80 years. How old is each?

---

31. 48 is 12% of what?

32. 35% of 180 is what?

33. What is 3% of 1250?

34. What percent of 60 is 210?

35. 2.5 is what percent of 7.5?

36. 1230 is 60% of what?

---

37. **CHEMISTRY** In a 250-ml salt solution there are 15 ml of salt. What is the percent of salt in the solution?

38. **SPORTS** A basketball player hit 12 shots in 20 attempts during one game. What was his shooting percentage?

39. **CONSUMER** Blue Carpet Realty received a commission of $4950 on the sale of a house. If the commission rate is 6%, what was the selling price of the house?

40. **INVESTMENT** Randee Wire received $845 interest on her savings last year. If she is paid 13% simple interest, what amount did she have invested?

41. **SPORTS** A quarterback completed 21 passes in one game for a completion percentage of 60%. How many passes did he attempt?

42. **CONSUMER** A sport coat was discounted 20% and the sale price was $68. What was the original price?

43. **SALARY** Fred now makes $18,920 per year. What was his salary before he received a 10% raise?

44. **CONSUMER** The price of a pet mouse rose 30% last year. If the present price is $1.56, what was the price one year ago?

45. **CONSUMER** Due to inflation, the cost of an item rose $7.20. This was a 12% increase. What was the former price? The new price?

46. **INTEREST** What sum invested at $8\frac{1}{2}\%$ simple interest will amount to $1410.50 in one year?

47. **SPORTS** A prize fighter won 38 of his 40 professional fights. What was his percent of wins?

48. **CONSUMER** The Perez family spent $125 last week for food. This was 20% of their weekly income. What was their weekly income?

49. **TAX** The sales-tax rate in Canyon City is 4%. How much tax would be charged on a purchase of $327?

50. **INTEREST** What sum at 11% simple interest will amount to \$7215 in 1 year?

51. **GEOMETRY** The area of the Wyler Ranch is 35% of the area of the Rodriguez Ranch. What is the area of the Wyler Ranch if the area of the Rodriguez Ranch is 1200 mi^2?

52. **POPULATION** One year the population of the United States was 5% of the total world population. If the U.S. population was 200,000,000, what was the world population?

FOR REVIEW

Exercises 53–56 review formulas from geometry that will help you prepare for the next section. These formulas with figures are on the inside cover of this text and are reviewed in the Geometry Appendix. A calculator will be helpful in some exercises.

53. **GEOMETRY** The perimeter P of a rectangle with length l and width w is given by $P = 2l + 2w$. Find the perimeter of a rectangle with length 8.6 m and width 5.3 m.

54. **GEOMETRY** The area A of a parallelogram with base b and altitude h is given by $A = bh$. Find the area of a parallelogram with base 246 cm and altitude 188 cm.

55. **GEOMETRY** The volume V of a cylinder with radius r and height h is given by $V = \pi r^2 h$. Find the volume of a cylinder, correct to the nearest tenth of a cubic foot, if the radius is 5.4 ft and height 11.2 ft.

56. **GEOMETRY** The volume V of a sphere with radius r is given by $V = \frac{4}{3}\pi r^3$. Find the volume, to the nearest tenth of a cubic inch, of a sphere with radius 3.8 inches.

3.5 ENRICHMENT EXERCISES

Solve each applied problem in Exercises 1–20.

1. **RECREATION** A climbing rope 27 m long is to be cut into three pieces in such a way that the second piece is one-fourth the first and the third is 3 m longer than the second. Find the length of each piece.

2. **CONSUMER** A retailer uses a 30% markup to make a profit on suits. If Chris Katsaropoulos bought a suit for \$124.02 and that included a 6% sales tax, what was the original cost of the suit to the dealer?

3. **EDUCATION** On a recent field trip, Cindy noticed that the bus was completely full and that there were 14 more girls than boys on the bus. If the bus has a capacity of 54 children, how many boys were on the bus?

4. **AGE** Bob, Mary, and Sharon were born in consecutive years. If the sum of their ages is 36, how old is each?

5. **GEOMETRY** A pole is standing in a pond. If one-fourth of the height of the pole is in the sand at the bottom of the pond, 9 ft are in the water, and three-eighths of the total height is in the air above the water, what is the length of the pole?

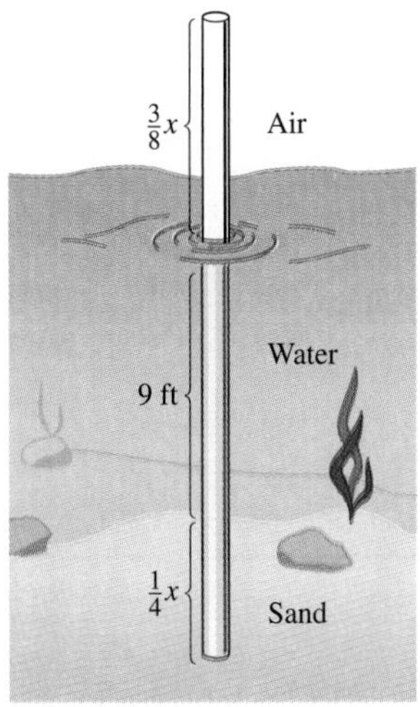

6. **PHYSICS** When ice floats in water, approximately $\frac{8}{9}$ of the height of the ice is below the surface of the water. If the tip of an iceberg is 35 feet above the surface of the water, what is the approximate depth of the iceberg?

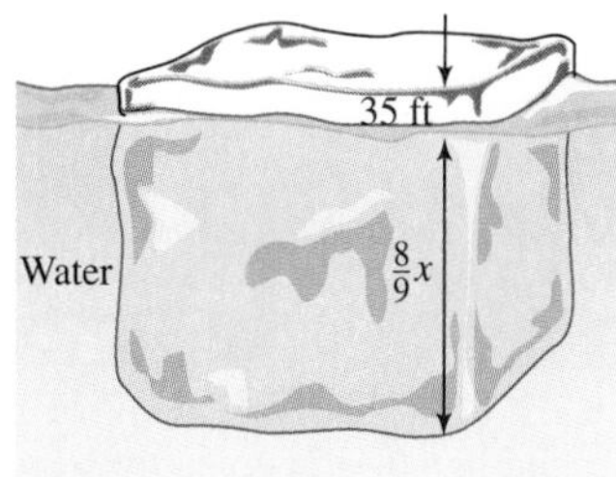

7. **ECONOMICS** Four-fifths of the operating budget of a community college goes for faculty salaries. If the total of all faculty salaries is $4,000,000, what is the total operating budget?
8. **TAX** If $16.80 is charged as tax on the sale of a washing machine priced at $420, what is the tax rate?
9. **CONSUMER** A fuel tank contained 840 gallons of fuel. An additional quantity of fuel was added making a total of 1092 gallons. What was the percent increase?
10. **TEMPERATURE** The relationship between °F and °C is given by the formula $F = \frac{9}{5}C + 32$. Determine °C for a temperature of 50°F.
11. **CONSUMER** International Car Rental will rent a compact car for $12.50 per day plus 10¢ per mile driven. If Charlene rented a compact for two days and was billed a total of $73.00, how many miles did she drive?
12. **CONSUMER** Tim Chandler bought a pair of running shoes on sale for $33.60. If the sale price was discounted 30% from the original price, what was the original price?
13. **CONSUMER** Barbara purchased a Ford Bronco for $16,500. If the options totaled $5800, what percent of the purchase price was the base price of the vehicle?
14. **INVESTMENT** Gene won $10,000 in the Illinois Lottery. He invested part in a savings account that earned 14% simple interest, and the rest in a fund that paid 11% simple interest. If at the end of one year he earned an income of $1310 from the two, how much was invested at each rate?
15. **POPULATION** The population of Deserted, Utah was 740 in 1990. This was a 20% decrease in the population of 1980. What was the population in 1980?
16. **CONSUMER** The Arnotes plan to sell their home. They must receive $82,000 after deducting the sales commission of 6% on the selling price. Rounded to the nearest dollar, at what selling price should the house be listed?
17. **EDUCATION** Becky must have an average of 90 on four tests in geology to get an A in the course. What is the lowest score she can make on the fourth test if her first three grades are 96, 78, and 91?
18. **SCIENCE** A meteorite weighing 4.5 tons was discovered near Meteor Crater, Arizona, in 1918. If the meteorite contains about 87% iron, how many pounds of iron does it contain?

---

19. Outline the **ATTACK** method of problem solving.
20. Give several reasons why it is important to write complete and accurate descriptions of the variable in the *Tabulation* step used in problem solving.

SECTION 3.6 Geometry and Motion Problems

Student guideposts ▶ *Geometry problems* ▶ *Motion problems*

▶ *Geometry problems*

Many geometry problems require knowledge of basic formulas that are summarized inside the front cover and reviewed in the Geometry Appendix. As you read and analyze a problem, try to determine which formula is appropriate. Keep in mind the

ATTACK method of problem solving, and always make a sketch and label the given parts of the figure in a geometry problem. In our first example, we will review the problem-solving method in detail.

EXAMPLE 1

Solving an Application in Geometry

Find the width of a rectangle if its area is 192 ft^2 and its length is 16 ft.

Analysis: We are asked to find the width of a rectangle. Since the area of the rectangle is given, we will probably use the formula for the area of a rectangle, $A = lw$.
Tabulation: Let $w =$ the width of the rectangle.
Make a sketch as in Figure 3.1.

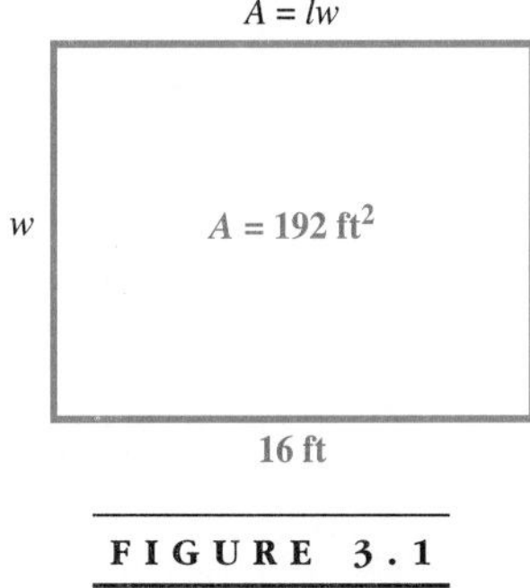

FIGURE 3.1

Translation: To obtain an equation involving w, all we need to do is substitute 192 for A and 16 for l in the formula for the area of a rectangle.

$$A = lw$$
$$192 = 16w \quad \text{Substitute}$$
$$12 = w \quad \text{Divide both sides by 16}$$

Approximation: Since 12 ft is a reasonable answer for the width of a rectangle whose length is 16 ft and area is 192 ft^2, we can proceed to the check.
Check: Since (16)(12) = 192, a width of 12 ft does indeed check.
Thus, the width of the rectangle is 12 ft. ■

In the following examples we present the solution more in the format you should use. Remember that even though we do not specifically write every step, we have performed them mentally. You should do the same.

EXAMPLE 2

Solving an Application in Geometry

If the perimeter of a rectangular room is 32 ft and its length is three times its width, find its dimensions. Make a sketch as in Figure 3.2.

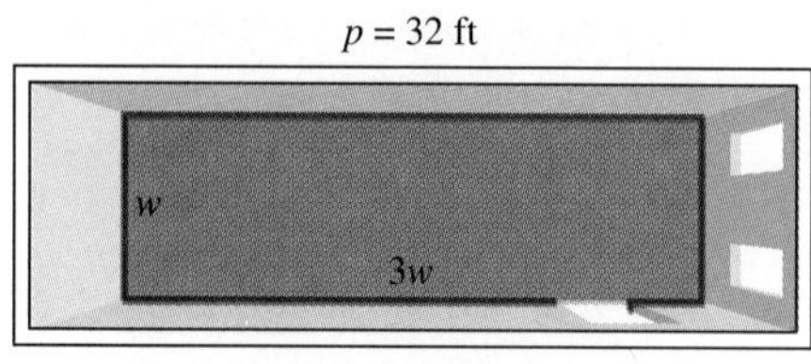

FIGURE 3.2

The perimeter of a rectangle is given by $P = 2l + 2w$.
Let w = width of room,
$3w$ = length of room.

$$\begin{aligned} P &= 2l + 2w \\ 32 &= 2(3w) + 2(w) \\ 32 &= 6w + 2w \\ 32 &= 8w \\ 4 &= w \\ \text{and} \quad 12 &= 3w \end{aligned}$$

The length of the room is 12 ft and the width is 4 ft. ■

EXAMPLE 3 **Solving a Geometry Problem**

The first angle of a triangle is three times as large as the second. The third angle is 40° larger than the first angle. What is the measure of each angle?

The sum of the measures of the angles of any triangle is 180°. Make a sketch as in Figure 3.3.

Let $3x$ = measure of the first angle,
x = measure of the second angle,
$3x + 40$ = measure of the third angle.

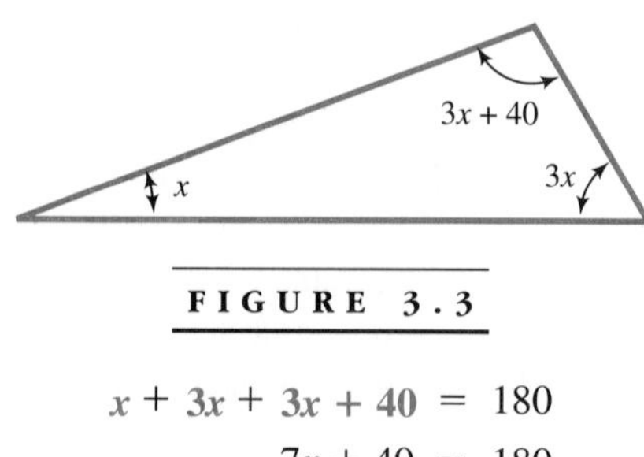

FIGURE 3.3

$$\begin{aligned} x + 3x + 3x + 40 &= 180 \\ 7x + 40 &= 180 \\ 7x &= 140 \\ x &= 20 \\ \text{and} \quad 3x &= 60 \\ \text{and} \quad 3x + 40 &= 100 \end{aligned}$$

The measures are 20°, 60°, and 100°. ■

EXAMPLE 4

Solving an Application in Geometry

The circumference of a circular flower bed is 182 ft. How many feet of pipe do we need to reach from the edge of the bed to a fountain in the center of the bed? The circumference of a circle is given by $C = 2\pi r$. [Use 3.14 for π]. Make a sketch as in Figure 3.4.

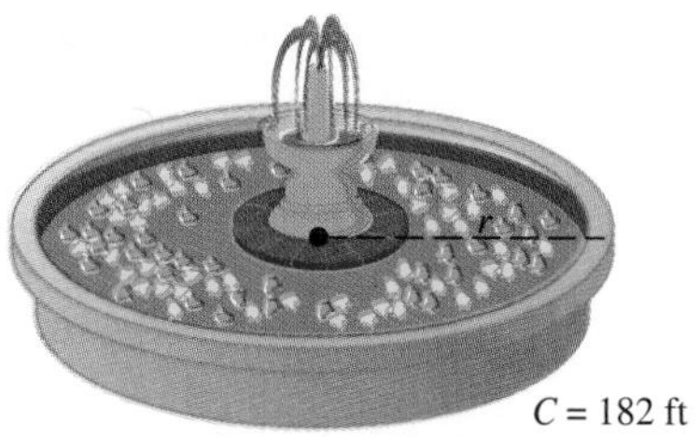

FIGURE 3.4

$$C = 2\pi r$$
$$182 = 2(3.14)r$$
$$\frac{182}{2(3.14)} = r$$
$$28.98 \approx r \quad \text{To the nearest hundredth}$$

We need about 29 ft of pipe. ∎

NOTE In Example 4 we used the symbol ≈ to represent the phrase "is *approximately equal* to." It is important to use ≈ whenever an approximate or rounded number is indicated.

EXAMPLE 5

Solving an Application in Geometry

A cylindrical storage bin with radius 10 ft is to be built. How high will it need to be to store 10,200 ft^3 of grain? (See Figure 3.5.)

The volume of a cylinder is given by $V = \pi r^2 h$. [Use 3.14 for π.]

$$V = \pi r^2 h$$
$$10{,}200 = (3.14)(10)^2 h$$
$$10{,}200 = 314h$$
$$\frac{10{,}200}{314} = h$$
$$32.48 \approx h \quad \text{To the nearest hundredth}$$

The bin must be about 32.5 ft high. ∎

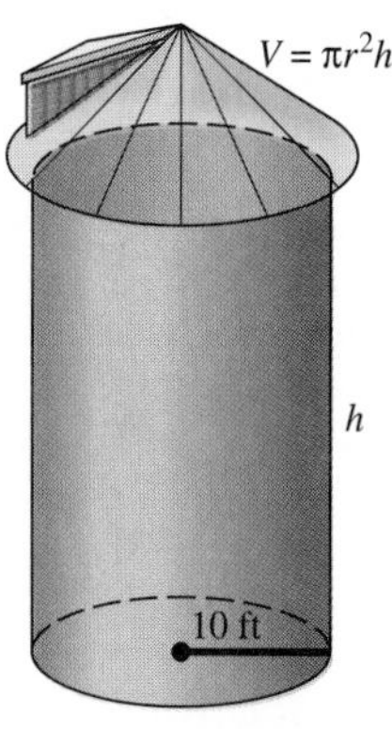

FIGURE 3.5

Motion problems

Problems that involve distances and rates of travel often result in simple linear equations. The distance d that an object travels in a given time t at a uniform rate r is given by the formula

$$\textbf{(distance)} = \textbf{(rate)} \cdot \textbf{(time)} \quad \text{or} \quad d = rt.$$

For example, a boy walking at a rate of 4 mph for 3 hr will travel a distance of

$$d = rt = 4 \cdot 3 = 12 \text{ miles}.$$

Most types of motion problems depend in some way on the formula $d = rt$.

EXAMPLE 6

Solving a Motion Problem

An automobile is driven 336 mi in 7 hr. How fast (at what rate) was the car driven?

Let r = average rate of travel,
336 = distance d driven,
7 = time t of travel.

We need to solve the following equation:

$$336 = r(7)$$

$$\frac{336}{7} = r$$

$$48 = r.$$

Thus, the average rate of travel was 48 mph. ■

EXAMPLE 7

Solving a Transportation Problem

Two trucks leave Denver at 9:00 A.M., one heading north and the other south. If one is traveling 8 mph faster than the other, and at 7:00 P.M. the same day they are 1280 miles apart, how fast is each traveling?

At 7:00 P.M. the two will have been traveling for 10 hours since they both started at 9:00 A.M. Consider the sketch given in Figure 3.6.

Let r = rate of one truck,
$r + 8$ = rate of other truck,
$10r$ = distance one travels,
$10(r + 8)$ = distance other travels.

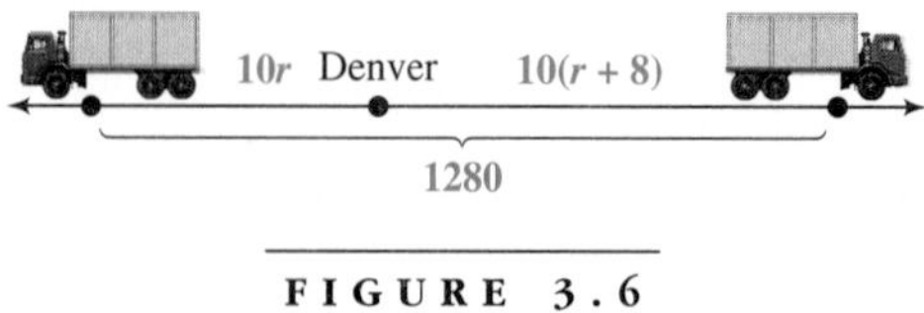

FIGURE 3.6

We must solve the following equation.

$$10r + 10(r + 8) = 1280$$
$$10r + 10r + 80 = 1280 \quad \text{Clear parentheses}$$
$$20r + 80 = 1280 \quad \text{Collect like terms}$$
$$20r = 1200 \quad \text{Subtract 80}$$
$$r = 60 \quad \text{Divide by 20}$$

One truck is traveling 60 mph and the other 68 mph ($r + 8 = 68$). ∎

3.6 EXERCISES

Solve each applied problem in Exercises 1–26. If necessary, check the inside front cover for a list of formulas.

1. **GEOMETRY** The perimeter of a rectangle is 60 in. If the length is 4 in more than the width, find the dimensions.

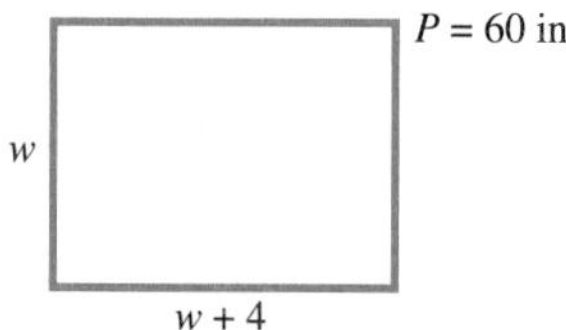

2. **GEOMETRY** If one angle of a triangle is 60° more than the smallest angle and the third angle is six times the smallest angle, find the measure of each angle.

3. **GEOMETRY** Find the length of a rectangle if its area is 104 in^2 and its width is 8 in.

4. **GEOMETRY** Find the height of a triangle whose base is 12 cm and whose area is 84 cm^2.

5. **GEOMETRY** A circular patio has a radius of 14 ft. How many feet of edging material will be needed to enclose the patio? [Use $\pi \approx 3.14$.]

6. **GEOMETRY** In a triangle, the longest side is twice the shortest side, and the third side is 5 ft shorter than the longest side. Find the three sides if the perimeter is 45 ft.

7. **GEOMETRY** Find the height of a parallelogram whose base is 19 in and whose area is 133 in^2.

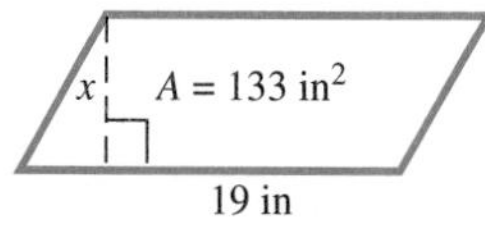

8. **GEOMETRY** If two angles of a triangle are equal and the third angle is equal to the sum of the first two, find the measure of each.

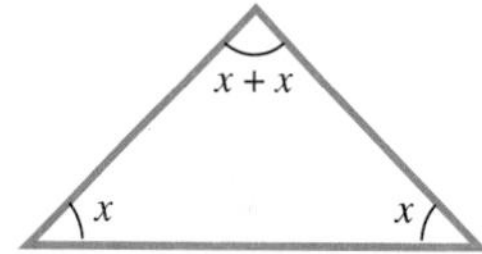

9. **GEOMETRY** An isosceles triangle has two equal sides called legs and a third side called the base. If each leg of an isosceles triangle is four times the base and the perimeter is 108 m, find the length of the legs and base.

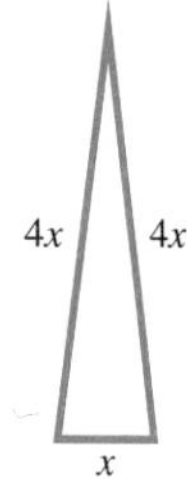

10. **GEOMETRY** The perimeter of a rectangle is 630 in. Find the dimensions if the length is 25 in more than the width.

11. **GEOMETRY** Find the height of a trapezoid if the area is 247 m^2 and the bases are 16 m and 22 m. [*Hint:* $A = \frac{1}{2}(b_1 + b_2)h$]

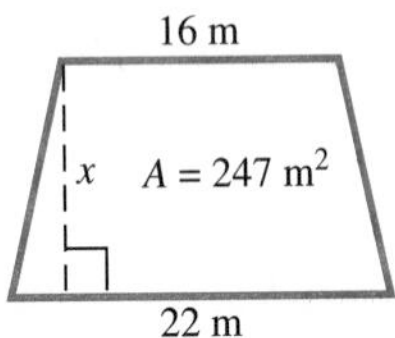

12. **GEOMETRY** Find the base of a parallelogram if the perimeter is 88 cm and a side is 20 cm.
13. **GEOMETRY** Find the area of a circular garden having a diameter of 96 yd.
14. **GEOMETRY** The volume of a grain storage silo in the shape of a rectangular solid is 4725 m^3. If both the width and the height are 15 m, what is the length?
15. **GEOMETRY** Find the height of a cylindrical tank with volume 3200 m^3 and radius 8 m.

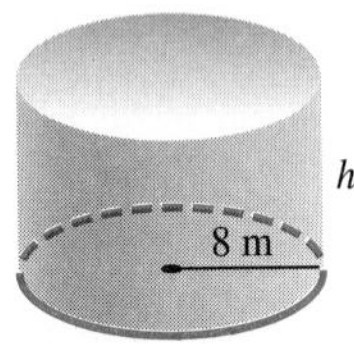

16. **GEOMETRY** The perimeter of a square is 48 ft. What is the length of a side?
17. **GEOMETRY** A cube with edge 10 ft is submerged in a rectangular tank containing water. If the tank is 40 ft by 50 ft, how much does the level of water in the tank rise?
18. **GEOMETRY** Find the volume, rounded to the nearest tenth, of a sphere with radius 2 m.
19. **GEOMETRY** The sphere in Exercise 18 is dropped into a rectangular tank that is 10 m long and 8 m wide. To the nearest tenth, how much does this raise the water level?

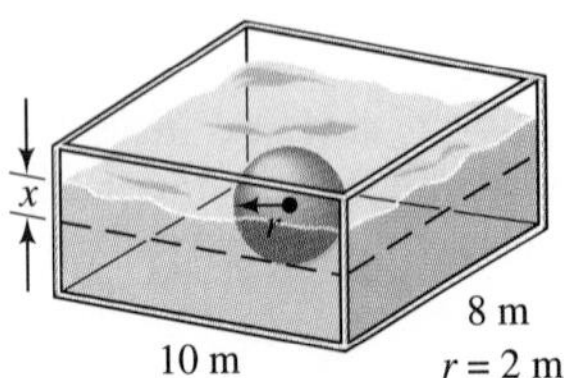

20. **GEOMETRY** A rancher wishes to enclose a pasture that is 3 mi long and 2 mi wide with a fence selling for 35¢ per linear foot. How much will the project cost?
21. **MOTION** Mary Lou Mercer walks for 7 hours at a rate of 5 km/hr. How far does she walk?
22. **MOTION** Bob Packard runs a distance of 20 miles at a rate of 8 mph. How many minutes does he run? [*Hint:* Note the units used.]
23. **RECREATION** A hiker crossed a valley by walking 5 mph the first 2 hr and 3 mph the next 4 hr. What was the total distance that she hiked?
24. **TRANSPORTATION** Two trains leave Omaha, one traveling east and the other traveling west. If one is moving 20 mph faster than the other, and if after 4 hr they are 520 mi apart, how fast is each going?

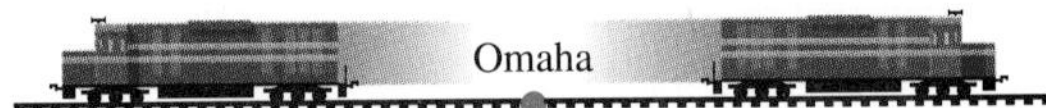

25. **NAVIGATION** Two ships sail north from Bermuda. One is traveling at 22 knots and the other at 17 knots. How many nautical miles will they be from each other after 8 hours?

26. **TRAVEL** Two cars that are 550 mi apart and whose speeds differ by 10 mph are moving towards each other. What is the speed of each if they meet in 5 hr?

FOR REVIEW

Solve each problem in Exercises 27–30. A calculator may be helpful in some problems.

27. **GEOMETRY** A wire is 42 in long. It is to be cut into three pieces in such a way that the second is twice the first and the third is equal to the sum of the lengths of the first two. How long is each piece?
28. **ECONOMICS** If the cost of an item rose 8¢, a 16% increase, what was the old price? What is the new price?
29. **EDUCATION** If a student answered 68 questions correctly on an 80-question exam, what was her percent score?
30. **SALARY** Betsy earned $11,130 one year after she received a 6% raise. What was her former salary?

Exercises 31–34 review material that we covered in Chapter 2. They will help you prepare for the next section. Place the correct symbol, $<$ or $>$, between the given pairs of numbers.

31. 2 5 **32.** −2 5 **33.** −2 −5 **34.** 2 −5

35. Consider the true inequality $-4 < 7$. **(a)** Does the inequality remain true if we multiply both sides by 2? **(b)** Does the inequality remain true if we multiply both sides by −2?

3.6 PARALLEL EXERCISES

Solve each applied problem in Exercises 1–26. If necessary, check the inside front cover for a list of formulas.

1. **GEOMETRY** The perimeter of a rectangle is 52 ft. If the length is 8 ft more than the width, find the dimensions.
2. **GEOMETRY** If one angle of a triangle is 72° more than the smallest angle, and the third angle is seven times the smallest angle, find the measure of each angle.
3. **GEOMETRY** The area of a rectangle is 32.5 ft^2 and the width is 5 ft. What is the length?
4. **GEOMETRY** If the area of a triangle is 78 cm^2 and its base is 12 cm, find its height.
5. **GEOMETRY** A circular garden is to be enclosed with edging material. How many meters of edging will be needed if the radius of the garden is 5 m? [Use $\pi \approx 3.14$.]
6. **GEOMETRY** In a triangle, the longest side is three times as long as the shortest side, and the third side is 2 ft shorter than the longest side. Find the three sides if the perimeter is 26 ft.
7. **GEOMETRY** Find the height of a parallelogram with a base of 17 cm and an area of 93.5 cm^2.
8. **GEOMETRY** If two angles of a triangle are equal and the third angle is equal to twice their sum, find the measure of each.
9. **GEOMETRY** An isosceles triangle with a base of 13 in has a perimeter of 53 in. Find the length of its legs.
10. **GEOMETRY** The perimeter of a rectangular table is 90 in. Find its dimensions if the length is 15 in more than the width.
11. **GEOMETRY** What is the height of a trapezoid with area 24 yd^2 and bases of length 4.5 yd and 3.5 yd?
12. **GEOMETRY** Find the base of a parallelogram if the perimeter is 100 in and a side is 15 in.
13. **GEOMETRY** What is the area of a circular rug having diameter 82 inches?

14. **GEOMETRY** The volume of a rectangular solid is 26,250 cm^3. If both the width and the height are 25 cm, what is the length?

15. **GEOMETRY** Find the height of a cylindrical storage tank with volume 1105.3 ft^3 and radius 4 ft.

16. **GEOMETRY** The perimeter of a square is 72 yd. What is the length of a side?

17. **GEOMETRY** A cube with edge 8 in is submerged in a rectangular tank containing water. If the tank is 10 in by 20 in, how much does the level of water in the tank rise?

18. **GEOMETRY** Find the volume of a sphere with radius 8 cm.

19. **GEOMETRY** If the sphere in Exercise 18 is submerged in a rectangular tank 20 cm wide by 30 cm long, how much will the level of the water increase?

20. **GEOMETRY** How much will it cost to enclose a garden with a picket fence if the garden is 12 yd long, 8 yd wide, and fencing costs 85¢ per linear foot?

21. **NAVIGATION** A ship travels for 15 hr at 20 knots, where a knot is 1 nautical mile per hour. How many nautical miles has it traveled?

22. **NAVIGATION** Sue Thompson drove her boat a distance of 45 miles at a rate of 30 mph. How many minutes did she drive?

23. **TRAVEL** Bill Young traveled by car for 6 hr at a rate of 55 mph and then by boat for 2 hr at 24 mph. What was the total distance traveled?

24. **RECREATION** Two campers leave Rocky Mountain National Park, one traveling north and the other traveling south. After 3 hr they are 255 mi apart, and one has been traveling 5 mph faster than the other. How fast is each traveling?

25. **TRANSPORTATION** Two truckers leave Atlanta at the same time heading west. How far apart will they be in 13 hr if one is traveling at a rate of 60 mph and the other at 56 mph?

26. **RECREATION** Two families leave home at 8:00 A.M., planning to meet for a picnic at a point between them. One travels at a rate of 45 mph and the other travels at 55 mph. If they live 500 miles apart, at what time do they meet?

FOR REVIEW

Solve each problem in Exercises 27–30. A calculator may be helpful in some problems.

27. **GEOMETRY** A 36-m steel rod is cut into three pieces. The second piece is twice as long as the first and the third is three times as long as the second. How long is each piece?

28. **CONSUMER** If the cost of a calculator rose \$1.92 and this was a 12% increase, what was the old price? What is the new price?

29. **TAX** If the sales-tax rate is 6%, how much tax will be charged on the purchase of a wallet costing \$14.50?

30. **SALARY** After an 8% salary increase, Henry makes \$24,300. What was his salary before the raise?

Exercises 31–34 review material that we covered in Chapter 2. They will help you prepare for the next section. Place the correct symbol, $<$ or $>$ between the given pairs of numbers.

31. 7 12 **32.** −7 12 **33.** −4 −15 **34.** 8 −10

35. Consider the true inequality $6 > -2$. **(a)** Does the inequality remain true if we multiply both sides by 3? **(b)** Does the inequality remain true if we multiply both sides by -3?

3.6 ENRICHMENT EXERCISES

Solve each applied problem in Exercises 1–18.

1. **GEOMETRY** Find the length of x in the figure below if the area enclosed is 162 ft^2. [*Hint:* Draw a line making two rectangles.]

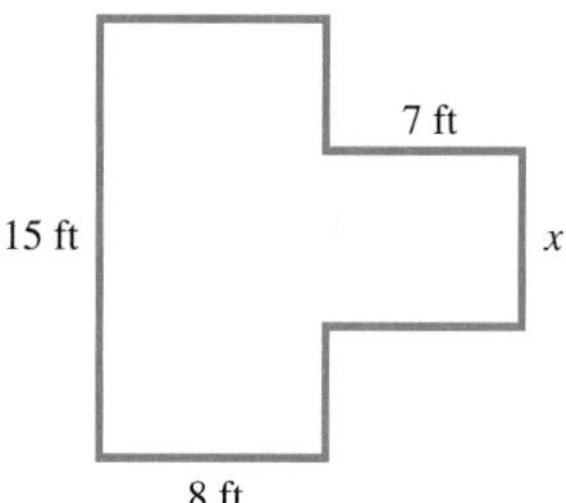

2. **GEOMETRY** Find the length of y in the figure below if the area enclosed is 297 in^2.

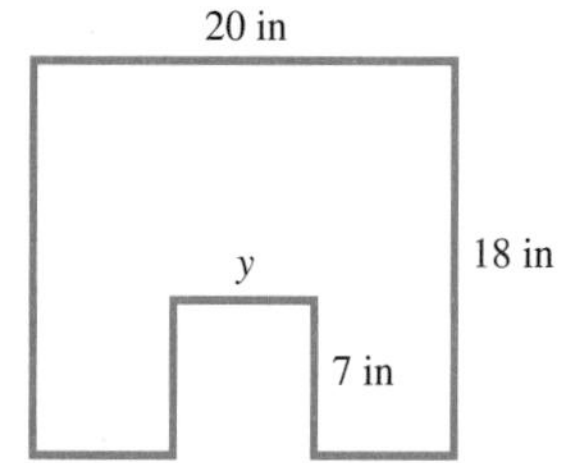

3. **GEOMETRY** The area shown required 124 m of fencing to enclose. Find the dimensions by finding the value of x.

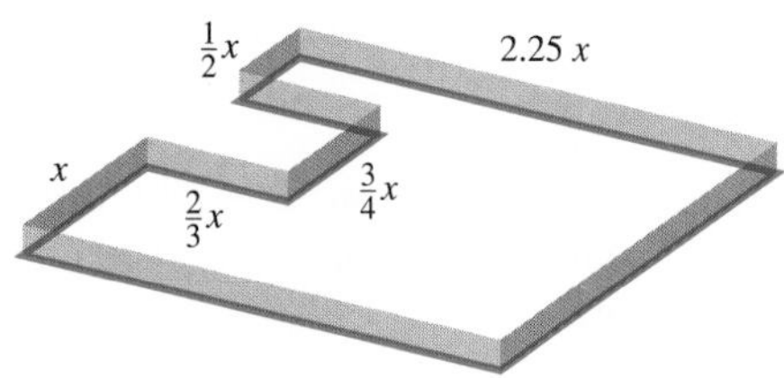

4. **GEOMETRY** The measure of the second angle of a triangle is one-fourth the measure of the third and 30° more than the first. Find the measure of each.

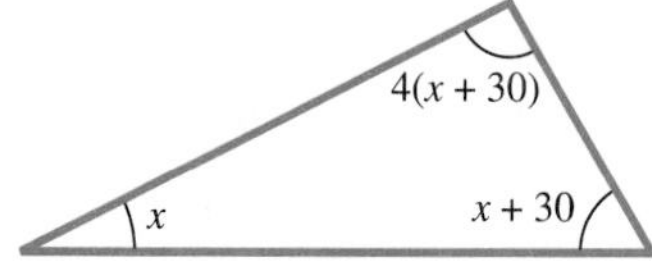

5. **GEOMETRY** The perimeter of a square is eleven cm less than five times the length of a side. Find the length of a side.

6. **GEOMETRY** A rectangular patio is twice as long as it is wide. If its length were decreased 8 ft and the width were increased 8 ft, it would be square. What are its dimensions?

7. **GEOMETRY** Dr. Cotera wishes to enclose a rectangular plot of land with 140 yards of fencing in such a way that the length is four times the width. What will be the dimensions of the plot?

8. **GEOMETRY** The perimeter of Ivan Danielson's yard is 528 yd. If the yard is rectangular in shape with length 24 yd more than the width, what are the dimensions?

9. **SPORTS** One year the Indianapolis 500 Memorial Day Race was won in 2 hours 36 minutes. To the nearest tenth, what was the average speed of the winner in this 500 mile race?

10. **TRAVEL** Melissa Martin drove her car at an average speed of 55 mph for one-half the distance of a trip and then traveled by boat at 20 mph the second half. How many miles did she travel if the total trip took 9 hours?

11. **TRAVEL** On a recent vacation, Leona Frezieres traveled one-third the total distance by car, 400 miles by boat, and one-half the total distance by air. What was the total distance traveled on the vacation?

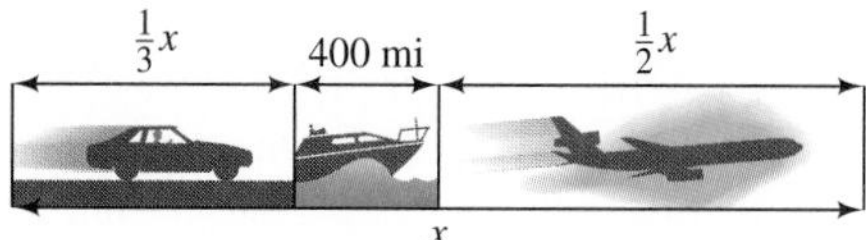

12. **RECREATION** Two hikers leave the same camp, one traveling east and the other traveling west. The one going east is hiking at a rate 1 mph faster than the other, and after 5 hr they are 35 mi apart. How fast is each hiking?

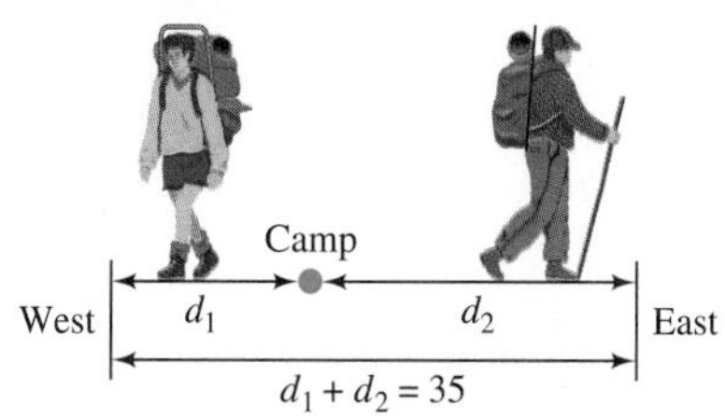

13. **POLITICS** In a school election, Morton beats his two opponents by 230 and 175 votes, respectively. If there were a total of 1635 votes cast, how many did Morton receive?

14. **NAVIGATION** A boat traveled from Puerto Vallarta to an island and back again in a total time of 10.5 hours. How far is the island from Puerto Vallarta if the boat averaged 15 mph going to the island and 20 mph returning?

15. **RECREATION** After draining their swimming pool to make several minor repairs, the Bonnetts plan to refill it using their garden hose. Suppose the hose lets water in at a rate of 20 gallons per minute and the pool holds 36,000 gallons. Will the pool be filled by noon on Sunday if the water is turned on at 9:00 A.M. Saturday?

16. **WILDLIFE MANAGEMENT** To estimate the trout population in Lake Louise, 400 banded trout were released on June 1, and the lake was closed to all fishing. On June 10, a sample of 100 trout were caught, 6 of which were banded. As a result, the ranger estimated that 6% of all the trout in Lake Louise were banded. Approximately how many trout were in the lake?

17. **SPORTS** Two cars are racing on an oval track that is 2 mi long. If they start at the same time, and one travels 185 mph and the other 175 mph, about how many minutes will it take for the faster car to overtake the slower car?

18. **TRAVEL** A camper and a sports car leave Phoenix at the same time headed west on interstate highway I-10. If the camper averages 50 mph and the sports car averages 68 mph, how long will it take for them to be 90 miles apart?

---

19. Write an interesting applied problem that has "18.5 ft" for the answer.

20. Write an interesting applied problem that has "20 minutes" for the answer.

SECTION 3.7 Solving and Graphing Linear Inequalities

Student guideposts

- ▶ *Graphing equations*
- ▶ *Graphing inequalities*
- ▶ *Solving linear inequalities*
- ▶ *Addition-subtraction rule*
- ▶ *Multiplication-division rule*
- ▶ *Solving by a combination of rules*
- ▶ *Method for solving linear inequalities*
- ▶ *Applications involving inequalities*

Often in algebra we try to picture abstract ideas. This was done in Chapter 2, for instance, using a number line. Recall that a number line is marked off in unit lengths with each point on the line associated with a real number. The origin is identified with the number zero, positive numbers correspond to points to the right of zero, and negative numbers correspond to points to the left of zero. We can identify any real number with exactly one point on a number line, and, conversely, every point on a number line corresponds to exactly one real number.

▶ *Graphing equations*

Linear equations in one variable like those we studied earlier can be graphed on a number line by plotting the points that correspond to solutions of the equation.

EXAMPLE 1 **Graphing Solutions to Equations**

Graph $2x + 1 = 3$.

First solve the equation.

$$2x + 1 - 1 = 3 - 1 \quad \text{Subtract 1}$$
$$2x = 2$$
$$x = 1$$

The solution is $x = 1$. Plot the point corresponding to 1 on a number line, as in Figure 3.7. ■

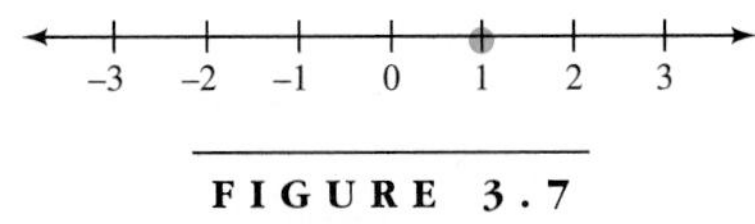

FIGURE 3.7

To graph $2x + 1 = 1 + 2x$, first solve the equation.

$$2x + 1 - 1 = 1 - 1 + 2x \quad \text{Subtract 1}$$
$$2x = 2x$$
$$2x - 2x = 2x - 2x \quad \text{Subtract } 2x$$
$$0 = 0$$

Since $0 = 0$ is always true, this equation is an identity and every number is a solution. Then every number must be plotted, and the graph of the solution is the entire number line shown in Figure 3.8.

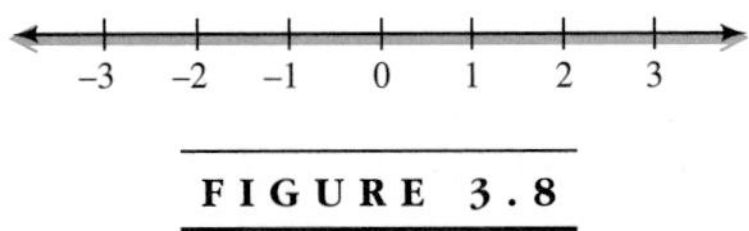

FIGURE 3.8

Suppose we graph $x + 1 = x$. If we solve the equation, we obtain the following result.

$$x - x + 1 = x - x \quad \text{Subtract } x$$
$$1 = 0$$

This equation is a contradiction because $1 \neq 0$. There are no solutions to the equation so we have no points to plot.

▶ *Graphing inequalities*

Graphing equations is a relatively simple procedure. The procedure for graphing **inequalities,** statements containing the symbols $<$, $\leq$, $>$, or $\geq$, is shown with the following figures.

In Figure 3.9, the graph of $x > 3$ has an open circle at 3. This means that the number 3 is not included among the solutions, while the colored line shows that all points to the right of 3 are included.

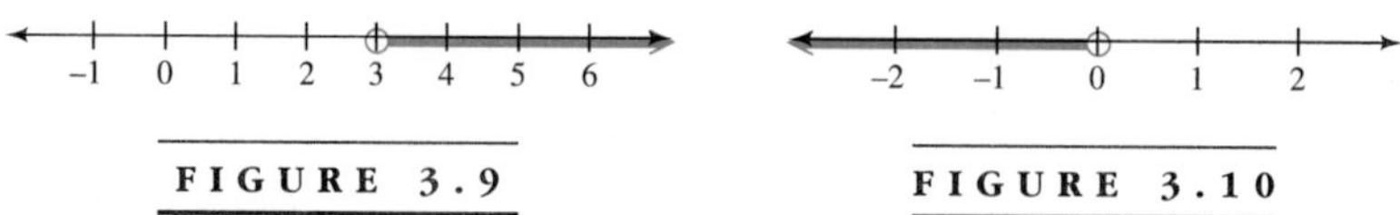

FIGURE 3.9

FIGURE 3.10

The graph of $x < 0$ is shown in Figure 3.10. In Figure 3.11, the graph of $x \geq -1$ has a solid circle at the point -1, indicating that -1 is included in the graph of $x \geq -1$. Finally, the graph of $x \leq 1$ is given in Figure 3.12.

FIGURE 3.11

FIGURE 3.12

Solving linear inequalities Now that we know how to graph simple inequalities such as $x > 3, x < 0, x \geq -1$, and $x \leq 1$, we can start to solve and graph more complex ones. Statements containing the inequality symbols $<, \leq, >$, and $\geq$, such as

$$x + 1 < 7, \quad 2x - 1 \geq 3, \quad 3x + 1 \leq 4x - 5, \quad \text{and} \quad x + 5 > 2(x - 3)$$

are called **linear inequalities.** A **solution** to a linear inequality is a number that, when substituted for the variable, makes the inequality true. For example, -6, 0, and 5 are some of the solutions to $x + 1 < 7$ since

$$-6 + 1 < 7, \quad 0 + 1 < 7, \quad \text{and} \quad 5 + 1 < 7$$

are all true.

Solving linear inequalities is much like solving linear equations since most of the same rules apply. There is one exception that will be discussed shortly. Like equivalent equations, **equivalent inequalities** have exactly the same solutions. Solving an inequality is a matter of transforming it to an equivalent inequality for which the solution is obvious.

Addition-subtraction rule If we start with the true inequality

$$7 < 15$$

and add 4 to both sides, we obtain another true inequality.

$$7 + 4 < 15 + 4$$
$$11 < 19$$

Likewise, if we subtract 3 from both sides, we again obtain a true inequality.

$$7 - 3 < 15 - 3$$
$$4 < 12$$

These observations lead to the addition-subtraction rule for inequalities.

Addition-Subtraction Rule

An equivalent inequality is obtained if the same quantity is added to or subtracted from both sides of an inequality.

Suppose a, b, and c are real numbers.

$$\text{If } a < b \quad \text{then} \quad a + c < b + c \text{ and } a - c < b - c.$$

NOTE We use this rule to solve inequalities in very much the same way that we used the similar addition-subtraction rule to solve equations. The key is to isolate the variable on one side of the inequality.

EXAMPLE 2

Using the Addition-Subtraction Rule

Solve and graph.

$$x + 1 < 7$$
$$x + 1 - 1 < 7 - 1 \quad \text{Subtract 1 from both sides}$$
$$x + 0 < 6$$
$$x < 6$$

All numbers less than 6 are solutions, and the graph is given in Figure 3.13. The fact that 6 is not part of the solution is indicated by the open circle. ■

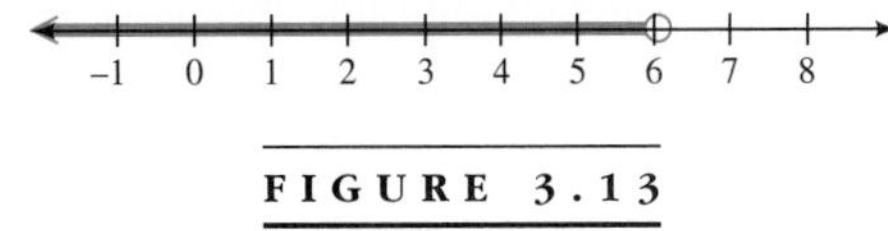

FIGURE 3.13

Most of the equations we have solved have had only one solution. For inequalities, there are many solutions.

EXAMPLE 3

Using the Addition-Subtraction Rule

Solve and graph.

$$x - 3 \geq 5$$
$$x - 3 + 3 \geq 5 + 3 \quad \text{Add 3 to both sides}$$
$$x + 0 \geq 8$$
$$x \geq 8$$

All numbers greater than or equal to 8 are solutions. Generally, we indicate the solution simply by writing $x \geq 8$. The graph is given in Figure 3.14. Notice that 8 is part of the solution, so the circle at the point corresponding to 8 is solid. ■

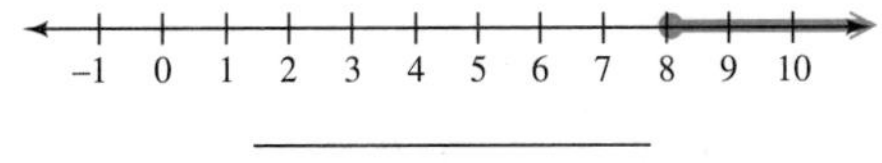

FIGURE 3.14

Multiplication-division rule

If we start with the true inequality

$$6 < 14$$

and multiply both sides by 3, we obtain the true inequality

$$18 < 42.$$

However, if we multiply both sides by -2, we obtain the false inequality

$$-12 < -28. \quad \text{This is false}$$

To obtain a true inequality here, we need to reverse the inequality symbol, that is, change $<$ to $>$. These observations lead to the multiplication-division rule for inequalities.

Multiplication-Division Rule

An equivalent inequality is obtained in the following situations.

1. Each side of the inequality is multiplied or divided by the same *positive* quantity.

$$\text{If } c > 0 \text{ and } a < b \text{ then } ac < bc \text{ and } \frac{a}{c} < \frac{b}{c}.$$

2. Each side of the inequality is multiplied or divided by the same *negative* quantity and the inequality symbol is reversed.

$$\text{If } c < 0 \text{ and } a < b \text{ then } ac > bc \text{ and } \frac{a}{c} > \frac{b}{c}.$$

EXAMPLE 4

Using the Multiplication-Division Rule

Solve and graph.

$$4x > 16$$

$$\frac{1}{4} \cdot 4x > \frac{1}{4} \cdot 16 \quad \frac{1}{4} \text{ is positive so inequality symbol remains the same}$$

$$1 \cdot x > 4$$

$$x > 4$$

The graph is given in Figure 3.15. ■

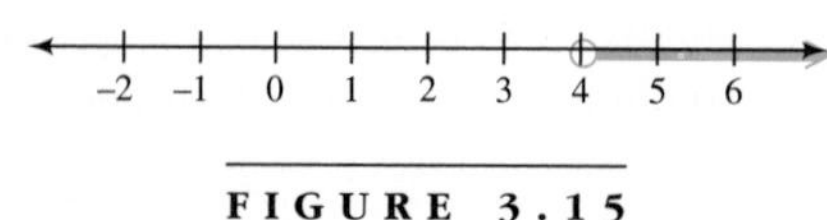

FIGURE 3.15

EXAMPLE 5 Using the Multiplication-Division Rule

Solve and graph.

$$-\frac{1}{2}x \leq 7$$

$$\downarrow$$

$$(-2)\left(-\frac{1}{2}x\right) \geq (-2)(7) \qquad \text{Multiply both sides by } -2 \text{ and } \textit{reverse} \text{ the inequality symbol}$$

$$1 \cdot x \geq -14$$

$$x \geq -14$$

The graph is given in Figure 3.16. ■

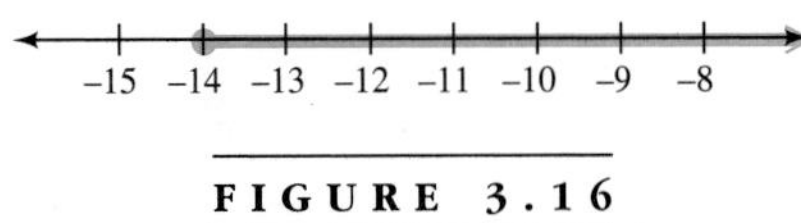

FIGURE 3.16

> CAUTION To multiply or divide by a negative number, always reverse the inequality symbol. Thus, if $-x < -5$, then $x > 5$ (not $x < 5$). This is the only substantial difference between solving an equation and solving an inequality.

▶ *Solving by a combination of rules*

We now solve inequalities that require both the addition-subtraction rule and the multiplication-division rule. As with solving equations, the basic idea is to isolate the variable on one side of the inequality.

EXAMPLE 6 Using a Combination of Rules

Solve and graph.

$$2x + 5 < 7$$

$$2x + 5 - 5 < 7 - 5 \qquad \text{Subtract 5}$$

$$2x < 2$$

$$\frac{1}{2} \cdot 2x < \frac{1}{2} \cdot 2 \qquad \text{Multiply by } \tfrac{1}{2} \text{ or divide by 2; the inequality remains the same}$$

$$1 \cdot x < 1$$

$$x < 1$$

The graph is given in Figure 3.17. ■

–2 –1 0 1 2 3 4

FIGURE 3.17

EXAMPLE 7 **Using a Combination of Rules**

Solve and graph.

$$6 - 4x \geq 2 - 3x$$

$$6 - 6 - 4x \geq 2 - 6 - 3x \qquad \text{Subtract 6}$$

$$-4x \geq -4 - 3x$$

$$-4x + 3x \geq -4 - 3x + 3x \qquad \text{Add } 3x$$

$$-x \geq -4$$

$$(-1)(-x) \leq (-1)(-4) \qquad \text{Multiply by } -1 \text{ and } \textit{reverse} \text{ inequality symbol}$$

$$x \leq 4$$

The graph is given in Figure 3.18. ■

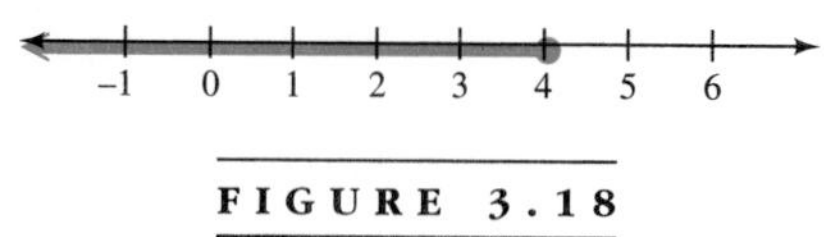

FIGURE 3.18

Often an inequality involves parentheses. When this occurs, first remove all parentheses and then proceed as in previous cases.

EXAMPLE 8 **Solving an Inequality with Parentheses**

Solve.

$$-6(2 + x) \geq 2(4x - 2)$$

$$-12 - 6x \geq 8x - 4 \qquad \text{Remove parentheses}$$

$$-12 + 12 - 6x \geq 8x - 4 + 12 \qquad \text{Add 12}$$

$$-6x \geq 8x + 8$$

$$-6x - 8x \geq 8x - 8x + 8 \qquad \text{Subtract } 8x$$

$$-14x \geq 8$$

$$\downarrow$$

$$\frac{-14x}{-14} \leq \frac{8}{-14} \qquad \text{Divide by } -14 \text{ and } \textit{reverse} \text{ inequality symbol}$$

$$x \leq -\frac{8}{14}$$

$$x \leq -\frac{4}{7}$$

The graph is given in Figure 3.19. ■

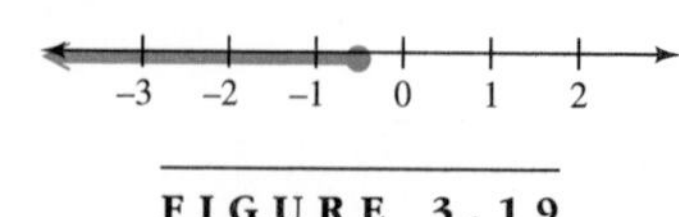

FIGURE 3.19

▶ *Method for solving linear inequalities*

The method for solving a linear inequality is summarized below.

To Solve a Linear Inequality

1. Simplify both sides of the inequality by clearing parentheses, fractions, and decimals.
2. Use the addition-subtraction rule to isolate all variable terms on one side and all constant terms on the other side. Collect like terms when possible.
3. Use the multiplication-division rule to obtain a variable with coefficient of 1. **Be sure to reverse the inequality symbol whenever multiplying or dividing both sides by a negative number.**

▶ *Applications involving inequalities*

Some applied problems result in inequalities. The following example solves the applied problem given in the chapter introduction.

EXAMPLE 9

Solving an Education Application

For Kevin Connors to get an A in his Spanish course, he must earn a total of 360 points on four tests each worth 100 points. If he got scores of 87, 96, and 91 on the first three tests, find (using an inequality) the range of scores he could make on the fourth test to get an A.

Let s = score Kevin must get on the fourth test. Since the total of his four test scores must be greater than or equal to 360, we must solve

$$87 + 96 + 91 + s \geq 360.$$

$$274 + s \geq 360$$

$$s \geq 86 \quad \text{Subtract 274 from both sides}$$

Kevin must make a score of 86 or better on the fourth test to get an A in the course. ■

There are some key words and phrases that translate into inequalities and which are often used in applications. Consider the statement:

You must be *at least* 21 years of age to be in the casinos in Las Vegas.

The phrase

at least means *greater than or equal to.*

If a represents your age, then the sentence above translates into

$$a \geq 21.$$

Consider the sentence:

An airport shuttle can seat *at most* 12 people.

The phrase

at most means *less than or equal to.*

If s is the number of seats on the shuttle, the sentence translates into

$$s \leq 12.$$

A third common term is illustrated in the sentence:

A profit is realized when the revenue received *exceeds* the cost of production.

The term

exceeds means *greater than.*

If R represents revenue received and C represents cost of production, this sentence translates into:

$$R > C.$$

3.7 EXERCISES

Graph each equation in Exercises 1–6 on a number line.

1. $2x - 3 = 1$
2. $x + 5 = x$
3. $x - 1 = x - 1$
4. $-\frac{1}{10} - \frac{3}{5}y = \frac{1}{5}$
5. $a - 3 + 4a = 2 + a - 5$
6. $12 - x = 3 + 2[4 - (x - 1)]$

Graph each inequality in Exercises 7–12 on a number line.

7. $x > 2$
8. $y \leq -1$
9. $-2a \leq -8$
10. $1 - 3x < 8$
11. $25 \geq 5(3 - z) - 10$
12. $-2a + 3 + a < 2(a + 3)$

Solve each inequality in Exercises 13–36.

13. $x + 9 > 12$
14. $x - 3 < 14$
15. $z + 2.3 > 4.7$
16. $3.9 > z - 5.2$
17. $z - \frac{3}{4} \leq \frac{2}{3}$
18. $2a + 1 > a - 3$
19. $a - 4 \leq 2a + 5$
20. $3(b + 1) > 2b - 5$
21. $\frac{1}{3}x < -4$
22. $-\frac{1}{4}y \geq 2$
23. $-3y < 7$
24. $2.1y > 4.2$
25. $-a \leq -7$
26. $-\frac{2}{3}z > \frac{4}{3}$
27. $-3b \geq \frac{1}{2}$
28. $1 - 3x \geq -8$
29. $-8y - 7 \geq 21 - 15y$
30. $4(z - 3) \leq 3(2z + 4)$
31. $3(2x + 3) - (3x + 2) < 12$
32. $5(x + 3) + 4 \geq x - 1$
33. $y + 3 - 4y > 2(y + 12)$
34. $3 - 2z < 5(z - 7)$
35. $0.05 + 3(z - 1.2) > 2z$
36. $\frac{3}{4}z - \frac{3}{8} < \frac{3}{2} + \frac{1}{8}z$

Are the statements in Exercises 37–42 true *or* false? *If the statement is false, tell why.*

37. If $x < 9$, then $-2x < -18$.
38. If $x > 4$, then $3x > 12$.
39. If $x \leq 7$, then $x + 1 \leq 8$.
40. If $x < -1$, then $-x > 1$.
41. If $x < 3$, then $x - 7 > -4$.
42. If $-x < -10$, then $1 - x < -9$.

Solve each applied problem in Exercises 43–48.

43. **NUMBER** The product of a number and 3 is greater than or equal to the number less 8. Find the numbers that satisfy this.

44. **AGE** If twice my age, increased by 7, is greater than or equal to 31 less my age, I am at least how old?

45. **EDUCATION** Professor Packard will given an F to any student with a point total less than 180 in a course having three 100 point exams. Burford made 38 points on the first exam and 54 on the second. Determine the minimum score he could make on the third exam to avoid failing the course.

46. **BUSINESS** For Darrell Fosberg to win a trip to Bermuda, his new car sales must average at least 50 over the three-month period June, July, and August. If he sold 47 cars in June and 62 cars in July, how many cars must he sell in August to qualify for the trip?

47. **BUSINESS** In the manufacture and sale of novelty items, the daily cost of producing n items is given by $C = 2n + 50$, and the revenue realized on the sale of n items is $R = 4n$. How many items must be produced and sold daily for the revenue to exceed the cost; that is, for a profit to be made?

48. **ELECTRICITY** In an electrical circuit, the power in watts W is given in terms of the pressure in volts E and the current in amperes I by the equation $W = EI$. If a 20-ampere fuse is in a 110-volt circuit, the total wattage of all items on the circuit can be at most what number of watts before "blowing" the fuse?

FOR REVIEW

Solve each applied problem in Exercises 49–52.

49. **GEOMETRY** The length of a rectangular room is 5 yd more than its width. If its perimeter is 54 yd, find its dimensions.

50. **GEOMETRY** Find the volume, rounded to the nearest tenth, of a sphere with radius 3 cm. [Use 3.14 for π.]

51. **MOTION** Roy drove 378 miles in 7 hr. What was his average speed?

52. **TRAVEL** Two families leave their homes at the same time planning to meet at a point between them. If one travels 55 mph, the other travels 50 mph, and they live 273 miles apart, how long will it take for them to meet?

3.7 PARALLEL EXERCISES

Graph each equation in Exercises 1–6 on a number line.

1. $2x - 5 = 1$

2. $4x + 3 = 4x - 3$

3. $x - 5 = x - 5$

4. $-\frac{1}{4} - \frac{3}{8}y = \frac{1}{2}$

5. $a - 2 + 3a = 4 + a - 5$

6. $7 - 2x = 3 + [2 - (x - 3)]$

Graph each inequality in Exercises 7–12 on a number line.

7. $x > 1$

8. $y \leq -3$

9. $-3a > -9$

10. $1 - 2x < 4$

11. $-4y - 4 \geq 3 - 11y$

12. $-3a - 4 + 2a \geq 3(a + 2)$

Solve each inequality in Exercises 13–36.

13. $x + 3 > 2$

14. $x - 4 \leq 7$

15. $z + 1.9 < 3.9$

16. $4.2 < z - 8.1$

17. $z - \frac{2}{3} \leq \frac{3}{4}$

18. $a - 5 \leq 2a + 3$

19. $4a - 12 \geq 3a - 1$

20. $2(b + 5) \geq b + 7$

21. $\frac{1}{3}x < -8$

22. $-\frac{1}{3}y < 2$

23. $-5y < 11$

24. $2.1y \leq 6.3$

25. $-a > -10$

26. $-4.1z > 8.2$

27. $-4b \geq \frac{1}{5}$

28. $1 - 4x \geq -7$

29. $-5y - 2 < 32 + 12y$

30. $5(y - 2) > 4(2y + 1)$

31. $2(3x + 1) - (5x + 4) \geq 2$

32. $3x - 1 \leq x - (3x - 14)$

33. $x - 2 + 2x \leq 2(x + 5)$

34. $3 - 2(z + 1) \geq 5 - z$

35. $0.01 + 2(z + 1.5) > 3z$

36. $\frac{1}{4}z + \frac{3}{8} \geq \frac{1}{2} - \frac{3}{8}z$

Are the statements in Exercises 37–42 true *or* false? *If the statement is false, tell why.*

37. If $x > 7$, then $-2x < -14$.

38. If $x < 5$, then $3x < 15$.

39. If $x \leq -1$, then $x + 1 \leq 0$.

40. If $-x \geq 1$, then $x \geq 1$.

41. If $x < 5$, then $x - 4 < 1$.

42. If $-x \leq -5$, then $2 - x \leq -3$.

Solve each applied problem in Exercises 43–48.

43. **NUMBER** The product of a number and 5 is less than or equal to that number increased by 8. Find the numbers that satisfy this.

44. **AGE** If Jeff's age is doubled, then diminished by 4, the result is greater than or equal to 5 plus his age. Jeff is at least how old?

45. **EDUCATION** To get an A in chemistry, Paula must have at least 270 points out of a total of 300 in the course. She has made 87 points on the first test and 98 on the second. At least how many points must she get on the third and final exam to receive an A?

46. **RECREATION** Each team of four members in a tug-of-war can have no more than 600 lb total weight to qualify for the finals. Ron's team has three members weighing 120 lb, 140 lb, and 128 lb. What is the greatest amount Ron can weigh in order for his team to qualify?

47. **BUSINESS** In the manufacture and sale of bird feeders, the daily cost of making n feeders is given by $C = 10n + 120$, and the revenue realized on the sale of n feeders is $R = 22n$. How many feeders must be made and sold daily for the revenue to exceed the cost; that is, for a profit to be made?

48. **ELECTRICITY** In an electrical circuit, the power in watts W is given in terms of the pressure in volts E and the current in amperes I by the equation $W = EI$. If a 30-ampere fuse is in a 220-volt circuit, the total wattage of all items on the circuit can be at most what number of watts before "blowing" the fuse?

FOR REVIEW

Solve each applied problem in Exercises 49–52.

49. **GEOMETRY** The width of a rectangular table is 22 in less than its length. If its perimeter is 216 in, find its dimensions.

50. **GEOMETRY** A circular cylinder has volume 117.75 cm^3 and radius 5 cm. What is the height of the cylinder? [Use 3.14 for π.]

51. **MOTION** Martha hiked 25 miles at an average rate of 3 mph. What length of time did she hike?

52. **AERONAUTICS** Two planes leave Atlanta at the same time, one heading east at 400 mph and the other heading west at 460 mph. How long will it take for them to be 3010 miles apart?

3.7 ENRICHMENT EXERCISES

Solve each inequality in Exercises 1–2.

1. $\frac{x-5}{3} - \frac{2x+1}{2} \le x - (2x - 1)$

△ 2. $\frac{x+3}{2} - 5(x-4) > \frac{x}{3} + \frac{43}{2}$

Solve each applied problem in Exercises 3–6.

△ 3. **ECONOMICS** A company that makes and sells computer software items makes a profit of \$20 on each item. How many items must be sold to realize a profit of at least \$10,000?

4. **TRAVEL** Barry can drive at most 450 miles a day. If he plans to take a trip of 3150 miles, he should plan to drive at least how many days?

5. **CONSUMER** Bob Carlton bought a new luxury car. The sales-tax rate in the state where he bought the car is 6%. Bob claims that the sales tax on his car exceeded \$1650. We know then that Bob must have paid more than what amount for his car?

6. **CONSUMER** The price of a hamburger is 20 cents more than the price of an order of French fries, and the price of a Pepsi is 30 cents more than a hamburger at the Burger Barn. During a special TV promotion, Burger Barn advertises that you can have a total meal (hamburger, fries, and Pepsi) for less than \$2.50. The price of a hamburger must not exceed what amount?

7. What is the only substantial difference between solving a linear inequality and solving a linear equation?

8. Explain what is wrong with Burford's work in the following problem.

$$\frac{6}{x} < 3$$
$$\left(\frac{6}{x}\right)x < 3x$$
$$6 < 3x$$
$$\frac{6}{3} < \frac{3x}{3}$$
$$2 < x$$

9. Outline the method to be used to solve any linear inequality.

10. Make up three word problems that use the terms *exceeds, at least,* and *at most.*

SECTION 3.8 Compound Inequalities (Optional)

Student guideposts ▶ And *statements* ▶ Or *statements*

▶ And *statements*

Problems can often involve combinations of two inequalities. Inequalities are usually combined one of two ways, with the word *and* or with the word *or*. The combination is called a **compound inequality.** For example, the compound inequality

$$x > -2 \quad \textit{and} \quad x < 3$$

could be restated as

$$-2 < x \quad \textit{and} \quad x < 3$$

or as the **chain** of inequalities

$$-2 < x < 3.$$

The numbers that satisfy this chain of inequalities are solutions to both inequalities: those numbers which are *both* greater than -2 *and* less than 3. The graph is shown in Figure 3.20.

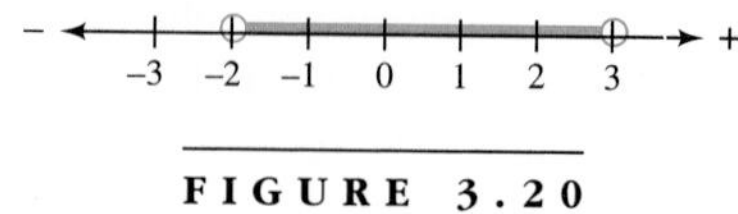

FIGURE 3.20

Similarly, the graph of $-1 \le x \le 2$ ($-1 \le x$ and $x \le 2$) is shown in Figure 3.21, the graph of $-3 \le x < 0$ ($-3 \le x$ and $x < 0$) in Figure 3.22,

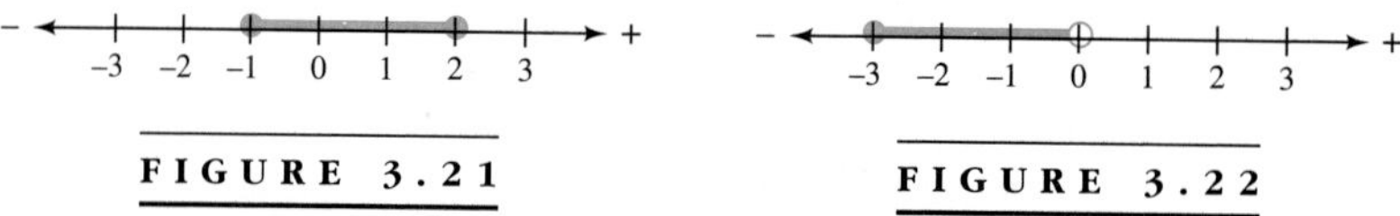

FIGURE 3.21 **FIGURE 3.22**

and the graph of $1 < x \le 2$ ($1 < x$ and $x \le 2$) in Figure 3.23.

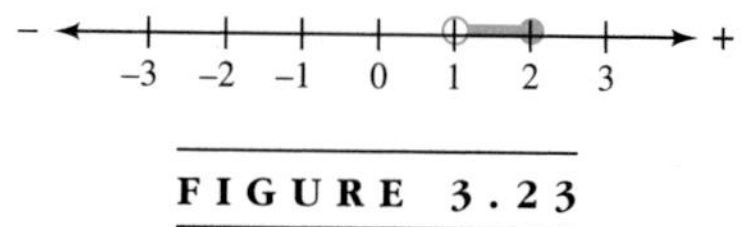

FIGURE 3.23

NOTE The compound inequality

$$2 < x \quad \text{and} \quad x < -1$$

has no solution since there are no numbers which are *both* less than -1 *and* greater than 2. If we try to merge the two inequalities into a single chain as before, we have

$$2 < x < -1 \qquad \text{This is wrong}$$

which states that 2 is less than -1, a contradiction.

A chain of inequalities may be more complex. For example,

$$-1 < 2x + 1 < 3$$

is restated as the compound

$$-1 < 2x + 1 \quad \textit{and} \quad 2x + 1 < 3$$

Since -1 is indeed less than 3, the chain makes sense.

EXAMPLE 1 **Solving an *and* Compound**

Solve and graph $-1 < 2x + 1 < 3$.

We need to solve two inequalities.

$$
\begin{array}{rcll}
-1 < 2x + 1 & \text{and} & 2x + 1 < 3 & \\
-1 - 1 < 2x + 1 - 1 & \text{and} & 2x + 1 - 1 < 3 - 1 & \text{Subtract 1} \\
-2 < 2x & \text{and} & 2x < 2 & \\
-1 < x & \text{and} & x < 1 & \text{Divide by 2}
\end{array}
$$

Rewritten as a single chain, the solution is

$$-1 < x < 1$$

and the graph is shown in Figure 3.24.

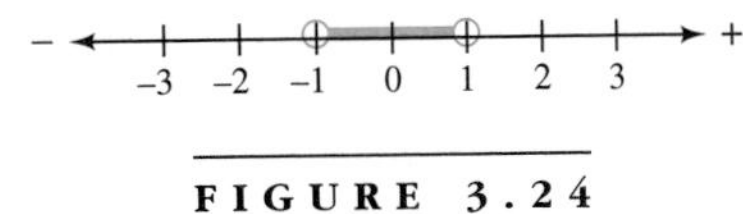

FIGURE 3.24

More compactly, we can solve the original chain as follows.

$$
\begin{array}{ll}
-1 < 2x + 1 < 3 & \\
-1 - 1 < 2x + 1 - 1 < 3 - 1 & \text{Subtract 1 throughout} \\
-2 < 2x < 2 & \\
\frac{1}{2}(-2) < \frac{1}{2}(2x) < \frac{1}{2}(2) & \text{Multiply throughout by } \frac{1}{2} \\
-1 < x < 1 \quad \blacksquare &
\end{array}
$$

▶ Or *statements* The other way inequalities are combined is with the connective *or*.

$$x < -1 \quad or \quad x > 2$$

Compound inequalities using *or* cannot be formed into a single chain. Trying to form this compound into a single chain would give us $2 < x < -1$, which makes no sense since 2 is not less than -1. The graph of an *or* compound is usually two segments of a number line, such as the graph in Figure 3.25 of $x < -1$ or $x > 2$.

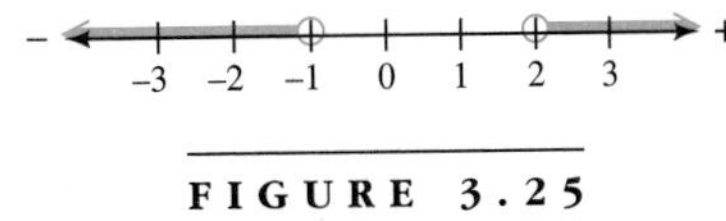

FIGURE 3.25

Similarly, $x < -2$ or $x \geq 1$ is graphed in Figure 3.26.

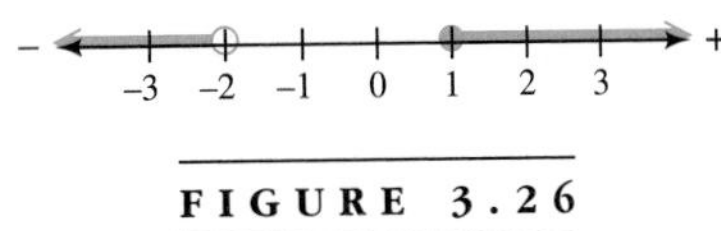

FIGURE 3.26

Also, the graph of $x \le 0$ or $x > 3$ is shown in Figure 3.27,

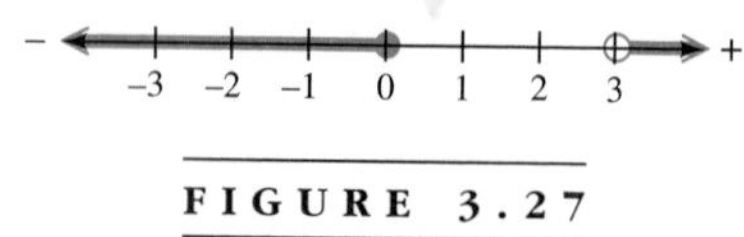

FIGURE 3.27

and the graph of $x \le -1$ or $x \ge 0$ is in Figure 3.28.

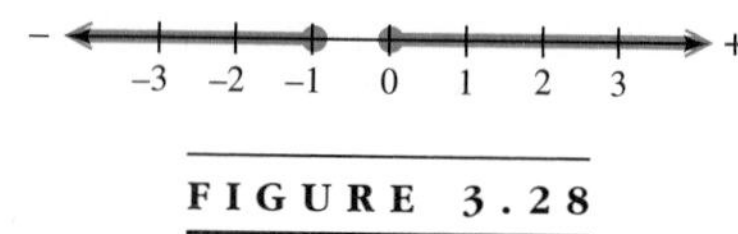

FIGURE 3.28

Finally, the graph of $x \le 2$ or $x \ge -1$ in Figure 3.29 is the entire number line.

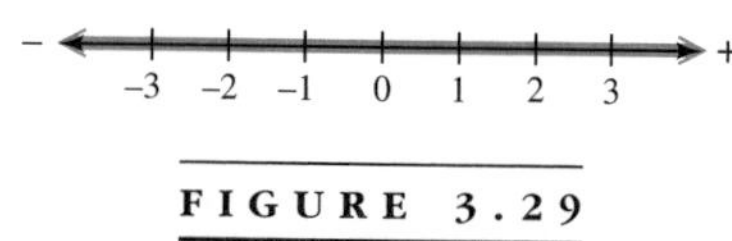

FIGURE 3.29

> **NOTE** If we tried to form the last compound into a single chain, we would get $-1 \le x \le 2$. Although this chain makes sense, its graph is only the 3 units on the number line between -1 and 2. But the graph of the compound statement $x \le 2$ or $x \ge -1$ is, as we have seen, the entire number line. So again, *or* statements can *never* be made into a chain.

As with *and* combinations, *or* combinations may be more complex.

EXAMPLE 2

Solving an *or* Compound

Solve and graph the following compound.

$$2x + 1 \le -1 \quad \text{or} \quad 2x + 1 > 3$$

$$2x + 1 - 1 \le -1 - 1 \quad \text{or} \quad 2x + 1 - 1 > 3 - 1 \qquad \text{Subtract 1}$$

$$2x \le -2 \quad \text{or} \quad 2x > 2$$

$$x \le -1 \quad \text{or} \quad x > 1 \qquad \text{Divide by 2}$$

The solution is

$$x \le -1 \quad \text{or} \quad x > 1$$

and the graph is shown in Figure 3.30. ■

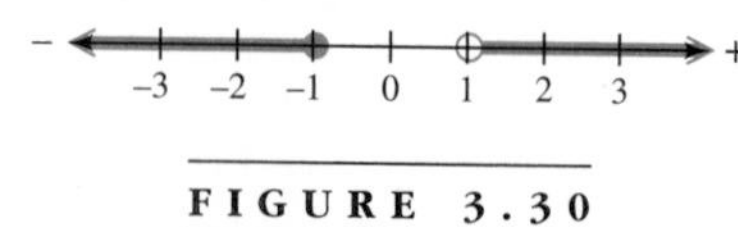

FIGURE 3.30

EXAMPLE 3 **Solving an *or* Compound**

Solve and graph the following compound.

$$3 - 4x < -1 \quad \text{or} \quad 3 - 4x \geq 9$$
$$-4x < -4 \quad \text{or} \quad -4x \geq 6$$
$$x > 1 \quad \text{or} \quad x \leq -\frac{6}{4} \quad \text{Reverse}$$
$$x \leq -\frac{3}{2}$$

The solution is

$$x > 1 \quad \text{or} \quad x \leq -\frac{3}{2}$$

and the graph is given in Figure 3.31. ■

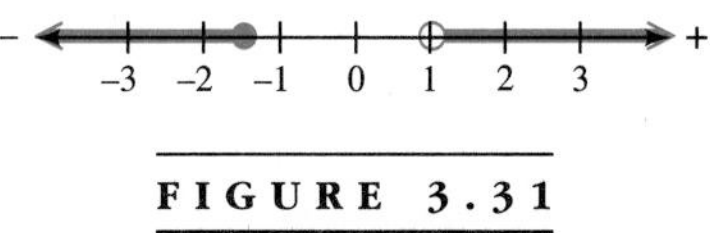

FIGURE 3.31

CAUTION Remember that an *and* compound (such as $-4 < x$ and $x \leq 3$) can be expressed as a single chain of inequalities ($-4 < x \leq 3$) and usually has as its graph a single segment of a number line. An *or* compound (such as $x < -1$ or $x > 2$) *cannot* be expressed as a single chain of inequalities (*never write* $2 < x < -1$) and usually has as its graph two separate segments of a number line.

Many applied problems can be solved using compound inequalities. A term that is often used in such problems is *between.* Consider the statement:

The temperature on Friday stayed between 55° and 72°.

If we use T for temperature, this statement translates to

$$55 < T < 72.$$

Sometimes the word *inclusive* is used with *between.* When this happens, the inequality symbols are changed to include equality. For example, the statement

My weight over the last year has stayed between 155 lb and 165 lb, inclusive.

translates to

$$155 \leq w \leq 165,$$

where w is used to represent my weight.

EXAMPLE 4 **Solving a Temperature Application**

The temperature at a hot-springs spa in Mexico is advertised to stay between 35°C and 40°C, inclusive. Use the formula $C = \frac{5}{9}(F - 32)$ and determine the range of temperatures in degrees Fahrenheit.

Since we are given that

$$35 \le C \le 40$$

substitute $\frac{5}{9}(F - 32)$ for C and solve for F.

$$35 \le \frac{5}{9}(F - 32) \le 40$$

Multiply throughout by 9. Since 9 is positive, the inequalities remain the same.

$$315 \le 5(F - 32) \le 360$$

Divide throughout by 5. Since 5 is positive, the inequalities remain the same.

$$63 \le F - 32 \le 72$$

Add 32 throughout.

$$95 \le F \le 104$$

Thus, the temperature is between 95°F and 104°F, inclusive. ■

3.8 EXERCISES

In Exercises 1–14, graph each compound inequality on a number line.

1. $x > -3$ and $x < 0$

2. $-3 < x < 0$

3. $x < -3$ or $x > 3$

4. $-2 \le x \le 2$

5. $x < 2$ or $x \ge 4$

6. $-5 \le 4x + 3 < 5$

7. $4x + 3 < -5$ or $4x + 3 \ge 5$

8. $2x - 5 \le -3$ or $2x - 5 > 3$

9. $0 > 3 - x$ or $3 - x \ge 1$

10. $0 > 2 - x$ or $2 - x \ge 2$

11. $0 \le 2 - (x - 1) < 1$

12. $0 \le 1 - (x - 1) < 2$

13. $6 - 5x \le -4$ or $7 - (5x + 1) > 1$

14. $5 - (3x + 1) \le -2$ or $4 - 3x \ge 1$

Solve each applied problem in Exercises 15–18.

15. **ECONOMICS** The profit on the sale of n shirts is given by $P = 20n - 80$. If it is known that the profit on sales was between \$400 and \$600, inclusive, how many shirts were sold? Give the answer as an inequality and also in words.

16. **ELECTRICITY** If W is the power in watts, E is the pressure in volts, and I is the current in amperes in an electrical circuit, then we know that $W = EI$. If the range of power in a particular 110-volt circuit is between 220 watts and 2200 watts, what is the range of current in the circuit? Give the answer as an inequality and also in words.

17. **EDUCATION** To receive a C in German, Harvey must have an average percent score between 70% and 80%, inclusive. If on the first three tests his scores were 82%, 60%, and 78%, what range of scores on the fourth and final test will give him a C?

18. **TEMPERATURE** If the Fahrenheit temperature is between 27° and 54° what is the range of temperatures, to the nearest tenth of a degree, on the Celsius scale? [*Hint:* $F = \frac{9}{5}C + 32$]

FOR REVIEW

Solve each inequality in Exercises 19–21.

19. $-\frac{1}{2}x > 4$ **20.** $1 - 2x \geq 5$ **21.** $2(x - 1) < 3 - (x - 4)$

22. The perimeter of a square is at least 36 inches. Each side must be at least how long?

3.8 PARALLEL EXERCISES

In Exercises 1–14, graph each compound inequality on a number line.

1. $x > -5$ and $x < 1$ **2.** $-1 < x < 4$ **3.** $x < -2$ or $x > 2$

4. $-3 \leq x \leq 0$ **5.** $x \leq -2$ or $x > 1$ **6.** $-3 < 2x - 3 \leq 3$

7. $3x + 1 < -8$ or $3x + 1 \geq 4$ **8.** $4x - 3 \leq -3$ or $4x - 3 > 3$

9. $0 > 2 - x$ or $2 - x \geq 3$ **10.** $0 > 5 - x$ or $5 - x \geq 5$

11. $0 \leq 3 - (x - 2) < 2$ **12.** $0 \leq 2 - (x - 2) < 2$

13. $7 - 2x \leq -5$ or $3 - (3x + 1) > -1$ **14.** $4 - (2x - 1) \leq -3$ or $5 - 3x \geq 2$

Solve each applied problem in Exercises 15–18.

15. **ECONOMICS** The profit on the sale of n cassette tapes is given by $P = 5n - 70$. If it is known that the profit on sales was between \$150 and \$350, inclusive, how many tapes were sold? Give the answer as an inequality and also in words.

16. **ELECTRICITY** If W is the power in watts, E is the pressure in volts, and I is the current in amperes in an electrical circuit, then we know that $W = EI$. If the range of power in a particular 220-volt circuit is between 1100 watts and 3300 watts, what is the range of current in the circuit? Give the answer as an inequality and also in words.

17. **EDUCATION** To receive a B in German, Cecilia must have an average percent score between 80% and 90%, inclusive. If on the first three tests her scores were 82%, 92%, and 88%, what range of scores on the fourth and final test will give her a B?

18. **TEMPERATURE** If the Fahrenheit temperature is between 10° and 35° what is the range of temperatures, to the nearest tenth of a degree, on the Celsius scale? [*Hint:* $F = \frac{9}{5}C + 32$]

FOR REVIEW

Solve each inequality in Exercises 19–21.

19. $-\frac{1}{3}x < 5$ **20.** $2 - 3x \leq 5$ **21.** $3(x - 2) < 1 - (x - 3)$

22. If the length of a room is 14 ft, and the floor area of the room is at least 126 ft^2, the width of the room is at least what?

3.8 ENRICHMENT EXERCISES

Solve each applied problem in Exercises 1–2.

1. **EDUCATION** Burford had scores of 45%, 51%, and 68% on the first three tests in algebra. (Burford is a party animal!) At the beginning of the term, his professor told the class that to receive a grade of C in the course, a student must have between 70% and 80%, inclusive, at the end of the term. The night before the final exam, Burford called his professor and asked what it would take for him to receive a C. What did his professor tell him?

2. **CONSUMER** Zach and Andy plan to buy their parents a new color television set for their anniversary. The sets that they are looking at range in price from \$500 to \$800, inclusive. Since Andy has a better paying job, he plans to contribute \$75 more than Zach towards the gift. What can Zach expect to pay for his parents' gift?
3. Explain the usual difference between an *and* compound and an *or* compound relative to their graphs on a number line.
4. What is the graph of the compound $x < -1$ and $x > 2$?
5. What is the graph of the compound $x < 2$ or $x > -1$?
6. Write an applied problem that has $10 < n < 25$ as its answer.

CHAPTER 3 REVIEW

KEY WORDS

3.1 An **equation** is a statement that two quantities are equal.

A **solution** to an equation is a number that makes the equation true.

A **linear equation** can be written in the form $ax + b = 0$.

A **conditional equation** is true for some replacements of the variable and false for others.

An **identity** has the entire set of real numbers for its solution set.

A **contradiction** has no solutions.

Equivalent equations have exactly the same solutions.

3.4 A **literal equation** is an equation that contains two or more variables.

3.5 A **commission** is income as a percent of total sales.

Interest is money we pay to borrow money or money earned on savings.

3.7 A **linear inequality** is a statement involving the inequality symbols $<$, $\leq$, $>$, or $\geq$, such as $x + 1 < 7$, $2x - 1 \geq 3$, $3x + 1 \leq 4x - 5$, and $x + 5 > 2(x - 3)$.

A **solution** to a linear inequality is a number that, when substituted for the variable, makes the inequality true.

Equivalent inequalities have exactly the same solutions.

3.8 An inequality formed by joining two inequalities using the words *and* or *or* is called a **compound inequality.**

KEY CONCEPTS

3.1 When using the addition-subtraction rule to solve an equation, add or subtract the same expression on both sides.

3.2 When using the multiplication-division rule to solve an equation, multiply by a number that makes the coefficient of x equal to 1. For example, to solve

$$\frac{x}{\frac{4}{5}} = 20$$

multiply by $\frac{4}{5}$, *not* by $\frac{5}{4}$.

3.3

1. Use the addition-subtraction rule before the multiplication-division rule when a combination is necessary to solve an equation.
2. When solving an equation involving parentheses, first use the distributive law to clear all parentheses.

3.4 When solving a literal equation, remember that the variables simply represent real numbers. As a result, use the same steps in the solution that you would use for any equation. Sometimes it will help to consider a numerical example similar to the given literal equation.

3.5

1. Use the ATTACK method to solve an applied problem. Remember that you might not write out each step in the method, but the steps should be kept in mind. For certain, you should write out complete descriptions of the variable (*Tabulation*).
2. For many applied problems involving percent, the following may be useful.
   Tax Problems:

$$\text{sales tax} = (\text{tax rate}) \cdot (\text{selling price})$$
$$\text{total cost} = (\text{selling price}) + (\text{sales tax})$$

Commission Problems:

$$\text{Commission} = (\text{commission rate}) \cdot (\text{total sales})$$

Percent Increase:

$$(\text{former amount}) + (\%\text{ of } \textit{former amount}) = \text{new amount}$$

Percent Decrease:

$$(\text{former amount}) - (\%\text{ of } \textit{former amount}) = \text{new amount}$$

Simple Interest:

$$I = Prt \text{ and } A = P + I = P + Prt$$

3.6

1. An accurate sketch is often helpful for solving a geometry problem.
2. The formula $d = rt$, or (distance) = (rate) · (time), is used in many motion problems.

3.7

1. The same expression can be added or subtracted on both sides of an inequality.
2. When you multiply or divide both sides of an inequality by a negative number, *reverse* the symbol of inequality. For example, $-x < 5$

$$(-1)(-x) > (-1)(5)$$
$$x > -5.$$

3. When graphing $x \geq c$ or $x \leq c$ on a number line, the point corresponding to c is part of the graph, shown with a solid dot at c. When graphing $x > c$ or $x < c$, the point corresponding to c is *not* part of the graph, shown with an "open" dot at c.
4. In applied problems involving inequalities, the following translations are often used:

at least	becomes	*greater than or equal to*
at most	becomes	*less than or equal to*
exceeds	becomes	*greater than*

3.8 1. When graphing an *and* compound such as $x > 1$ *and* $x < 5$, the graph consists of all real numbers between the numbers 1 and 5. That is, the graph is a single segment of the number line. This compound can also be written as the chain $1 < x < 5$.

2. When graphing an *or* compound such as $x < 1$ or $x > 5$, the graph consists of all real numbers "below" 1 or (together with) all real numbers "above" 5. That is, the graph is two segments of the number line. An *or* compound can never be written as a chain. For example, **do not write** $5 < x < 1$ for the *or* statement above. This is a meaningless statement since 5 is **not** less than 1.
3. In an applied problem, if x is *between* a and b *where* $a < b$, this translates to the *and* compound

$$a < x < b$$

written as a chain of inequalities. When the word *inclusive* is added, the inequality becomes

$$a \leq x \leq b.$$

CHAPTER 3 REVIEW EXERCISES

PART I

3.1 1. Use the equation $2(x + 1) = 2x + 2$ to answer Exercises (a)–(f).

(a) What is the variable?
(b) What is the left side?
(c) What is the right side?
(d) What is the solution?
(e) Is this an identity?
(f) Is this a contradiction?

Solve for x in Exercises 2–9.

2. $x + 9 = 13$
3. $\dfrac{2}{3} - x = \dfrac{4}{9}$

3.2 4. $-2.3x = 4.6$

5. $\dfrac{x}{\frac{1}{3}} = 15$

3.3 6. $2x + 3 = x + 3 - 4x$

7. $3(x - 4) + 5 = 2(x + 1) - 3$
8. $5(2x - 2) - 3(x - 4) = 0$
9. $20 - 3(x + 5) = 0$

3.4 *Solve each literal equation for the indicated variable in Exercises 10–13.*

10. $2a + 2b = w$ for b
11. $M = 3(y - d)$ for y
12. $2x + 5y - 20 = 0$ for y
13. $\dfrac{y}{2} + \dfrac{x}{3} = 1$ for y

14. **ECONOMICS** The total cost T of purchasing a number of items n each at a cost c is given by the formula $T = nc$. Find a formula for c, and use it to calculate the value of c when T is \$48.00 and n is 16.

3.5 *Letting x represent the unknown number, translate each sentence in Exercises 15–18 into symbols.*

15. A number increased by 5 is 7.
16. Four times a number is 23.
17. Twice a number, increased by 7, is -12.
18. When 5 is added to six times a number, the result is the same as 3 less than the number.

Solve each applied problem in Exercises 19–30.

19. **AGE** Fred is 12 years older than Bertha. Twice the sum of their ages is 100. How old is each?
20. **COMMISSION** Terry works on a commission selling cars. Last year he had a commission of \$34,200 on total sales of \$285,000. What was Terry's commission rate?
21. **TAX** If the sales-tax rate is 4%, how much tax would be charged on a purchase of \$420?
22. 30% of what is 198?
23. 14% of 50 is what?
24. What percent of 900 is 585?
25. **CONSUMER** The price of an item rose 15% last year. If the present price is \$41.40, what was the price last year?
26. **INVESTMENT** What sum of money invested at 12% simple interest will amount to \$716.80 in 1 year?

3.6

27. **GEOMETRY** The diameter of a circle is 7.56 cm. What is the radius?
28. **GEOMETRY** The area of a rectangle is 25.2 ft^2 and the length is 6 ft. What is the width?
29. **GEOMETRY** The perimeter of a rectangle is 80 ft. If the length is 10 ft more than the width, what are the dimensions?
30. **TRANSPORTATION** Two trains leave the same city, one heading north and the other south. If one train is moving 5 mph faster than the other, and if after 4 hr they are 556 mi apart, how fast is each traveling?

3.7 *Graph each equation or inequality in Exercises 31–34 on a number line.*

31. $3x + 1 = 10$
32. $\frac{y}{\frac{1}{8}} = 16$
33. $-2a \leq -2$
34. $3(y - 1) \leq 2(y - 2)$

Solve each inequality in Exercises 35–40.

35. $x - 3 > 4$
36. $-2z \geq -8$
37. $6 - 2x > -4 + 3x$
38. $5 + x > 3 - (x + 10)$
39. $3(x + 2) \leq 5x - 4$
40. $2 - (x - 2) < 7(x - 3)$
41. In solving an inequality, when is the symbol of inequality reversed?
42. **ECONOMICS** In the manufacture and sale of patio wind chimes, the daily cost of producing n chimes is $C = 5n + 120$, and the revenue realized on the sale of n chimes is $R = 10n$. How many chimes must be made and sold daily for the revenue to exceed the cost; that is, for a profit to be made?

43. **GEOMETRY** The area of a rectangular pasture must be at least 18,000 yd^2. If the width is to be 120 yd, what are the possibilities for the length of the pasture? Give the answer as an inequality and also in words.

3.8 *In Exercises 44–49, graph each compound inequality on a number line.*

44. $x > -4$ and $x < 2$

45. $-4 < x < 2$

46. $x \leq -4$ or $x \geq 2$

47. $0 \leq 1 - (x + 3) < 2$

48. $1 - (x - 2) \leq 0$ or $1 - (x - 2) > 3$

49. $x + 2 < 0$ and $x - 5 > 0$

50. Celsius temperature is given in terms of Fahrenheit temperature by $C = \frac{5}{9}(F - 32)$. If the Celsius temperature is predicted to be between 20° and 30°, inclusive, what is the range of temperatures using the Fahrenheit scale?

PART II

Solve each equation or applied problem in Exercises 51–55.

51. **CONSUMER** After receiving a 20% discount on the selling price, Holly paid \$6.60 for a record. What was the price of the record before the discount?

52. **GEOMETRY** A sphere with radius 7 cm is submerged in a rectangular tank 20 cm wide and 25 cm long. How much will the level of the water rise in the tank?

53. $-y = -4.7$

54. $1\frac{1}{2} = z + 2$

55. $3(x - 2) = 5 - (x + 1)$

Solve each inequality in Exercises 56–58.

56. $6x + 1 < 2(x - 3)$

57. $-3x \geq \frac{6}{5}$

58. $4 - 2(x - 1) \leq 6 - (x - 1)$

59. Solve $u + b = t - v$ for v.

60. Solve $2x - 3y - 5 = 0$ for y.

In Exercises 61–64, graph each inequality or compound inequality on a number line.

61. $-\frac{1}{4}y > 1$

62. $2 - 3(x + 1) < x + 3$

63. $-2 \leq 1 - x \leq 4$

64. $1 - x < -2$ or $1 - x > 4$

65. **TEMPERATURE** The temperature in degrees Celsius C is given in terms of degrees Fahrenheit F by the formula $C = \frac{5}{9}(F - 32)$. Find a formula for F, and use it to calculate the value of F when C is 45°.

Answer true *or* false *in Exercises 66–80. If the statement is false, tell why.*

66. A statement that two quantities are equal is called an inequality.

67. The equation $x + 5 = 5 + x$ is an example of an identity.

68. The equation $x + 5 = x - 5$ is an example of a conditional equation.

69. Two equations that have exactly the same solutions are called equivalent.

70. The inequalities $2x + 1 < 3$ and $3 > 2x + 1$ are equivalent.

71. If $x = 2$ is a solution to $x + a = -3$, then $a = -5$.

72. If $x < 5$, then $x + 2 < 7$.

73. If $-x > -3$, then $x > 3$.

74. If $x + 1 \leq 4$, then $x \geq 3$.

75. If x is at most 20, then $x \leq 20$.

76. If x exceeds 35, then $x < 35$.

77. If $x > 2$, then $-3x > -6$.

78. If x is between 10 and 20, inclusive, then $10 < x < 20$.

79. The compound $x < 5$ and $x > -3$ can also be written as $-3 < x < 5$.

80. The compound $x < -5$ or $x > 3$ can also be written as $3 < x < -5$.

CHAPTER 3 TEST

Solve.

1. $x - 5 = 10$

2. $4x = 32$

3. $x + \frac{3}{4} = \frac{5}{4}$

4. $5.1x = -10.2$

5. $\frac{1}{4}x = 9$

6. $\frac{x}{\frac{1}{5}} = 20$

7. $3x - 5 = 8x + 10$

8. $3(x + 2) - 5(x - 4) = 0$

9. $4x - (x + 6) = 3$

10. Last year Gail's income was \$20,000 plus a 5% commission on all sales. If her total income was \$29,000, what was the amount of total sales?

11. The price of a dress was \$54 but the price was increased by 15%. What is the new price?

12. The area of a triangle is 240 cm^2 and its height is 12 cm. What is the length of the base?

13. Two trains that are 840 miles apart and whose speeds differ by 9 mph are traveling towards each other. If they will meet in 8 hours, at what speed is each traveling?

14. Clem hiked to a waterfall at a rate of 3 mph and returned at a rate of 4 mph. If the total time he spent hiking was 7 hours, how long did it take him to reach the waterfall? What was the total distance hiked?

15. Solve $U = W + Wmg$ for g.

16. The perimeter of a rectangle is given in terms of its length l and width w by the formula $P = 2l + 2w$. Find a formula for w and use it to calculate w when P is 8.6 cm and l is 2.6 cm.

Solve the inequalities.

17. $3x - 6 \leq 9x + 12$

18. $3 - (2x - 5) > 6x + 4$

Graph on a number line.

19. $2x + 5 = 9$

20. $2(y + 1) \geq 1 - (y + 5)$

21. $x + 2 \leq 1$ or $x + 2 \geq 5$

22. $-3 < 2 - x < 2$

23. Give the different types of equations with examples of each.

24. Discuss the types of compound inequalities and how each can be written.

Graphing

In Chapter three we graphed linear equations and inequalities in one variable on a number line. In this chapter we introduce graphing which requires the use of a rectangular coordinate system since two variables are involved.

To illustrate the applications of this material we state a problem below which is solved in Example 4 of Section 4.1.

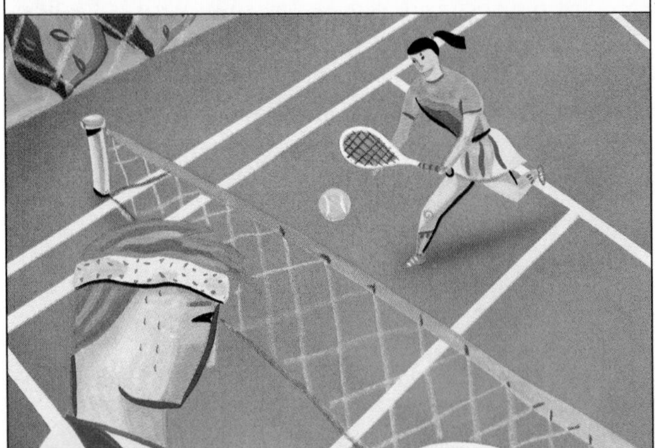

MANUFACTURING Mr. Paducci has a small business that manufactures tennis rackets. He has found that the cost in dollars y of producing a certain number of rackets x is given by the equation

$$y = 150x + 80.$$

Find the cost to produce 1, 2, and 5 rackets.

We begin this chapter by developing the rectangular coordinate system in which linear equations in two variables can be graphed. Next we consider the notion of slope and several forms of the equation of a straight line. We conclude the chapter with solving and graphing linear inequalities in two variables.

SECTION 4.1 The Rectangular Coordinate System

Student guideposts

- ▶ *Rectangular coordinate system*
- ▶ *Ordered pairs*
- ▶ *Quadrants*
- ▶ *Linear equations in two variables*

In Section 3.7 we graphed linear equations and inequalities in one variable by plotting points on a number line. Now we develop a system in which equations and inequalities in two variables can be graphed. Consider a horizontal number line and a vertical number line as shown in Figure 4.1.

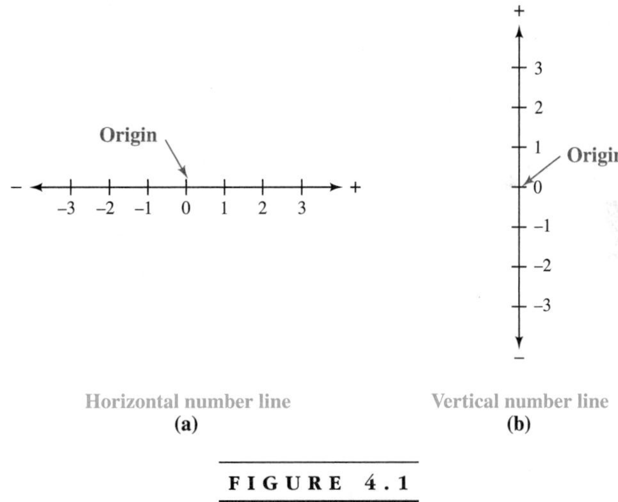

FIGURE 4.1

▶ *Rectangular coordinate system*

When the horizontal number line and the vertical number line are placed together so that the two origins coincide and the lines are perpendicular, as in Figure 4.2, the result is called a **rectangular** or **Cartesian coordinate system** or a **coordinate plane.** (The word Cartesian comes from the name of the French mathematician René Descartes (1596–1650) who first used the coordinate system to combine the ancient discipline of geometry with the more modern algebra.)

The horizontal number line is called the ***x*-axis,** and the vertical number line is called the ***y*-axis.** Together the number lines are referred to as **axes,** and the point of intersection of the lines is the **origin.**

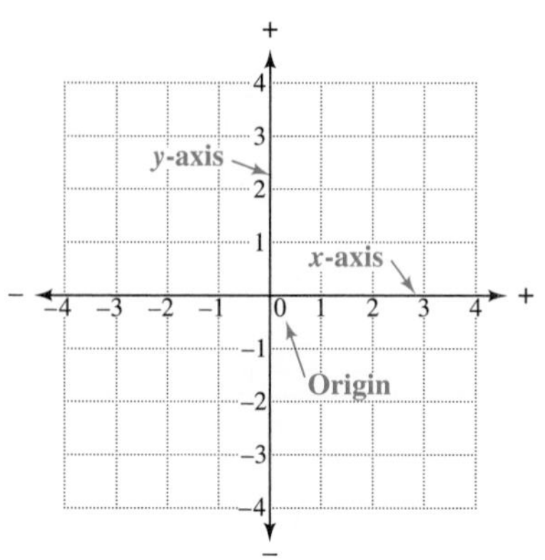

FIGURE 4.2
Rectangular or Cartesian Coordinate System

▶ *Ordered pairs*

Just as there is one and only one point on a number line associated with each number, there is one and only one point in a plane associated with each **ordered pair** of numbers. For example, the ordered pair (3, 2) is identified with a point in a coordinate plane as follows:

The first number, 3, the ***x*-coordinate** of the point, is associated with a value on the x-axis.

The second number, 2, the ***y*-coordinate,** is associated with a value on the y-axis.

The ordered pair (3, 2), is identified with the point where the vertical line through 3 on the x-axis intersects the horizontal line through 2 on the y-axis. See Figure 4.3. Note that the point (2, 3) is different from (3, 2).

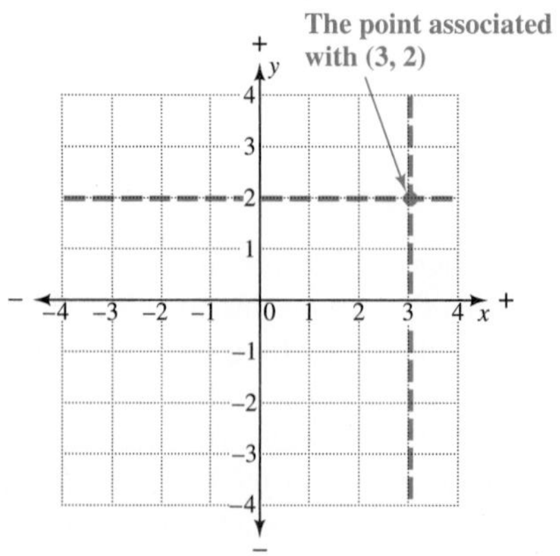

FIGURE 4.3
Plotting the Point (3, 2)

EXAMPLE 1

Plotting Points

The points associated with (1, 3), (−2, 1), (−3, −2), and (2, −2) are given in the coordinate plane in Figure 4.4.

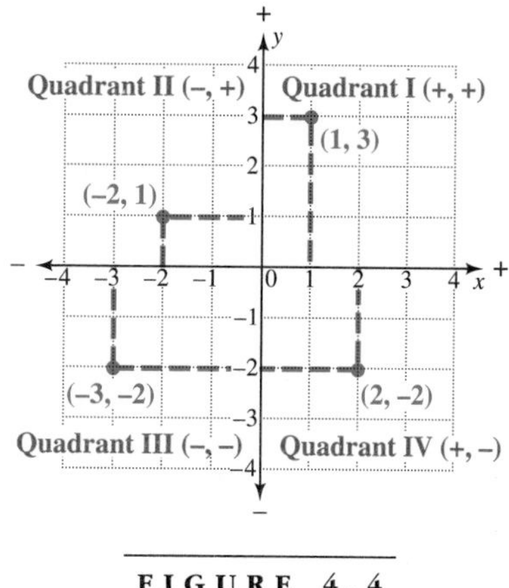

FIGURE 4.4

(1, 3): Go 1 unit right and 3 units up.

(−2, 1): Go 2 units left and 1 unit up.

(−3, −2): Go 3 units left and 2 units down.

(2, −2): Go 2 units right and 2 units down. ■

▶ *Quadrants*

The axes in a rectangular coordinate system divide the plane into four sections called **quadrants.** The first, second, third, and fourth quadrants are identified by the Roman numerals I, II, III, and IV in Figure 4.4. The x-coordinate (first) and the y-coordinate (second) have the following signs in each quadrant:

I: (+, +), II: (−, +), III: (−, −), IV: (+, −)

We often use (x, y) to refer to a general ordered pair of numbers. The point P in the plane associated with the pair (x, y) has x-coordinate x and y-coordinate y. We plot a point P when we identify it with a given pair of numbers in a plane, and we often refer to "the point (x, y)" or write $P(x, y)$.

EXAMPLE 2

Determining Ordered Pairs

Determine the coordinates of the points A, B, C, D, E, F, G, and H shown in Figure 4.5. Also give the quadrant in which A, D, E, and G are located.

The coordinates of the points are $A(4, 1)$, $B(0, 2)$, $C(0, 0)$, $D(-2, 1)$, $E(-4, -2)$, $F(0, -3)$, $G(1, -2)$, and $H(3, 0)$. Point A is in quadrant I, D is in II, E is in III, and G is in IV. Notice that the remaining points are on one of the axes and are not considered to be in any of the quadrants. ■

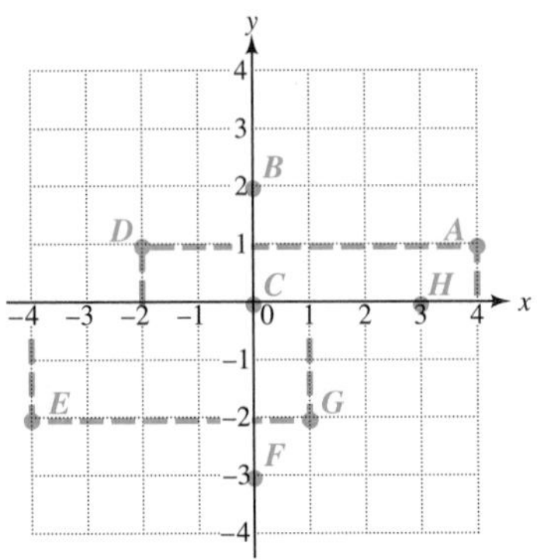

FIGURE 4.5

Linear equations in two variables

In Chapter 3 we solved linear equations in one variable. Such equations can always be written in the form

$$ax + b = 0. \qquad a, b \text{ constants and } a \neq 0$$

We now consider linear equations in two variables. A **linear equation in two variables** x and y, is an equation of the form

$$ax + by = c. \qquad a, b, c \text{ constants, } a \text{ and } b \text{ not both zero.}$$

A **solution** to a linear equation in two variables is an ordered pair of numbers which when substituted for the variables results in a true equation. In an *ordered pair* the x-value is always written first and the y-value is always written second.

We can show that the ordered pairs $(1, 3)$ and $(10, 0)$ are two solutions to the linear equation $x + 3y = 10$.

For the ordered pair $(1, 3)$, we must substitute 1 for x and 3 for y in the equation.

$$\begin{aligned} x + 3y &= 10 \\ 1 + 3(3) &= 10 \qquad x = 1 \text{ and } y = 3 \\ 1 + 9 &= 10 \\ 10 &= 10 \qquad \text{True} \end{aligned}$$

Thus, $(1, 3)$ is a solution.

For the ordered pair $(10, 0)$, we substitute 10 for x and 0 for y.

$$\begin{aligned} x + 3y &= 10 \\ 10 + 3(0) &= 10 \qquad x = 10 \text{ and } y = 0 \\ 10 + 0 &= 10 \\ 10 &= 10 \qquad \text{True} \end{aligned}$$

Thus, (10, 0) is a solution. You might verify that (4, 2) and $(0, \frac{10}{3})$ are also solutions to this equation. However, (9, 0) is *not* a solution.

$$\begin{aligned} x + 3y &= 10 \\ 9 + 3(0) &\stackrel{?}{=} 10 && x = 9 \text{ and } y = 0 \\ 9 + 0 &\stackrel{?}{=} 10 \\ 9 &\neq 10 && \text{False} \end{aligned}$$

EXAMPLE 3

Completing Ordered Pairs

Given the equation $3x + 2y = 6$, complete the ordered pairs so that they are solutions to the equation.

$$(0,\ ),\quad (\ ,0),\quad (1,\ ),\quad (\ ,1),\quad (-2,\ )$$

To complete the ordered pair (0,), substitute 0 for x in $3x + 2y = 6$ and solve for y.

$$\begin{aligned} 3(0) + 2y &= 6 \\ 2y &= 6 \\ y &= 3 && \text{The completed ordered pair is } (0, 3) \end{aligned}$$

To complete the ordered pair (, 0), substitute 0 for y in $3x + 2y = 6$ and solve for x.

$$\begin{aligned} 3x + 2(0) &= 6 \\ 3x &= 6 \\ x &= 2 && \text{The ordered pair is } (2, 0) \end{aligned}$$

To complete the ordered pair (1,), substitute 1 for x and solve for y.

$$\begin{aligned} 3(1) + 2y &= 6 \\ 3 + 2y &= 6 \\ 2y &= 3 \\ y &= \frac{3}{2} && \text{The completed ordered pairs is } (1, \tfrac{3}{2}) \end{aligned}$$

Similarly, substitute 1 for y and solve for x to complete (, 1), obtaining $(\frac{4}{3}, 1)$, and to complete (−2,), substitute −2 for x and solve to obtain (−2, 6). ■

We now solve the applied problem given in the chapter introduction.

EXAMPLE 4

Application to Business

Mr. Paducci has a small business that manufactures tennis rackets. He has found that the cost in dollars y of producing a certain number of rackets x is given by the equation

$$y = 150x + 80.$$

Find the cost to produce 1, 2, and 5 rackets.

Complete the ordered pairs (1,), (2,), and (5,). Let $x = 1$ and solve for y.

$$y = 150(1) + 80$$
$$y = 230$$

Thus, (1,) becomes (1, 230). Similarly, (2,) becomes (2, 380) and (5,) becomes (5, 830). This means that it costs Mr. Paducci \$230 to produce 1 racket, \$380 to produce 2 rackets, and \$830 to produce 5 rackets. ■

4.1 EXERCISES

1. Plot the points associated with the given pairs of numbers: $A(2, 4)$, $B(4, -1)$, $C(-3, 4)$, $D(-3, 0)$, $E(2, 0)$, $F(-2, -2)$, $G(1, -4)$, and $H(4, -4)$.

2. Give the coordinates of the points A, B, C, D, E, F, G, and H.

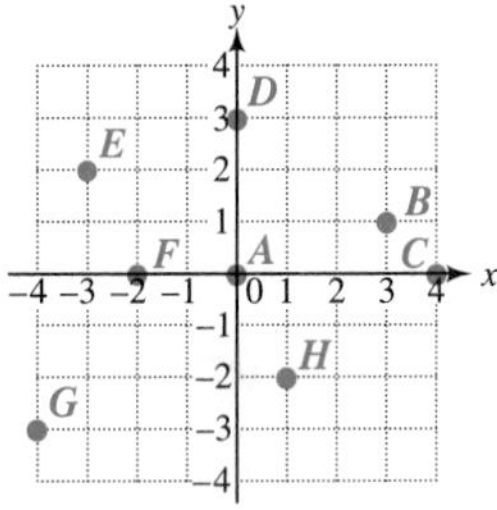

3. Plot the points associated with the given pairs of numbers: $M(\frac{1}{2}, 2)$, $N(-\frac{3}{2}, 3)$, $P(-2, -\frac{3}{4})$, and $Q(3, -\frac{5}{2})$.

4. In which quadrant are the points M, N, P, and Q of Exercise 3 located?

In Exercises 5–8, give the quadrant in which each point is located.

5. $(-8, -8)$ **6.** $(6, -3)$ **7.** $(4, 12)$ **8.** $(-2, 7)$

9. What are the four regions called into which a plane is separated by a Cartesian coordinate system?

10. What is the x-coordinate of the point named by the ordered pair $(-2, 5)$?

11. What is the y-coordinate of the point named by the ordered pair $(3, -8)$?

12. What are the coordinates of the origin?

13. What is another name for the horizontal axis in a Cartesian coordinate system?

14. If the first coordinate of a point is positive and the second is negative, in which quadrant is the point located?

15. If the x-coordinate of a point is negative and the y-coordinate is positive, in which quadrant is the point located?

Using the given equation, complete each ordered pair in Exercises 16–21 so that it will be a solution to the equation.

16. $x - y = 2$
(a) (0,) **(b)** (, 0)
(c) (4,) **(d)** (, −3)

17. $x - 5 = 0$
(a) (0,) **(b)** (, 0)
(c) (5,) **(d)** (, −10)

18. $x + y = 5$
(a) $(0, \quad)$ **(b)** $(\quad, 0)$
(c) $(3, \quad)$ **(d)** $(\quad, -4)$

19. $2x - y = 4$
(a) $(0, \quad)$ **(b)** $(\quad, 0)$
(c) $(-2, \quad)$ **(d)** $(\quad, 6)$

20. $x + 5y = 10$
(a) $(0, \quad)$ **(b)** $(\quad, 0)$
(c) $(-10, \quad)$ **(d)** $(\quad, 3)$

21. $5x - 2y = 10$
(a) $(0, \quad)$ **(b)** $(\quad, 0)$
(c) $(7, \quad)$ **(d)** $(\quad, -4)$

22. **TRAVEL** The distance traveled y by a car averaging 55 mph over x hours is given by the equation

$$y = 55x.$$

Complete the ordered pairs $(1, \quad)$, $(5, \quad)$, and $(10, \quad)$. How far does the car travel **(a)** in 1 hour? **(b)** in 5 hours? **(c)** in 10 hours?

23. **SALARY** If a salesperson gets a monthly salary of \$1200 plus a 5% commission on all sales, her monthly income y is given by $y = 0.05x + 1200$ where x is her sales for the month. Find her salary for the month of February if she sold \$22,000 worth of clothing for the month.

24. Draw the triangle with vertices $(3, 4)$, $(-3, 1)$, and $(1, -2)$.

25. Draw the rectangle with corners $(3, 1)$, $(1, 3)$, $(-3, -1)$, and $(-1, -3)$.

26. What is the y-coordinate of the origin?

27. What is the x-coordinate of a point on the y-axis?

28. Find five ordered pairs in which the coordinates of each pair have a sum equal to 2. Plot these points in a rectangular coordinate system. Do you notice anything special about the points?

FOR REVIEW

Exercises 29–34 review material from Chapter 3 to help you prepare for the next section. In Exercises 29–30 graph each equation on a number line.

29. $a + 3 = 3(a - 1)$

30. $3x + 8 = 8 + 3x$

In Exercises 31–32 graph each inequality on a number line.

31. $2x \geq 7$

32. $3(y - 1) < 4 - (y - 1)$

33. Solve the equation $4x + 3y = 12$ for y.

34. Write $y = 5x - 6$ in the form $ax + by = c$ with a positive.

4.1 PARALLEL EXERCISES

1. Plot the points associated with the given pairs of numbers: $A(1, 3)$, $B(2, -1)$, $C(-3, 4)$, $D(-1, 1)$, $E(-3, -3)$, $F(2, -3)$.

2. Give the coordinates of the points A, B, C, D, E, and F.

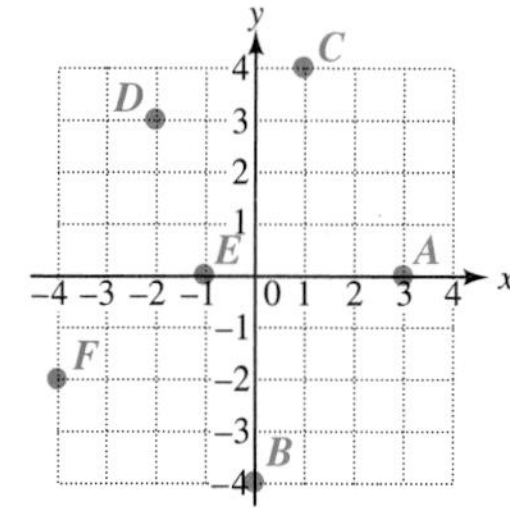

3. Plot the points associated with the given pairs of numbers: $M(-\frac{1}{2}, 1)$, $N(\frac{3}{2}, 2)$, $P(2, -\frac{3}{4})$, and $Q(-3, -\frac{5}{2})$.

4. In which quadrants are the points M, N, P, and Q of Exercise 3 located?

In Exercises 5–8, give the quadrant in which each point is located.

5. $(4, -1)$ **6.** $(-4, 3)$ **7.** $(6, 6)$ **8.** $(-12, -4)$

9. What is another name for a Cartesian coordinate system?

10. What is the y-coordinate of the point named by the ordered pair $(-2, 5)$?

11. What is the x-coordinate of the point named by the ordered pair $(3, -8)$?

12. What is the name of the point with coordinates $(0, 0)$?

13. What is another name for the vertical axis in a Cartesian coordinate system?

14. If the first coordinate of a point is negative and the second is positive, in which quadrant is the point located?

15. If the x-coordinate of a point is negative and the y-coordinate is also negative, in which quadrant is the point located?

Using the given equation, complete each ordered pair in Exercises 16–21 so that it will be a solution to the equation.

16. $x + y = 2$
(a) (0,) **(b)** (, 0)
(c) (3,) **(d)** (, −2)

17. $y + 1 = 0$
(a) (0,) **(b)** (, 0)
(c) (3,) **(d)** (, −1)

18. $x - y = 3$
(a) (0,) **(b)** (, 0)
(c) (2,) **(d)** (, −4)

19. $2x + y = 4$
(a) (0,) **(b)** (, 0)
(c) (−2,) **(d)** (, 6)

20. $x - 5y = 10$
(a) (0,) **(b)** (, 0)
(c) (−10,) **(d)** (, 3)

21. $5x + 2y = 10$
(a) (0,) **(b)** (, 0)
(c) (7,) **(d)** (, −4)

22. **PRODUCTION** The cost in dollars y of producing a number of items x has been estimated by the equation

$$y = 300x + 15.$$

Complete the ordered pairs (1,), (3,), and (10,). Give the cost of producing **(a)** 1 item, **(b)** 3 items, **(c)** 10 items.

23. **SALES** If the sales-tax rate in Garden City is 6%, the total cost y of merchandise is given by the equation $y = 1.06x$ where x is the price of the item. What is the total cost of a mixer which sells for \$27.50?

24. Draw the triangle with vertices $(-2, 7)$, $(1, 1)$, and $(-4, -5)$.

25. Draw the rectangle with corners $(-4, 2)$, $(-1, 5)$, $(5, -1)$, and $(2, -4)$.

26. What is the x-coordinate of the origin?

27. What is the y-coordinate of a point on the x-axis?

28. Find five ordered pairs with the property that the y-coordinate subtracted from the x-coordinate is equal to 2. Plot these points in a rectangular coordinate system. Do you notice anything special about the points?

FOR REVIEW

Exercises 29–34 review material from Chapter 3 to help you prepare for the next section. In Exercises 29–30 graph each equation on a number line.

29. $2a + 1 = 3(a - 2)$

30. $3x - 8 = 3x + 8$

In Exercises 31–32 graph each inequality on a number line.

31. $3x < -5$

32. $2(y - 3) \geq 3 - (y - 6)$

33. Solve the equation $4x - 3y = 12$ for y.

34. Write $y = 7x + 2$ in the form $ax + by = c$ with a positive.

4.1 ENRICHMENT EXERCISES

Using the equation given in Exercises 1–2, complete each ordered pair so that it will be a solution to the equation. A calculator might be helpful.

1. $0.012x - 1.565y = 1.878$
(a) (0,) **(b)** (, 0)
(c) (234.75,) **(d)** (, 2.4)

2. $-\frac{3}{16}x + \frac{7}{12}y = 3\frac{5}{8}$
(a) (0,) **(b)** (, 0)
(c) $(-\frac{5}{9},\ )$ **(d)** $(\ , 1\frac{3}{7})$

3. Suppose that the point $A(x, y)$ is exactly halfway between the points $B(2, -5)$ and $C(4, 1)$. Find the coordinates of A.

4. Suppose that the point $A(2, -1)$ is exactly halfway between the points $B(-1, 3)$ and $C(x, y)$. Find the coordinates of C.

5. Learn enough about René Descartes to write several paragraphs about his major accomplishments.

SECTION 4.2 Graphing Linear Equations

Student guideposts

- ▶ *Graphing equations*
- ▶ *Standard form of a linear equation*
- ▶ *Graphing using intercepts*

▶ *Graphing equations*

The **graph** of an equation in two variables x and y is the set of points in a rectangular coordinate system that corresponds to solutions of the equation. Since there are usually infinitely many solutions, we cannot find and plot each pair. Generally, we plot enough points to see a pattern, and then connect these points with a line or curve to graph the equation.

An excellent way to display a collection of ordered-pair solutions to an equation such as

$$y = 2x + 5$$

is to make a table of values. Choose several values for x and substitute these values into the equation to compute the corresponding value for y. Place each y-value beside the x-value used to calculate it. (Calculations are usually done mentally or as scratch work.)

Substitution	*Results in* $y = 2x + 5$	x	y
$x = 0$	$y = 2(0) + 5 = 5$	0	5
$x = 1$	$y = 2(1) + 5 = 7$	1	7
$x = -1$	$y = 2(-1) + 5 = 3$	−1	3
$x = 2$	$y = 2(2) + 5 = 9$	2	9
$x = -2$	$y = 2(-2) + 5 = 1$	−2	1
$x = 3$	$y = 2(3) + 5 = 11$	3	11
$x = -3$	$y = 2(-3) + 5 = -1$	−3	−1

This table lists seven (of the infinitely many) solutions to the equation $y = 2x + 5$.

$$(0, 5),\quad (1, 7),\quad (-1, 3),\quad (2, 9),\quad (-2, 1),\quad (3, 11),\quad (-3, -1)$$

Now plot the points that correspond to these ordered-pair solutions in a rectangular coordinate system, as in Figure 4.6.

It appears that all seven points lie on a straight line. It is reasonable to assume that the graph of this equation is the straight line passing through these seven points, as in Figure 4.7.

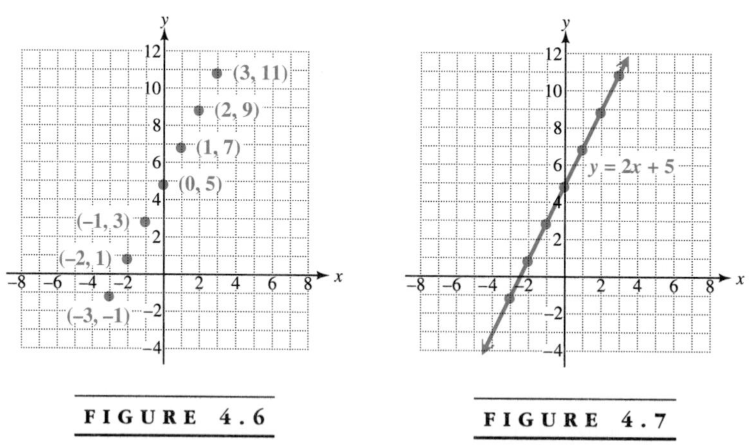

FIGURE 4.6

FIGURE 4.7

To Graph an Equation in the Two Variables x and y

1. Make a table of values. These values represent the ordered-pair solutions of the equation.
2. Plot the points that correspond to the ordered-pair solutions in a rectangular coordinate system.
3. Connect the points with a line or curve.

EXAMPLE 1

Graphing by Plotting Points

Graph $y + x = 3$.

Before making a table, it is often helpful to solve the equation for one of the variables (usually for y):

$$y = -x + 3.$$

To make a table of values, choose several values for x and substitute each into the equation to compute the corresponding value of y. See the table below. Plot the points that correspond to the ordered pairs from the table:

$$(0, 3), \quad (1, 2), \quad (-1, 4), \quad (2, 1), \quad (-2, 5), \quad (3, 0), \quad (-3, 6).$$

Connecting these points gives us a straight line, as in Figure 4.8. ∎

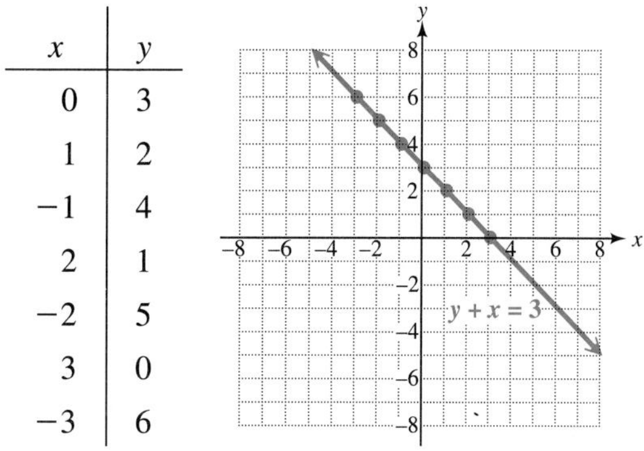

x	y
0	3
1	2
−1	4
2	1
−2	5
3	0
−3	6

FIGURE 4.8

In Chapter 3, we graphed an equation in one variable on a number line. Usually, for graphing purposes, an equation in one variable such as

$$x = 5 \quad \text{or} \quad y + 2 = 0$$

is thought of as an equation in two variables with the coefficient of the missing variable equal to zero. That is,

$$x = 5 \text{ is the same as } x + 0 \cdot y = 5$$

and

$$y + 2 = 0 \text{ is the same as } 0 \cdot x + y + 2 = 0.$$

With this in mind, such equations can be graphed in a rectangular coordinate system.

EXAMPLE 2

Graphing Lines Parallel to the Axes

(a) Graph $x = 5$ in a rectangular coordinate system.

Solutions to this equation always have an x-coordinate of 5 and can have any number as y-coordinate. For example,

$$(5, 0), \quad (5, -1), \quad (5, 1), \quad (5, 2)$$

are all solutions, since $x = 5$ is the same as $x + 0 \cdot y = 5$, and we know

$$5 + 0 \cdot (\text{any number}) = 5 + 0 = 5.$$

Plot the points from the table and draw a line through them. The graph of $x = 5$ is a straight line parallel to the y-axis, 5 units to the right of the y-axis. See Figure 4.9.

x	y
5	0
5	1
5	-1
5	2
5	-2
5	3
5	-3

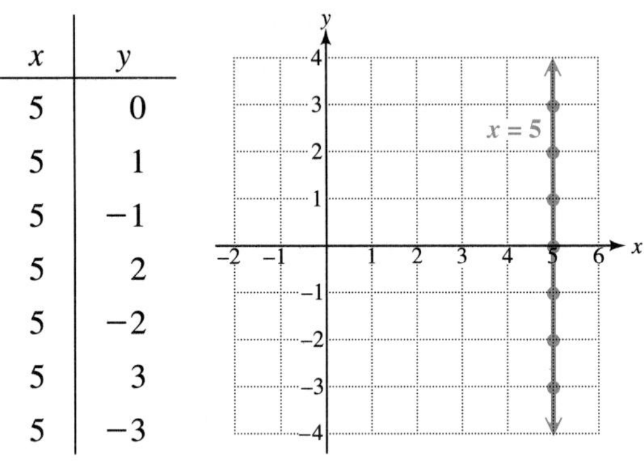

FIGURE 4.9

(b) Graph $y + 2 = 0$ in a Cartesian coordinate system.

We can write this equation as $y = -2$. Thus, solutions to this equation always have a y-coordinate of -2 and can have any number as x-coordinate. For example,

$$(0, -2), \quad (1, -2), \quad (-1, -2), \quad (2, -2)$$

are all solutions since $y + 2 = 0$ is the same as $0 \cdot x + y + 2 = 0$, and we know that

$$0 \cdot (\text{any number}) + (-2) + 2 = -2 + 2 = 0.$$

x	y
0	-2
1	-2
-1	-2
2	-2
-2	-2
3	-2
-3	-2

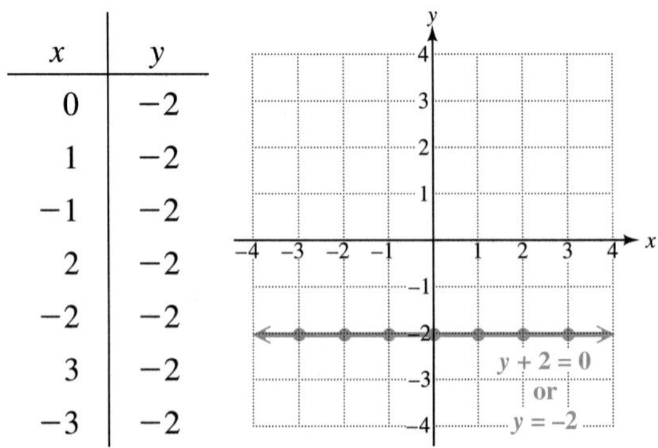

FIGURE 4.10

Plot the points given in the table and draw a line through them. The graph of $y + 2 = 0$ ($y = -2$) is a straight line parallel to the x-axis, 2 units below the x-axis. (See Figure 4.10). ■

If we are asked to graph an equation such as $x = 5$ or $y + 2 = 0$, we must first know whether it is considered an equation in one variable or an equation in two variables having a zero coefficient on the missing variable. In the first case, the graph would be a point on a number line, while in the second, the graph would be a straight line in a rectangular coordinate system. From this point on, we will look only at equations in two variables, and all graphs will be in the coordinate plane.

▶ *Standard form of a linear equation*

In graphing we can sometimes minimize the number of points that we plot by knowing the nature of the graph. When an equation can be written in the form

$$ax + by = c$$

it is a linear equation in two variables. The numbers a, b, and c are constant real numbers, a and b not both zero, and this form of the equation is called the **standard form.** The graph of a **line**ar equation is always a straight **line** and can be determined by plotting just two points. Linear equations are also called **first-degree equations** since the variables are raised to the first power only. The following table provides practice at identifying linear equations.

Equation	*Nature*	*Standard Form*
$2x + y = 7$	linear	$2x + y = 7$
$x = -y - 8$	linear	$x + y = -8$
$2y = 3x - 5$	linear	$3x - 2y = 5$
$x + 5 = 0$	linear	$x + 0 \cdot y = -5$
$2y = 3$	linear	$0 \cdot x + 2y = 3$
$y = x^2 + 3$	not linear (x to second power)	
$x - y^3 + 7 = 0$	not linear (y to third power)	
$y = \frac{5}{x}$	not linear (cannot be put in the form $ax + by = c$)	

▶ *Graphing using intercepts*

Suppose we are given a linear equation such as

$$2x - 3y = 6.$$

Knowing that the graph of a linear equation is a straight line and that only two points are needed to determine a straight line, our work graphing linear equations can be shortened considerably. Rather than making a table of values that includes many solutions, we need only two solutions. In most instances, the two pairs that are easiest to find are the **intercepts.** The point at which a line crosses the x-axis, where y is zero, is the ***x*-intercept.** The point at which a line crosses the y-axis, where x is zero, is the ***y*-intercept.** To find the intercepts, fill in the following table.

x	y
0	
	0

The x-intercept, which is a point on the x-axis, has y-coordinate 0 while the y-intercept, which is a point on the y-axis, has x-coordinate 0. We substitute 0 for x in $2x - 3y = 6$ and solve for y to find the y-intercept.

$$\begin{aligned} 2(0) - 3y &= 6 \\ 0 - 3y &= 6 \\ -3y &= 6 \\ y &= -2 \end{aligned}$$

Find the x-intercept by substituting 0 for y in $2x - 3y = 6$ and solving.

$$\begin{aligned} 2x - 3(0) &= 6 \\ 2x &= 6 \\ x &= 3 \end{aligned}$$

The completed table

x	y
0	-2
3	0

displays the y-intercept $(0, -2)$ and the x-intercept $(3, 0)$. Plot these two intercepts and draw the straight line through them for the graph of $2x - 3y = 6$ in Figure 4.11. We can check our work by showing that $(-3, -4)$ satisfies the equation and is on the graph in Figure 4.11.

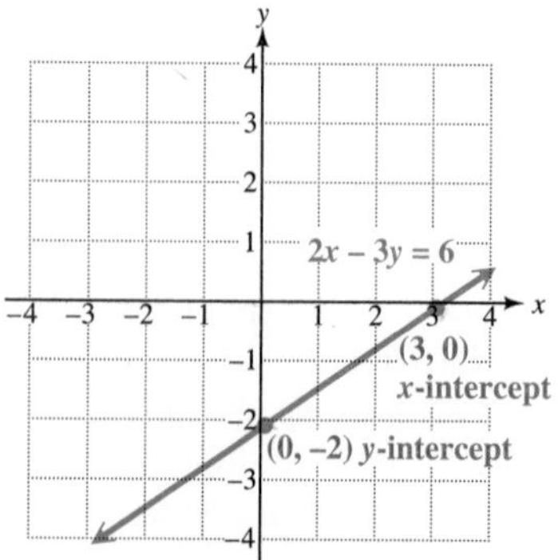

FIGURE 4.11

To Graph a Linear Equation $ax + by = c$

1. If $a \neq 0$ and $b \neq 0$, find the x- and y-intercepts, plot them, and draw the line through them. If both intercepts are $(0, 0)$ (that is, if $c = 0$), find and plot another point and draw the line through $(0, 0)$ and this point.
2. If $a = 0$, the equation becomes $by = c$ or $y = c/b$. The graph is a horizontal line through the y-intercept $(0, c/b)$ parallel to the x-axis.
3. If $b = 0$, the equation becomes $ax = c$ or $x = c/a$. The graph is a vertical line through the x-intercept $(c/a, 0)$ parallel to the y-axis.

EXAMPLE 3 **Graphing Using Intercepts**

(a) Graph $3x + 4y = 12$.

First find the x- and y-intercepts by completing the following table.

x	y
0	
	0

When $x = 0$, $4y = 12$, so that $y = 3$. When $y = 0$, $3x = 12$, so that $x = 4$. The completed table,

x	y
0	3
4	0

shows that the x-intercept is $(4, 0)$ and the y-intercept is $(0, 3)$. Plot $(0, 3)$ and $(4, 0)$ and connect the points to obtain the graph. See Figure 4.12.

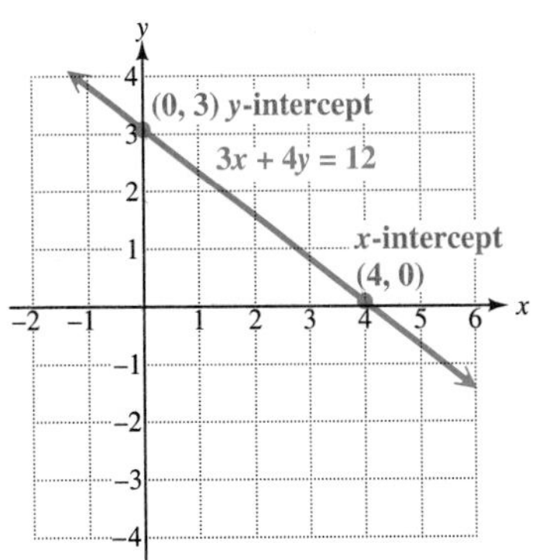

FIGURE 4.12

(b) Graph $x + 3y = 0$.

First find the x- and y-intercepts by completing the table.

x	y
0	
	0

This time both intercepts are $(0, 0)$, so we need to find another point on the line. When $x = 3$, $3 + 3y = 0$, so that $y = -1$. This leads to the table below.

x	y
0	0
3	-1

Plot $(0, 0)$ and $(3, -1)$ and connect the points to obtain the graph in Figure 4.13. ■

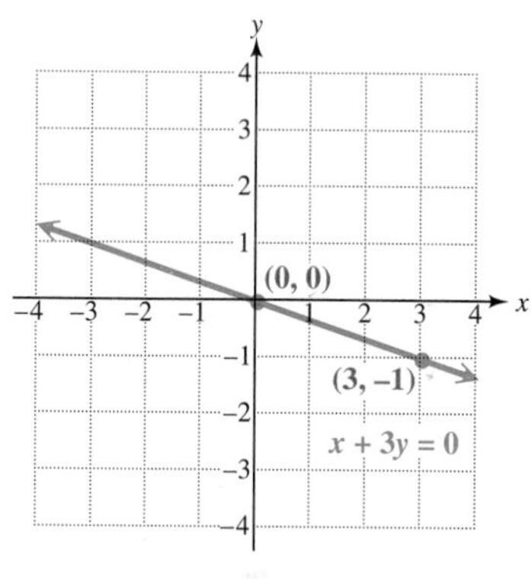

FIGURE 4.13

> NOTE When both intercepts are $(0, 0)$ as in Example 3(b), to find one additional point, **any** value of x can be substituted to find the corresponding value of y.

EXAMPLE 4

Graphing Vertical and Horizontal Lines

(a) Graph $x = 2$.

In this case, with no y term, the solution will be $(2, y)$ for any number y. Thus, the graph is the line through the x-intercept $(2, 0)$ parallel to the y-axis, as in Figure 4.14.

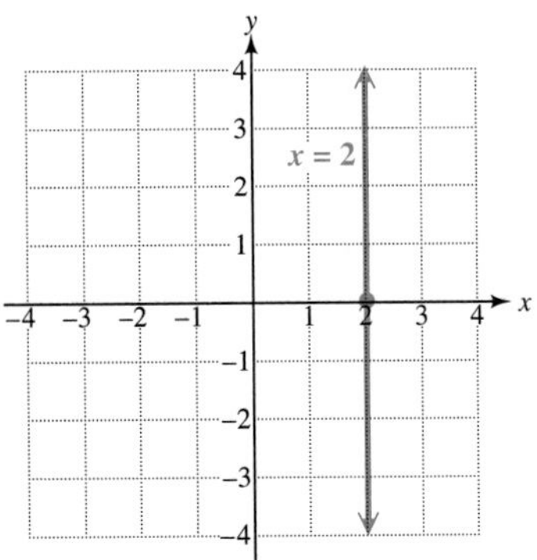

FIGURE 4.14

(b) Graph $2y = -2$.

The equation can be simplified to $y = -1$. In this case, with no x term, the solutions will be $(x, -1)$ for any number x. Thus, the graph is the line through the y-intercept $(0, -1)$ parallel to the x-axis, as shown in Figure 4.15. ■

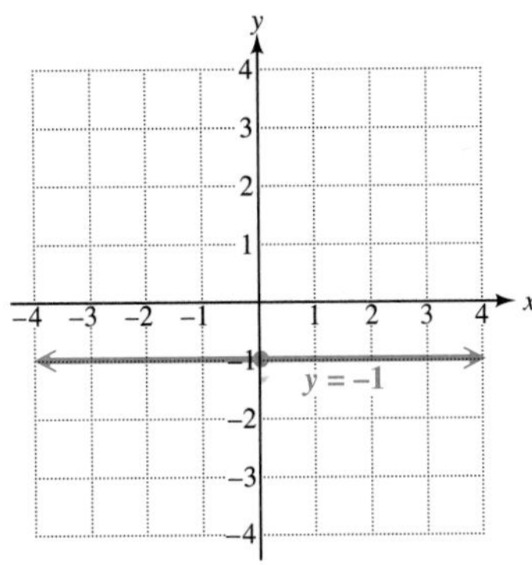

FIGURE 4.15

4.2 EXERCISES

In Exercises 1–6 each is an equation in the two variables x and y. Make a table of values and graph each equation in a rectangular coordinate system.

1. $y = x + 2$

2. $x - y = 1$

3. $y = 3x + 1$

4. $y = \frac{1}{2}x - 1$

5. $y = 2$

6. $x = -1$

7. Which of the following are linear equations? Explain.
(a) $2x + y = 4$ (b) $x - y^3 = 5$ (c) $2xy = 7$
(d) $\frac{3}{x} + y = 7$ (e) $x^2 + y^2 = 5$ (f) $x = y - 8$

8. Why is a linear equation also called a first-degree equation?

9. What is an equation of the form $ax + by = c$ ($a \neq 0$ or $b \neq 0$) called?

10. An equation of the type $x = c$ (c a constant) has as its graph a line parallel to which axis?

11. An equation of the type $y = c$ (c a constant) has as its graph a line parallel to which axis?

12. What is a point where a graph crosses the x-axis called?

13. What is a point where a graph crosses the y-axis called?

14. To graph a general linear equation, only two points are necessary. What are the best points to use?

In Exercises 15–23, find the intercepts and graph each equation.

15. $y + 2x = 4$ **16.** $3y - 2x = 12$ **17.** $y + x = 0$

18. $y = 3$ **19.** $2x - 1 = 0$ **20.** $y + 2x = 0$

21. $2x + 3y = 6$ **22.** $2x - 5y = 10$ **23.** $y = \frac{3}{4}x + 3$

24. What are the intercepts of the line $x = 0$? What is the graph?

25. Burford tried to graph $6x - y = 0$ using the intercept method and failed because he could find only one intercept. Write Burford a paragraph explaining how to graph this type of equation.

FOR REVIEW

Using the equation given in Exercises 26–27, complete each ordered pair so that it will be a solution to the equation.

26. $5x - 3y = 15$
(a) (0,) (b) (, 0)
(c) (, −1) (d) (−1,)

27. $y = 3$
(a) (1,) (b) (−1,)
(c) (5,) (d) (−3,)

28. **SALARY** The annual salary of a salesman y is given in terms of his total sales x by the equation

$$y = \$10{,}000 + (0.1)x.$$

Complete the ordered pairs (10,000,), (20,000,), and (50,000,). How much does the salesman earn if he sells **(a)** 10,000 items, **(b)** 20,000 items, **(c)** 50,000 items?

29. Find the area of the rectangle with corners (4, −3), (4, 5), (−3, −3), and (−3, 5).

Exercises 30–33 will help you prepare for the next section. Starting with the point $A(1, 2)$, give the coordinates of point B.

30. B is 2 units up from A and then 1 unit to the right.

31. B is 2 units down from A and then 3 units to the right.

32. B is 3 units up from A and then 2 units to the left.

33. B is 3 units down from A and then 4 units to the left.

4.2 PARALLEL EXERCISES

In Exercises 1–6 each is an equation in the two variables x and y. Make a table of values and graph each equation in a rectangular coordinate system.

1. $y = x + 1$
2. $y = 3x - 1$
3. $y = \frac{1}{2}x + 1$
4. $x + y = -1$
5. $x = 4$
6. $y = -2$

7. Which of the following are linear equations? Explain.
(a) $3x - y = 8$
(b) $x + y^2 = 7$
(c) $3xy = -1$
(d) $\frac{5}{y} + x = 3$
(e) $x^2 + y^2 = 16$
(f) $x = y - 3$

8. Why is a first-degree equation also called a linear equation?

9. Give the standard form of a linear equation.

10. Give the standard form of the equation of a line parallel to the x-axis.

11. Give the standard form of the equation of a line parallel to the y-axis.

12. The x-intercept of the graph of a line is a point on which axis?

13. The y-intercept of the graph of a line is a point on which axis?

14. In general, what are the two best points to use when graphing a linear equation?

In Exercises 15–23, find the intercepts and graph each equation.

15. $y - 2x = -4$
16. $3y + 2x = -12$
17. $2y + x = 0$
18. $y = -4$
19. $2x + 3 = 0$
20. $x - 3y = 0$
21. $4x - 3y = 12$
22. $5x + 2y = 10$
23. $y = -\frac{3}{2}x - 3$

24. What are the intercepts of the line $y = 0$? What is the graph?

25. Burford tried to graph $6x - 6 = 0$ using the intercept method and failed because he could find only one intercept. Write Burford a paragraph explaining how to graph this type of equation.

FOR REVIEW

Using the equation given in Exercises 26–27, complete each ordered pair so that it will be a solution to the equation.

26. $x - 3y = 6$
(a) (0,) **(b)** (, 0)
(c) (, −1) **(d)** (−1,)

27. $x = -1$
(a) (, 1) **(b)** (, −1)
(c) (, 5) **(d)** (, −3)

28. **FORESTRY** The number of deer y that can live in a forest preserve is related to the number of acres x in the preserve. If this relationship is given by the equation

$$y = 0.5x + 3$$

complete the ordered pairs (20,), (100,), and (200,). How many deer can the preserve sustain if it contains **(a)** 20 acres, **(b)** 100 acres, **(c)** 200 acres?

29. Find the area of the triangle with vertices (1, 2), (−3, −2), and (5, −2).

Exercises 30–33 will help you prepare for the next section. Starting with the point $A(-3, 5)$, give the coordinates of point B.

30. B is 4 units up from A and then 3 units to the right.

31. B is 4 units down from A and then 2 units to the right.

32. B is 1 unit up from A and then 4 units to the left.

33. B is 6 units down from A and then 1 unit to the left.

4.2 ENRICHMENT EXERCISES

Graph each equation in Exercises 1–2.

1. $0.05x - 0.02y = 0.10$

2. $\frac{2}{5}x + \frac{3}{10}y = \frac{6}{5}$

3. Give the equation of the line parallel to the x-axis passing through the point $(0, 2)$.

4. Give the equation of the line parallel to the x-axis passing through the point $(5, -3)$,

5. Give the equation of the line parallel to the y-axis passing through the point $(2, 0)$.

6. Give the equation of the line parallel to the y-axis passing through the point $(-3, 7)$.

7. Discuss the various possibilities that can occur when graphing $ax + by = c$.

SECTION 4.3 Slope of a Line

Student guideposts

- ▶ *Definition of slope*
- ▶ *Nature of the slope of a line*
- ▶ *Parallel lines*
- ▶ *Perpendicular lines*

▶ *Definition of slope*

The graph of a linear equation may be horizontal (parallel to the x-axis), may be vertical (parallel to the y-axis), may "slope" upward from lower left to upper right, or may "slope" downward from upper left to lower right. The way that a line slopes or does not slope can be precisely defined.

The formal definition of slope uses any two points on the line. The coordinates of the points are written (x_1, y_1) and (x_2, y_2) where the subscript distinguishes between the two while identifying the x- and y-coordinates. We read x_1 as "x-sub-one" and y_1 as "y-sub-one," for example. The *slope* of the line passing through (x_1, y_1) and (x_2, y_2) is defined as the ratio of the vertical change, *rise,* to the horizontal change, *run,* as we move from (x_1, y_1) to (x_2, y_2) along the line. See Figure 4.16. This ratio will be the same for any two points on the line.

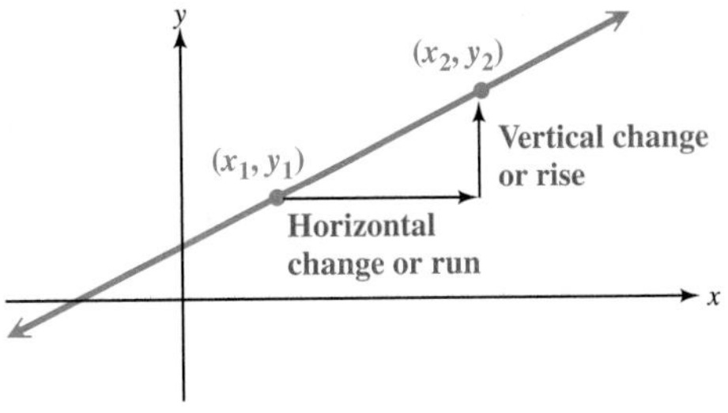

FIGURE 4.16
Rise and Run of a Line

We can define the rise and run as numbers by using the coordinates of the points. The ratio of these numerical values gives us a precise definition of slope. Refer to Figure 4.17.

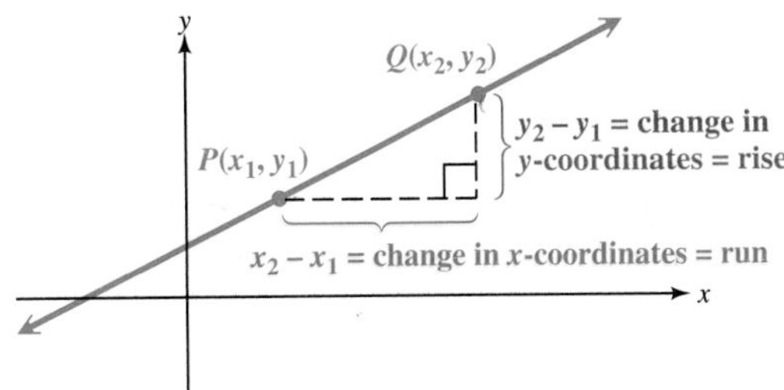

FIGURE 4.17
Slope $= \dfrac{y_2 - y_1}{x_2 - x_1} = \dfrac{\textit{rise}}{\textit{run}}$

The Slope of a Line

Let $P(x_1, y_1)$ and $Q(x_2, y_2)$ be two points on a nonvertical line. The **slope** of the line, denoted m, is given by the equation

$$m = \frac{y_2 - y_1}{x_2 - x_1} = \frac{\text{change in } y\text{-coordinates}}{\text{change in } x\text{-coordinates}} = \frac{\text{rise}}{\text{run}}.$$

EXAMPLE 1

Finding the Slope of a Line

Find the slope of the line passing through the given points.

(a) (4, 3) and (1, 2).

See the graph in Figure 4.18. Suppose we identify point $P(x_1, y_1)$ with (1, 2) and point $Q(x_2, y_2)$ with (4, 3). The slope will then be given by

$$m = \frac{y_2 - y_1}{x_2 - x_1} = \frac{3 - 2}{4 - 1} = \frac{1}{3}.$$

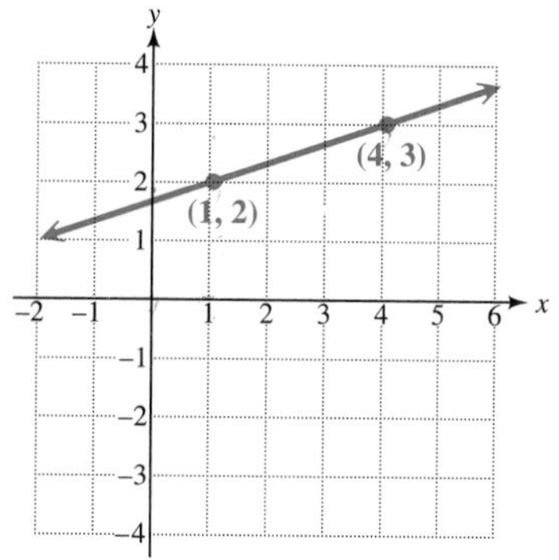

FIGURE 4.18

What happens if we identify $P(x_1, y_1)$ with (4, 3) and, $Q(x_2, y_2)$ with (1, 2)? In this case we have

$$m = \frac{y_2 - y_1}{x_2 - x_1} = \frac{2 - 3}{1 - 4} = \frac{-1}{-3} = \frac{1}{3}.$$

Thus, we see that *the slope is the same regardless of how the two points are identified.*

(b) $(-3, 2)$ and $(1, -1)$.

Let us identify $P(x_1, y_1)$ with $(-3, 2)$ and $Q(x_2, y_2)$ with $(1, -1)$ as in Figure 4.19. The slope is given by

$$m = \frac{y_2 - y_1}{x_2 - x_1} = \frac{(-1) - (2)}{(1) - (-3)} \quad \text{Watch signs}$$

$$= \frac{-3}{1 + 3} = -\frac{3}{4}.$$ ■

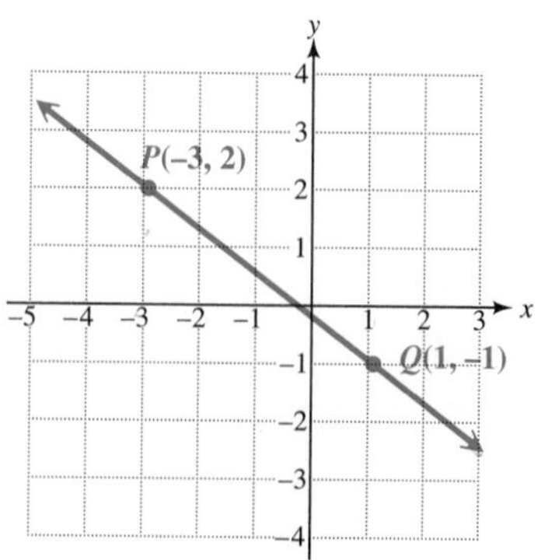

FIGURE 4.19

> **CAUTION** Make sure that the coordinates are subtracted in the same order. *Do not compute*
>
> $$\frac{y_2 - y_1}{x_1 - x_2}. \qquad \text{This is wrong}$$

EXAMPLE 2

Working with Zero and Undefined Slope

Find the slope of the line passing through the given points

(a) $(3, 2)$ and $(-1, 2)$.

Identifying $P(x_1, y_1)$ with $(3, 2)$ and $Q(x_2, y_2)$ with $(-1, 2)$ in Figure 4.20, we obtain

$$m = \frac{y_2 - y_1}{x_2 - x_1} = \frac{2 - 2}{-1 - 3} = \frac{0}{-4} = 0.$$

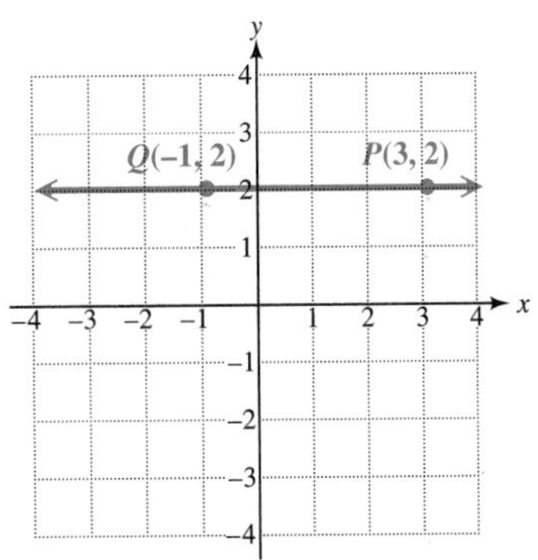

FIGURE 4.20

(b) $(-1, 4)$ and $(-1, -2)$.

Identifying $P(x_1, y_1)$ with $(-1, 4)$ and $Q(x_2, y_2)$ with $(-1, -2)$ in Figure 4.21, we obtain

$$m = \frac{y_2 - y_1}{x_2 - x_1} = \frac{-2 - 4}{-1 - (-1)} = \frac{-6}{-1 + 1} = \frac{-6}{0}, \text{ which is undefined.}$$

In this case we say that the slope of the line is undefined. Notice that the two points are on a vertical line. The slope of any vertical line is undefined. ∎

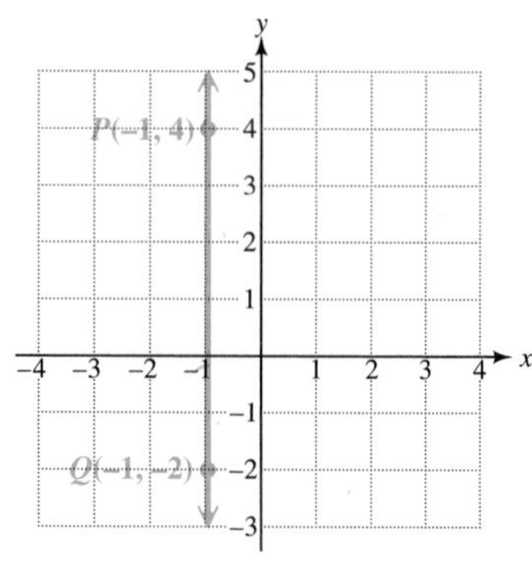

FIGURE 4.21

Nature of the slope of a line

The nature of the slope of a line is summarized below.

Summary of the Slope of a Line

1. A line which slopes from lower left to upper right has a **positive slope.**
2. A line which slopes from upper left to lower right has a **negative slope.**
3. A horizontal line (parallel to the x-axis) has **zero slope.**
4. A vertical line (parallel to the y-axis) has **undefined slope.**

The graphs in Figure 4.22 show these four cases.

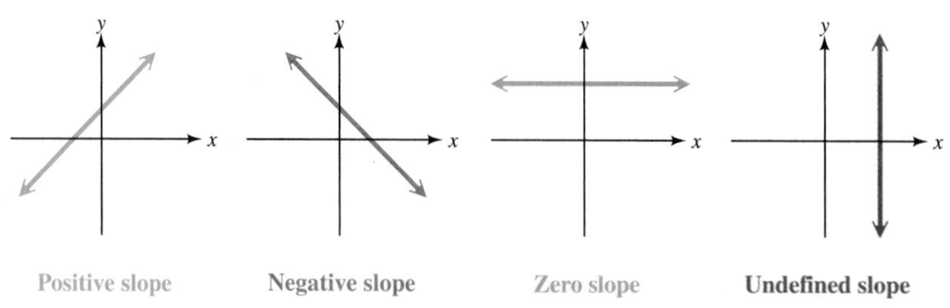

FIGURE 4.22
Summary of Slopes

Parallel Lines

Slope can be used to determine when two lines are **parallel** (never intersect).

Parallel Lines

If two nonvertical lines have slopes m_1 and m_2 and $m_1 = m_2$, then the lines are parallel. (Equal slopes determine parallel lines).

EXAMPLE 3

Finding Parallel Lines

Verify that the line l_1 through (1, 8) and $(-2, -1)$ and the line l_2 through (2, 4) and $(-1, -5)$ in Figure 4.23 are parallel.

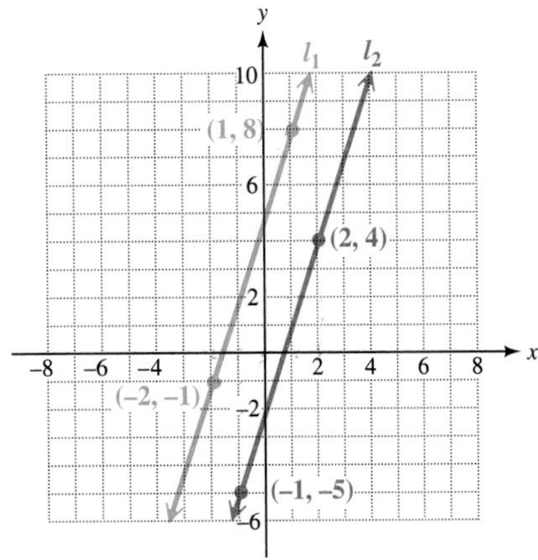

FIGURE 4.23

The slope of l_1 is

$$m_1 = \frac{8-(-1)}{1-(-2)} = \frac{8+1}{1+2} = \frac{9}{3} = 3.$$

The slope of l_2 is

$$m_2 = \frac{4-(-5)}{2-(-1)} = \frac{4+5}{2+1} = \frac{9}{3} = 3.$$

Since $m_1 = m_2$, the lines are parallel. ■

▶ *Perpendicular lines* Two lines are **perpendicular** if they intersect at right (90°) angles. The slopes of perpendicular lines have the following property.

Perpendicular Lines

If two nonvertical lines have slopes m_1 and m_2 and $m_1 m_2 = -1$, then the lines are perpendicular. (Notice that $m_1 = -\frac{1}{m_2}$ and $m_2 = -\frac{1}{m_1}$.)

EXAMPLE 4 **Finding Perpendicular Lines**

Verify that the line l_1 through $(-1, 3)$ and $(2, -1)$ and the line l_2 through $(2, 1)$ and $(-2, -2)$ in Figure 4.24 are perpendicular.

The slope of l_1 is

$$m_1 = \frac{3-(-1)}{-1-2} = \frac{3+1}{-3} = -\frac{4}{3}$$

The slope of l_2 is

$$m_2 = \frac{1-(-2)}{2-(-2)} = \frac{1+2}{2+2} = \frac{3}{4}.$$

Since $m_1 m_2 = \left(-\frac{4}{3}\right)\left(\frac{3}{4}\right) = -1$, l_1 and l_2 are perpendicular. ■

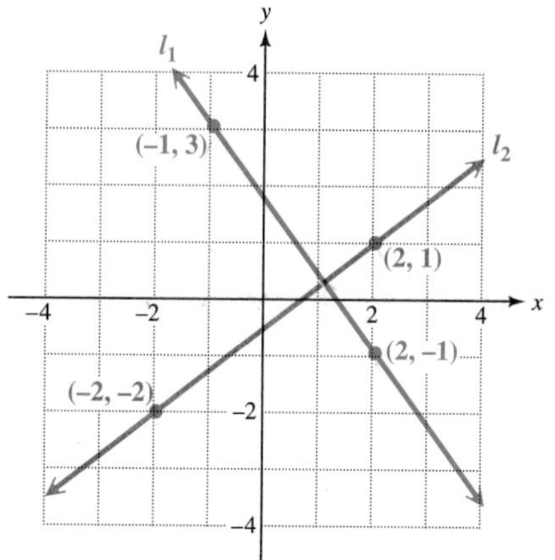

FIGURE 4.24
Perpendicular Lines

4.3 EXERCISES

In Exercises 1–3, find the slope of the line passing through the given pair of points.

1. (3, 5) and (1, 3) **2.** (3, 4) and (−1, 4) **3.** (0, 2) and (5, 0)

Answer Exercises 4–7 with one of the following phrases: ***(a)*** *positive slope* ***(b)*** *negative slope* ***(c)*** *zero slope* ***(d)*** *undefined slope.*

4. A line parallel to the y-axis has __?__.

5. A line that slopes from lower left to upper right has __?__.

6. A line perpendicular to the y-axis has __?__.

7. The x-axis has __?__.

In Exercises 8–10, m_1 and m_2 represent the slopes of two lines. State whether the lines are parallel, perpendicular, or neither. Justify your answer.

8. $m_1 = -3$ and $m_2 = -3$ **9.** $m_1 = -2$ and $m_2 = \frac{1}{2}$ **10.** $m_1 = \frac{1}{5}$ and $m_2 = 5$

11. Do the three points (2, 3), (0, 2), and (−2, 1) all lie on the same straight line? Explain using slopes.

In Exercises 12–14, find the slope of the given line by first finding two points on the line then using the definition of slope.

12. $4x - y + 7 = 0$ **13.** $5x + 1 = 0$ **14.** $3x + 5y = 0$

In Exercises 15–20, the lines l_1 and l_2 pass through the given points. Without graphing determine if the lines are parallel or perpendicular. Verify your answer.

15. l_1: (−2, −1) and (1, 5)
l_2: (4, 3) and (−1, −7)

16. l_1: (−1, 3) and (2, 4)
l_2: (6, −1) and (5, 2)

17. l_1: (−2, 5) and (−2, −4)
l_2: (4, 3) and (4, −1)

18. l_1: (1, 1) and (5, 5)
l_2: (−1, 1) and (4, −4)

19. l_1: (−3, 6) and (2, 6)
l_2: (1, −2) and (1, 4)

20. l_1: (0, 3) and (2, 0)
l_2: (−2, 0) and (0, −3)

21. Show that if two lines with slopes m_1 and m_2 are perpendicular, then $m_2 = -\dfrac{1}{m_1}$.

22. **AERONAUTICS** By the time an airplane is one mile (5280 feet) from the runway it has climbed to an altitude of 7920 feet. Find the slope of the line followed in the climb.

23. **CONSTRUCTION** A roof rises 6.25 feet in a horizontal distance of 10.31 feet. Find the slope of the roof.

FOR REVIEW

In Exercises 24–27, give the intercepts and graph.

24. $x - 6y = 2$
25. $5x + y = 0$
26. $x = -5$
27. $y = 6$
28. Is $\frac{3}{x} + \frac{2}{y} = 5$ a linear equation? Explain.

4.3 PARALLEL EXERCISES

In Exercises 1–3, find the slope of the line passing through the given pairs of points.

1. (4, 8) and (10, 2)
2. (6, 1) and (6, −5)
3. (0, 1) and (−2, 0)

*Answer Exercises 4–7 with one of the following phrases: **(a)** positive slope **(b)** negative slope **(c)** zero slope **(d)** undefined slope.*

4. A line parallel to the x-axis has __?__.
5. A line that slopes from upper left to lower right has __?__.
6. A line perpendicular to the x-axis has __?__.
7. The y-axis has __?__.

In Exercises 8–10, m_1 and m_2 represent the slopes of two lines. State whether the lines are parallel, perpendicular, or neither. Justify your answer.

8. $m_1 = \frac{1}{4}$ and $m_2 = \frac{1}{4}$
9. $m_1 = \frac{1}{5}$ and $m_2 = -5$
10. $m_1 = \frac{3}{2}$ and $m_2 = \frac{2}{3}$
11. Do the three points (1, 2), (−1, −1), and (3, 6) all lie on the same straight line? Explain using slopes.

In Exercises 12–14, find the slope of the given line by first finding two points on the line then using the definition of slope.

12. $x + 4y - 9 = 0$
13. $3y - 7 = 0$
14. $3x - 5y + 2 = 0$

In Exercises 15–20, the lines l_1 and l_2 pass through the given points. Without graphing determine if the lines are parallel or perpendicular. Verify your answer.

15. l_1: (4, −2) and (1, 1)
    l_2: (3, 3) and (7, −1)
16. l_1: (−2, 4) and (2, 5)
    l_2: (3, 2) and (4, −2)
17. l_1: (−6, −3) and (−6, 4)
    l_2: (1, −4) and (1, −5)
18. l_1: (2, 1) and (6, 5)
    l_2: (−1, 2) and (4, −3)
19. l_1: (−4, 2) and (5, 2)
    l_2: (−1, 2) and (−1, −6)
20. l_1: (0, 5) and (−4, 0)
    l_2: (4, 0) and (0, −5)

21. Show that if two lines have slopes m_1 and m_2, and $m_2 = -\dfrac{1}{m_1}$, then the lines are perpendicular.

22. **AERONAUTICS** An airplane covered 10 miles of its route while decreasing its altitude by 10,560 feet. Find the slope of the line followed.

23. **CONSTRUCTION** The road in a tunnel rises 26.9 feet in a horizontal distance of 0.2 miles. Find the slope of the road. [*Hint:* Be careful with the units.]

FOR REVIEW

In Exercises 24–27, give the intercepts and graph.

24. $6x + y = 3$
25. $3x + y = 0$
26. $y = 5$
27. $x = -3$
28. Is $3x^2 + 2y^2 = 5$ a linear equation? Explain.

4.3 ENRICHMENT EXERCISES

1. Tell whether the lines $ax = c$ and $by = c$ are parallel, perpendicular, or neither.
2. Find the slope of the line with equation $ax + by = c$. [*Hint:* a, b, and c are constants.]
3. Find the x-intercept of the line with equation $ax + by = c$.
4. Find the y-intercept of the line with equation $ax + by = c$.

In Exercises 5–6, find another point on the line that contains the given point and has the given slope. [Hint: Use the fact that slope is rise over run.]

5. $(-5, 1)$; $m = \frac{4}{3}$
6. $(2, -1)$; $m = \frac{-4}{3}$
7. Find the slope of a line parallel to the line with equation $y = -2x + 5$.
8. Find the slope of a line perpendicular to the line with equation $y = -2x + 5$.
9. Find several examples of the use of slope in practical problems and write a paragraph or two outlining what you discover.

SECTION 4.4 Forms of the Equation of a Line

Student guideposts

- ▶ *Standard form*
- ▶ *Slope-intercept form*
- ▶ *Graphing using slope*
- ▶ *Point-slope form*

▶ *Standard form*

The equation of a line can be written in several forms. In Section 4.2 the **standard form** was defined to be

$$ax + by = c \qquad a, b, c \text{ constants}$$

where a and b are not both zero. For example, consider the equation $x - 3y = -6$.

▶ *Slope-intercept form* Suppose we solve this equation for y. The result is a special form of the equation called the **slope-intercept form.**

$$x - 3y = -6$$
$$-3y = -x - 6$$
$$y = \frac{1}{3}x + 2 \qquad \text{Divide through by } -3$$

To explain why this is called the slope-intercept form first calculate y when $x = 0$.

$$y = \frac{1}{3}(0) + 2 = 2$$

Thus, the y-intercept of the line is $(0, 2)$. Also, if x increases by 3, say from 0 to 3, y increases by 1. That is, y was 2 when $x = 0$, and when $x = 3$,

$$y = \frac{1}{3}(3) + 2 = 3.$$

Hence the slope of the line is

$$m = \frac{\text{change in } y}{\text{change in } x} = \frac{\text{rise}}{\text{run}} = \frac{1}{3}.$$

When an equation is in slope-intercept form the coefficient of x is the slope, and the constant term is the y-coordinate of the y-intercept of the line.

Slope-Intercept Form of the Equation of a Line

If the equation of a line is solved for y, the resulting equation is in **slope-intercept form**

$$y = mx + b,$$

where m is the slope of the line and $(0, b)$ is the y-intercept.

EXAMPLE 1 **Finding the Slope and y-Intercept**

What are the slope and y-intercept of the line with equation $4x + 2y = -1$?

First solve for y to obtain the slope-intercept form.

$$4x + 2y = -1$$
$$2y = -4x - 1$$
$$y = -2x - \frac{1}{2} \qquad \text{Divide by 2}$$

$m = -2 =$ slope $\quad \left(0, -\frac{1}{2}\right) = y$-intercept $\quad \left[b = -\frac{1}{2}\right]$ ■

> NOTE Example 1 shows how to find the slope of a nonvertical line when its equation is given in standard form. Solve the equation for y to obtain the slope-intercept form. The slope is always the numerical coefficient of x.

EXAMPLE 2

Using the Slope-Intercept Forms

Find the standard form of the equation of the line with slope -2 and y-intercept $(0, 5)$.

We first find the slope-intercept form of the equation by substituting -2 for m and 5 for b in

$$y = mx + b.$$
$$y = -2x + 5$$

By writing all terms with the variables on the left side of this equation we obtain the standard form

$$2x + y = 5. \quad ■$$

Graphing using slope

In Section 4.2 we learned how to graph a line by finding the intercepts. The graph of a line in slope-intercept form can be obtained in a different way using what we know about slope. This technique is illustrated by graphing the equation $y = \frac{2}{3}x - 1$.

Since the y-intercept is $(0, -1)$, we know the graph passes through this point. But since there are infinitely many lines containing $(0, -1)$, we need to find the one with slope $\frac{2}{3}$. To do this we find a second point on the line that can be obtained from $(0, -1)$ by considering the rise and run specified by a slope of $\frac{2}{3}$. If we start at $(0, -1)$ and move up 2 units (a rise of 2) then move right 3 units (a run of 3), we are at the point $(3, 1)$. The line passes through $(0, -1)$ and $(3, 1)$, as shown in Figure 4.25.

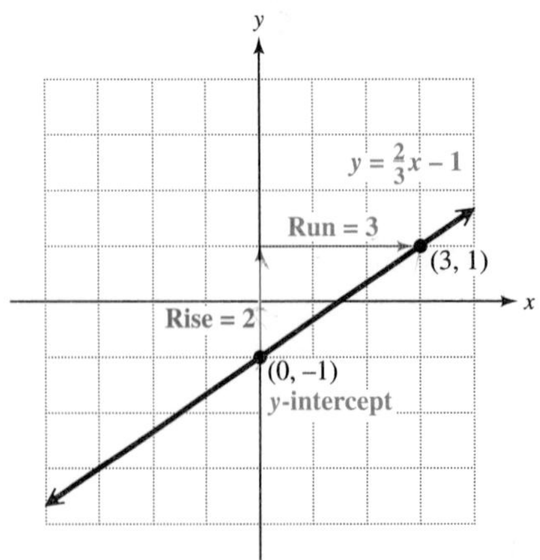

FIGURE 4.25
Graphing with Slope

▶ *Point-slope form* If we know that the slope of a line is m and that (x_1, y_1) is a point on the line, we can obtain the equation of the line. Suppose (x, y) is an arbitrary point on the line. Then using the formula for the slope of a line with (x, y) as (x_2, y_2), we have

$$m = \frac{y - y_1}{x - x_1}.$$

Multiplying both sides of this equation by $x - x_1$,

$$m(x - x_1) = y - y_1,$$

gives us another form of the equation of a line.

Point-Slope Form of the Equation of a Line

To find the equation of a line which has slope m and passes through the point (x_1, y_1), substitute these values into the **point-slope form**

$$y - y_1 = m(x - x_1).$$

EXAMPLE 3

Using Point-Slope Form

Find the slope-intercept form of the equation of the line with slope -3 passing through the point $(1, -2)$. Graph the line.

Use the point-slope form of the equation with $m = -3$ and $(x_1, y_1) = (1, -2)$.

$$y - y_1 = m(x - x_1)$$

$$y - (-2) = -3(x - 1) \qquad y_1 = -2,\ x_1 = 1,\ m = -3$$

$$y + 2 = -3x + 3 \qquad \text{Watch the signs}$$

$$y = -3x + 1 \qquad \text{Subtract 2 to obtain slope-intercept form}$$

Since the slope $m = -3 = \frac{-3}{1} = \frac{\text{rise}}{\text{run}}$, the rise is -3 and the run is 1. Start at the y-intercept $(0, 1)$ and move down 3 units (the rise is -3), then right 1 unit (the run is 1). This locates another point on the line, $(1, -2)$. See Figure 4.26. ■

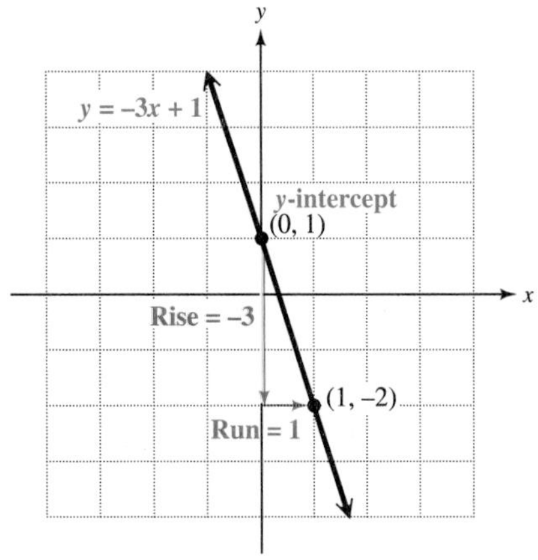

FIGURE 4.26

To find the equation of a line passing through two points, we use both the slope formula and the point-slope form. This is shown in the next example.

EXAMPLE 4 **Finding an Equation of a Line Through Two Points**

Find the standard form of the equation of the line passing through two points $(3, -2)$ and $(-1, 5)$.

First find the slope of the line using $(3, -2) = (x_1, y_1)$ and $(-1, 5) = (x_2, y_2)$.

$$m = \frac{y_2 - y_1}{x_2 - x_1} = \frac{5 - (-2)}{-1 - 3} = \frac{7}{-4} = -\frac{7}{4}$$

Next, substitute $-\frac{7}{4}$ for m and $(3, -2)$ for (x_1, y_1) in the point-slope form. (We would get the same equation by using $(-1, 5)$ for (x_1, y_1).)

$$y - y_1 = m(x - x_1).$$

$$y - (-2) = -\frac{7}{4}(x - 3)$$

$$4(y - (-2)) = -7(x - 3) \quad \text{Multiply both sides by 4}$$

$$4y + 8 = -7x + 21$$

$$7x + 4y = 13$$

This is the standard form of the equation of the desired line. ■

We conclude this section with a summary of forms of the equation of a line.

Forms of the Equation of a Line

Standard Form	$ax + by = c$	
Slope-Intercept Form	$y = mx + b$	Slope m, y-intercept $(0, b)$
Point-Slope Form	$y - y_1 = m(x - x_1)$	Slope m, point (x_1, y_1) on line

NOTE The names *slope-intercept* and *point-slope form* help you decide which form should be used in a particular problem.

4.4 EXERCISES

In Exercises 1–6, write each equation in slope-intercept form and give the slope and y-intercept.

1. $5x + y - 12 = 0$
2. $2x - 5y + 10 = 0$
3. $4y + 7 = 0$
4. $5x + 1 = 0$
5. $x + y = 5$
6. $2x - 3y + 1 = 0$

In Exercises 7–9, write each equation in slope-intercept form and use the y-intercept and slope to graph the equation.

7. $x + y + 2 = 0$ **8.** $2x - 5y + 10 = 0$ **9.** $4x + 3y = 15$

In Exercises 10–12, find the standard form of the equation of the line with the given slope and y-intercept.

10. $m = 2, (0, 4)$ **11.** $m = 4, (0, -3)$ **12.** $m = -\frac{1}{2}, (0, 6)$

In Exercises 13–15, find the standard form of the equation of the line with the given slope passing through the given point.

13. $m = 3, (2, -4)$ **14.** $m = -2, (1, 5)$ **15.** $m = -\frac{1}{2}, (3, -2)$

In Exercises 16–18, find the standard form of the equation of the line passing through the given points.

16. $(2, 5)$ and $(4, 7)$ **17.** $(-1, 3)$ and $(2, 4)$ **18.** $(3, -2)$ and $(-1, -1)$

BUSINESS *Some business problems can be described by a linear equation. For example, the cost y of producing a number of items x is given by $y = mx + b$, where b is the overhead cost (the cost when no items are produced) and m is the variable cost (the cost of producing a single item). Use this information to find the cost equation in Exercises 19–20.*

19. Overhead cost: \$25
Variable cost: \$10

20. Overhead cost: \$300
Variable cost: \$10.50.

21. Which of the two equations, $x = 2$ or $y = -3$, is the equation of the vertical line through $(2, -3)$?

22. Which of the two equations, $x = 2$ or $y = -3$, is the equation of the horizontal line through $(2, -3)$?

23. Find the standard form of the equation of the line through $(1, -2)$ that is perpendicular to a line with slope -3.

24. Find the standard form of the equation of the line through $(-1, 5)$ that is parallel to the line $3x + 2y = 4$.

25. Find the standard form of the equation of the line through $(-2, -4)$ that is perpendicular to the line $5x - 2y = -10$.

FOR REVIEW

Exercises 26–28 review material from Section 3.7 to help you prepare for the next section. Solve each inequality.

26. $2x + 1 < 5$ **27.** $-2(x - 1) \geq 8$ **28.** $3(x - 1) - (2 - x) \geq 5$

4.4 PARALLEL EXERCISES

In Exercises 1–6, write each equation in slope-intercept form and give the slope and y-intercept.

1. $7x - y + 13 = 0$ **2.** $5x - 9y + 9 = 0$ **3.** $2x - 1 = 0$

4. $4y + 12 = 0$ **5.** $y - x = 3$ **6.** $3x - 5y + 2 = 0$

In Exercises 7–9, write each equation in slope-intercept form and use the y-intercept and slope to graph the equation.

7. $x + y - 6 = 0$ **8.** $3x - 4y - 12 = 0$ **9.** $5x + 2y = 6$

In Exercises 10–12, find the standard form of the equation of the line with the given slope and y-intercept.

10. $m = 3$, $(0, 1)$ **11.** $m = 5$, $(0, -2)$ **12.** $m = -\frac{1}{4}$, $(0, 2)$

In Exercises 13–15, find the standard form of the equation of the line with the given slope passing through the given point.

13. $m = 5$, $(-3, 1)$ **14.** $m = -4$, $(2, 6)$ **15.** $m = -\frac{1}{5}$, $(-1, 4)$

In Exercises 16–18, find the standard form of the equation of the line passing through the given points.

16. $(2, 6)$ and $(5, 9)$ **17.** $(-3, 2)$ and $(2, 5)$ **18.** $(-4, 6)$ and $(-2, -2)$

BUSINESS *Some business problems can be described by a linear equation. For example, the cost y of producing a number of items x is given by $y = mx + b$, where b is the overhead cost (the cost when no items are produced) and m is the variable cost (the cost of producing a single item). Use this information to find the cost equation in Exercises 19–20.*

19. Overhead cost: \$50
Variable cost: \$30

20. Overhead cost: \$500
Variable cost: \$8.50.

21. Which of the two equations $x = -1$ or $y = 5$, is the equation of the vertical line through $(-1, 5)$?

22. Which of the two equations, $x = -1$ or $y = 5$, is the equation of the horizontal line through $(-1, 5)$?

23. Find the standard form of the equation of the line through $(-3, 2)$ that is perpendicular to a line with slope 4.

24. Find the standard form of the equation of the line through $(3, 6)$ that is parallel to the line $3x - 2y = -5$.

25. Find the standard form of the equation of the line through $(-1, -5)$ that is perpendicular to the line $5x + 2y = 9$.

FOR REVIEW

The following exercises review material from Section 3.7 to help you prepare for the next section. Solve each inequality.

26. $1 - 3x \le -5$ **27.** $4(2 - x) > 7 - 3x$ **28.** $3(x + 2) - (1 - 2x) \ge 10$

4.4 ENRICHMENT EXERCISES

1. Find the standard form of the equation of the horizontal line through the point $(6, -4)$.

2. Find the standard form of the equation of the vertical line through the point $(5, 8)$.

3. Find the standard form of the equation of a line through $(4, -5)$ that is parallel to $4x = 7$.

4. Find the standard form of the equation of a line through $(4, -5)$ that is perpendicular to $4x = 7$.

5. The midpoint of the line segment joining (x_1, y_1) and (x_2, y_2) is $\left(\frac{x_1 + x_2}{2}, \frac{y_1 + y_2}{2}\right)$. Find the standard form of the perpendicular bisector of the line segment joining $(2, -1)$ and $(-6, 3)$.

6. Explain why it is important to know the name of the form of the equation of a line as well as the form itself.

SECTION 4.5

Graphing Linear Inequalities in Two Variables

Student guideposts

- ▶ ***Linear inequalities in two variables***
- ▶ ***Graph of solution***
- ▶ ***Test point***
- ▶ ***Method of graphing***

In Section 3.7 we graphed linear inequalities in one variable, such as

$$3x + 2 > 5 \quad \text{and} \quad x - 1 \le 3(x - 5) + 1,$$

on a number line. For example, if we solve

$$\begin{aligned} 3x + 2 &> 5 \\ 3x &> 3 && \text{Subtract 2} \\ x &> 1, && \text{Divide by 3} \end{aligned}$$

the solution $x > 1$ is graphed in Figure 4.27.

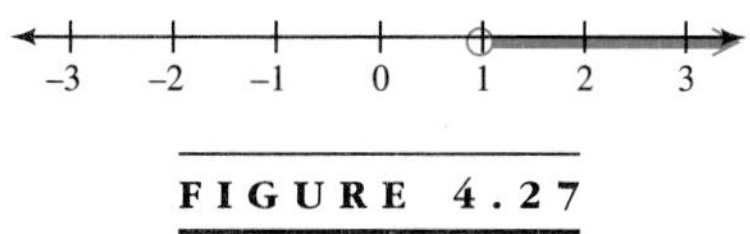

FIGURE 4.27

▶ ***Linear inequalities in two variables***

We now consider **linear inequalities in two variables** in which the variables are raised only to the first power. For example,

$$2x + y < -1$$

is a linear inequality in the two variables x and y. A **solution** to such an inequality is an ordered pair of numbers which when substituted for x and y yields a true statement. Thus, $(-1, 0)$ is a solution to $2x + y < -1$ since by replacing x with -1 and y with 0 we obtain

$$\begin{aligned} 2x + y &< -1 \\ 2(-1) + 0 &< -1 \\ -2 &< -1, && \text{which is true.} \end{aligned}$$

On the other hand, $(4, -3)$ is not a solution since

$$\begin{aligned} 2x + y &< -1 \\ 2(4) + (-3) &< -1 \\ 8 - 3 &< -1 \\ 5 &< -1, && \text{is false.} \end{aligned}$$

EXAMPLE 1 **Finding Solutions to an Inequality**

Tell whether $(-1, -3)$, $(1, 1)$ and $(-2, 0)$, are solutions to $3x - 2y \geq 1$.

$$3(-1) - 2(-3) \geq 1$$
$$-3 + 6 \geq 1$$
$$3 \geq 1 \quad \text{True. } (-1, -3) \text{ is a solution.}$$

$$3(1) - 2(1) \geq 1$$
$$3 - 2 \geq 1$$
$$1 \geq 1 \quad \text{True. } (1, 1) \text{ is a solution.}$$

$$3(-2) - 2(0) \geq 1$$
$$-6 - 0 \geq 1$$
$$-6 \geq 1 \quad \text{False. } (-2, 0) \text{ is not a solution.}$$ ■

▶ *Graph of solution* The set of all solutions to a linear inequality in two variables can be displayed in a rectangular coordinate system. Consider

$$2x + y > -3.$$

If we replace the inequality symbol with an equal sign, the resulting equation is

$$2x + y = -3.$$

To graph this equation we first plot the intercepts $(-\frac{3}{2}, 0)$ and $(0, -3)$ and draw the line as in Figure 4.28. Notice that the graph of the line divides the plane into a region above the line, the line itself, and a region below the line.

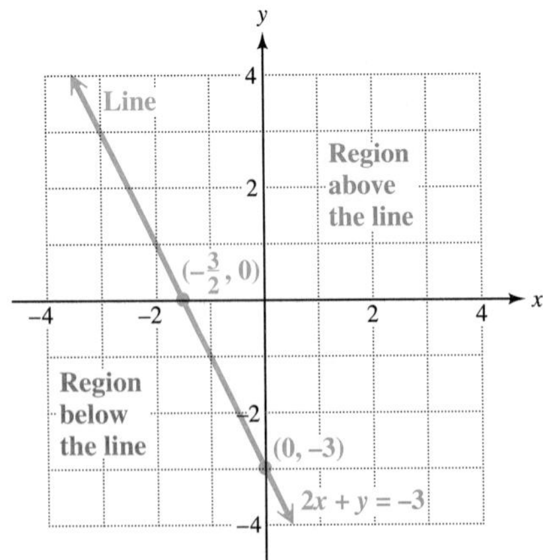

FIGURE 4.28

▶ *Test point* The graph of an inequality such as $2x + y > -3$ consists of all the points on one side of the boundary line $2x + y = -3$. The graph of $2x + y < -3$ is all the points on the other side of the line. To determine the correct side of the line to graph for an inequality such as $2x + y > -3$, we select any point not on the line as a **test point.** If we use (0, 0) in this case the arithmetic is easy:

$$2x + y > -3$$
$$2(0) + 0 > -3$$
$$0 > -3. \quad \text{This is true}$$

Since this inequality is true, we graph the points on the side of the line containing the test point (0, 0). If the inequality to be graphed had been $2x + y < -3$, a false inequality would have resulted using (0, 0) as a test point:

$$2x + y < -3$$
$$2(0) + 0 < -3$$
$$0 < -3. \quad \text{This is false}$$

In the case when a false inequality is obtained, shade the region that does *not* contain the test point. The graphs of both $2x + y < -3$ and $2x + y > -3$ are shown in Figure 4.29 by shading the region that satisfies the inequality. The figure also has graphs of $2x + y \leq -3$ and $2x + y \geq -3$.

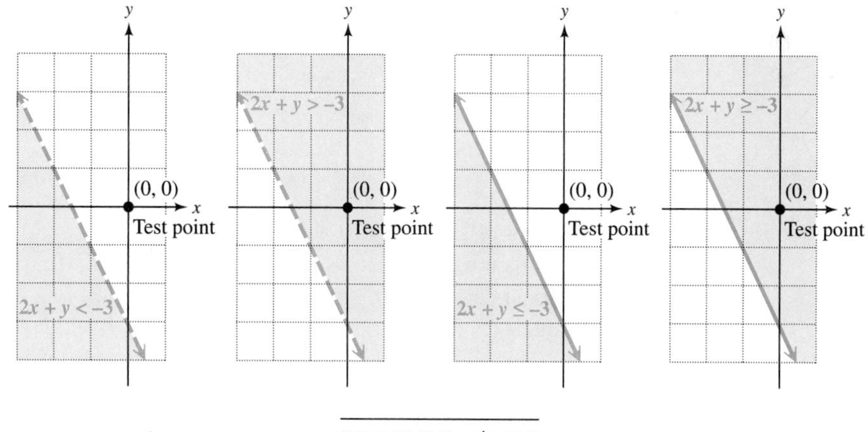

FIGURE 4.29

> NOTE We use a dashed line for the boundary when the inequality is $<$ or $>$ to show that the boundary is *not* part of the graph. For the inequalities $\leq$ and $\geq$ a solid line is used to indicate that the boundary *is* part of the graph.

EXAMPLE 2 **Graphing Inequalities**

(a) Graph $x + 3y > 6$.

Graph the line $x + 3y = 6$ using the intercepts (0, 2) and (6, 0). Since the inequality is $>$, use a dashed line. Select the test point (0, 0). (It is not on the line and the arithmetic is easy with (0, 0).)

$$x + 3y > 6$$
$$0 + 3(0) > 6$$
$$0 > 6 \quad \text{This is false}$$

The inequality is false. Shade the region in Figure 4.30 that does not contain (0, 0).

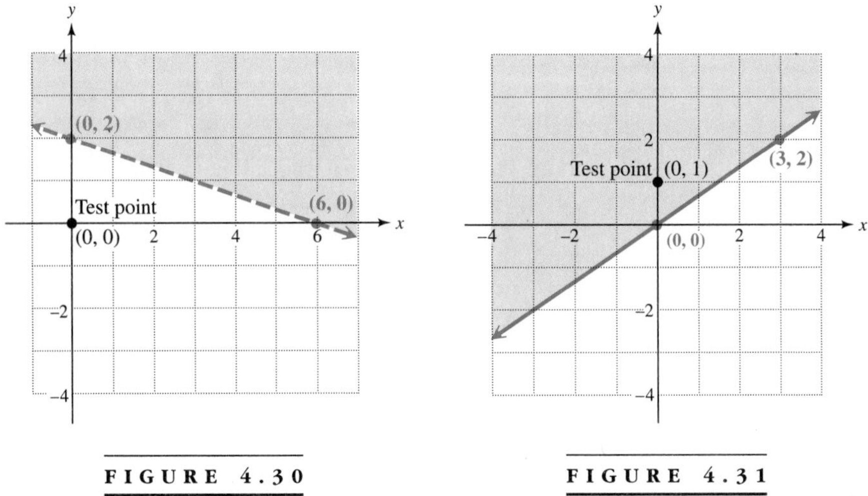

FIGURE 4.30

FIGURE 4.31

(b) Graph $2x - 3y \leq 0$.

Since both intercepts of $2x - 3y = 0$ are (0, 0), we need to find another point on the boundary line. If $x = 3$ then $y = 2$, so (3, 2) is a second point. Draw a solid line through (0, 0) and (3, 2) as in Figure 4.31.

This time (0, 0) cannot be used as a test point. Choosing (0, 1) as a test point we obtain a true inequality:

$$2x - 3y \leq 0$$
$$2(0) - 3(1) \leq 0$$
$$-3 \leq 0.$$

Thus, we shade the region containing the test point (0, 1). ■

Some linear inequalities in two variables are missing either the x-term or the y-term. The solution techniques are the same for these equations, but sometimes our work can be simplified by first solving the inequality for the remaining variable.

EXAMPLE 3 **Solving Inequalities Involving Vertical and Horizontal Lines**

(a) Graph $2x - 4 \geq 0$.

$$2x - 4 \geq 0$$
$$2x \geq 4$$
$$x \geq 2$$

Replacing $\geq$ with $=$ we recognize the graph of $x = 2$ as a vertical line with x-intercept $(2, 0)$. Since the inequality is $\geq$, we draw the boundary $x = 2$ as a solid line and use $(0, 0)$ as a test point.

$$x \geq 2$$
$$0 \geq 2 \quad \text{This is false}$$

Since the inequality is false, shade the region not containing $(0, 0)$ in Figure 4.32.

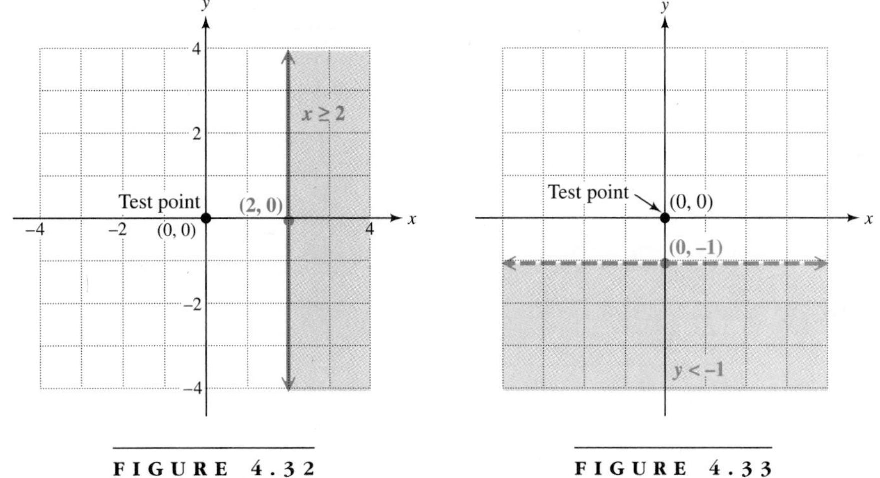

FIGURE 4.32

FIGURE 4.33

(b) Graph $3y + 3 < 0$.

$$3y + 3 < 0$$
$$3y < -3$$
$$y < -1$$

Replacing $<$ with $=$ we recognize the graph of $y = -1$ as a horizontal line with y-intercept $(0, -1)$. Since the inequality is $<$, we draw the boundary $y = -1$ as a dashed line and use $(0, 0)$ as a test point.

$$y < -1$$
$$0 < -1 \quad \text{This is false}$$

Since the inequality is false, shade the region not containing $(0, 0)$ in Figure 4.33. ∎

▶ *Method of graphing* We now summarize the techniques that we have learned.

To Graph a Linear Inequality in Two Variables

1. Graph the boundary line using a dashed line if the inequality is $<$ or $>$ and a solid line if it is $\leq$ or $\geq$.
2. Choose a test point that is not on the boundary line and substitute it into the inequality.
3. Shade the region that includes the test point if a true inequality is obtained, and shade the region that does not contain the test point if a false inequality results.

4.5 EXERCISES

1. In the graph of the inequality $3x - 2y \leq 5$, would the line $3x - 2y = 5$ be solid or dashed?
2. In the graph of the inequality $2x + y > 9$, would the line $2x + y = 9$ be solid or dashed?

In Exercises 3–6 the boundary line for the inequality has been given. Complete each graph by shading the appropriate region.

3. $x + y \leq 5$

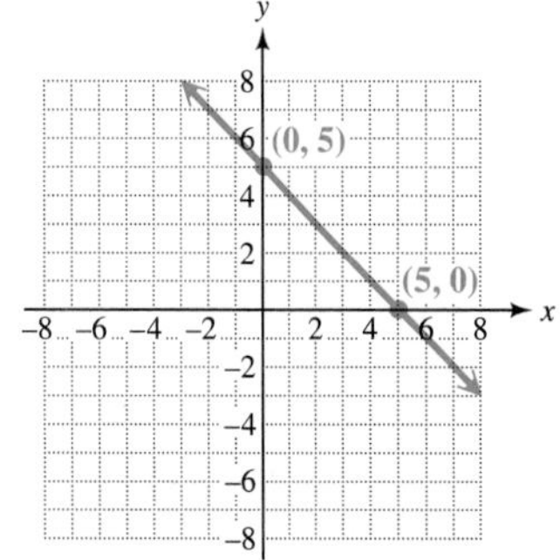

4. $2x - y < 6$

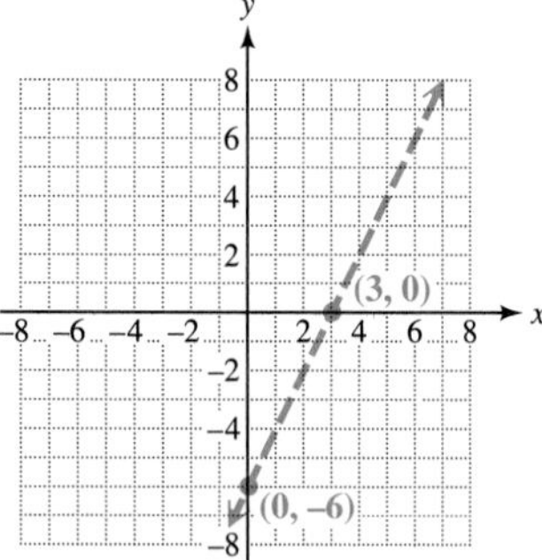

5. $3x + 12 > 0$

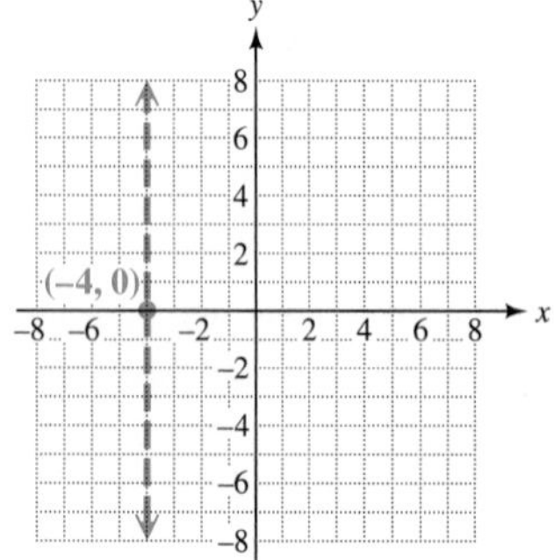

6. $1 - y \geq 0$

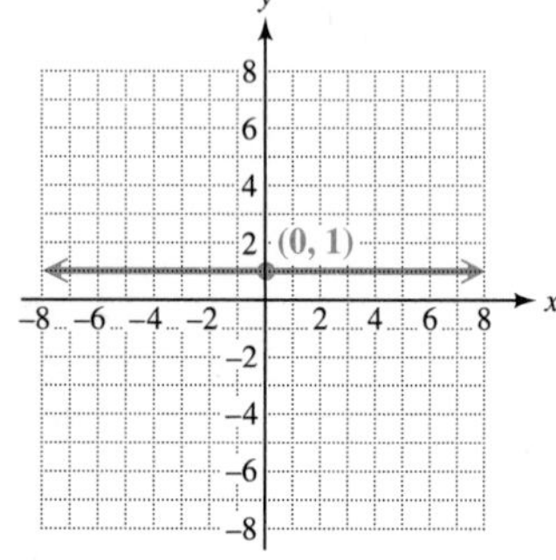

Graph the solutions of the linear inequalities in two variables in Exercises 7–14.

7. $x + y > 3$ **8.** $x + y \leq 3$ **9.** $x - y \geq -2$ **10.** $x - y < -2$
11. $x + 4y < 4$ **12.** $4x + 12 \leq 0$ **13.** $2y - 8 > 0$ **14.** $x + y \geq 0$

FOR REVIEW

Find the slope of the line passing through each pair of points in Exercises 15–17.

15. $(-3, 7)$ and $(10, -1)$ **16.** $(6, 3)$ and $(6, -5)$ **17.** $(2, -5)$ and $(-8, -5)$

In Exercises 18–19, write each equation in slope-intercept form and give the slope and y-intercept.

18. $12x - 9y + 36 = 0$ **19.** $5y - 15 = 0$

Find the standard form of the equation of the line in Exercises 20–21.

20. $m = \frac{1}{5}$, through $(-1, 4)$ **21.** through $(2, 6)$ and $(-4, -3)$

22. Verify that the line l_1 through $(-9, 2)$ and $(0, 5)$ and the line l_2 through $(1, -4)$ and $(19, 2)$ are parallel.

4.5 PARALLEL EXERCISES

1. In the graph of the inequality $5x + y \geq 1$, would the line $5x + y = 1$ be solid or dashed?

2. In the graph of the inequality $4x - 2y < 5$, would the line $4x - 2y = 5$ be solid or dashed?

In Exercises 3–6 the boundary line for the inequality has been given. Complete each graph by shading the appropriate region.

3. $x + y > 5$

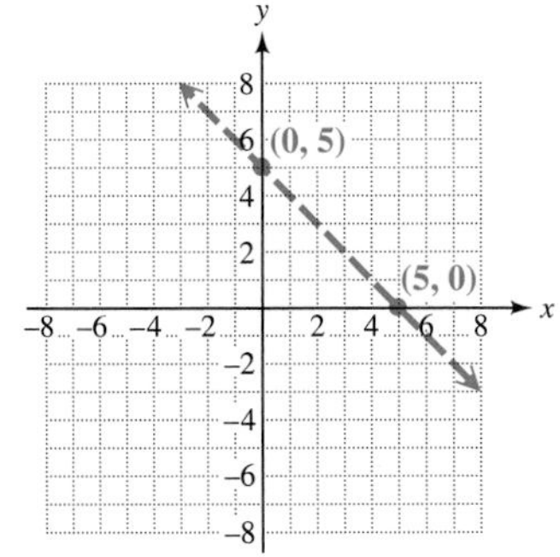

4. $2x - y \geq 6$

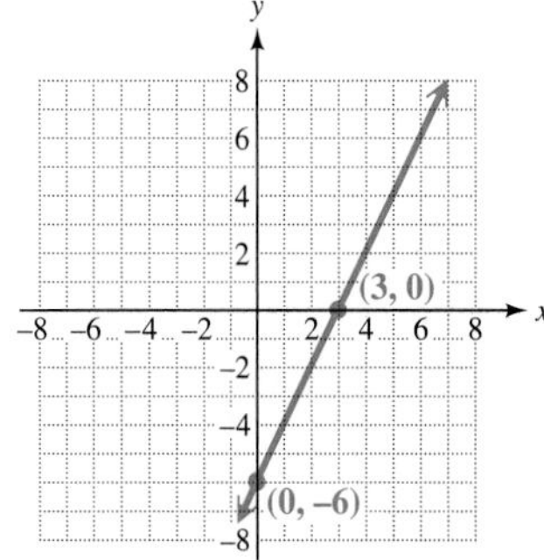

5. $3x + 12 \leq 0$

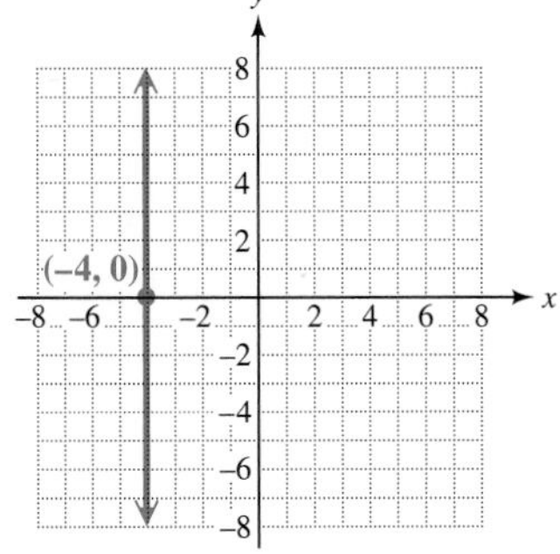

6. $1 - y < 0$

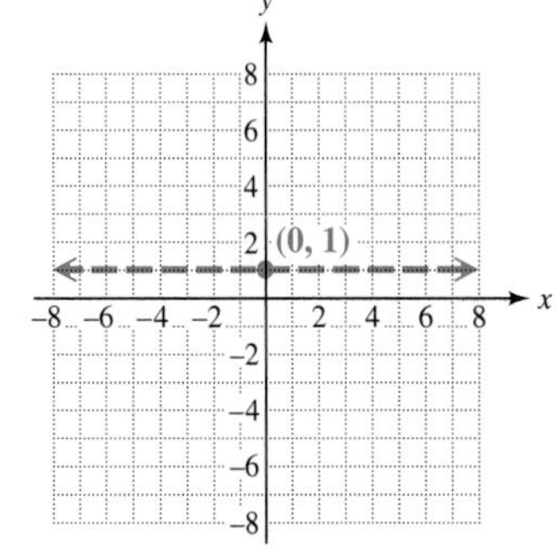

Graph the solutions of the linear inequalities in two variables in Exercises 7–14.

7. $x + y > 2$ **8.** $x + y \leq 2$ **9.** $x - y \geq -1$ **10.** $x - y < -1$

11. $3x + 4y \geq 12$ **12.** $4x + 8 > 0$ **13.** $2y - 6 \leq 0$ **14.** $2x + y < 0$

FOR REVIEW

Find the slope of the line passing through each pair of points in Exercises 15–17.

15. $(-5, 5)$ and $(3, -2)$ **16.** $(-3, 10)$ and $(2, 10)$ **17.** $(-9, 0)$ and $(-9, -7)$

In Exercises 18–19, write each equation in slope-intercept form and give the slope and y-intercept.

18. $14x - 7y + 21 = 0$ **19.** $2y + 1 = 0$

Find the standard form of the equation of the line in Exercises 20–21.

20. $m = -3$, through $(-2, 5)$ **21.** through $(8, -1)$ and $(-4, 2)$

22. Verify that the line l_1 through $(3, 6)$ and $(5, -4)$ and the line l_2 through $(1, -2)$ and $(-1, 8)$ are parallel.

4.5 ENRICHMENT EXERCISES

Tell whether the given point satisfies both of the inequalities in Exercises 1–2.

1. $3x - y < 4$
$y \geq -2$

(a) $(0, 2)$ **(b)** $(2, 0)$

△ **(c)** $(-1, 5)$ △ **(d)** $(-3, -4)$

2. $x + 4y \geq 5$
$-2x + 3y < 0$

(a) $(0, -1)$ **(b)** $(-1, 0)$

(c) $(5, 2)$ **(d)** $(-3, 4)$

3. In your own words, describe the method used to graph a linear inequality in two variables.

CHAPTER 4 REVIEW

KEY WORDS

4.1 A **rectangular** or **Cartesian coordinate system** is formed by using both a horizontal and a vertical number line.

The ***x*-axis** is the horizontal number line in a rectangular coordinate system.

The ***y*-axis** is the vertical number line in a rectangular coordinate system.

An **ordered pair** has x-coordinate in the first position and y-coordinate in the second position.

The **quadrants** are the four sections formed by the axes in a rectangular coordinate system.

A **linear equation in two variables** x and y is an equation of the form $ax + by = c$.

A **solution** to a linear equation in two variables is an ordered pair of numbers which when substituted for the variables results in a true equation.

4.2 The **graph** of an equation in two variables x and y is the set of points in a rectangular coordinate system that corresponds to solutions of the equation.

The **standard form** of a linear equation is $ax + by = c$.

The **x-intercept** is the point where the line crosses the x-axis.

The **y-intercept** is the point where the line crosses the y-axis.

4.3 The **slope** of a line gives a measure of its direction in a coordinate system.

Parallel lines never intersect.

Perpendicular lines intersect at right angles.

4.5 A **linear inequality in two variables** is an expression using $<$, $\leq$, $>$, or $\geq$ in which the variables are raised to the first power.

A **test point** is a point used to determine which side of the line is the solution of a linear inequality.

KEY CONCEPTS

4.2
1. When graphing an equation in a rectangular coordinate system, construct a table of values.
2. Two convenient points to use for graphing a linear equation are the intercepts (if they exist).
3. An equation of the form $x = c$ is parallel to the y-axis with x-intercept $(c, 0)$.
4. An equation of the form $y = c$ is parallel to the x-axis with y-intercept $(0, c)$.

4.3
1. The slope of the line passing through points (x_1, y_1) and (x_2, y_2) is given by

$$m = \frac{y_2 - y_1}{x_2 - x_1} = \frac{\textbf{change in } y\textbf{-coordinates}}{\textbf{change in } x\textbf{-coordinates}}$$

   and can be positive, negative, zero, or undefined.
2. Let m_1 and m_2 be the slopes of two distinct lines. If $m_1 = m_2$, the lines are parallel.
3. Let m_1 and m_2 be the slopes of two distinct lines. If $m_1 m_2 = -1$, the lines are perpendicular.

4.4
1. The slope-intercept form of the equation of a line is

$$y = mx + b,$$

   where m is the slope and $(0, b)$ is the y-intercept.
2. The best way to find the slope of a line quickly is to solve the equation for y (if possible), putting the equation into slope-intercept form. The coefficient of x is the slope.
3. The point-slope form of the equation of a line is

$$y - y_1 = m(x - x_1),$$

   where m is the slope and (x_1, y_1) is any point on the line.

4.5 To graph a linear inequality in two variables, first graph the boundary line using a dashed line (for $<$ or $>$) or a solid line (for $\leq$ or $\geq$). Choose a test point not on the boundary line and substitute it into the inequality. Shade the region containing the test point if a true inequality results, and shade the region not containing the test point if a false inequality results.

CHAPTER 4 REVIEW EXERCISES

PART I

4.1

1. Plot the points associated with the pairs $A(-1, 3)$, $B(0, 0)$, $C(1, -2)$, $D(4, 2)$, and $E(-4, -3)$, and state which quadrant each is in.
2. Complete the ordered pairs $(0,\ )$, $(\ , 0)$, and $(-2,\ )$ so that they will be solutions to the equation $2x + 3y = 6$.
3. **BIOLOGY** The number, y, of bacteria in a culture is approximated using time x, in days, by the equation $y = 4000x + 5000$. Complete the ordered pair $(3,\ )$. After 3 days, what is the bacteria count?

4.2

4. Which of the following are linear equations?
   (a) $2x + 3 = y$ **(b)** $xy = 5$ **(c)** $x + y^2 = 2$
   (d) $x^3 + y = 3$ **(e)** $x = 4$ **(f)** $3y = -1$

In Exercises 5–8, give the intercepts and graph in the Cartesian coordinate system.

5. $3x - 4y = 12$
   x-intercept =
   y-intercept =
6. $2x + 3 = 0$
   x-intercept =
   y-intercept =
7. $x - 2y = 0$
   x-intercept =
   y-intercept =
8. $y - 3 = 0$
   x-intercept =
   y-intercept =

4.3

Find the slope of the line through the given pair of points in Exercises 9–11.

9. $(-9, -2)$ and $(3, 6)$
10. $(0, 2)$ and $(-3, 0)$
11. $(-1, 8)$ and $(-1, 7)$
12. What can be said about two distinct lines that both have slope $\frac{2}{3}$?
13. What can be said about two lines with slopes $\frac{1}{3}$ and -3?

4.4

14. Write $8x + y - 3 = 0$ in slope-intercept form and give the slope and y-intercept.
15. Write $3y + 4 = 0$ in slope-intercept form and give the slope and y-intercept.
16. Find the standard form of the equation of the line with slope $-\frac{2}{3}$ and y-intercept $(0, 4)$.
17. Find the standard form of the equation of the line passing through $(-1, -2)$ and $(5, 3)$.

4.5

In Exercises 18–21, graph each inequality in a Cartesian coordinate system.

18. $x - 2y > -2$
19. $2y + 4 \leq 0$
20. $3 - 3x < 0$
21. $3x + 2y \geq 6$

PART II

22. What can be said about two lines both with slope $\frac{1}{5}$ and y-intercept -5?

Write each equation in Exercises 23–24 in slope-intercept form and give its slope and y-intercept.

23. $3x - 2y = 8$
24. $-x + 5y + 4 = 0$
25. Find the standard form of the equation of a line through $(6, -1)$ and $(4, 5)$.
26. Find the standard form of the equation of a line through $(-2, 7)$ and parallel to a line with slope $-\frac{1}{3}$.

Answer true *or* false *in Exercises 27–36. If the statement is false, tell why.*

27. If (a, b) is on the x-axis and on the y-axis, then (a, b) is $(0, 0)$.

28. The line with equation $x = 5$ passes through the points $(5, -1)$ and $(5, 27)$.

29. The line with equation $y = -3$ has x-intercept $(-3, 0)$.

30. All the points that are needed to graph $2x + 7y = 0$ are the intercepts.

31. The graph of $3x - y > 6$ includes the point $(4, 5)$.

32. There is only one vertical line through the point $(2, 8)$

33. The line with equation $y = 5$ has slope 1.

34. The line with equation $2x - 4y = 0$ has slope 0.

35. The lines with equations $y = x$ and $y = -x$ are perpendicular.

36. The lines with equations $y = x + 2$ and $x = y + 2$ are parallel.

CHAPTER 4 TEST

1. The point with coordinates $(2, -3)$ is located in which quadrant?

2. Complete the ordered pair $(-3, \quad)$ so that it will be a solution to the equation $x + 5y = -1$.

3. The number, y, of items in a store during the week is approximated by using time x, in days, in the equation $y = -200x + 1000$. Complete the ordered pair $(3, \quad)$ to find the number of items in the store after three days.

4. True or false: $x - 2y^2 = 3$ is a linear equation.

5. Find the slope of the line through the points $(2, -3)$ and $(-4, -5)$.

6. Write $2x + 5y = 20$ in slope-intercept form and give the slope and the y-intercept.

7. Find the standard form of the equation of the line with slope -6 and passing through $(4, -5)$.

8. Are lines with slopes $-\frac{1}{7}$ and 7 parallel, perpendicular, or neither?

Graph each equation in a rectangular coordinate system.

9. $y = 2x + 4$

10. $3x + y = 0$

Graph each inequality in a rectangular coordinate system.

11. $2y + x - 3 > 0$

12. $y - 4 \leq 0$

Answer true *or* false *in Problems 13–14. If the statement is false, tell why.*

13. If $(a, 4)$ is a solution to $x + 2y = 8$, then $a = 4$.

14. The line $x = 7$ is perpendicular to the line $y = 7$.

15. An equation for the horizontal line through $(-1, 6)$ is $y = 6$.

16. Why do we say that the slope of a vertical line is undefined?

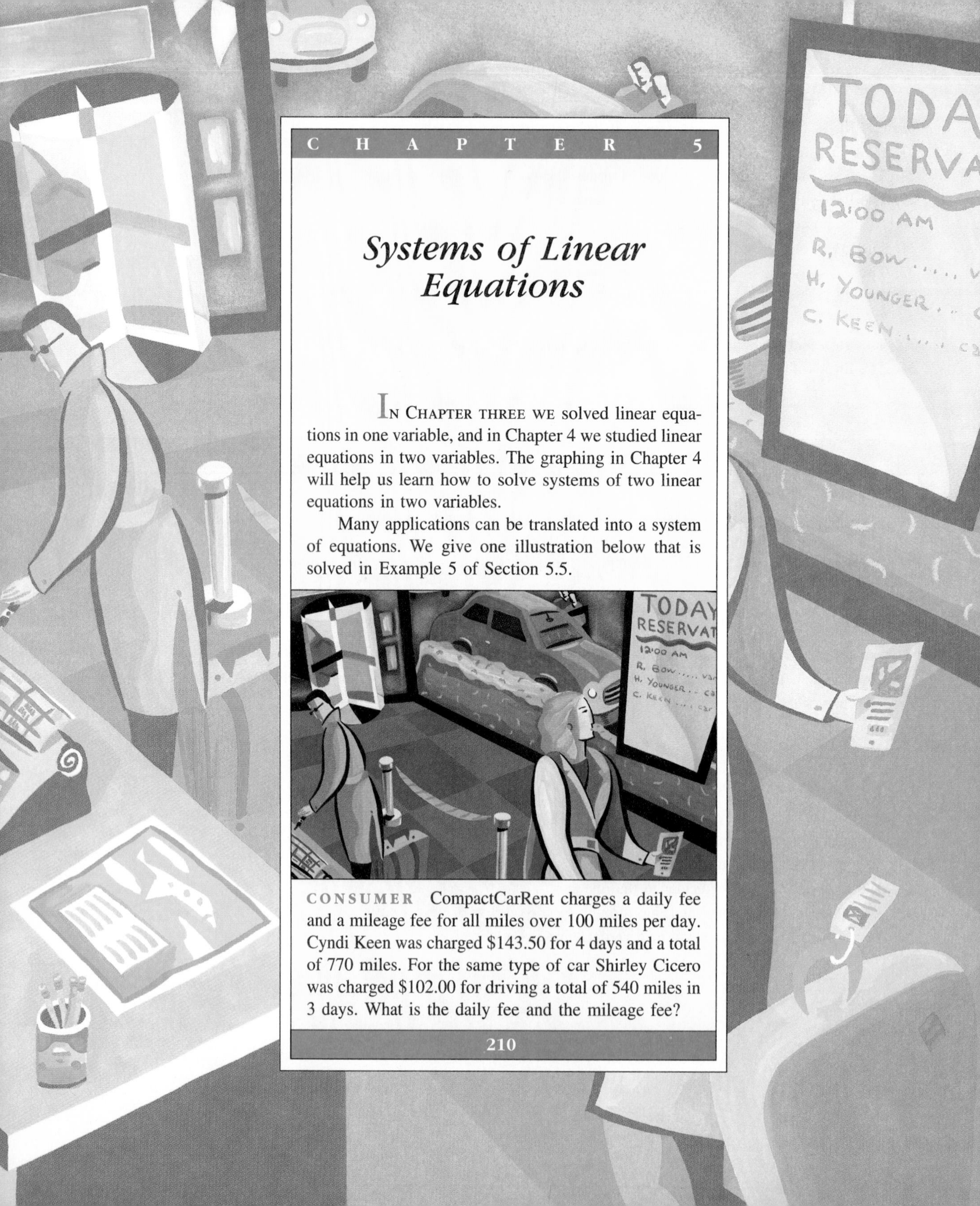

CHAPTER 5

Systems of Linear Equations

IN CHAPTER THREE WE solved linear equations in one variable, and in Chapter 4 we studied linear equations in two variables. The graphing in Chapter 4 will help us learn how to solve systems of two linear equations in two variables.

Many applications can be translated into a system of equations. We give one illustration below that is solved in Example 5 of Section 5.5.

CONSUMER CompactCarRent charges a daily fee and a mileage fee for all miles over 100 miles per day. Cyndi Keen was charged \$143.50 for 4 days and a total of 770 miles. For the same type of car Shirley Cicero was charged \$102.00 for driving a total of 540 miles in 3 days. What is the daily fee and the mileage fee?

We begin this chapter with a study of the nature of the graph of a system of equations. This includes parallel, coinciding, and intersecting lines as well as solving systems using graphing. We then consider the algebraic solution methods of substitution and elimination before concluding the chapter with a variety of applications.

SECTION 5.1 Parallel, Coinciding, and Intersecting Lines

Student guideposts

- ▶ *Systems of linear equations*
- ▶ *Graphing a system*
- ▶ *Relation of the graphs of a system*

▶ *Systems of linear equations*

In Chapter 4 we discovered that a solution to a linear equation in two variables such as

$$2x - y = -1$$

is an ordered pair of numbers that when substituted for x and y makes the equation true. Often in applied situations, two quantities are compared using two different equations. For example, a small businessman may discover that total sales and profit are related in two different ways. If the following pair of linear equations describes the relationships between sales x and profit y, it is called a **system of two linear equations in two variables,** or simply a **system of equations.**

$$3x - 2y = -1$$
$$3x + y = 5$$

A **solution** to a system of equations is an ordered pair of numbers (x, y) that is a solution to *both* equations. We can verify (check) that (1, 2) is a solution to the above system by direct substitution.

$$3(1) - 2(2) \stackrel{?}{=} -1 \quad x = 1 \text{ and } y = 2 \quad 3(1) + (2) \stackrel{?}{=} 5$$
$$3 - 4 \stackrel{?}{=} -1 \qquad\qquad 3 + 2 \stackrel{?}{=} 5$$
$$-1 = -1 \qquad\qquad 5 = 5$$

▶ *Graphing a system*

Finding a solution to a system of equations is easier to understand if we first examine the graphs of the system. Remember that a linear equation in x and y has a straight line for its graph. When the linear equations in a given system are graphed together in a rectangular coordinate system, one of three possibilities occurs:

1. The lines coincide (the two equations represent the same line).
2. The lines are parallel (do not intersect).
3. The lines intersect in exactly one point.

The following three pairs of linear equations, graphed in Figure 5.1, illustrate these three possible relationships.

(a) $3x - 2y = -1$ **(c)** $3x - 2y = -1$ **(e)** $3x - 2y = -1$
(b) $6x - 4y = -2$ **(d)** $3x - 2y = 4$ **(f)** $3x + y = 5$

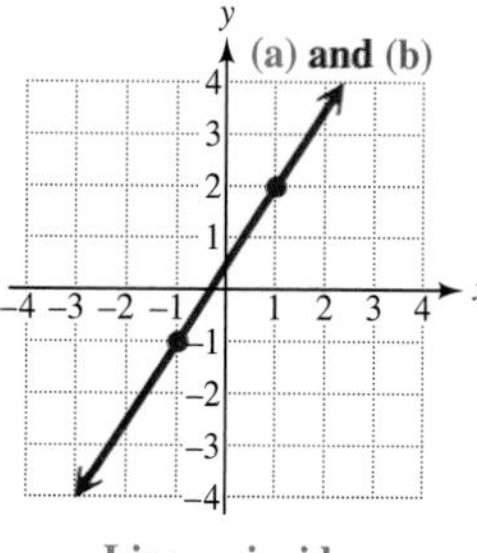

Lines coincide

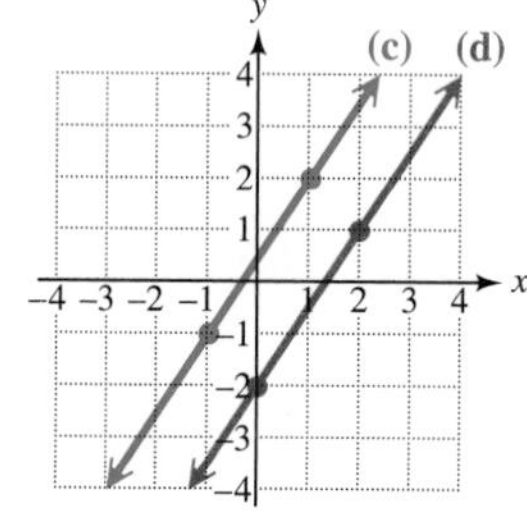

Lines are parallel

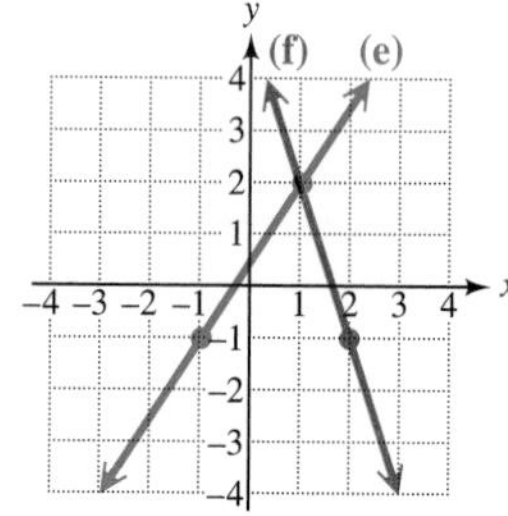

Lines intersect in exactly one point

FIGURE 5.1

In the first case, lines **(a)** and **(b)** coincide, in the second case, lines **(c)** and **(d)** are parallel, and in the third case, lines **(e)** and **(f)** intersect in one point.

▶ ***Relation of the graphs of a system***

We need a way to tell quickly which case we have in a given situation. Let us solve each linear equation above for y, writing it in slope-intercept form.

(a) $y = \frac{3}{2}x + \frac{1}{2}$

Slopes are the same. y-intercepts are the same. **Lines coincide.**

(b) $y = \frac{3}{2}x + \frac{1}{2}$

(c) $y = \frac{3}{2}x + \frac{1}{2}$

Slopes are the same. y-intercepts are different. **Lines are parallel.**

(d) $y = \frac{3}{2}x - 2$

(e) $y = \frac{3}{2}x + \frac{1}{2}$

Slopes are different. **Lines intersect in exactly one point.**

(f) $y = -3x + 5$

Notice that all lines with equation $y = b$ are parallel since the slopes are zero. Now we have covered all cases except when one (or both) of the equations in a system is of the form $ax = c$, since such equations cannot be solved for y. However, recalling that the graph of an equation of this form is always a line parallel to the y-axis, parallel or coinciding lines result only if both equations in the system are of this type.

EXAMPLE 1

Finding Intersecting Lines

Tell how the graphs of the system are related.

$$\begin{aligned} 2x + 3y &= -1 \\ x - 2y &= -5 \end{aligned}$$

Solve for y.

$$\begin{aligned} 2x + 3y &= -1 \\ 3y &= -2x - 1 \\ \frac{1}{3} \cdot 3y &= \frac{1}{3}(-2x - 1) \\ y &= -\frac{2}{3}x - \frac{1}{3} \end{aligned} \qquad \begin{aligned} x - 2y &= -5 \\ -2y &= -x - 5 \\ \left(-\frac{1}{2}\right)(-2y) &= \left(-\frac{1}{2}\right)(-x - 5) \\ y &= \frac{1}{2}x + \frac{5}{2} \end{aligned}$$

Since the slopes of the lines are $-\frac{2}{3}$ and $\frac{1}{2}$ (unequal), the lines are neither parallel nor coinciding, they intersect. ■

EXAMPLE 2

Finding Parallel Lines

Tell how the graphs of the system are related.

$$\begin{aligned} 2x - 3y &= -1 \\ 4x - 6y &= 3 \end{aligned}$$

Solve for y.

$$\begin{aligned} 2x - 3y &= -1 \\ -3y &= -2x - 1 \\ \left(-\frac{1}{3}\right)(-3y) &= \left(-\frac{1}{3}\right)(-2x - 1) \\ y &= \frac{2}{3}x + \frac{1}{3} \end{aligned} \qquad \begin{aligned} 4x - 6y &= 3 \\ -6y &= -4x + 3 \\ \left(-\frac{1}{6}\right)(-6y) &= \left(-\frac{1}{6}\right)(-4x + 3) \\ y &= \frac{4}{6}x - \frac{3}{6} \\ y &= \frac{2}{3}x - \frac{1}{2} \end{aligned}$$

Since the slopes of the lines are both $\frac{2}{3}$ (equal), the lines are either parallel or coinciding. Since the constants $\frac{1}{3}$ and $-\frac{1}{2}$ are unequal, the lines have two different y-intercepts, namely $\left(0, \frac{1}{3}\right)$ and $\left(0, -\frac{1}{2}\right)$, and the lines do not coincide. Thus, the lines are parallel. ■

EXAMPLE 3 **Finding Coinciding Lines**

Tell how the graphs of the system are related.

$$x - 2y = -2$$
$$-3x + 6y = 6$$

Solve for y.

$$x - 2y = -2 \qquad\qquad -3x + 6y = 6$$
$$-2y = -x - 2 \qquad\qquad 6y = 3x + 6$$
$$\left(-\frac{1}{2}\right)(-2y) = \left(-\frac{1}{2}\right)(-x - 2) \qquad\qquad \frac{1}{6}(6y) = \frac{1}{6}(3x + 6)$$
$$y = \frac{1}{2}x + 1 \qquad\qquad y = \frac{3}{6}x + \frac{6}{6}$$
$$y = \frac{1}{2}x + 1$$

Since both slopes are $\frac{1}{2}$ and both y-intercepts are (0, 1), the lines coincide. ■

EXAMPLE 4 **Working with One Line Vertical**

Tell how the graphs are related.

$$2x + 3y = 6$$
$$2x = 6$$

Since $2x = 6$ becomes $x = 3$, its graph is a line parallel to the y-axis, 3 units to the right of the y-axis. Since there is a y term in $2x + 3y = 6$, the graph of this equation cannot be a line parallel to the y-axis. Thus, the two lines must intersect in one point. ■

EXAMPLE 5 **Working with One Line Horizontal**

Tell how the graphs are related.

$$3y = -5$$
$$4x - 2y = -3$$

Solve for y.

$$3y = -5 \qquad\qquad 4x - 2y = -3$$
$$-2y = -4x - 3$$
$$\left(\frac{1}{3}\right)(3y) = \left(\frac{1}{3}\right)(-5) \qquad\qquad \left(-\frac{1}{2}\right)(-2y) = \left(-\frac{1}{2}\right)(-4x - 3)$$
$$y = -\frac{5}{3} \qquad\qquad y = \frac{4}{2}x + \frac{3}{2}$$
$$y = 0 \cdot x - \frac{5}{3} \qquad\qquad y = 2x + \frac{3}{2}$$

Since the slopes are 0 and 2 (not equal), the lines intersect in one point. ■

5.1 EXERCISES

Complete Exercises 1–4 with one of the following words **(a)** *parallel,* **(b)** *coinciding, or* **(c)** *intersecting.*

1. When the two linear equations are both solved for y and the coefficients of x are unequal, the graphs are ____ lines.

2. When two linear equations are both solved for y and the coefficients of x are equal as are the constants, the graphs are ____ lines.

3. If the y-term is missing in both of two linear equations, the graphs are **(a)** ____ lines or lines **(b)** ____ to the y-axis.

4. If the y-term is missing in only one of two linear equations, the graphs are ____ lines.

Tell how the graphs of each system are related in Exercises 5–13.

5. $-2x + 3y = -5$
$-2x - 3y = -5$

6. $x - 5y = -2$
$2x - 10y = -4$

7. $2x - 7y + 1 = 0$
$-6x + 21y + 3 = 0$

8. $2y + x = 5$
$2x = 10$

9. $x = 3y + 7$
$y = 3x + 7$

10. $2y = 8$
$2x = 8$

11. $2x + 1 = 3$
$4x - 3 = 1$

12. $x + y = 5$
$3y = 15$

13. $8y - 5 = -3x$
$-6x + 10 = 16y$

In Exercises 14–16, tell whether $(-3, 2)$ *is a solution to each system.*

14. $2x + 3y = 0$
$x + 8y = 19$

15. $3x + y + 7 = 0$
$x + 4y - 5 = 0$

16. $3y = 6$
$x - 5y = -13$

In Exercises 17–19, tell whether $(4, 0)$ *is a solution to each system.*

17. $2x - 3y = 8$
$x - 4 = 0$

18. $x + y - 2 = 0$
$2y + 2x = 4$

19. $2y + 1 = x$
$2x - 8 = y$

FOR REVIEW

To help you prepare for graphing systems in the next section, Exercises 20–22 review material from Chapter 4. Find the intercepts of each line.

20. $2x - y = 4$

21. $6x + 2y = 5$

22. $3x - 5y + 2 = 0$

5.1 PARALLEL EXERCISES

Complete Exercises 1–4 with one of the following words: **(a)** *parallel,* **(b)** *coinciding, or* **(c)** *intersecting.*

1. When the slopes of the lines in a system of equations are equal but the y-intercepts are unequal, the graphs are ____ lines.

2. When the slopes of the lines in a system of equations are unequal, the graphs are ____ lines.

3. If the x-term is missing in both equations in a system of equations, the graphs are **(a)** ____ lines or are lines **(b)** ____ to the x-axis.

4. If the x-term is missing in only one of the equations in a system of equations, the graphs are ____ lines.

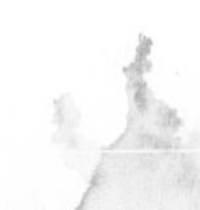

Tell how the graphs of each system are related in Exercises 5–13.

5. $-5x + y = 3$
$5x - y = 3$

6. $x + 2y = -3$
$-3x - 6y = 9$

7. $4x - y + 1 = 0$
$x - 4y - 1 = 0$

8. $2x + 3y = 1$
$y = 2$

9. $x = 3y - 1$
$y = -x - 1$

10. $3x = 1$
$3y = 1$

11. $3y + 1 = 4$
$-y + 2 = 1$

12. $y - 3x = 11$
$2x = 8$

13. $x + 2 = y$
$y + 1 = x$

In Exercises 14–16, tell whether $(1, 0)$ *is a solution to each system.*

14. $2x + 3y = 2$
$-x - 4y = -1$

15. $3x - y = 1$
$x + y = 1$

16. $3x = 3$
$-x + 9y = -1$

In Exercises 17–19, tell whether $(-2, 1)$ *is a solution to each system.*

17. $x - y = -3$
$y - 1 = 0$

18. $2x - 3y + 7 = 0$
$6y - 4x = 14$

19. $y + 2x = 3$
$2x + 5 = y$

FOR REVIEW

To help you prepare for graphing systems in the next section, Exercises 20–22 review material from Chapter 4. Find the intercepts of each line.

20. $x - 3y = 6$

21. $4x + 5y = 8$

22. $2x - 4y + 7 = 0$

5.1 ENRICHMENT EXERCISES

1. Find the value of a so that the line with equation $ax - 3y + 7 = 0$ will be parallel to the line with equation $5x + y - 2 = 0$. [*Hint:* Write each equation in slope-intercept form.]

2. Find the value of c so that the line with equation $2x - 3y + c = 0$ will have the same y-intercept as the line with equation $4x + 2y + 3 = 0$.

In Exercises 3–5, if a, b, and c are nonzero constants, tell how the graphs of the system are related.

3. $ax + by = c$
$ax + by = -c$

4. $ax + by = c$
$ax - by = c$

5. $ax + ay = c$
$bx + by = c$

6. Determine the standard form of the equation of a line that is perpendicular to the line with equation $ax + by = c$ where a, b, and c are nonzero constants.

7. Discuss how to determine the nature of the graphs of the lines in a system (parallel, intersecting, or coinciding) by considering slopes and y-intercepts.

SECTION 5.2 Solving Systems of Equations by Graphing

Student guideposts

▶ *The graphing method*

▶ *Finding the number of solutions*

▶ ***The graphing method***

Consider the system of equations

$$x + y = 1$$
$$2x - y = 5.$$

Solve each equation for y.

$$y = -x + 1$$
$$y = 2x - 5$$

The slopes are different, so the lines intersect in exactly one point. Since every point on each line corresponds to an ordered pair of numbers that is a solution to that equation, the point of intersection must correspond to the ordered pair that solves both equations. Hence it is the solution to the system. If we graph both equations in the same rectangular coordinate system, as in Figure 5.2, it appears that the point of intersection has coordinates $(2, -1)$. We can check to see if $(2, -1)$ is indeed a solution by substitution.

$$\begin{aligned} x + y &= 1 \\ 2 + (-1) &\stackrel{?}{=} 1 \\ 1 &= 1 \end{aligned} \qquad \begin{aligned} 2x - y &= 5 \\ 2(2) - (-1) &\stackrel{?}{=} 5 \\ 4 + 1 &\stackrel{?}{=} 5 \\ 5 &= 5 \end{aligned}$$

This method for solving a system is the **graphing method.**

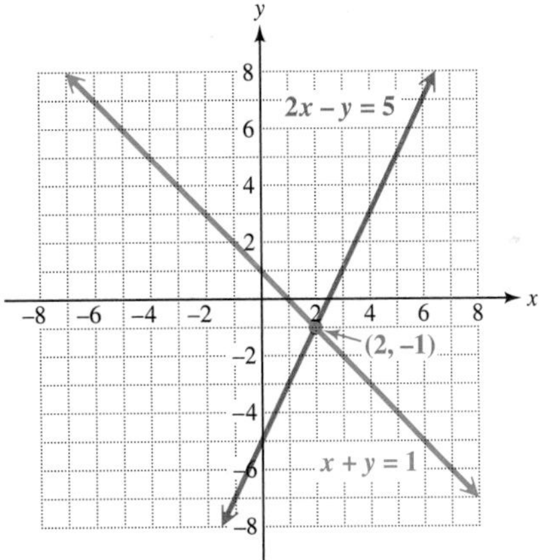

FIGURE 5.2

▶ *Finding the number of solutions*

If the graphs of the lines in a system are parallel, there can be no point of intersection, so the system has no solution. If the graphs of the lines coincide, then any solution to one equation is also a solution to the other equation, and the system has infinitely many solutions. These observations are summarized in the following statement.

Number of Solutions to a System

A system of equations has:

1. infinitely many solutions if the graphs of the equations coincide;
2. no solution if the graphs of the equations are parallel;
3. exactly one solution if the graphs of the equations intersect in one point.

EXAMPLE 1 **Finding Infinitely Many Solutions**

Find the number of solutions to the system.

$$3x - 4y + 1 = 0$$
$$8y - 2 = 6x$$

Solve each equation for y.

$$-4y = -3x - 1 \qquad\qquad 8y = 6x + 2$$
$$\left(-\frac{1}{4}\right)(-4y) = \left(-\frac{1}{4}\right)(-3x - 1) \qquad \left(\frac{1}{8}\right)(8y) = \left(\frac{1}{8}\right)(6x + 2)$$
$$y = \frac{3}{4}x + \frac{1}{4} \qquad\qquad y = \frac{6}{8}x + \frac{2}{8}$$
$$y = \frac{3}{4}x + \frac{1}{4}$$

Since the lines coincide (why?), there are infinitely many solutions to the system. ■

EXAMPLE 2 **Finding No Solution**

Find the number of solutions to the system.

$$x - 5y + 1 = 0$$
$$15y - 3x = 1$$

Solve for y.

$$-5y = -x - 1 \qquad 15y = 3x + 1$$
$$y = \frac{1}{5}x + \frac{1}{5} \qquad y = \frac{3}{15}x + \frac{1}{15}$$
$$y = \frac{1}{5}x + \frac{1}{15}$$

Since the lines are parallel (why?), there is no solution to the system. ■

EXAMPLE 3 **Finding Exactly One Solution**

Find the number of solutions to the system.

$$3x - 5 = 0$$
$$3x + y = -5$$

Since the y term is missing in the first equation, it cannot be solved for y. The graph of $3x - 5 = 0$, however, is a line parallel to the y-axis, so it intersects the line $3x + y = -5$ in only one point (why?). Thus, there is exactly one solution to the system. ■

EXAMPLE 4 **Using the Graphing Method**

Solve the system by graphing.

$$x - 2y = 1$$
$$2x + y = 7$$

We graph each equation by finding its intercepts.

$x - 2y = 1$

x	y
0	$-\frac{1}{2}$
1	0

$2x + y = 7$

x	y
0	7
$\frac{7}{2}$	0

The point of intersection of the two lines, graphed in Figure 5.3, appears to have coordinates (3, 1). We check by substitution in both equations.

$$\begin{aligned} x - 2y &= 1 & 2x + y &= 7 \\ 3 - 2(1) &\stackrel{?}{=} 1 & 2(3) + 1 &\stackrel{?}{=} 7 \\ 3 - 2 &\stackrel{?}{=} 1 & 6 + 1 &\stackrel{?}{=} 7 \\ 1 &= 1 & 7 &= 7 \end{aligned}$$

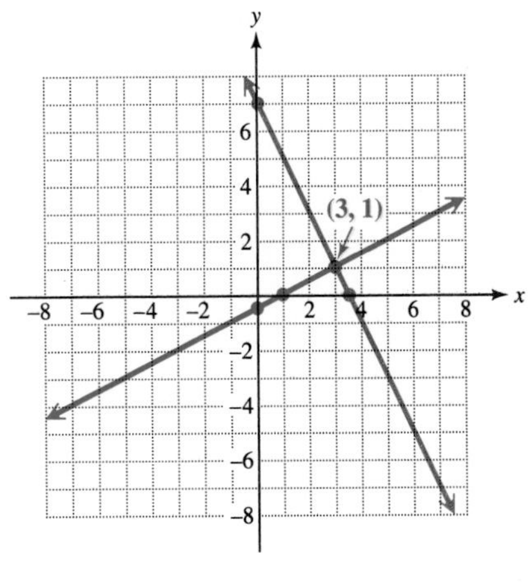

FIGURE 5.3

Thus, the solution to the system is (3, 1). ∎

5.2 EXERCISES

1. How many solutions will a system of equations have if the lines in the system are parallel?
2. How many solutions will a system of equations have if the lines in the system are intersecting?
3. How many solutions will a system of equations have if the lines in the system are coinciding?

In Exercises 4–11, find the number of solutions to each system. For those that have exactly one solution, find that solution by graphing. Check each solution.

4. $x + 3y = 4$
$-x + y = 0$

5. $x + 3y = 4$
$-2x - 6y = -8$

6. $x + 3y = 4$
$-2x - 6y = 0$

7. $2x + y = 5$
$2x - y = 3$

8. $3x - y = 1$
$2y = 4$

9. $2y = 3$
$3x = 2$

10. $x = y + 1$
$y = x - 1$

11. $x + 4y = 1$
$-x - 4y = 1$

FOR REVIEW

In Exercises 12–14, tell whether $(0, 4)$ *is a solution to each system.*

12. $2x + 3y - 12 = 0$
$x - 2y + 8 = 0$

13. $x - y = -4$
$2x + y = -4$

14. $y = 4$
$2x - 2y + 8 = 0$

Exercises 15–16 will help you prepare for the next section. Find the value of each expression when x is -2.

15. $3x - 1$

16. $4 - 5x$

5.2 PARALLEL EXERCISES

1. If a system of equations has exactly one solution, how are the graphs of the system related?
2. If a system of equations has no solution, how are the graphs of the system related?
3. If a system of equations has infinitely many solutions, how are the graphs of the system related?

In Exercises 4–11, find the number of solutions to each system. For those that have exactly one solution, find that solution by graphing. Check each solution.

4. $x + 2y = 1$
$x - y = -2$

5. $x + 2y = 1$
$-x - 2y = -1$

6. $x + 2y = 1$
$-x - 2y = 1$

7. $x + 2y = 5$
$x - 2y = -3$

8. $2x + 3y = 6$
$3x = 3$

9. $3x = 4$
$4y = 3$

10. $x - 5y = 2$
$-x + 5y = 2$

11. $y = x + 2$
$x = y - 2$

FOR REVIEW

In Exercises 12–14, tell whether $(1, -5)$ *is a solution to each system.*

12. $2x - y - 7 = 0$
$x + y = -4$

13. $x - 2y = 11$
$2x - 7 = y$

14. $x + 5 = 0$
$y - 1 = 0$

Exercises 15–16 will help you prepare for the next section. Find the value of each expression when x is -5.

15. $6x - 3$

16. $-7 - 4x$

5.2 ENRICHMENT EXERCISES

1. Find the value of c so that the system will have infinitely many solutions.

$$x - 5y + c = 0$$
$$-3x + 15y - 7 = 0$$

2. Find the value of a so that the system will have no solution.

$$ax - 5y + 8 = 0$$
$$4x + y - 1 = 0$$

3. Write a paragraph describing the relationship between the graphs of a system and the number of solutions.

SECTION 5.3 Solving Systems of Equations by Substitution

Student guideposts

- *The substitution method*
- *Contradictions and identities*

The substitution method

Solving a system by graphing is time-consuming, and estimating the point of intersection depends on the accuracy of the graph. A better method for solving some systems is the **method of substitution.** Consider the system

$$x - 2y = 1$$
$$2x + y = 7.$$

We will change the system into one equation in one unknown. Solve the first equation for x,

$$x - 2y = 1$$
$$x = 2y + 1,$$

and substitute this value of x into the second equation.

$$2x + y = 7$$
$$2(2y + 1) + y = 7 \qquad x = 2y + 1$$

The result is an equation in the single variable y, which we can solve.

$$4y + 2 + y = 7$$
$$5y + 2 = 7$$
$$5y = 5$$
$$y = 1 \qquad \text{This is the } y\text{-coordinate of the solution}$$

Substitute this value of y into either of the original equations. Using the first, solve for x.

$$x - 2y = 1$$
$$x - 2(1) = 1 \qquad y = 1$$
$$x - 2 = 1$$
$$x = 3 \qquad \text{This is the } x\text{-coordinate of the solution}$$

We check the possible solution pair (3, 1) by substituting it into both original equations.

$$\begin{aligned} x - 2y &= 1 \\ 3 - 2(1) &\stackrel{?}{=} 1 \\ 3 - 2 &\stackrel{?}{=} 1 \\ 1 &= 1 \end{aligned} \qquad \begin{aligned} 2x + y &= 7 \\ 2(3) + 1 &\stackrel{?}{=} 7 \\ 6 + 1 &\stackrel{?}{=} 7 \\ 7 &= 7 \end{aligned}$$

Thus, the solution to the system is (3, 1), the same result obtained in Example 4 in Section 5.2 using the graphing method.

To Solve a System of Equations Using the Substitution Method

1. Solve one of the equations for one of the variables.
2. Substitute that expression for the variable in the *remaining* equation.
3. Solve this new equation (which has just one variable), and substitute the numerical solution into either of the two *original* equations to find the numerical value of the second variable.
4. Check your solution in both original equations.

EXAMPLE 1 **Using Substitution**

Solve by the substitution method.

$$\begin{aligned} 5x + 3y &= 17 \\ x + 3y &= 1 \end{aligned}$$

We could solve either equation for either variable. However, since the coefficient of x in the second equation is 1, we can avoid fractions if we solve for x using that equation.

$$x = 1 - 3y$$

Substitute $1 - 3y$ for x in the first equation.

$$\begin{aligned} 5x + 3y &= 17 \\ 5(1 - 3y) + 3y &= 17 \\ 5 - 15y + 3y &= 17 \\ 5 - 12y &= 17 \\ -12y &= 12 \\ y &= -1 \qquad \text{y-coordinate of the solution} \end{aligned}$$

Substitute -1 for y in the second equation.

$$\begin{aligned} x + 3y &= 1 \\ x + 3(-1) &= 1 \\ x - 3 &= 1 \\ x &= 4 \qquad \text{x-coordinate of the solution} \end{aligned}$$

The solution is $(4, -1)$.

Check:

$$\begin{aligned} 5x + 3y &= 17 \\ 5(4) + 3(-1) &\stackrel{?}{=} 17 \\ 20 - 3 &\stackrel{?}{=} 17 \\ 17 &= 17 \end{aligned} \qquad \begin{aligned} x + 3y &= 1 \\ (4) + 3(-1) &\stackrel{?}{=} 1 \\ 4 - 3 &\stackrel{?}{=} 1 \\ 1 &= 1 \end{aligned}$$

EXAMPLE 2

Working with a System with No Solution

Solve by substitution.

$$\begin{aligned} 4x + 2y &= 1 \\ 2x + y &= 8 \end{aligned}$$

If we solve the second equation for y, we obtain

$$y = 8 - 2x.$$

Substitute this value into the first equation.

$$\begin{aligned} 4x + 2y &= 1 \\ 4x + 2(8 - 2x) &= 1 \\ 4x + 16 - 4x &= 1 \\ 16 &= 1 \end{aligned}$$

But $16 \neq 1$. What went wrong? Return to the original system and solve both equations for y.

$$\begin{aligned} 2y &= 1 - 4x \\ y &= \frac{1}{2} - \frac{4}{2}x \\ y &= -2x + \frac{1}{2} \end{aligned} \qquad \text{and} \qquad \begin{aligned} y &= 8 - 2x \\ y &= -2x + 8 \end{aligned}$$

Both slopes are -2 but the constant terms are different. Thus the two lines are parallel, and there is no solution. If there is no solution (the lines are parallel), substitution results in an equation that is a contradiction (such as $16 = 1$).

EXAMPLE 3

Solving a System with Infinitely Many Solutions

Solve by substitution.

$$\begin{aligned} x + 2y &= 1 \\ 2y &= 1 - x \end{aligned}$$

We solve the first equation for x.

$$x = 1 - 2y$$

Substitute this value into the second equation.

$$2y = 1 - (1 - 2y)$$
$$2y = 1 - 1 + 2y \qquad \text{Watch the signs}$$
$$2y = 2y$$

Clearly, $2y = 2y$ no matter what number replaces y so that we end up with an equation that is an identity. Return to the original equations and solve them for y.

$$\begin{aligned} x + 2y &= 1 \\ 2y &= -x + 1 \\ y &= -\frac{1}{2}x + \frac{1}{2} \end{aligned} \qquad \begin{aligned} 2y &= 1 - x \\ 2y &= -x + 1 \\ y &= -\frac{1}{2}x + \frac{1}{2} \end{aligned}$$

The slopes are equal, as are the constants. The two lines coincide so there are infinitely many solutions to this system (any pair of numbers that is a solution to one equation is a solution to both, hence a solution to the system). ■

▶ *Contradictions and identities*

Examples 2 and 3 lead to the following.

When Solving a System of Equations

1. If you get a **contradiction** (an equation that is never true), the lines are parallel and there is no solution to the system.
2. If you get an **identity** (an equation that is always true for every value of the variable), the lines coincide and there are infinitely many solutions to the system.

5.3 EXERCISES

1. Suppose while solving a system of equations using substitution we obtain the equation $3x = 3x$. What would this tell us about the system?

2. Suppose while solving a system using substitution we obtain the equation $5 = 0$. What would this tell us about the system?

In Exercises 3–11, solve each system using the substitution method.

3. $y = 3x + 2$, $5x - 2y = -7$

4. $2x - 3y = 14$, $x = y + 10$

5. $13x - 4y = -66$, $5x + 2y = 10$

6. $x - 3y = 14$, $x - 2 = 0$

7. $3x - 3y = 1$, $x - y = -1$

8. $2x + 2y = -6$, $-x - y = 3$

9. $y = 5$, $4x - y = 19$

10. $2x + 3y = 5$, $4x + 7y = 11$

11. $3x + 5y = 30$, $5x + 3y = 34$

12. Which variable in which equation is easiest to solve for in Exercise 11? (The next section explains a method for solving equations that may be better for systems such as this.)

In Exercises 13–14, for which variable in which equation should you solve to avoid fractions in the substitution method? a, b, and c are nonzero constants.

13. $abx + by = bc$
$12x + 4y = 22$

14. $3ax + 4ay = 12$
$3bx + 6by = 9b$

FOR REVIEW

15. If the lines in a system of equations are parallel, how many solutions does the system have?

Solve by the graphing method in Exercises 16–17.

16. $x + y = 5$
$3x - y = -1$

17. $2x + y = 4$
$x - 2 = 0$

5.3 PARALLEL EXERCISES

1. Suppose while solving a system of equations using substitution we obtain the equation $-3 = 0$. What would this tell us about the system?

2. Suppose while solving a system using substitution we obtain the equation $x + 1 = x + 1$. What would this tell us about the system?

In Exercises 3–11, solve each system using the substitution method.

3. $y = -2x + 3$
$3x - 4y = -1$

4. $x + y = 0$
$5x + 2y = -3$

5. $2x - y = 3$
$-4x + 2y = -6$

6. $3x - y = 2$
$-6x + 2y = 2$

7. $2x - y = -2$
$y - 4 = 0$

8. $4x + y = -2$
$-2x - 3y = 1$

9. $3x - y = 14$
$x - 4 = 0$

10. $2x + 3y = -4$
$3x - 2y = 7$

11. $3x + 7y = 32$
$7x + 3y = 8$

12. What is the difficulty in using the substitution method on a system like the one in Exercise 11?

In Exercises 13–14, for which variable in which equation should you solve to avoid fractions in the substitution method? a, b, and c are nonzero constants.

13. $ax + aby = ac$
$6x + 14y = 26$

14. $9ax + 3ay = 6a$
$4bx + 8by = 6b$

FOR REVIEW

15. If the lines in a system of equations are coinciding, how many solutions does the system have?

Solve by the graphing method in Exercises 16–17.

16. $3x - y = -4$
$-x + y = 0$

17. $x - 3y = 3$
$y + 1 = 0$

5.3 ENRICHMENT EXERCISES

Solve using the substitution method in Exercises 1–2.

1. $0.03x - 0.01y = 0.02$
   $0.04x - 0.05y = 0.045$

2. $\dfrac{x}{10} + \dfrac{2y}{5} = 1$
   $\dfrac{2x}{5} + \dfrac{3y}{2} = 2$

3. Burford's solution to the given system using the substitution method is shown below. What is wrong with his work? What is the correct answer?

$$x + y = 3$$
$$2x - y = 9$$

Solve for y in first equation. $y = 3 - x$

Substitute into first equation. $x + 3 - x = 3$

This gives $3 = 3$ so there are infinitely many solutions.

4. In your own words, explain how to solve a system of equations using the substitution method.

SECTION 5.4 Solving Systems of Equations by Elimination

Student guideposts

- *The elimination method*
- *Multiplication rule*
- *Method to use*

The elimination method

Consider the following system.

$$3x + 5y = 30$$
$$5x + 3y = 34$$

Solving for either variable in either equation will result in fractional coefficients. Another method, better than substitution for systems like this one, is known as the **elimination method.** The goal of the elimination method is to "eliminate" one variable and obtain an equation in a single variable. It is based on the addition-subtraction rule from Chapter 3: if the same quantity is added to or subtracted from both sides of an equation, another equation with the same solutions is obtained. Suppose we illustrate the method using the following system.

$$x + y = 6$$
$$3x - y = 2.$$

In the second equation, $3x - y$ and 2 are both names for the same number, 2. Therefore we can add $3x - y$ to the left side of the first equation, and 2 to the right of it, to obtain another equation with the same solution.

$$(x + y) + (3x - y) = 6 + 2$$
$$4x = 8 \quad y \text{ has been eliminated}$$

Generally, we add the equations vertically.

$$\begin{aligned} x + y &= 6 \\ 3x - y &= 2 \\ \hline 4x \quad &= 8 \quad && y \text{ has been eliminated} \\ x &= 2 && \text{Divide by 4 to obtain the } x\text{-coordinate of the solution} \end{aligned}$$

By adding the two equations, we obtain one equation in one variable, x. Once we know x is 2, we substitute this value into either one of the original equations (just as in the substitution method) to find the value of y.

$$\begin{aligned} x + y &= 6 \\ 2 + y &= 6 && \text{Substitute in the first equation since it is simpler} \\ y &= 4 && \text{The } y\text{-coordinate of the solution} \end{aligned}$$

Thus, the solution is (2, 4). Check this by substituting into both equations.

EXAMPLE 1 **Using the Elimination Method**

Solve by the elimination method.

$$\begin{aligned} x + y &= 5 \\ -2x + y &= -4 \end{aligned}$$

If we add both equations, the resulting equation still has both variables. (Try it.) So in this case, we subtract instead of adding, to obtain an equation in one variable.

$$\begin{aligned} x + y &= 5 \\ +2x - y &= 4 && \text{Change all signs when subtracting and add} \\ \hline 3x \quad &= 9 \\ x &= 3 \end{aligned}$$

Substitute 3 for x in the first equation.

$$\begin{aligned} x + y &= 5 \\ 3 + y &= 5 \\ y &= 2 \end{aligned}$$

The solution is the ordered pair (3, 2). Check by substitution. ■

▶ *Multiplication rule*

Sometimes addition or subtraction does not yield one equation in only one variable. When this occurs, we may have to multiply one (or both) of the equations by a number so that the coefficients of one variable are opposites of each other. We then add to eliminate that variable.

EXAMPLE 2 **Using Multiplication and Elimination**

Solve by the elimination method.

$$2x - 5y = 13$$
$$x + 2y = 11$$

We would not obtain one equation with one variable by simply adding or subtracting in this case. However, if we multiply both sides of the second equation by -2 the resulting equation is

$$-2x - 4y = -22. \qquad -2 \text{ times second equation}$$

Now add this equation to the first equation.

$$\begin{aligned} 2x - 5y &= 13 \\ -2x - 4y &= -22 \\ \hline -9y &= -9 \\ y &= 1 \end{aligned}$$

Substitute 1 for y in the second equation.

$$\begin{aligned} x + 2y &= 11 \\ x + 2(1) &= 11 \\ x + 2 &= 11 \\ x &= 9 \end{aligned}$$

The solution is (9, 1). Check by substitution. ■

Sometimes the multiplication rule has to be applied to both equations before adding or subtracting. In Example 3 this technique is used to solve the system at the beginning of this section.

EXAMPLE 3 **Using Multiplication and Elimination**

Solve by the elimination method.

$$3x + 5y = 30$$
$$5x + 3y = 34$$

Multiply the first equation by -5 and the second equation by 3 (making the coefficients of x negatives of each other).

$$\begin{aligned} -15x - 25y &= -150 \qquad -5 \text{ times first equation} \\ 15x + 9y &= 102 \qquad 3 \text{ times second equation} \end{aligned}$$

Add to get one equation in one variable.

$$\begin{aligned} -16y &= -48 \\ y &= 3 \end{aligned}$$

Substitute 3 for y in the first equation.

$$\begin{aligned} 3x + 5y &= 30 \\ 3x + 5(3) &= 30 \\ 3x + 15 &= 30 \\ 3x &= 15 \\ x &= 5 \end{aligned}$$

The solution is (5, 3). Check by substitution. ∎

Compare this example with your work on Exercise 14 in the last section. In this case the elimination method is faster and easier to use than the substitution method.

To Solve a System by the Elimination Method

1. Write both equations in the form $ax + by = c$.
2. If necessary, apply the multiplication rule to each equation so that addition or subtraction will eliminate one of the variables.
3. Solve the resulting single-variable equation. Substitute this value into one of the original equations. The resulting pair of numbers is the ordered-pair solution to the system.
4. Check your answer by substitution in both original equations.

EXAMPLE 4

Working with Contradictions and Identities

Solve by the elimination method.

(a) $2x = 3y + 5$
$-2x + 3y = -1$

Rewrite the first equation as $2x - 3y = 5$. Notice that by adding the equations, we can eliminate x.

$$\begin{aligned} 2x - 3y &= 5 \\ -2x + 3y &= -1 \\ \hline 0 &= 4 \end{aligned}$$

We actually eliminated both variables and obtained a contradiction. Just as with the substitution method, this means there is no solution to the system. Verify that the lines are parallel by solving each equation for y.

(b) $2x + y = 3$
$-4x - 2y = -6$

Multiply the first equation by 2 and add.

$$\begin{aligned} 4x + 2y &= 6 \\ -4x - 2y &= -6 \\ \hline 0 &= 0 \end{aligned}$$

Again, both variables are eliminated by this process, but this time we obtain an identity. This means there are infinitely many solutions to the system. Verify that the lines coincide by solving each equation for y. ■

When a system of equations contains fractions or decimals, it is best to eliminate them before trying to solve the system. The next example illustrates this technique.

EXAMPLE 5 **Solving a System with Fractions**

Solve the system.

$$\frac{x+y}{2} + \frac{x-y}{3} = \frac{4}{3}$$
$$\frac{2x+y}{3} + \frac{x-2y}{4} = \frac{5}{12}$$

We can clear the fractions in the first equation if we multiply both sides by 6, the least common denominator of 2 and 3.

$$6\left[\frac{x+y}{2} + \frac{x-y}{3}\right] = 6 \cdot \frac{4}{3}$$
$$3(x+y) + 2(x-y) = 2 \cdot 4 \qquad \text{Use parentheses}$$
$$3x + 3y + 2x - 2y = 8$$
$$5x + y = 8$$

Multiply both sides of the second equation by 12 to clear the fractions.

$$12\left[\frac{2x+y}{3} + \frac{x-2y}{4}\right] = 12 \cdot \frac{5}{12}$$
$$4(2x+y) + 3(x-2y) = 5 \qquad \text{Use parentheses}$$
$$8x + 4y + 3x - 6y = 5$$
$$11x - 2y = 5$$

Thus, the original system has been transformed into the following simpler equivalent system.

$$5x + y = 8$$
$$11x - 2y = 5$$

Multiply the first equation by 2 and add the result to the second.

$$\begin{aligned} 10x + 2y &= 16 \\ 11x - 2y &= 5 \\ \hline 21x &= 21 \\ x &= 1 \end{aligned}$$

Substitute 1 for x in $5x + y = 8$.

$$5(1) + y = 8$$
$$y = 3$$

The solution is (1, 3). Check this in the original system. ■

▶ *Method to use* The question is often asked: "Which method should I use?" If a coefficient of one of the variables is 1 (or -1), it may be better to solve first for that variable using the substitution method. If none of the coefficients is 1 (or -1), it is probably better to use the elimination method. Keep in mind that with either method, the system has no solution if at any step a contradiction is obtained, and the system has infinitely many solutions if at any step an identity is obtained.

5.4 EXERCISES

1. If we obtain an equation such as $0 = -3$ when using the elimination method, how many solutions does the system have?
2. If we obtain an equation such as $0 = 0$ when using the elimination method, how many solutions does the system have?

In Exercises 3–10, solve each system using the elimination method. Check by substitution.

3. $x + y = 6$, $x - y = 4$
4. $3x - 2y = 12$, $2x + 2y = 13$
5. $6x + 5y = 11$, $3x - 7y = -4$
6. $4x + y = -3$, $-8x - 2y = 6$
7. $-2y = 2 - x$, $3x - 6y = -4$
8. $2x + 3y = -4$, $1 + 2y = -3x$
9. $3x + 7y = -21$, $7x + 3y = -9$
10. $5x - 2y = 1$, $3x + 7y = -24$

In Exercises 11–18, decide whether the substitution or the elimination method is more appropriate, then use it to solve the system.

11. $x + 5y = 0$, $x - 5y = 20$
12. $3x + 3y = 3$, $4x + 4y = -3$
13. $2x + 3y = -4$, $5x + 7y = -10$
14. $3x = 9$, $x - y = 7$
15. $y - 5 = 0$, $x + 2 = 0$
16. $\frac{1}{3}y = x + \frac{1}{3}$, $\frac{1}{6}x + \frac{5}{24}y = 1$
17. $\frac{2}{5}x + \frac{3}{5}y = 1$, $\frac{4}{11}x + \frac{7}{11}y = 1$
18. $0.1x + 1.3y = 13.5$, $0.3x - 1.2y = -10.5$

FOR REVIEW

Exercises 19–23 review material from Section 3.5 to help you prepare for the next section. Use x for the variable and translate each sentence into symbols. Do not solve.

19. The sum of a number and 5 is 12.
20. Four times my age in 2 years is 60.
21. The measure of an angle is 10° less than twice its measure.
22. 40% of the cost of an item is \$20.
23. \$60 is the sale price of an item discounted by 20%.

5.4 PARALLEL EXERCISES

1. When solving a system of equations using the elimination method, if a contradiction results, how many solutions does the system have?

2. When solving a system of equations using the elimination method, if an identity results, how many solutions does the system have?

In Exercises 3–10, solve each system using the elimination method. Check by substitution.

3. $x + y = 3$
$x - y = -1$

4. $2x - 3y = -7$
$3x + 3y = 27$

5. $x - y = 0$
$x - 5y = -12$

6. $2x + 3y = -4$
$3x - 2y = 7$

7. $5x - 2y = 1$
$7 + 10x = 4y$

8. $2x - 2y = 5$
$4y = 3x - 7$

9. $4x - 2y = 2$
$-2x + y = -1$

10. $3x + 2y = -10$
$5x - 3y = 15$

In Exercises 11–18, decide whether the substitution or the elimination method is more appropriate, then use it to solve the system.

11. $x + 3y = 4$
$x + 8y = -6$

12. $3x - 7y = -4$
$7x + 3y = 10$

13. $2x = 8$
$x - y = 1$

14. $2x + 5y = -10$
$3x + 11y = -22$

15. $y + 7 = 0$
$x - 3 = 0$

16. $\frac{1}{8}x = \frac{1}{2}y - \frac{3}{8}$
$\frac{1}{5}x + \frac{3}{10}y = \frac{1}{2}$

17. $\frac{1}{4}x + \frac{3}{8}y = -\frac{1}{2}$
$\frac{3}{7}x - \frac{2}{7}y = 1$

18. $4.2x - 0.3y = -6.0$
$0.7x + 1.5y = 8.3$

FOR REVIEW

Exercises 19–23 review material from Section 3.5 to help you prepare for the next section. Use x for the variable and translate each sentence into symbols. Do not solve.

19. A number less 2 is 14.

20. Twice a number added to 6 is 28.

21. The measure of an angle is 25° less than three times its measure.

22. 15% of the population is 3000.

23. Her salary plus a 12% increase is $22,400.

5.4 ENRICHMENT EXERCISES

In Exercises 1–8, solve using the elimination method.

1. $0.015x - 0.007y = 0.032$
$-0.009x + 0.014y = -0.001$

2. $-\frac{3x}{4} + \frac{7y}{10} = \frac{1}{5}$
$\frac{5x}{2} - \frac{4y}{3} = -\frac{1}{12}$

3. $1.35x + 2.05y = 14.35$
$0.45x - 3.25y = -22.75$

4. $2.25x + 1.15y = -5.65$
$1.45x - 3.65y = 0.75$

5. $2(3x + y) = 3(x - y) - 2$
$4(2x - y) = 5(x + y) + 12$

6. $3(2x + y) = 5(x - y) + 16$
$4(x - 2y) = 2(x + y) - 20$

7. $\frac{x + y}{2} + \frac{2x - y}{3} = \frac{13}{6}$
$\frac{3x + y}{3} + \frac{x - y}{4} = \frac{29}{12}$

8. $\frac{x - y}{4} + \frac{3x - y}{2} = 1$
$\frac{3x + y}{3} + \frac{x + y}{2} = \frac{7}{3}$

9. Explain why the method used in this section is called the *elimination* method.
10. Write a paragraph or two telling which of the substitution method or elimination method that you prefer to use. Give your reasons why.

SECTION 5.5 Problem Solving Using Systems

Student guideposts

- ▶ *Problem-solving techniques*
- ▶ *Mixture problems*
- ▶ *Motion problems*

▶ ***Problem-solving techniques***

Many applied problems are more easily solved if they are translated into a system of two equations in two variables. In order to do this we need to review the ATTACK method that was introduced in Section 3.5. We will use this method in detail in the first example and will keep the steps in mind as we do other examples.

EXAMPLE 1 **Solving a Number Problem**

The sum of two numbers is 21 and their difference is 9. Find the numbers.

Analysis: We must find two numbers which have both properties. Their sum must be 21 and their difference 9.

Tabulation: Let $x =$ the larger of the two numbers,
$y =$ the smaller number.

Translation: Since their sum is 21, we can write the equation

$$x + y = 21.$$

Since their difference is 9 and x is larger than y, the second equation is

$$x - y = 9.$$

Then we have the following system:

$$x + y = 21 \quad \text{Represents "their sum is 21"}$$
$$x - y = 9 \quad \text{Represents "their difference is 9"}$$

We should solve the system by the simplest method. In this case, one method is as easy as the other so we add the two equations.

$$2x = 30$$
$$x = 15$$

Now substitute 15 for x in $x + y = 21$.

$$15 + y = 21$$
$$y = 6$$

Approximation: These numbers seem to be reasonable as solutions. We might suspect a mistake if they were too large or they were negative.

Check: Since $15 + 6 = 21$ and $15 - 6 = 9$, the numbers fit the words of the problem and are the solution.

Key: Remember that the key to success with problem solving is to try something. ■

The examples that follow are in a format that you should strive to attain without specifically pointing out the steps in the **ATTACK** method. Remember, however, that you must always give complete and accurate descriptions of the variables that you use.

EXAMPLE 2

Solving a Problem Involving Ages

The sum of Bob's and Joe's ages is 14. In 2 years Bob will be twice as old as Joe. What are their present ages?

Let x = Bob's present age,
y = Joe's present age.

Then both Bob and Joe will age 2 years and

$$x + 2 = \text{Bob's age in 2 years},$$
$$y + 2 = \text{Joe's age in 2 years}.$$

In two years Bob will be twice as old as Joe

$$(x + 2) \quad = \quad 2 \quad (y + 2)$$

$$x + 2 = 2(y + 2)$$
$$x + 2 = 2y + 4$$
$$-2 = 2y - x \quad \text{or} \quad -x + 2y = -2$$

Since the sum of their ages is 14, $x + y = 14$. This gives us the following system.

$$-x + 2y = -2$$
$$x + y = 14$$

Add these equations.

$$3y = 12$$
$$y = 4$$

Now substitute 4 for y in $x + y = 14$.

$$x + 4 = 14$$
$$x = 10$$

Bob is 10 and Joe is 4. Check. ∎

EXAMPLE 3

Solving a Geometry Problem

Two angles are **supplementary** (their sum is 180°). If one is 60° more than twice the other, find the angles.

Let x = one angle,
y = the other angle.

Then $x + y = 180$. The angles are supplementary

If x is 60° more than $2y$, then we would add 60° to $2y$ to get x. This gives the following system.

$$x + y = 180$$
$$2y + 60 = x$$

Substitute $2y + 60$ for x in $x + y = 180$.

$$(2y + 60) + y = 180$$
$$3y + 60 = 180$$
$$3y = 120$$
$$y = 40$$

Now substitute 40 for y in $x + y = 180$.

$$x + 40 = 180$$
$$x = 140$$

The angles are 40° and 140°. Check. ■

▶ *Mixture problems*

A useful application of systems is the **mixture problem.** The two equations in the system of the mixture problem are the *quantity equation* and the *value equation.*

To set up a value equation, we need to look at the idea of *total value.* For a given number of units, each of equal value, the total value can be computed by

total value = (value per unit)(number of units).

The following are examples of total value calculations.

Price Given Per Pound

Find the value of 5 lb of candy worth \$1.10 per lb.

total value = (value per lb)(number of lb)
= (\$1.10)(5)
= \$5.50

Value of Coins

Find the value of 30 nickels.

total value = (value per nickel)(number of nickels)
= (5¢)(30)
= 150¢ or \$1.50

The next examples are applications of the total value idea.

Percent Solutions
Find the amount of acid in 16 liters of 20% acid solution.

$$\begin{aligned} \text{total value} &= \text{amount of acid in solution} \\ &= (\text{percent acid})(\text{liters of solution}) \\ &= (0.20)(16) \\ &= 3.2 \text{ liters of acid} \end{aligned}$$

Interest
Find the annual interest on \$8000 invested at 6.5% simple interest.

$$\begin{aligned} \text{total value} &= \text{amount of interest} \\ &= (\text{percent interest})(\text{amount invested}) \\ &= (0.065)(\$8000) \\ &= \$520 \end{aligned}$$

These examples will be helpful in solving the following mixture problems.

EXAMPLE 4

Solving a Mixture Problem

A man wishes to mix candy selling for 75¢ a pound with nuts selling for 50¢ per pound to obtain a party mix to be sold for 60¢ per pound. How many pounds of each must be used to obtain 50 pounds of the mixture?

Let x = number of pounds of candy,
y = number of pounds of nuts.

It sometimes helps to place all given information into a summary table.

	Number of pounds	*Value per pound*	*Value*
Candy	x	75	$75x$
Nuts	y	50	$50y$
Total	50	60	60(50)

The first equation we set up is the quantity equation (first column in the table)

$$(\text{no. lb of candy}) + (\text{no. lb of nuts}) = (\text{no. lb of mixture}),$$

which translates to

$$x + y = 50.$$

Next we find the value equation which comes from the last column in the table. Since the value of a quantity equals the sum of the values of its parts,

$$(\text{total value of candy}) + (\text{total value of nuts}) = \text{total value of mixture}.$$

$$\begin{aligned} 75x &= \text{value of candy} \\ 50y &= \text{value of nuts} \\ 60(50) &= \text{value of mixture} \end{aligned}$$

This gives the value equation

$$75x + 50y = 60(50).$$

We need to solve the following system of equations.

$$\begin{aligned} x + \quad y &= 50 \\ 75x + 50y &= 3000 \end{aligned}$$

Solve the first equation for x,

$$x = 50 - y,$$

and substitute in the second equation

$$\begin{aligned} 75(50 - y) + 50y &= 3000 \\ 3750 - 75y + 50y &= 3000 \\ -25y &= -750 \\ y &= 30 \end{aligned}$$

Now substitute 30 for y in $x = 50 - y$.

$$x = 50 - 30 = 20$$

The man must use 20 lb of candy and 30 lb of nuts. ■

We now solve the applied problem given in the chapter introduction.

EXAMPLE 5

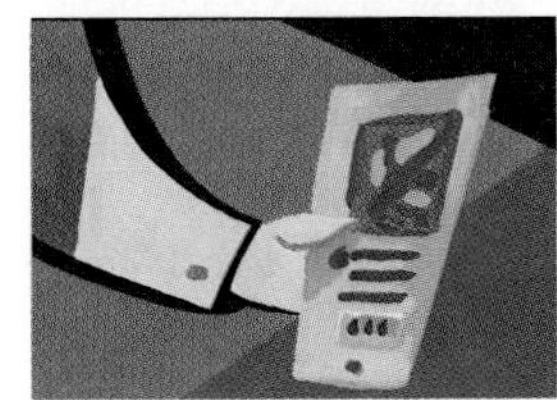

Working with a Consumer Application

CompactCarRent charges a daily fee and a mileage fee for all miles over 100 miles per day. Cyndi Keen was charged \$143.50 for 4 days and a total of 770 miles. For the same type of car Shirley Cicero was charged \$102.00 for driving a total of 540 miles in 3 days. What is the daily fee and the mileage fee?

Let x = the cost per day for this type of car,

y = the cost per mile for this type of car.

Since Cyndi got 400 miles free in 4 days, she was charged for $770 - 400 = 370$ miles. Shirley got 300 miles free in 3 days and was charged for $540 - 300 = 240$ miles. Again we will use a table for the given information.

	Cyndi	*Shirley*
Daily cost	$4x$	$3x$
Mileage cost	$370y$	$240y$
Total	$4x + 370y$	$3x + 240y$

We can now write the equation for Cyndi's charges.

$$4x + 370y = 143.50$$

The equation for Shirley's charges is written below.

$$3x + 240y = 102.00$$

This can be simplified by dividing by 3.

$$x + 80y = 34.00$$

Multiply this equation by 4 and subtract from the first equation.

$$\begin{aligned} 4x + 370y &= 143.50 \\ \underline{4x + 320y} &\underline{= 136.00} \\ 50y &= 7.50 \\ y &= 0.15 \end{aligned}$$

The mileage fee is \$0.15 per mile. Substitute this into $x + 80y = 34.00$ to find the daily fee.

$$\begin{aligned} x + 80(0.15) &= 34.00 \\ x + 12.00 &= 34.00 \\ x &= 34.00 - 12.00 \\ &= 22.00 \end{aligned}$$

CompactCarRent charges \$22.00 per day and \$0.15 per mile for each mile over 100 miles per day. ■

EXAMPLE 6 **Solving an Agriculture Problem**

To fertilize a field properly, a farmer must use 3200 pounds of nitrogen and 660 pounds of iron. He places an order with the local chemical company which has two mixtures of fertilizer available, SuperGro and EverGreen. SuperGro contains, among other things, 20% nitrogen and 5% iron, and EverGreen is composed of 15% nitrogen and 2% iron. How many pounds of each mixture should the company combine to fill the farmer's order?

Let x = number of pounds of SuperGro in the mixture,
y = number of pounds of EverGreen in the mixture.

Then $0.20x$ = number of pounds of nitrogen in SuperGro,
$0.15y$ = number of pounds of nitrogen in EverGreen,
$0.05x$ = number of pounds of iron in SuperGro,
$0.02y$ = number of pounds of iron in EverGreen.

We can put this information in a table for better interpretation.

	Number of pounds	*Pounds of nitrogen*	*Pounds of iron*
SuperGro	x	$0.20x$	$0.05x$
EverGreen	y	$0.15y$	$0.02y$
Total		3200	660

Since the total number of pounds of nitrogen needed is 3200, one equation is (add the second column)

$$0.20x + 0.15y = 3200.$$

Since the total number of pounds of iron needed is 660, a second equation is (add the third column)

$$0.05x + 0.02y = 660.$$

We must solve the system

$$\begin{aligned} 0.20x + 0.15y &= 3200 \\ 0.05x + 0.02y &= 660. \end{aligned}$$

To simplify each equation, multiply both sides by 100, clearing the decimals.

$$\begin{aligned} 20x + 15y &= 320{,}000 \\ 5x + 2y &= 66{,}000 \end{aligned}$$

Multiply the second equation by -4 and add.

$$\begin{aligned} 20x + 15y &= 320{,}000 \\ -20x - 8y &= -264{,}000 \\ \hline 7y &= 56{,}000 \\ y &= 8000 \end{aligned}$$

Substitute 8000 for y in $5x + 2y = 66{,}000$.

$$\begin{aligned} 5x + 2(8000) &= 66{,}000 \\ 5x + 16{,}000 &= 66{,}000 \\ 5x &= 50{,}000 \\ x &= 10{,}000 \end{aligned}$$

The company should blend 10,000 pounds of SuperGro with 8000 pounds of Ever-Green to obtain the necessary fertilizer mixture. ■

▶ *Motion problems*

Another type of problem that can be solved using systems is the **motion problem.**

EXAMPLE 7

Solving a Motion Problem

A boat travels 60 mi upstream in 4 hr and returns to the starting place in 3 hr. What is the speed of the boat in still water, and what is the speed of the stream?

Let x = speed of the boat in still water,
y = speed of the stream,
$x - y$ = speed of the boat going upstream (against current),
$x + y$ = speed of the boat going downstream (with current).

Since $d = rt$ (distance equals rate times time), we have the following system.

$$\begin{aligned} 60 &= (x - y)(4) \\ 60 &= (x + y)(3) \end{aligned}$$

Here we can simplify the system by dividing the first equation by 4 and the second equation by 3.

$$
\begin{aligned}
x - y &= 15 \\
x + y &= 20 \\
\hline
2x \quad &= 35 \qquad \text{Add the equations} \\
x &= \frac{35}{2} \\
x &= 17.5
\end{aligned}
$$

Substituting 17.5 into $x + y = 20$ gives

$$
\begin{aligned}
17.5 + y &= 20 \\
y &= 2.5.
\end{aligned}
$$

Thus, the speed of the boat is 17.5 mph, and the speed of the stream is 2.5 mph. ■

> **CAUTION** Do not write $y - x$ for the speed of the boat against the current in Example 7. The quantity $y - x$ is actually negative since the speed of the stream must be less than the speed of the boat in still water.

5.5 EXERCISES

Solve each applied problem in Exercises 1–22.

1. **NUMBER** The sum of two numbers is 39 and their difference is 13. Find the numbers.
2. **AGE** Mike is 2 years younger than Burford. Four years from now the sum of their ages will be 36. How old is each now?
3. **GEOMETRY** Two angles are supplementary (their sum is 180°) and one is 5° more than six times the other. Find the angles.
4. **NUMBER** If three times the smaller of two numbers is increased by five times the larger, the result is 195. Find the two numbers if their sum is 47.
5. **AGE** Mr. Smith has two sons. If the sum of their ages is 19 and the difference between their ages is 3, how old are his sons?
6. **AGE** Bill is three times as old as Jim. Find the age of each if the sum of their ages is 24.
7. **NUMBER** One-third of one number is the same as twice another. The sum of the first and five times the second is 33. Find the numbers.
8. **GEOMETRY** Two angles are *complementary* (their sum is 90°) and their difference is 66°. Find the angles.
9. **CONSTRUCTION** A 30-ft rope is cut into two pieces. One piece is 8 ft longer than the other. How long is each?

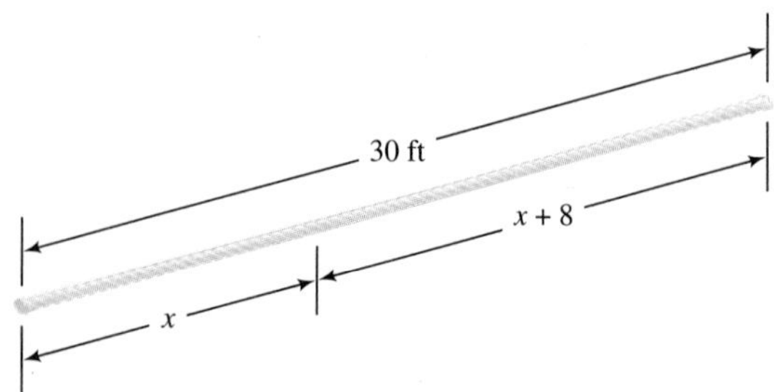

10. **SPORTS** The starting players on a basketball team scored 40 points more than the reserves. If the team scored a total of 90 points, how many points did the starters score?

11. **BUSINESS** A candy mix sells for \$1.10 per lb. If it is composed of two kinds of candy, one worth 90¢ per lb and the other worth \$1.50 per lb, how many pounds of each would be in 30 lb of the mixture?
12. **MIXTURE** A collection of nickels and dimes is worth \$2.85. If there are 34 coins in the collection, how many of each are there?
13. **MIXTURE** A collection of 13 coins consists of dimes and quarters. If the value of the collection is \$2.80, how many of each are there?
14. **BUSINESS** A man wishes to mix two grades of nuts selling for 48¢ and 60¢ per lb. How many pounds of each must he use to get a 20-lb mixture that sells for 54¢ per lb? (Does your answer seem reasonable?)
15. **RECREATION** There were 450 people at a play. If the admission price was \$2.00 for adults and 75¢ for children and the receipts were \$600.00, how many adults and how many children were in attendance?
16. **BUSINESS** A painter needs to have 24 gallons of paint that contains 30% solvent. How many gallons of paint containing 20% solvent and how many gallons containing 60% solvent should be mixed to obtain the desired paint?
17. **RECREATION** When riding his bike against the wind, Terry Larsen can go 40 mi in 4 hr. He takes 2 hr to return riding with the wind. What are Terry's average speed in still air and the average wind speed?
18. **RECREATION** Karin Wagner can ride her bike 120 mi with the wind in 5 hr and return against the wind in 10 hr. What are her speed in still air and the speed of the wind?
19. **INVESTMENT** Vince McKee has \$10,000 to invest, part at 10% simple interest, and the rest at 12% simple interest. If he wants to have \$1160 in interest at the end of the year, how much should he invest at each rate?
20. **INVESTMENT** Gail Taggart has \$20,000 invested. Part of the money earns 9% simple interest and the rest earns 11% simple interest. If her interest income for one year was \$2060, how much did she have invested at each rate?
21. **CONSUMER** International Car Rentals charges a daily fee plus a mileage fee. Jack Pritchard was charged \$82.00 for 3 days and 400 mi, while John Young was charged \$120.00 for 5 days and 500 mi. What are the daily rate and the mileage rate?
22. **CONSUMER** Harder-Than-Ever Car Rentals charged Liz Lee \$76.00 for 2 days and 300 mi. For the same type of car, Linda Youngman was charged \$132.00 for 6 days and 100 mi. What are the daily fee and the mileage fee?

FOR REVIEW

In Exercises 23–24, solve each system using either the elimination or the substitution method, whichever seems more appropriate.

23. $2x - 3y = 20$
    $7x + 5y = -54$

24. $x - 11y = -5$
    $7x + 13y = -35$

5.5 PARALLEL EXERCISES

Solve each applied problem in Exercises 1–22.

1. **NUMBER** If three times the smaller of two numbers is increased by two times the larger, the result is 16. Find the two numbers if their sum is 7.
2. **AGE** Julie is 4 years older than Randy. Five years from now the sum of their ages will be 24. How old is each now?
3. **GEOMETRY** Two angles are supplementary (their sum is 180°) and one is 15° more than twice the other. Find the angles.
4. **NUMBER** If four times the larger of two numbers is decreased by six times the smaller, the result is 4. Find the two numbers if they sum up to 16.

5. **AGE** Tim Chandler has two sons. If the sum of their ages is 30 and the difference between their ages is 4, how old are his sons?

6. **AGE** Sherry Maducci is five times as old as Mac Davis. Find the age of each if the sum of their ages is 42.

7. **NUMBER** One half of one number is the same as three times a second. The sum of twice the second and the first is 80. Find the numbers.

8. **GEOMETRY** Two angles are complementary (their sum is 90°) and one is 15° more than four times the other. Find each angle.

9. **CONSTRUCTION** A 45-inch wire is cut into two pieces. One piece is 11 inches longer than the other. How long is each?

10. **SPORTS** The starting five on the Memphis State basketball team scored 35 more points than the reserves. If the team scored a total of 85 points, how many points did the starters score?

11. **MIXTURE** A collection of nickels and dimes is worth $2.00. If the number of dimes minus the number of nickels is 5, how many of each are there?

12. **BUSINESS** A man wishes to make a party mix consisting of nuts worth 50¢ per lb and candy worth 80¢ per lb. How many pounds of each must he use to make 100 lb of the mixture that will sell for 68¢ per lb?

13. **MIXTURE** Mark Bonnett has 40 coins in his piggy bank, consisting of dimes and quarters. If the value of the collection is $5.80, how many of each are in the bank?

14. **BUSINESS** A grocer mixes two types of candy selling for 50¢ and 70¢ per lb. How many pounds of each must he use to obtain a 30-lb mixture that sells for 60¢ per lb?

15. **RECREATION** There were 12,000 people at a rock concert at Colorado State University. If the admission price was $7.00 for a student with an I.D. and $10.00 for a nonstudent, how many of each were in attendance if the total receipts amounted to $94,500?

16. **MEDICINE** Dr. Karen Winter needs 20 liters of 70% alcohol solution in her clinic. How many liters of 40% solution and how many liters of 90% solution must be mixed to obtain the desired solution?

17. **RECREATION** While driving his boat upstream, Charlie Moore can go 75 mi in 5 hr. It takes him 3 hr to make the return trip downstream. What are the average speed of the boat in still water and the average stream speed?

18. **RECREATION** Maria Lopez traveled 60 mi downstream in 2 hr but needed 5 hr to go back upstream to her starting point. What are the average speed of her boat in still water and the average speed of the stream?

19. **INVESTMENT** Grady and Barbara wish to invest $5000, part at 8% simple interest, and the rest at 14% simple interest. If they must earn $610 by the end of one year, how much should they invest at each rate?

20. **INVESTMENT** A student has $1200 invested. Part of this money earns 12% simple interest, and the rest earns 10% simple interest. How much is invested at each rate if the interest income for the year will be $140?

21. **CONSUMER** Horn Rentals charges a daily fee and a mileage fee to rent a truck. Syd was charged $375 for 5 days and 1500 mi while Barry was charged $165 for 3 days and 600 mi. What are the daily rate and the mileage rate?

22. **CONSUMER** Better-Than-Ever Car Rentals charges a daily fee and a mileage fee. Renee paid $110 for 10 days and 200 mi, while Pamela rented the same type of car and paid $168 for 6 days and 800 mi. What are the daily fee and the mileage fee?

FOR REVIEW

In Exercises 23–24, solve the system using either the elimination or the substitution method, whichever seems more appropriate.

23. $3x + 2y = 2$
$5x - 2y = 30$

24. $4x - y = 6$
$3x + 5y = -30$

5.5 ENRICHMENT EXERCISES

Solve each applied problem in Exercises 1–5. A calculator would be helpful in these exercises.

1. **RECREATION** On a Pacific island Angie is charged $157.92 after driving a rented car for 420 km in 5 days. Andy paid $217.56 for 7 days and 560 km. If each bill includes a 5% pleasure tax, what was the daily fee and what was the fee charged per km? [*Hint:* Find the fees before tax first.]
2. **INVESTMENT** John and Pat Woods invested $22,000, part at 14% simple interest and the rest at 9% simple interest. How much was invested at 14% if the total interest received in three years was $8040?
3. **CHEMISTRY** A chemist plans to mix two saline solutions, one that is 20% salt and the other that is 50% salt, to obtain 100 milliliters of a solution that is 40% salt. How many milliliters of each should he combine?
4. **AGRICULTURE** A farmer places an order for fertilizer with a chemical supplier. He must have a total of 1400 pounds of nitrogen and 400 pounds of iron. The supplier has two fertilizer blends on hand, GroFast and HiYield. GroFast contains 25% nitrogen and 8% iron while HiYield contains 15% nitrogen and 4% iron. How many pounds of each should be blended to fill the farmer's order?
5. **SCIENCE** In a laboratory experiment, a scientist is required to keep a control group of animals on a strict diet. Each animal must receive 55 grams of protein and 11 grams of fat each day. Two food blends are available, GroChow and EatRite. If GroChow contains 20% protein and 4% fat and EatRite contains 15% protein and 3% fat, how many grams of each should be mixed to provide the correct diet for one animal?
6. Write a complete description of all the steps in the **ATTACK** method. Tell exactly how you use each step when you are solving an applied problem.

CHAPTER 5 REVIEW

KEY WORDS

5.1 A **system of equations** is a pair of linear equations.

A **solution** to a system of equations is an ordered pair of numbers (x, y) that is a solution to both equations.

Coinciding lines are the graphs of equations that represent the same line.

Parallel lines are lines that do not intersect.

Intersecting lines have exactly one point in common.

5.5 **A mixture problem** involves two quantities mixed together and is solved by finding a quantity equation and a value equation.

A motion problem makes use of the equation $d = rt$, distance equals rate times time.

KEY CONCEPTS

5.1, 5.2 A system of equations has:

1. infinitely many solutions if the lines coincide,
2. no solution if the lines are parallel,
3. exactly one solution if the lines intersect.

5.2 The method of graphing is not usually used to solve a system since it is time-consuming and depends on our ability to graph accurately.

5.3, 5.4

1. To solve a system of equations, use either the substitution method or the elimination method, whichever seems more appropriate.
2. If you reach an identity (such as $0 = 0$) when solving a system, the system has infinitely many solutions.
3. If you reach a contradiction (such as $3 = 0$) when solving a system, the system has no solution.
4. When solving a system, be sure to find the value of both variables, not just one of them. For example, when solving

$$\begin{aligned} x + y &= 3 \\ x - y &= 1 \\ \hline 2x \quad &= 4 \qquad \text{Adding the two} \\ x &= 2 \end{aligned}$$

do not stop here. Solve for y also.

5.5

1. The total value of a given number of units each of equal value is found with the following equation.

(total value) = (value per unit)(no. of units)

2. The value of a quantity is equal to the sum of the values of its parts.

CHAPTER 5 REVIEW EXERCISES

PART I

5.1 *In Exercises 1–3, tell how the graphs of the system are related.*

1. $2x + y = -3$
$-4x - 2y = 6$

2. $x - 3y = 7$
$4x - 12y = -3$

3. $x + y = 3$
$2x + y = -4$

5.2, 5.3, 5.4 *In Exercises 4–9, solve by whichever method seems more appropriate.*

4. $3x - y = 9$
$2x + 5y = -11$

5. $2x - 3y = -14$
$5x + 2y = 3$

6. $8x - 2y = 4$
$-4x + y = -2$

7. $x + 3 = 0$
$3x + 2y = -7$

8. $3x + y = -2$
$-6x - 2y = -2$

9. $x - 8 = 0$
$2y + 1 = 0$

5.5 *Solve each applied problem in Exercises 10–15.*

10. **NUMBER** The sum of two numbers is 37 and twice one minus the other is 14. Find the numbers.

11. **AGE** The sum of Barb's and Cindy's ages is 17. In 4 years Barb will be twice as old as Cindy is now. What is the present age of each?

12. **MIXTURE** A collection of nickels and dimes is worth \$2.00. If the number of dimes minus the number of nickels is 5, how many of each are there?

13. **BUSINESS** A dealer wishes to mix tea worth 80¢ per lb with tea worth \$1.00 per lb to obtain a 50-lb mixture worth 94¢ per lb. How many pounds of each must he use?

14. **TRAVEL** A boat travels 96 mi downstream in 4 hr and returns to the starting point in 6 hr. What is the speed of the boat in still water?

15. **INVESTMENT** Cecilia Lause invested \$7000, part at 8% simple interest and the rest at 12% simple interest. How much did she have invested at 12% if her total interest income for the year was \$640?

PART II

Solve the applied problem or system in Exercises 16–22.

16. **CHEMISTRY** A chemist has one solution that is 50% acid and a second that is 25% acid. If she wishes to obtain 10 liters of a 40% acid solution, how many liters of each should be combined to obtain the mixture?

17. **AERONAUTICS** Mike Brown flew his plane 600 mi with the wind in 5 hr and returned against the wind in 6 hr. What was the speed of the wind?

18. $\begin{aligned} 2x + y &= 0 \\ x - y &= 6 \end{aligned}$

19. $\begin{aligned} 4x - y &= -3 \\ 6x - 2y &= -7 \end{aligned}$

20. $\begin{aligned} 3x + 2 &= 0 \\ 2y - 3 &= 0 \end{aligned}$

21. **GEOMETRY** Two angles are complementary (their sum is 90°) and one is 6° more than five times the other. Find each angle.

22. **AGE** Mrs. Carlson has two sons. If the sum of their ages is 17 and the difference between their ages is 7, how old are her sons?

Answer true *or* false *in Exercises 23–28. If the statement is false, tell why.*

23. If the graph of one of the equations in a system is a horizontal line and the graph of the other equation is a vertical line, then the system has exactly one solution.

24. The graphing method cannot be used to solve every system.

25. The substitution method is always faster than the elimination method.

26. When solving a system if an identity is obtained, there is no solution.

27. When solving a system either variable can be eliminated first.

28. When a system has no solution and the lines have slope, the slopes are equal.

CHAPTER 5 TEST

1. Without graphing, tell how the graphs of the pair of linear equations are related (intersecting, parallel, or coinciding).

$$\begin{aligned} x + 3y &= 1 \\ 2x - y &= 5 \end{aligned}$$

2. Tell whether $(4, -2)$ is a solution to the following system.

$$\begin{aligned} 3x + 4y &= 4 \\ -2x - y &= -10 \end{aligned}$$

Solve the system of equations by whichever method seems more appropriate.

3. $\begin{aligned} 2x - 5y &= 11 \\ x + 3y &= 0 \end{aligned}$

4. $\begin{aligned} 3x - 2y &= 1 \\ -6x + 4y &= -1 \end{aligned}$

5. In a system of equations, if the lines are coinciding, how many solutions will the system have?
6. The sum of two numbers is 18 and their difference is 12. Find the two numbers.
7. Two angles are supplementary and one is 12° more than six times the other. Find each angle.
8. A collection of nickels and dimes has a value of \$3.70. If there are 52 coins in the collection, how many of each are there?
9. An airplane can fly 1000 mi with the wind in 2 hr and return against the wind in 2.5 hr. What is the speed of the plane in still air?
10. A specialty store wishes to sell a party mix of candy and nuts for \$1.80 per lb. If candy is \$1.20 per lb and nuts cost \$2.20 per lb, how many pounds of each should be used to make 100 lb of the mixture?
11. In the process of solving a system, how will you know if the system has infinitely many solutions?

CHAPTER 6

Exponents and Polynomials

In Chapter 2 we defined an exponential expression. We now consider rules of exponents and use them in working with more complex expressions called *polynomials.* Several other properties of our number system, especially the distributive law, are also needed in the study of this chapter.

The following applied problem uses the concepts introduced in this chapter. It will be solved in Example 9 of Section 6.5.

SALES Angelica would like to begin publishing a small environmental magazine which she will call EnviroLife. She has determined that the number n of new magazine subscriptions that can be sold during each month is related to the price in dollars p of a subscription by the equation $n = 200 - 10p$. Find an equation that gives the monthly revenue R in terms of p and use it to find R when p is \$15, \$10, and \$8.

We begin this chapter with a careful study of exponents including scientific notation. After introducing the basic terminology of polynomials, we then consider the operations of addition, subtraction, and multiplication, including special products, on polynomials. Division of polynomials concludes the chapter.

SECTION 6.1 Integer Exponents

Student guideposts

- ▶ *Exponential notation*
- ▶ *Product rule*
- ▶ *Quotient rule*
- ▶ *Power rule*
- ▶ *Powers of products and quotients*
- ▶ *Zero exponents*
- ▶ *Negative exponents*
- ▶ *Summary of rules for exponents*

▶ *Exponential notation*

In Section 2.1 we introduced exponents and exponential notation.

Exponential Notation

If a is any number and n is a positive integer,

$$a^n = \underbrace{a \cdot a \cdot a \cdots a}_{n \text{ factors}},$$

where a is the base, n the exponent, and a^n the exponential expression.

EXAMPLE 1

Using Exponential Notation

Write without using exponents.

(a) $4^5 = \underbrace{4 \cdot 4 \cdot 4 \cdot 4 \cdot 4}_{5 \text{ factors}}$ The product is 1024

(b) $3y^2 = 3\underbrace{yy}_{2\ y\text{s as factors}}$ 3 *is not* squared

(c) $(3y)^2 = \underbrace{(3y)(3y)}_{2\ (3y)\text{s as factors}}$ 3 *is* squared

(d) $2^2 + 3^2 = \underbrace{2 \cdot 2}_{2\ 2\text{s}} + \underbrace{3 \cdot 3}_{2\ 3\text{s}}$ This simplifies to 13, *not* $(2 + 3)^2 = 5^2 = 25$

(e) $-4^2 = -4 \cdot 4 = -16$ This is *not* $(-4)^2 = 16$

(f) $1^{32} = \underbrace{1 \cdot 1 \cdot 1 \cdots 1}_{\text{32 factors}} = 1$ — 1 to any power is always 1

(g) $(-1)^3 = (-1)(-1)(-1)$
$= (+1)(-1) = -1$ — -1 to an *odd* power is -1

(h) $(-1)^4 = (-1)(-1)(-1)(-1)$
$= (-1)(-1) = 1$ — -1 to an *even* power is $+1$ or 1 ■

CAUTION Three of the most common errors made with exponents have been shown in the above examples:

$$3y^2 \neq (3y)^2,\ 2^2 + 3^2 \neq (2 + 3)^2, \text{ and } -4^2 \neq (-4)^2$$

Parts **(g)** and **(h)** of Example 1 illustrate the following general rule: An odd power of a negative number is negative, and an even power of a negative number is positive.

▶ *Product rule*

When we combine terms containing exponential expressions by multiplication, division, or taking powers, our work can be simplified by using the basic properties of exponents. For example,

$$a^3a^2 = \underbrace{(a \cdot a \cdot a)}_{\substack{3\\ \text{factors}}}\underbrace{(a \cdot a)}_{\substack{2\\ \text{factors}}} = \underbrace{a \cdot a \cdot a \cdot a \cdot a}_{\substack{5\\ \text{factors}}} = a^5.$$

When two exponential expressions *with the same base* are multiplied, the product is that base raised to the sum of the exponents on the original expressions.

Product Rule for Exponents

If a is any number, and m and n are positive integers.

$$a^m a^n = a^{m+n}.$$

(To multiply powers with the same base, add exponents.)

EXAMPLE 2

Using the Product Rule

Find the product.

(a) $a^3a^4 = a^{3+4} = a^7$

(b) $5^3 \cdot 5^7 = 5^{3+7} = 5^{10}$ — *Not* 25^{10}

(c) $2^3 \cdot 2^2 \cdot 2^6 = 2^{3+2+6} = 2^{11}$ — The rule applies to more than two factors

(d) $3x^3x^2 = 3x^{3+2} = 3x^5$ — The 3 is not raised to the powers ■

Quotient rule When two powers with the same base are divided, for example,

$$\frac{a^5}{a^2} = \frac{\overbrace{a \cdot a \cdot a \cdot a \cdot a}^{\text{5 factors}}}{\underbrace{a \cdot a}_{\text{2 factors}}} = \frac{a \cdot a \cdot a \cdot \not{a} \cdot \not{a}}{\not{a} \cdot \not{a}} = \underbrace{a \cdot a \cdot a}_{\text{3 factors}} = a^3,$$

the quotient can be found by raising the base to the difference of the exponents $(5 - 2 = 3)$.

Quotient Rule for Exponents

If a is any number except zero, and m, n, and $m - n$ are positive integers, then

$$\frac{a^m}{a^n} = a^{m-n}.$$

(To divide powers with the same base, subtract exponents.)

EXAMPLE 3

Using the Quotient Rule

Find the quotient.

(a) $\dfrac{a^7}{a^3} = a^{7-3} = a^4$

(b) $\dfrac{5^8}{5^5} = 5^{8-5} = 5^3$

(c) $\dfrac{2^3}{3^4}$ Cannot be simplified using the rule of exponents since the bases are different

(d) $\dfrac{3x^3}{x^2} = 3x^{3-2} = 3x^1 = 3x$ $x^1 = x$

(e) $\dfrac{2yy^3}{y^2} = \dfrac{2y^1y^3}{y^2} = \dfrac{2y^{1+3}}{y^2}$

$= \dfrac{2y^4}{y^2} = 2y^{4-2} = 2y^2$ ∎

Power rule When a power is raised to a power, for example,

$$(a^2)^3 = \underbrace{(a^2)(a^2)(a^2)}_{\text{3 factors}} = (a \cdot a)(a \cdot a)(a \cdot a)$$

$$= \underbrace{a \cdot a \cdot a \cdot a \cdot a \cdot a}_{\text{6 factors}} = a^6,$$

the resulting exponential expression can be found by raising the base to the product of the exponents ($2 \cdot 3 = 6$).

Power Rule

If a is any number, and m and n are positive integers,

$$(a^m)^n = a^{mn}.$$

(To raise a power to a power, multiply exponents.)

CAUTION Do not confuse the power rule with the product rule. For example,

$$(a^5)^2 = a^{5 \cdot 2} = a^{10},$$

but

$$a^5 a^2 = a^{5+2} = a^7.$$

EXAMPLE 4

Using the Power Rule

Find the powers.

(a) $(a^3)^8 = a^{3 \cdot 8} = a^{24}$ Not $a^{3+8} = a^{11}$

(b) $2(x^3)^2 = 2x^{3 \cdot 2} = 2x^6$ Not $(2x^3)^2 = 4x^6$ ■

▶ *Powers of products and quotients*

A product or quotient of expressions is often raised to a power. For example,

$$(3x^2)^4 = \underbrace{(3x^2) \cdot (3x^2) \cdot (3x^2) \cdot (3x^2)}_{\text{4 factors}}$$

$$= \underbrace{3 \cdot 3 \cdot 3 \cdot 3}_{\text{4 factors}} \cdot \underbrace{x^2 \cdot x^2 \cdot x^2 \cdot x^2}_{\text{4 factors}} = 3^4(x^2)^4,$$

and

$$\left(\frac{2}{y^2}\right)^3 = \underbrace{\frac{2}{y^2} \cdot \frac{2}{y^2} \cdot \frac{2}{y^2}}_{\text{3 factors}} = \frac{\overbrace{2 \cdot 2 \cdot 2}^{\text{3 factors}}}{\underbrace{y^2 \cdot y^2 \cdot y^2}_{\text{3 factors}}} = \frac{2^3}{(y^2)^3}.$$

These illustrate the next rule.

Powers of Products and Quotients

If a and b are any numbers, and n is a positive integer, then

$$(ab)^n = a^n b^n \quad \text{and} \quad \left(\frac{a}{b}\right)^n = \frac{a^n}{b^n} \quad (b \text{ not zero}).$$

EXAMPLE 5 **Working with Powers of Products and Quotients**

Simplify.

(a) $(2y)^5 = 2^5 \cdot y^5 = 2^5y^5 = 32y^5$

(b) $(3a^2b^3)^4 = 3^4 \cdot (a^2)^4 \cdot (b^3)^4$ Raise each factor to the fourth power

$= 3^4a^8b^{12}$

$= 81a^8b^{12}$

(c) $\left(\frac{2}{x^3}\right)^4 = \frac{2^4}{(x^3)^4}$ $\quad \left(\frac{a}{b}\right)^n = \frac{a^n}{b^n}$

$= \frac{16}{x^{3\cdot 4}}$ $\quad (a^m)^n = a^{mn}$

$= \frac{16}{x^{12}}$

(d) $\left(\frac{3a^2}{b}\right)^3 = \frac{(3a^2)^3}{b^3}$ $\quad \left(\frac{a}{b}\right)^n = \frac{a^n}{b^n}$

$= \frac{3^3(a^2)^3}{b^3}$ $\quad (ab)^n = a^nb^n$ ■

$= \frac{27a^6}{b^3}$

CAUTION Rules similar to the product and quotient rules above do not exist for sums and differences. For example,

$$(2^2 + 3^2)^3 \text{ is } not\ (2^2)^3 + (3^2)^3,$$

and

$$(1^3 - 4^3)^2 \text{ is } not\ (1^3)^2 - (4^3)^2.$$

Also, exponential expressions with different bases cannot be combined by adding exponents. For example, in general,

$$a^2b^5 \text{ is } not\ (ab)^7.$$

▶ *Zero exponents*

We know that if a is not zero,

$$\frac{a^m}{a^n} = a^{m-n}.$$

Suppose we extend the quotient rule to include $m = n$. Then

$$\frac{a^m}{a^m} = a^{m-m} = a^0 \quad \text{and also} \quad \frac{a^m}{a^m} = 1.$$

(Any number divided by itself is 1.) This suggests the following definition.

Zero Exponent

If a is any number except zero,

$$a^0 = 1.$$

EXAMPLE 6

Using Zero Exponents

Simplify.

(a) $5^0 = 1$

(b) 0^0 is undefined

(c) $3x^0 = 3(1) = 3 \quad (\text{assuming } x \neq 0)$

(d) $(2a^2b^3)^0 = 1 \quad (\text{assuming } a \neq 0 \text{ and } b \neq 0)$ ■

▶ *Negative exponents*

Again, consider

$$\frac{a^m}{a^n} = a^{m-n} \ (a \neq 0).$$

What happens when $n > m$? For example, if we let $n = 5$ and $m = 2$ and we extend the quotient rule to include $m - n < 0$, we have

$$\frac{a^m}{a^n} = \frac{a^2}{a^5} = a^{2-5} = a^{-3}.$$

If we look at the problem another way, we have

$$\frac{a^2}{a^5} = \frac{\not{a} \cdot \not{a}}{\not{a} \cdot \not{a} \cdot a \cdot a \cdot a} = \frac{1}{a \cdot a \cdot a} = \frac{1}{a^3}.$$

Thus, we conclude that $a^{-3} = \frac{1}{a^3}$. This suggests a way to define exponential expressions with negative integer exponents.

Negative Exponents

If $a \neq 0$ and n is a positive integer ($-n$ is a negative integer), then

$$a^{-n} = \frac{1}{a^n}.$$

EXAMPLE 7

Using Negative Exponents

Simplify and write without negative exponents.

(a) $5^{-3} = \frac{1}{5^3} = \frac{1}{125}$ $\quad$ 5^{-3} is *not* -5^3 nor $(-3)(5)$

(b) $4^{-2} = \frac{1}{4^2} = \frac{1}{16}$

(c) $\frac{1}{3^{-2}} = \frac{1}{\frac{1}{3^2}} = \frac{1}{\frac{1}{9}} = 1 \cdot \frac{9}{1} = 9 = 3^2$

(d) $(-2)^{-5} = \frac{1}{(-2)^5} = \frac{1}{-32} = -\frac{1}{32}$ ■

NOTE Example 7 shows that we can "remove" negative exponents simply by moving an exponential expression with a negative exponent from numerator to denominator (or denominator to numerator) and changing the sign of the exponent. For example,

$$4^{-2} = \frac{4^{-2}}{1} = \frac{1}{4^2} \quad \text{and} \quad \frac{1}{3^{-2}} = \frac{3^2}{1} = 3^2.$$

CAUTION a^{-n} is not equal to $-a^n$ nor to $(-n)a$. As shown in Example 7 (a), 5^{-3} is $\frac{1}{125}$ and not -5^3, which is -125, nor $(-3)(5)$, which is -15.

Summary of rules for exponents

All the rules of exponents stated for positive integer exponents apply to all integer exponents: positive, negative, and zero. These are summarized as follows.

Rules for Exponents

Let a and b be any two numbers, m and n any two integers.

1. $a^m a^n = a^{m+n}$
2. $\frac{a^m}{a^n} = a^{m-n} \quad (a \neq 0)$
3. $(a^m)^n = a^{mn}$
4. $(ab)^n = a^n b^n$
5. $\left(\frac{a}{b}\right)^n = \frac{a^n}{b^n} \quad (b \neq 0)$
6. $a^0 = 1 \quad (a \neq 0)$
7. $a^{-n} = \frac{1}{a^n} \quad (a \neq 0)$
8. $\frac{1}{a^{-n}} = a^n \quad (a \neq 0)$

EXAMPLE 8 **Using All Rules**

Simplify and write without negative exponents.

(a) $(2a)^{-1} = \frac{1}{(2a)^1} = \frac{1}{2a}$ $\quad$ $(2a)^{-1}$ is *not* $-2a$

(b) $2a^{-1} = 2\frac{1}{a} = \frac{2}{a}$ $\quad$ The exponent -1 is only on a, not on 2

(c) $y^3y^{-5} = y^{3+(-5)} = y^{-2} = \dfrac{1}{y^2}$

(d) $\dfrac{a^2b^{-3}}{a^{-1}b^5} = a^{2-(-1)}b^{-3-5} = a^3b^{-8} = a^3 \cdot \dfrac{1}{b^8} = \dfrac{a^3}{b^8}$

(e) $\dfrac{1}{x^{-3}} = x^3$ Using $\frac{1}{a^{-n}} = a^n$

(f) $(2a^{-2}b)^{-3} = 2^{-3}(a^{-2})^{-3}b^{-3} = \dfrac{1}{2^3}a^{(-2)(-3)}\dfrac{1}{b^3}$

$$= \frac{1}{8} \cdot a^6\frac{1}{b^3} = \frac{a^6}{8b^3}$$

(g) $\left(\dfrac{a^2}{2y^{-3}}\right)^{-2} = \dfrac{(a^2)^{-2}}{2^{-2}(y^{-3})^{-2}} = \dfrac{a^{-4}}{\frac{1}{2^2}y^6} = \dfrac{\frac{1}{a^4}}{\frac{y^6}{2^2}}$

$$= \frac{1}{a^4} \cdot \frac{2^2}{y^6} = \frac{4}{a^4y^6} \quad \blacksquare$$

In the next example we give a step-by-step procedure that can be followed when several of the rules of exponents are needed to simplify an expression.

EXAMPLE 9

Simplifying a More Complex Expression

Simplify the expression and describe each step in the procedure.

$\left(\dfrac{3x^4y^{-2}}{x^{-2}y^5}\right)^{-3} = \dfrac{3^{-3}(x^4)^{-3}(y^{-2})^{-3}}{(x^{-2})^{-3}(y^5)^{-3}}$ Use powers of products and quotients: $(ab)^n = a^nb^n$ and $\left(\frac{a}{b}\right)^n = \frac{a^n}{b^n}$

$= \dfrac{3^{-3}x^{-12}y^6}{x^6y^{-15}}$ Use power rule: $(a^m)^n = a^{mn}$

$= 3^{-3}x^{-12-6}y^{6-(-15)}$ Use quotient rule: $\frac{a^m}{a^n} = a^{m-n}$ (and product rule when necessary)

$= 3^{-3}x^{-18}y^{21}$ Simplify

$= \dfrac{1}{3^3}\dfrac{1}{x^{18}}y^{21}$ Use $a^{-n} = \frac{1}{a^n}$

$= \dfrac{y^{21}}{27x^{18}}$ Evaluate: $3^3 = 27$ $\blacksquare$

We conclude this section with an example of evaluation of exponential expressions.

EXAMPLE 10 **Evaluating Exponential Expressions**

Evaluate the following when $a = -2$ and $b = 3$.

(a) $a^{-1} = (-2)^{-1} = \frac{1}{-2} = -\frac{1}{2}$ $(-2)^{-1}$ is *not* $+2$

(b) $\frac{a^{-2}}{b} = \frac{(-2)^{-2}}{3} = \frac{\frac{1}{(-2)^2}}{3} = \frac{\frac{1}{4}}{3} = \frac{1}{4} \cdot \frac{1}{3} = \frac{1}{12}$

(c) $(a + b)^{-1} = (-2 + 3)^{-1} = 1^{-1} = \frac{1}{1} = 1$

(d) $a^{-1} + b^{-1} = (-2)^{-1} + (3)^{-1}$

$= \frac{1}{-2} + \frac{1}{3} = -\frac{3}{6} + \frac{2}{6} = -\frac{1}{6}$ ■

6.1 EXERCISES

Write in exponential notation in Exercises 1–3.

1. $8 \cdot 8 \cdot 8 \cdot 8$
2. $2 \cdot 2 \cdot y \cdot y \cdot y$
3. $(2x)(2x)(2x)(2x)$

Write without using exponents in Exercises 4–6.

4. $2y^4$
5. $(2y)^4$
6. $a^2 + b^2$

Simplify and write without negative exponents in Exercises 7–42.

7. x^2x^5
8. $a^3a^2a^4$
9. $2y^2y^8$
10. $\frac{a^4}{a^3}$
11. $\frac{2y^5}{y^3}$
12. $(a^3)^4$
13. $(2x^3)^4$
14. $2(x^3)^4$
15. $\left(\frac{2}{x^3}\right)^4$
16. $\frac{a^3}{b^5}$
17. 5^0
18. 0^0
19. $(2a)^0$ $(a \neq 0)$
20. $(2x)^{-1}$
21. $2x^{-1}$
22. $\frac{2x^7}{x^9}$
23. $3y^4y^{-7}$
24. $(3y)^{-2}$
25. $3y^{-2}$
26. $(3y^{-2})^3$
27. $\left(\frac{2y}{x^3}\right)^{-2}$
28. $\frac{b^{-2}}{a^{-4}}$
29. $\frac{a^{-4}b^2}{b^{-2}}$
30. $\frac{a^{-2}b^2}{a^4b^{-3}}$
31. $(3xy^2)(4x^2y^3)$
32. $(2x^2y^2)^2(3x^2y)^3$
33. $(-xy)(2x^3y)(4xy^3)$
34. $\frac{x^3y^{-5}}{x^4y^{-6}}$
35. $\frac{3^0a^3b^{-8}}{ab^4}$
36. $\frac{3^{-1}x^{-1}y^{-5}}{x^{-6}y^2}$

37. $(x^{-2}y^{-1})^{-2}$ 38. $(x^2y^{-3})^{-4}$ 39. $(3x^{-1}y)^{-2}$

40. $\left(\frac{a^{-5}}{b^{-1}}\right)^{-1}$ 41. $\left(\frac{2a^{-3}}{b^3}\right)^{-2}$ 42. $\left(\frac{2a^3b^{-2}}{a^{-5}b}\right)^{-3}$

In Exercises 43–60, evaluate when $a = -2$ and $b = 3$.

43. $3a^2$ 44. $(3a)^2$ 45. $-3a^2$

46. $(-3a)^2$ 47. $-b^2$ 48. $(-b)^2$

49. $a^2 - b^2$ 50. $(a - b)^2$ 51. a^{-2}

52. $-2a$ 53. $-a^2$ 54. $a^{-2} + b^{-2}$

55. $(a + b)^{-2}$ 56. $\frac{a^{-1}}{b^{-2}}$ 57. a^{-3}

58. $(-a)^{-3}$ 59. $a^{-1}b^{-1}$ 60. $(ab)^{-1}$

6.1 PARALLEL EXERCISES

Write in exponential notation in Exercises 1–3.

1. $4 \cdot 4 \cdot z \cdot z \cdot z$ 2. $(3w)(3w)(3w)$ 3. $3www$

Write without using exponents in Exercises 4–6.

4. $4y^3$ 5. $(4y)^3$ 6. $x^2 + y^2$

Simplify and write without negative exponents in Exercises 7–42.

7. y^2y^7 8. $x^3x^2x^6$ 9. $2z^2z^5$

10. $\frac{b^5}{b^2}$ 11. $\frac{2y^7}{y^4}$ 12. $(w^3)^5$

13. $(2c^2)^4$ 14. $2(y^3)^5$ 15. $\left(\frac{2}{a^2}\right)^3$

16. $\frac{x^3}{y^4}$ 17. 7^0 18. -0^0

19. $(4x)^0$ $(x \neq 0)$ 20. $(5y)^{-1}$ 21. $5y^{-1}$

22. $\frac{3a^3}{a^7}$ 23. $4z^4z^{-9}$ 24. $(5w)^{-2}$

25. $5w^{-2}$ 26. $(2a^{-2})^3$ 27. $\left(\frac{2y}{x^3}\right)^2$

28. $\frac{b^{-5}}{a^{-3}}$ 29. $\frac{a^{-3}b^{-3}}{b^{-4}}$ 30. $\frac{x^{-2}y^4}{x^3y^{-3}}$

31. $(-5x^2y^2)(3x^3y)$ 32. $(x^3y^2)^3(2x^3y)^2$ 33. $(-2x)(5x^5y)(-3xy^2)$

34. $\frac{a^4b^{-3}}{a^{-2}b^2}$ 35. $\frac{5^0a^{-5}b^{-2}}{a^4b^{-1}}$ 36. $\frac{2^{-2}x^3y^{-4}}{x^{-2}y^{-2}}$

37. $(a^{-1}b^{-5})^{-1}$ 38. $(a^{-6}b^3)^{-3}$ 39. $(4a^{-1}b^{-1})^{-3}$

40. $\left(\frac{x^{-4}}{y^{-2}}\right)^{-2}$ 41. $\left(\frac{3x^4}{y^3}\right)^{-1}$ 42. $\left(\frac{3x^{-2}y^{-1}}{x^3y^{-5}}\right)^{-4}$

In Exercises 43–60, evaluate when $x = -3$ and $y = 2$.

43. $4x^2$
44. $(4x)^2$
45. $-4x^2$
46. $(-4x)^2$
47. $-x^2$
48. $(-x)^2$
49. $y^2 - x^2$
50. $(y - x)^2$
51. x^{-2}
52. $-3y$
53. $-y^3$
54. $x^{-2} + y^{-2}$
55. $(x + y)^{-2}$
56. $\frac{x^{-1}}{y^{-2}}$
57. x^{-3}
58. $(-x)^{-3}$
59. $x^{-1}y^{-1}$
60. $(xy)^{-1}$

6.1 ENRICHMENT EXERCISES

In Exercises 1–12, simplify and write without negative exponents.

1. $\frac{(a^3b^2)^2}{(a^2b^4)^3}$
2. $\frac{(a^5b)^4}{(a^{10}b^2)^2}$
3. $\frac{(a^{-2}b^3)^{-1}}{(a^5b^{-2})^2}$
4. $\frac{(a^7b^{-5})^{-2}}{(a^4b^{-3})^{-3}}$
5. $\frac{(x^{-2}y^{-2})^{-3}(xy^{-3})^{-1}}{(x^{-5}y^{-1})^2(x^{-4}y^2)^{-1}}$
6. $\frac{[(x^2y)^{-1}]^{-3}(x^{-1}y)^{-2}}{[(x^{-1}y)^{-2}]^3x^{-2}y^{-3}}$
7. $\frac{a^{-2}b^3c^2}{a^{-3}b^{-2}c^{-2}}$
8. $\frac{3^0x^{-6}(y^{-1})^{-2}}{x^{-2}y^{-3}}$
△ **9.** $\frac{2^{-2}(x^2)^{-3}y^3z^{-2}}{3^{-1}x^{-1}(yz)^{-1}}$
10. $\left(\frac{5^0a^{-6}b^2c^3}{a^2b^{-1}c^{-2}}\right)^{-1}$
11. $\left(\frac{2^{-1}x^{-5}y^{-8}}{4^{-1}x^3y^{-4}}\right)^{-2}$
△ **12.** $\left[\left(\frac{a^2b^{-2}}{a^{-5}b^{-1}}\right)^{-1}\right]^{-2}$

Verify that each rule of exponents given in Exercises 13–14 is true by expanding the left side of the equation.

13. $(a^3)^4 = a^{12}$
14. $(ab)^3 = a^3b^3$

15. Burford said that $-x^2$ was the same as $(-x)^2$ for all values of x. Can you show that he is wrong? Are there any values of x for which the two expressions are equal?

SECTION 6.2 Scientific Notation

Student guideposts

- ▶ *Scientific notation*
- ▶ *Calculations using scientific notation*

FIGURE 6.1

When we compute with very large or very small numbers on a calculator, problems can arise because the display is limited (usually 8 digits). For example, if we use a calculator to multiply

$$(290{,}000)(15{,}000),$$

the product, 4,350,000,000, has too many digits for the display and might be given as in Figure 6.1.

This shorthand notation, representing 4.35×10^9 and called *scientific notation,* depends on the use of integer exponents.

▶ *Scientific notation* A scientist might use the number

$$235{,}000{,}000{,}000{,}000{,}000{,}000$$

but, instead of writing out all the zeros, he or she would write

$$2.35 \times 10^{20}.$$

This short form is easier to use in computations. Likewise, the number

$$0.000000000057$$

could be written as 5.7×10^{-11}.

A number is written in **scientific notation** if it is the product of a power of 10 and a number that is greater than or equal to 1 and less than 10.

To Write a Number in Scientific Notation

1. Move the decimal point to the position immediately to the right of the first nonzero digit.
2. Multiply by a power of ten that is equal to the number of decimal places moved. The exponent on 10 is positive if the original number is greater than 10 and negative if the number is less than 1.

EXAMPLE 1

Converting to Scientific Notation

Write in scientific notation.

First nonzero digit ↓

(a) $2{,}500{,}000 = 2.5 \times 10^{6}$ Count 6 decimal places

6 places

First nonzero digit ↓

(b) $0.0000025 = 2.5 \times 10^{-6}$ Count 6 decimal places

6 places

(c) $4{,}321{,}000{,}000 = 4.321 \times 10^{9}$

9 places

(d) $0.00000000001 = 1 \times 10^{-11}$

11 places

(e) $0.1 = 1 \times 10^{-1}$

1 place

(f) $4.8 = 4.8 \times 10^{0}$ ■

EXAMPLE 2 **Converting to Standard Notation**

Write in standard notation.

(a) $5.4 \times 10^5 = 540{,}000$ Count 5 decimal places

(b) $5.4 \times 10^{-5} = 0.000054$ Count 5 decimal places

(c) $8.94 \times 10^{13} = 89{,}400{,}000{,}000{,}000$

(d) $2.113 \times 10^{-8} = 0.00000002113$ ■

▶ *Calculations using scientific notation*

Scientific notation not only shortens the notation for many numbers, but also helps in calculations.

EXAMPLE 3 **Calculating with Scientific Notation**

Perform the indicated operations using scientific notation.

(a)
$$\begin{aligned}(30{,}000)(2{,}000{,}000) &= (3 \times 10^4)(2 \times 10^6)\\ &= (3 \cdot 2) \times (10^4 \times 10^6) \quad \text{Change order}\\ &= 6 \times 10^{10} \quad \text{Add exponents}\end{aligned}$$

(b)
$$\begin{aligned}(2.4 \times 10^{-12})(4.0 \times 10^{11}) &= (2.4)(4.0) \times (10^{-12} \times 10^{11})\\ &= 9.6 \times 10^{-1}\end{aligned}$$

(c) $\dfrac{3.2 \times 10^{-1}}{1.6 \times 10^5} = \dfrac{3.2}{1.6} \times \dfrac{10^{-1}}{10^5} = 2 \times 10^{-6}$ ■

6.2 EXERCISES

In Exercises 1–6, write in scientific notation.

1. 370 **2.** 0.0037 **3.** 98,000

4. 0.0000000000756 **5.** 2,650,000,000 **6.** 0.01

In Exercises 7–12, write in standard notation.

7. 2.3×10^2 **8.** 2.3×10^{-2} **9.** 8.7×10^{-5}

10. 4.58×10^6 **11.** 7.51×10^{-8} **12.** 6.64×10^{10}

In Exercises 13–18, perform the indicated operations using scientific notation.

13. $(4 \times 10^5)(1 \times 10^6)$ **14.** $(40{,}000{,}000)(20{,}000)$

15. $(1 \times 10^{-10})(5 \times 10^7)$ **16.** $(0.0000022)(300)$

17. $\dfrac{3.3 \times 10^{12}}{1.1 \times 10^{-2}}$ **18.** $\dfrac{0.0000006}{0.03}$

19. **SCIENCE** The measure of one calorie is equal to 0.000000278 kilowatt-hours. Write this number in scientific notation.

20. **SCIENCE** The distance that light will travel in 1 year is approximately 5,870,000,000,000 miles. Write the number in scientific notation.

FOR REVIEW

Evaluate each expression in Exercises 21–26 when $a = -2$ and $b = 5$.

21. a^{-1} **22.** a^{-2} **23.** $-2a$

24. $(a + b)^{-1}$ **25.** $(a - b)^{-2}$ **26.** $a^{-2} - b^{-2}$

6.2 PARALLEL EXERCISES

In Exercises 1–6, write in scientific notation.

1. 5400 **2.** 0.0054 **3.** 386

4. 0.000000000254 **5.** 4,620,000,000 **6.** 0.001

In Exercises 7–12, write in standard notation.

7. 8.4×10^3 **8.** 8.4×10^{-3} **9.** 5.42×10^{-7}

10. 7.25×10^7 **11.** 2.06×10^{-6} **12.** 4.99×10^{12}

In Exercises 13–18, perform the indicated operations using scientific notation.

13. $(5 \times 10^3)(1 \times 10^4)$ **14.** (60,000,000)(50,000)

15. $(1 \times 10^{-12})(3 \times 10^8)$ **16.** (0.00000044)(500)

17. $\dfrac{4.4 \times 10^{15}}{1.1 \times 10^{-3}}$ **18.** $\dfrac{0.00000008}{0.04}$

19. **SCIENCE** The earth is approximately 93,000,000 miles from the sun. Write this number in scientific notation.

20. **CHEMISTRY** Chemists use 602,000,000,000,000,000,000,000, known as Avogadro's number, in calculations. Write this number in scientific notation.

FOR REVIEW

Evaluate each expression in Exercises 21–26 when $x = -3$ and $y = 2$.

21. x^{-1} **22.** x^{-2} **23.** $-2x$

24. $(x + y)^{-1}$ **25.** $(x - y)^{-2}$ **26.** $x^{-2} - y^{-2}$

6.2 ENRICHMENT EXERCISES

In Exercises 1–4, perform the indicated operations using scientific notation.

1. $\dfrac{(2.5 \times 10^{-3})(4.2 \times 10^{-8})}{(5.0 \times 10^7)(8.4 \times 10^{-10})}$ △ **2.** $\dfrac{(0.000036)(0.0001)^{-1}}{(1{,}200{,}000)(1 \times 10^7)^{-2}}$

3. **HEALTH** A government estimates that it will cost an average of $2500 per person to give proper medical care to the people for one year. What will be the total cost for the year if the population of the country is 30,000,000?

4. **ECONOMICS** The national debt of a country is $\$5.2 \times 10^9$. If the population is 4×10^6, what is the amount of debt per person?

5. Burford said that he could do anything in math without ever learning scientific notation. Using your calculator, explain to him a good reason for learning scientific notation.

SECTION 6.3 Basic Concepts of Polynomials

Student guideposts

- *Polynomials*
- *Monomials, binomials, and trinomials*
- *Degree of a polynomial*
- *Ascending and descending order*
- *Like terms*
- *Evaluating polynomials*

In Chapter 2 we defined a **variable** as a letter that represents a number and said that an **algebraic expression** involves sums, differences, products, quotients, or powers of numbers and variables. The **terms** in an algebraic expression are the parts that are separated by plus and minus signs. For example,

$$3x^2 - y + 2uv^3 - 9$$

is an algebraic expression with four terms, $3x^3$, $-y$, $2uv^3$, and -9. Notice that the minus sign goes with the terms $-y$ and -9.

Polynomials

A **polynomial** is an algebraic expression whose terms are products of numbers and variables with whole-number exponents.

These Are Polynomials:

$$3x^2 + x - 5, \quad 2m + 1, \quad 3x, \quad \frac{1}{2}z^2 - 5z^3, \quad \text{and} \quad -2x^2y + xy^2 + 3$$

The polynomial $3x^2 + x - 5$ has three terms, $3x^2$, x (or $1 \cdot x$), and -5. The **numerical coefficients** (usually just called the coefficients) of these terms are 3, 1, and -5. Similarly, the polynomial $\frac{1}{2}z^2 - 5z^3$ has terms $\frac{1}{2}z^2$ and $-5z^3$ with coefficients $\frac{1}{2}$ and -5.

These Are Not Polynomials:

$$3\sqrt{x} + 5, \quad \frac{x+2}{x-y}, \quad x^{-2}$$

The examples above are algebraic expressions that are not polynomials. In a polynomial, a variable cannot appear under a radical, in a denominator, or with a negative exponent.

Monomials, binomials, and trinomials

A polynomial with one term is a **monomial,** a **binomial** has two terms, and a **trinomial** has three terms. When a polynomial has more than three terms, no special name is used and we simply call it a polynomial. Study the polynomials in the following table.

Polynomial	*Type*	*Terms*	*Coefficients*
$5x - 2$	binomial	$5x, -2$	$5, -2$
6	monomial	6	6
$\frac{1}{3}y^2 + 2y - 3$	trinomial	$\frac{1}{3}y^2, 2y, -3$	$\frac{1}{3}, 2, -3$
$7a^3 + 2a^2 - 6a + 5$	polynomial	$7a^3, 2a^2, -6a, 5$	$7, 2, -6, 5$
$0.5x^3 + 0.1$	binomial	$0.5x^3, 0.1$	$0.5, 0.1$
$-4b^2a^3$	monomial	$-4b^2a^3$	-4

A **polynomial in one variable,** such as $3x^3 + 5x^2 - x + 7$, has the same variable in each of its terms. A **polynomial in several variables,** such as $-2a^2b - 3ab - b$, has two or more variables. Our primary interest is in polynomials in one variable, but some properties of polynomials with several variables will also be discussed.

▶*Degree of a polynomial*

For polynomials in one variable, the **degree of a term** is the exponent on the variable. The **degree of a polynomial** is the degree of the term of highest degree.

EXAMPLE 1

Finding the Degree of a Term

For the polynomial $-3y^2 + 9y^4 - 6y^7 + y + 8$, list the terms and their degree. Also give the degree of the polynomial.

Term	*Degree of the Term*	*Reason*
$-3y^2$	2	Exponent on y is 2
$9y^4$	4	Exponent on y is 4
$-6y^7$	7	Exponent on y is 7
y	1	Exponent on y is 1, since $y = y^1$
8	0	Exponent on y is 0, since $8 = 8 \cdot 1 = 8y^0$ (Remember that $y^0 = 1$)

Since $-6y^7$ has the highest degree, 7, the degree of the polynomial is 7. ∎

▶*Ascending and descending order*

If the polynomial in Example 1 is written in the order

$$-6y^7 + 9y^4 - 3y^2 + y + 8,$$

we say that it is in **descending order.** Note that the highest degree term is first, followed by the next highest, and so forth. The constant term is last since 8 can be written as $8y^0$. Written in **ascending order** the same polynomial would appear as

$$8 + y - 3y^2 + 9y^4 - 6y^7.$$

Most of the time we will use descending order.

EXAMPLE 2

Writing in Ascending and Descending Order

Write $-3x + 5 - x^6 + x^3$ in both descending and ascending order.

$-x^6 + x^3 - 3x + 5$ Descending order

$5 - 3x + x^3 - x^6$ Ascending order ■

▶ *Like terms*

Terms that have the variable raised to the same power are called **like terms.** The like terms for the polynomial

$$7a^2 - 3a^3 + 2a - 5a^2 + 1 - 2a - 5,$$

for example, are

$$7a^2 \text{ and } -5a^2, \quad 2a \text{ and } -2a, \quad \text{and} \quad 1 \text{ and } -5.$$

A polynomial like this one can be simplified by **collecting** or **combining like terms** using the distributive law. Both words, collecting and combining, are used to describe this operation which is illustrated in the next example.

EXAMPLE 3

Collecting and Combining Like Terms

Collect like terms and write each polynomial in descending order.

(a) $7a^2 - 3a^3 + 2a - 5a^2 + 1 - 2a - 5$

$= 7a^2 - 5a^2 - 3a^3 + 2a - 2a + 1 - 5$ Commute to collect like terms

$= (7 - 5)a^2 - 3a^3 + (2 - 2)a + (1 - 5)$ Use distributive law to combine like terms

$= 2a^2 - 3a^3 + 0 \cdot a - 4$

$= 2a^2 - 3a^3 - 4$

$= -3a^3 + 2a^2 - 4$ Descending order

(b) $-8x^3 + x^3 - 3x + 2 + 5x - 7$

$= -8x^3 + x^3 - 3x + 5x + 2 - 7$ Commute

$= (-8 + 1)x^3 + (-3 + 5)x + (2 - 7)$ Distributive law

$= -7x^3 + 2x - 5$

(c) $-3x^3 + x^7 - 7x - 4x^7 + x^3 + 1$

$= x^7 - 4x^7 - 3x^3 + x^3 - 7x + 1$

$= (1 - 4)x^7 + (-3 + 1)x^3 - 7x + 1$ This step may be omitted

$= -3x^7 - 2x^3 - 7x + 1$ ■

Like terms in polynomials with several variables must contain exactly the same variables raised to the same power. The following table lists several terms along with like and unlike terms.

Term	*Like Term*	*Unlike Term*
$-2xy$	$5xy$	$6y$
$8a^2b^3$	$-2a^2b^3$	$3a^3b^2$
$9xy^4z$	$4xy^4z$	$-7x^2y^4z$
2	-10	$5a^2b^2$

EXAMPLE 4

Collecting and Combining Like Terms

Collect like terms.

$$3x^2y - 5xy - 2x - 4x^2y + 4x + 2xy^2$$
$$= 3x^2y - 4x^2y - 5xy - 2x + 4x + 2xy^2$$
$$= (3 - 4)x^2y - 5xy + (-2 + 4)x + 2xy^2$$ With more practice, this step may be omitted
$$= -x^2y - 5xy + 2x + 2xy^2$$ ■

▶ *Evaluating polynomials*

Since a variable represents a real number, a polynomial in that variable also represents a real number. We can **evaluate** a polynomial when specific values for the variable(s) are given. The value of a polynomial will usually be different when different values for the variable(s) are used.

EXAMPLE 5

Evaluating Polynomials

Evaluate the polynomials for the given values of the variables.

(a) $5x^2 - 3x + 1$ for $x = -2$

$$5x^2 - 3x + 1 = 5(-2)^2 - 3(-2) + 1$$ Substitute -2 for x
$$= 5(4) + 6 + 1$$ Square first, then multiply
$$= 20 + 6 + 1 = 27$$ Add

(b) $5x^2 - 3x + 1$ for $x = 2$

$$5x^2 - 3x + 1 = 5(2)^2 - 3(2) + 1$$ Substitute 2 for x
$$= 5(4) - 6 + 1$$
$$= 20 - 6 + 1 = 15$$

Notice from (a) and (b) that the values of the polynomial are different for the different values of x.

(c) $3ab + 2a - 5b$ for $a = -1$ and $b = 0$

$$3ab + 2a - 5b = 3(-1)(0) + 2(-1) - 5(0)$$ Substitute -1 for a and 0 for b
$$= 0 - 2 - 0 = -2$$ ■

EXAMPLE 6

Manufacturing Application

The profit made by a machine manufacturer who sells x machines per week is given by the expression $100x^3 - 2500$. This means that fixed costs are \$2500 and the profit increases with the sale of each machine.

(a) Find the profit when 5 machines are sold.

$$100x^3 - 2500 = 100(5)^3 - 2500$$ Substitute 5 for x
$$= 100(125) - 2500$$
$$= 12{,}500 - 2500$$
$$= 10{,}000$$

The profit for the week was \$10,000.

(b) Find the profit when 2 machines are sold.

$$\begin{aligned} 100x^3 - 2500 &= 100(2)^3 - 2500 \\ &= 100(8) - 2500 \\ &= 800 - 2500 \\ &= -1700 \end{aligned}$$

Since the profit is negative, the company lost \$1700 that week. ■

6.3 EXERCISES

Give the type and list the terms and coefficients of the polynomials in Exercises 1–4.

1. $-3x^3 + 2$

2. $2a$

3. $-4y^2 + 2y^3 - 7y + 1$

4. $x^2 - 2xy + y^2$

Give the degree of each term in Exercises 5–8.

5. $3x^2$

6. $9b$

7. -5

8. $-7b^{14}$

Give the degree of each polynomial in Exercises 9–11.

9. $x^2 - 6x^3 + x^4 - 9x$

10. 6

11. $-y^2 - 8y + y^4 - 3y^3 + 5$

In Exercises 12–20, collect like terms and write in descending order.

12. $8x - 3x$

13. $-5y + 2y$

14. $10a^2 - 7a + 5a^2 + 3a$

15. $-4b^2 - 9 + 12 - 6b^2$

16. $2x^4 - 2x^3 + x^3 - 3x^4 + 7 - 5$

17. $7y^3 + 3y^2 - 7y^3 - 3y^2$

18. $4y^4 - 2y^3 + 2y^3 - 4y^4 + 8$

19. $\frac{3}{4}y^2 - \frac{1}{8}y^2$

20. $-0.5b^3 + 0.77b^3$

Collect like terms in Exercises 21–26.

21. $2xy - 5xy$

22. $5x^2 + 2y^2$

23. $2xy - 3y^2 + 5xy + y^2$

24. $a^2b^2 - ab + a^2b^2 + ab$

25. $-4x^2y + 2xy^2 + x^2 - 3x^2y$

26. $5ab^2 - 3ab + 3ab - 5ab^2$

Evaluate the polynomials for the given value of the variables in Exercises 27–30.

27. $3x + 2$ for $x = 5$

28. $7y^2 - 2y - 5$ for $y = -2$

29. $8a^3 - 5$ for $a = -3$

30. $2a^2 + 5b^2$ for $a = 1$ and $b = -1$

31. **MANUFACTURING** The cost in dollars of manufacturing x bolts is given by the expression $0.05x + 15.5$. Find the cost when 440 bolts are made.

32. **BUSINESS** The cost of typing a manuscript is given as two times the number of pages plus ten. Use x as the number of pages to be typed and write a polynomial to describe this cost. Find the cost of typing a one-hundred-page manuscript.

FOR REVIEW

Write in scientific notation in Exercises 33–34.

33. 265,000

34. 0.000000902

Write in standard notation in Exercises 35–36.

35. 6.75×10^{-4}

36. 1.06×10^8

Exercises 37–40 review material from Chapter 2 to help you prepare for the next section. Simplify each expression by removing the parentheses.

37. $-(-x)$ **38.** $-(x - 1)$ **39.** $-(-x - 1 + a)$ **40.** $-(a + x - 2)$

6.3 PARALLEL EXERCISES

Give the type and list the terms and coefficients of the polynomials in Exercises 1–4.

1. $7x - 5$
2. $3y^2 - 2y + 3$
3. 22
4. $9x^4y^6$

Give the degree of each term in Exercises 5–8.

5. $5y^7$ **6.** $-2x^{32}$ **7.** $4a^0$ **8.** $44b^{12}$

Give the degree of each polynomial in Exercises 9–11.

9. $3 + 4x^{10}$ **10.** $-2 - 3a$ **11.** $5y^{10} + 14y^{20} - 2y^{15} + 3$

In Exercises 12–20, collect like terms and write in descending order.

12. $-2x + 10x$ **13.** $y - 9y$ **14.** $a^3 - 3a^2 + 4a^3 - a^2$
15. $5 - b^4 + 3b^4 - 8$ **16.** $3y + 2 - 7y^2 - 2y - 5$ **17.** $-3b + 21b^7 - 5b^3 + 12b - b^7$
18. $10 - 3y + 7y^2 - 8y^3$ **19.** $0.2b - 0.8b^2 + 0.7b^2$ **20.** $\frac{3}{2}a^3 - \frac{1}{3}a^4 + \frac{1}{4}a^3 + \frac{2}{9}a^4$

Collect like terms in Exercises 21–26.

21. $-9xy + 7xy$
22. $5x^2y^2 - 5$
23. $x^2 - 3xy + 8xy - 4x^2$
24. $2a^2b - a^2b^2 - 2a^2b + a^2b^2$
25. $2x^2y^2 - 3xy^2 + 5x^2y^2 + xy^2$
26. $5ab - 2a^2 - 2a^2 + 5ab + 6$

Evaluate the polynomials for the given values of the variables in Exercises 27–30.

27. $-8x + 5$ for $x = 4$
28. $-2y^2 + 3y - 2$ for $y = -3$
29. $2a^3 + a^2$ for $a = 5$
30. $5a^2b^2 - 2$ for $a = 9$ and $b = 0$

31. **SALES** The profit in dollars when x pairs of shoes are sold is given by the expression $2x^2 - 120$. Find the profit when 10 pairs are sold.

32. **MANUFACTURING** The cost of making dresses is described as 10 times the number of dresses plus 8. Use x as the number of dresses and write a polynomial to describe this cost. Find the cost of making 20 dresses.

FOR REVIEW

Write in scientific notation in Exercises 33–34.

33. 0.0000205
34. 8,600,000,000

Write in standard notation in Exercises 35–36.

35. 8.11×10^5
36. 6.25×10^{-2}

Exercises 37–40 review material from Chapter 2 to help you prepare for the next section. Simplify each expression by removing the parentheses.

37. $-(x + 1)$ **38.** $-(-x + 1)$ **39.** $-(a - x + 2)$ **40.** $-(-a - x + 2)$

6.3 ENRICHMENT EXERCISES

The degree of a term of polynomial in several variables is found by adding the exponents on the variables. Find the degree of each term in Exercises 1–4.

1. $3x^2y^3$ **2.** $-8xy^6$ **3.** $6xyz$ **4.** $-9a^4b^2c^5$

Write each polynomial in descending powers of x in Exercises 5–6.

5. $7xy^3 - 4x^2y + 8x^4y^4$ **6.** $-3x^2yz^4 + 4yz - 8xyz$

Evaluate the polynomials for the given values of the variables in Exercises 7–12.

7. $3x^4 - 2x^3 + 4x^2 + x - 1$ for $x = 2$

8. $2y^5 - 3y^4 + 2y^3 - y^2 + 4y - 5$ for $y = 2$

9. $3x^4 - 2x^3 + 4x^2 + x - 1$ for $x = -2$

10. $2y^5 - 3y^4 + 2y^3 - y^2 + 4y - 5$ for $y = -2$

11. $3a^2b + 2ab^2 - ab$ for $a = -2$ and $b = 3$

12. $4x^3y + 3xy^2 - 2xy$ for $x = -1$ and $y = 2$

13. Burford said that $3x^2y + 4xy^2$ could be simplified by collecting like terms. Why was Burford wrong?

14. Write a paragraph describing how to tell the difference between a polynomial and other algebraic expressions.

SECTION 6.4 Addition and Subtraction of Polynomials

Student guideposts

- *Adding polynomials*
- *Subtracting polynomials*

Adding polynomials

Adding polynomials is simply a matter of collecting like terms. We work as follows.

To Add Polynomials

1. Indicate the addition with a plus sign.
2. Remove parentheses and collect like terms.

EXAMPLE 1 Adding Polynomials

Add $2x^2 - 3x + 5$ and $-x^2 + 6x + 2$.

$(2x^2 - 3x + 5) + (-x^2 + 6x + 2)$

$= 2x^2 - 3x + 5 - x^2 + 6x + 2$ Remove parentheses

$= (2 - 1)x^2 + (-3 + 6)x + (5 + 2)$ Collect like terms using the distributive law

$= x^2 + 3x + 7$ ■

When adding polynomials in one variable, we usually arrange the terms in descending order. This aids in collecting like terms and helps avoid forgetting a term.

EXAMPLE 2 **Arranging in Descending Order and Adding**

Add $-2x^3 - 4x^4 + 36 - 3x$ and $-14x^2 + 3x^3 - 6 + 5x$.

$(-4x^4 - 2x^3 - 3x + 36) + (3x^3 - 14x^2 + 5x - 6)$ — Arrange in descending order and indicate addition

$= -4x^4 - 2x^3 - 3x + 36 + 3x^3 - 14x^2 + 5x - 6$ — Remove parentheses

$= -4x^4 + (3 - 2)x^3 - 14x^2 + (5 - 3)x + (36 - 6)$ — Collect like terms using the distributive law

$= -4x^4 + x^3 - 14x^2 + 2x + 30$ ∎

Another way to add polynomials is to arrange like terms in vertical columns as illustrated in Example 3. This technique will also be used later when we multiply polynomials.

EXAMPLE 3 **Adding in Columns**

Add $2 - 3x^2$, $-x^4 + 7x - 3x^3 - 5$, and $-8x^3 + 4x^2 - 7$ using vertical columns.

$$\begin{array}{rrrrr} & & -3x^2 & & +2 \\ -x^4 & -3x^3 & & +7x & -5 \\ & -8x^3 & +4x^2 & & -7 \\ \hline -x^4 & -11x^3 & +x^2 & +0x & -3 \end{array} = -x^4 - 11x^3 + x^2 - 3$$

Note the spaces where terms are missing ∎

▶ *Subtracting polynomials*

Since addition is commutative, the arrangement of the polynomials for addition does not matter. However, when subtracting we must be sure to write the problem in the right order. For example, to subtract

$$2x + 5 \quad \text{from} \quad x^2 - 3x + 1,$$

we need to write

$$(x^2 - 3x + 1) - (2x + 5).$$

However, if we are given, for example,

$$(y^2 + 3) - (-2y + 1),$$

the problem is already set up for us.

Recall the definition of subtraction given in Chapter 1.

$$a - b = a + (-b)$$

That is, to subtract one expression from another, we add the negative of the second expression to the first. If a and b represent polynomials, $-b$ is found by changing all the signs in b. We can proceed as follows.

To Subtract Polynomials

1. Indicate the subtraction by putting a minus sign before the polynomial to be subtracted.
2. Remove parentheses, changing *all* signs in the polynomial being subtracted.
3. Collect like terms as in addition and simplify.

It helps to arrange terms in descending order when subtracting polynomials in one variable.

EXAMPLE 4

Subtracting Polynomials

Subtract $7x - 3x^2$ from $4 - 2x - 4x^2$.

$(-4x^2 - 2x + 4) - (-3x^2 + 7x)$ — Arrange in descending order and indicate the subtraction using parentheses

$= -4x^2 - 2x + 4 + 3x^2 - 7x$ — Remove parentheses, changing signs

$= -x^2 - 9x + 4$ — Combine like terms ■

CAUTION Be sure to change *all* signs in the polynomial being subtracted. This is shown in Example 4.

To do the same subtraction vertically, change the signs in $7x - 3x^2$. It becomes $-7x + 3x^2$. Now arrange the terms in vertical columns.

$$\begin{array}{r} -4x^2 - 2x + 4 \\ +3x^2 - 7x \phantom{{}+4} \\ \hline -x^2 - 9x + 4 \end{array}$$

Change signs

Add

EXAMPLE 5

Subtracting Polynomials

Subtract $-3x + 7x^4 + 5x^5 - 2$ from $2x^4 - 8x^5 - 4x + 12x^2 - x^3$.

$(-8x^5 + 2x^4 - x^3 + 12x^2 - 4x) - (5x^5 + 7x^4 - 3x - 2)$

$= -8x^5 + 2x^4 - x^3 + 12x^2 - 4x - 5x^5 - 7x^4 + 3x + 2$ — Change signs

$= -8x^5 - 5x^5 + 2x^4 - 7x^4 - x^3 + 12x^2 - 4x + 3x + 2$ — Commute

$= -13x^5 - 5x^4 - x^3 + 12x^2 - x + 2$

Subtracting vertically gives the same result.

$$\begin{array}{r} -8x^5 + 2x^4 - x^3 + 12x^2 - 4x \phantom{{}+2} \\ -5x^5 - 7x^4 \phantom{{}- x^3 + 12x^2} + 3x + 2 \\ \hline -13x^5 - 5x^4 - x^3 + 12x^2 - x + 2. \end{array}$$

Arrange in descending order

Change signs

Add ■

EXAMPLE 6

Adding and Subtracting

Perform the indicated operations.

$$\begin{aligned}
&(5x^3 - 6 + x^2) + (7x^2 - 3) - (-4x^3 + 7x - 5)\\
&\quad = (5x^3 + x^2 - 6) + (7x^2 - 3) - (-4x^3 + 7x - 5)\\
&\quad = 5x^3 + x^2 - 6 + 7x^2 - 3 + 4x^3 - 7x + 5 \qquad \text{Change signs on polynomial being subtracted}\\
&\quad = (5 + 4)x^3 + (1 + 7)x^2 - 7x + (5 - 6 - 3)\\
&\quad = 9x^3 + 8x^2 - 7x - 4
\end{aligned}$$

We add and subtract vertically as follows.

$$\begin{array}{rrrrl}
5x^3 + & x^2 & & -\ 6 & \\
 & 7x^2 & & -\ 3 & \\
+4x^3 & & -\ 7x & +\ 5 & \text{Change all signs}\\
\hline
9x^3 + & 8x^2 & -\ 7x & -\ 4. & \text{Add} \ \blacksquare
\end{array}$$

For polynomials in several variables, the procedures are exactly the same. Be sure that only like terms are combined.

EXAMPLE 7

Adding in Several Variables

Add $8x^2 + 2y^2 - 3xy$ and $6x^2 - 7y^2 - 9xy + 3$.

$$\begin{aligned}
&(8x^2 + 2y^2 - 3xy) + (6x^2 - 7y^2 - 9xy + 3)\\
&\quad = 8x^2 + 2y^2 - 3xy + 6x^2 - 7y^2 - 9xy + 3\\
&\quad = (8 + 6)x^2 + (2 - 7)y^2 + (-3 - 9)xy + 3\\
&\quad = 14x^2 - 5y^2 - 12xy + 3 \quad \blacksquare
\end{aligned}$$

EXAMPLE 8

Subtracting in Several Variables

Subtract $3ab - 5a + 9$ from $-6ab + 2a + b$.

$$\begin{aligned}
&(-6ab + 2a + b) - (3ab - 5a + 9) && \text{Use parentheses}\\
&\quad = -6ab + 2a + b - 3ab + 5a - 9 && \text{Change signs}\\
&\quad = (-6 - 3)ab + (2 + 5)a + b - 9 && \text{Collect like terms}\\
&\quad = -9ab + 7a + b - 9 \quad \blacksquare
\end{aligned}$$

EXAMPLE 9

Subtracting Several Times

Perform the indicated operations.

$$\begin{aligned}
&(7x^2y^2 - 2xy) - (5x^2y + 9xy) - (-x^2y^2 + 3xy^2 - 4xy)\\
&\quad = 7x^2y^2 - 2xy - 5x^2y - 9xy + x^2y^2 - 3xy^2 + 4xy && \text{Change signs}\\
&\quad = (7 + 1)x^2y^2 + (-2 - 9 + 4)xy - 5x^2y - 3xy^2 && \text{Collect like terms}\\
&\quad = 8x^2y^2 - 7xy - 5x^2y - 3xy^2
\end{aligned}$$

Note that $-5x^2y$ and $-3xy^2$ are not like terms. ■

6.4 EXERCISES

Add the polynomials in Exercises 1–10.

1. $3x - 5$ and $-8x + 4$

2. $7x^2 + 6$ and $x^2 - 2$

3. $3x^5 - 2x^3 + 5x^2$ and $-5x^5 + 8x^4 - 7x^2$

4. $-x^6 + 2x^4$ and $2x^7 - x^6 + 5x^2 + 2$

5. $2 - x^2 + 7x$, $9x - 7 + x^3$, $-6x$, and $12 - 3x^3$

6. $25x^4 - 7x^5$, $12x - 17x^2 + 40x^3 - 18x^4$, and $x - 21 + 18x^5$

7.
$$\begin{array}{r} 3y^2 - 2y + 1 \\ \underline{-2y^2 + 2y + 8} \end{array}$$

8.
$$\begin{array}{rrrrr} 5x^5 & & + x^3 & & - 2x \\ \underline{2x^5} & \underline{- 8x^4} & \underline{- 7x^3} & \underline{+ 6x^2} & \end{array}$$

9.
$$\begin{array}{rrrrr} & 5x^3 & + 6x^2 & & - 7 \\ -4x^4 & + 3x^3 & - 3x^2 & - 8x & \\ \underline{3x^4} & \underline{- 2x^3} & \underline{+ 4x^2} & & \underline{+ 1} \end{array}$$

10.
$$\begin{array}{rrrr} 0.03y^3 & - 0.75y^2 & - 3y & + 2 \\ -0.15y^3 & & + 5y & - 0.3 \\ \underline{0.21y^3} & \underline{- 0.13y^2} & & \underline{+ 0.6} \end{array}$$

Subtract the polynomials in Exercises 11–16.

11. $2x + 5$ from $3x - 6$

12. $6x^2 - 2$ from $4x^2 + 5$

13. $-3y^2 + 2y - 7$ from $-8y^2 + y - 9$

14. $-3y + 2$ from $y^2 - 4y - 5$

15. $a^4 + 5a^3 - 3a^2$ from $7a^5 - 2a^4 - a^2 + 3a$

16. $7x^{10} - 4x^4 + 1$ from $3x^5 + 1 - x^6 - 3x^2$

Perform the indicated operations in Exercises 17–28.

17. $(-8y^2 + 4) - (7y^2 - 3)$

18. $(-8a^2 - 2a + 5) - (-8a^2 + a + 1)$

19. $(6y^7 - y + y^5 + 2) - (2y + 3y^2 - 4y^5 - 2)$

20. $(8y^{10} - y^8) - (3y^{12} + 2y^{10} - y^8)$

21. $(3y^2 + 2) + (-5y - 5) - (y^2 - 2y + 10)$

22. $(-2a^2 + 3a) - (a^2 + a + 1) - (a^2 - 2a - 5)$

23. $(4x^2y^2 - 2xy) - (5x^2y^2 + 9xy)$

24. $(3x^2 + 2y^2 + 3) - (-6x^2 + 2y^2 - 2)$

25. $(-2a^2b + ab - 4ab^2) + (6a^2b + 4ab^2)$

26. $(-2a^2b + ab - 4ab^2) - (6a^2b + 4ab^2)$

27. $(6x^2y - xy) + (3x^2y - 7xy^2) - (4xy - 5xy^2)$

28. $(6x^2y - xy) - (3x^2y - 7xy^2) - (4xy - 5xy^2)$

BUSINESS *A toy maker finds that his manufacturing costs are given by the polynomial $M = n^2 - 2n + 5$, his sales costs are $S = n^2 - 3n + 2$, and the revenue from sales is $R = 3n^2 + n + 3$, where n is the number of toys made and sold. Use this information in Exercises 29–32.*

29. Find the polynomial that represents the total cost of manufacturing and sales.

30. Find the polynomial for the profit P of the operation if $P = R - (M + S)$.

31. Use the result of Exercise 29 to find the total cost when 10 toys are made and sold.

32. Use the result of Exercise 30 to find the profit when 10 toys are made and sold.

33. **GEOMETRY** A rectangle has sides of $5x + 4$ and $7x - 1$. Find the polynomial that represents its perimeter.

34. **GEOMETRY** If two of the angles of a triangle are $x^2 - 5$ and $2x^2 + 3x - 1$, find the polynomial that represents the third angle. [*Hint:* The sum of the angles of a triangle is 180 degrees.]

FOR REVIEW

Give the degree of each polynomial in Exercises 35–37.

35. $-6y + 8y^5 + y^4 - 2$

36. 14

37. $x^{10} - 6x^{20} + x^{30}$

Evaluate the polynomial for the given value of the variable in Exercises 38–39.

38. $-7a + 3$ for $a = -2$

39. $3y^3 + 2y^2$ for $y = -1$

40. **BUSINESS** The profit in dollars when x suits are sold is given by the expression $7x - 50$. Find the profit when 60 suits are sold.

Exercises 41–44 review material from Chapter 2 to help you prepare for the next section. Find the product.

41. $(3x)(-2x)$ **42.** $(-3x)(-2x)$ **43.** $(x^2)(4x)$ **44.** $(2x^2)(-5x^2)$

6.4 PARALLEL EXERCISES

Add the polynomials in Exercises 1–10.

1. $9x + 3$ and $-4x - 2$

2. $-8x^2 + 5$ and $3x^2 + 2$

3. $6x^4 + 2x^3 - 7x^2$ and $-9x^5 + 3x^4 - x^3 + 7$

4. $3y - 5y^3 - 2y^2 + 2$ and $9 + 2y^2 - y^3$

5. $x^2 - x^3 + x$, $5x - 6x^3 + 3$, 9, and $3 + 2x^3$

6. $-3x^5 + 9x^2$, $6 - 12x^5 + 6x^2$, and $3 - 6x + 5x^5 + x^2$

7.
$$\begin{array}{r} -9y^2 + 2y - 6 \\ 6y^2 + 3y + 9 \\ \hline \end{array}$$

8.
$$\begin{array}{rrrr} -8x^4 & & -\ 2x^2 + 6x & -\ 8 \\ 7x^4 & +\ 12x^3 & +\ 2x^2 & +\ 4 \\ \hline \end{array}$$

9.
$$\begin{array}{rrrrr} & -\ 2x^3 & +\ 8x^2 & -\ 9x & +\ 9 \\ 7x^4 & & +\ 2x^2 & +\ 9x & -\ 8 \\ -6x^4 & +\ 6x^3 & -\ 4x^2 & & +\ 7 \\ \hline \end{array}$$

10.
$$\begin{array}{rrrr} 0.23y^3 & +\ 0.98y^2 & -\ 0.6y & +\ 0.8 \\ 0.54y^3 & -\ 0.82y^2 & +\ 0.1y & \\ -0.77y^3 & & +\ 0.9y & -\ 0.3 \\ \hline \end{array}$$

Subtract the polynomials in Exercises 11–16.

11. $3x - 5$ from $2x + 8$

12. $2x^2 - 9$ from $-5x^2 + 7$

13. $6y^2 - 2y + 8$ from $-4y^2 - 2y + 1$

14. $-3y^2 + 9$ from $2y^2 - 9y + 2$

15. $5a - 3a^2 + 5a^3$ from $a^4 + 5a^2 + 5a^3 + 3$

16. $10x^8 + 10x^6 - 13$ from $2x^4 - 13 + 8x^8 - x^2$

Perform the indicated operations in Exercises 17–28.

17. $(7y^2 - 8) - (-2y^2 + 7)$

18. $(9a^2 + 7a - 4) - (-2a^2 + 7a - 7)$

19. $(-6y + 4y - y^5 + 8) - (5y - 4y^2 + 7y^5 - 2)$

20. $(3y^{14} - 2y^{10}) - (-y^{14} + 2y^{10} + y^6)$

21. $(5y + 6) + (-2y^2 + 5) - (2y^2 - 3y - 8)$

22. $(-8a^2 - 2a) - (2a^2 + 3a - 1) - (a^2 - 9a + 6)$

23. $(8x^2y^2 - 9xy) - (-4x^2y^2 + 7xy)$

24. $(5x^2 + 3y^2 - 7) - (-2x^2 + 3y^2 + 7)$

25. $(5a^2b - 2ab - 2ab^2) + (2a^2b - 6ab^2)$

26. $(5a^2b - 2ab - 2ab^2) - (2a^2b - 6ab^2)$

27. $(11x^2y - 2xy) + (4x^2y - 9xy^2) - (8xy - 10xy^2)$

28. $(11x^2y - 2xy) - (4x^2y - 9xy^2) - (8xy - 10xy^2)$

BUSINESS *A rug maker finds that his manufacturing costs are given by the polynomial $M = n^2 - 4n + 3$, his sales costs are $S = n^2 - 2n + 8$, and the revenue from sales is $R = 3n^2 + 2n + 5$, where n is the number of rugs made and sold. Use this information in Exercises 29–32.*

29. Find the polynomial that represents the total cost of manufacturing and sales.

30. Find the polynomial for the profit P of the operation if $P = R - (M + S)$.

31. Use the result of Exercise 29 to find the total cost when 20 rugs are made and sold.

32. Use the result of Exercise 30 to find the profit when 20 rugs are made and sold.

33. **GEOMETRY** A rectangle has sides of $6x - 2$ and $3x + 4$. Find the polynomial that represents its perimeter.

34. **GEOMETRY** If two of the angles of a triangle are $x^2 + x + 1$ and $x^2 - 4x + 5$, find the polynomial that represents the third angle. [*Hint:* The sum of the angles of a triangle is 180 degrees.]

FOR REVIEW

Give the degree of each polynomial in Exercises 35–37.

35. $8y^2 - 6y^{10} - y^{14}$ **36.** $22a$ **37.** $x^{20} + 2x^{40}$

Evaluate the polynomial for the given value of the variable in Exercises 38–39.

38. $6a^2 - 2a$ for $a = 3$ **39.** $y^4 - 6y^2 + 8$ for $y = -2$

40. **BUSINESS** The cost in dollars when x suits are made is given by the expression $4x^2 + 5x - 100$. Find the cost when 15 suits are made.

Exercises 41–44 review material from Chapter 2 to help you prepare for the next section. Find the product.

41. $(-7y)(4y)$ **42.** $(-7y)(-4y)$ **43.** $(-3x^3)(6x)$ **44.** $(6x^3)(5x^3)$

6.4 ENRICHMENT EXERCISES

Perform the indicated operations in Exercises 1–4.

△ **1.** $\left(\frac{1}{3}x^4 - \frac{1}{2}x^3 + \frac{7}{8}\right) + \left(-\frac{1}{9}x^4 + \frac{3}{4}x^3 - \frac{2}{3}x^2 + x\right) + \left(\frac{2}{9}x^4 - \frac{3}{2}x^3 + \frac{4}{3}x^2 + \frac{1}{3}x + \frac{3}{8}\right)$

2. $(100a^3 - 97a^2 + 21a - 105) + (16a^3 + 45a^2 - 115a) - (88a^3 - 19a^2 - 47)$

△ **3.** $(-2.13a^2 + 3.25a + 7.98) - (0.32a^3 - 2.10a + 1.92)$

4. $\left(-\frac{1}{9}x^5 + \frac{1}{3}x^4 - \frac{2}{3}x + \frac{1}{3}\right) - \left(-\frac{5}{9}x^5 - \frac{2}{9}x^4 + \frac{8}{9}x + \frac{7}{9}\right)$

5. Consider the polynomials $x^2 + 3x - 1$ and $2x^2 - x + 3$.

(a) Evaluate $x^2 + 3x - 1$ when $x = -2$.

(b) Evaluate $2x^2 - x + 3$ when $x = -2$.

(c) Find the sum of these two polynomials and evaluate the sum when $x = -2$.

(d) Compare the results of parts (a), (b), and (c).

6. Consider the polynomials $3x^2 + x - 2$ and $2x^2 - 3x + 4$.

(a) Evaluate $3x^2 + x - 2$ when $x = -1$.

(b) Evaluate $2x^2 - 3x + 4$ when $x = -1$.

(c) Subtract $3x^2 + x - 2$ from $2x^2 - 3x + 4$ and evaluate the difference when $x = -1$.

(d) Compare the results of parts (a), (b), and (c).

7. Burford was told to subtract $8x - 7$ from $12x + 5$ and showed his work below. What did he do wrong?

$$\begin{aligned} 8x - 7 - (12x + 5) &= 8x - 7 - 12x - 5 \\ &= -4x - 12 \end{aligned}$$

8. Burford shows his work on another problem below. What did he do wrong this time? Give the correct answer.

$$\begin{aligned} 18ab - (3ab - 4) &= 18ab - 3ab - 4 \\ &= 15ab - 4 \end{aligned}$$

9. Discuss the method used to add or subtract polynomials. Why is it important to use parentheses in a subtraction problem?

SECTION 6.5 Multiplication of Polynomials

Student guideposts

- ▶ *Multiplying monomials*
- ▶ *Multiplying a binomial by a monomial*
- ▶ *Multiplying polynomials*
- ▶ *The FOIL method for multiplying binomials*

▶ *Multiplying monomials*

In Section 6.1 we multiplied powers of a variable by adding their exponents using the product rule

$$x^m x^n = x^{m+n}.$$

This rule is used repeatedly when we multiply polynomials. We begin by reviewing multiplication of monomials.

EXAMPLE 1 Multiplying a Monomial by a Monomial

Multiply.

(a) $(-3x^2)(7x^5) = (-3)(7)x^2x^5$ The order of the factors can be changed

$= -21x^{2+5}$ Use $x^m x^n = x^{m+n}$

$= -21x^7$

(b) $(5x^4)(-x) = (5)(-1)x^4x$ $-x = (-1)\cdot x$

$= -5x^{4+1}$ $x = x^1$

$= -5x^5$ ■

▶ *Multiplying a binomial by a monomial*

In Section 2.5 we introduced the distributive law. Examples in that section showed multiplication of a binomial by a monomial. Example 2 reviews this idea.

EXAMPLE 2 Multiplying a Monomial by a Binomial

Multiply.

(a) $a(3a^2 + 2) = (a)(3a^2) + (a)(2)$ Distributive law

$= 3aa^2 + 2a$

$= 3a^3 + 2a$

(b) $-3a^2(8a^3 - 5a) = (-3a^2)(8a^3) + (-3a^2)(-5a)$ Distributive law

$= (-3)(8)a^2a^3 + (-3)(-5)a^2a$

$= -24a^{2+3} + 15a^{2+1}$

$= -24a^5 + 15a^3$ ■

▶ *Multiplying polynomials*

Polynomials can be multiplied by repeated use of the distributive law. This is illustrated in Example 3.

EXAMPLE 3 **Using the Distributive Law**

Multiply.

(a) $(3x + 2)(x^2 - 5x)$

$= (3x + 2)x^2 + (3x + 2)(-5x)$ Distributive law

$= (3x)(x^2) + (2)(x^2) + (3x)(-5x) + (2)(-5x)$ Distributive law

$= 3x^3 + 2x^2 - 15x^2 - 10x$

$= 3x^3 - 13x^2 - 10x$

(b) $(4x + 1)(3x^2 - x + 5)$

$= (4x + 1)3x^2 + (4x + 1)(-x) + (4x + 1)5$

$= (4x)(3x^2) + (1)(3x^2) + (4x)(-x) + (1)(-x) + (4x)(5) + (1)(5)$

$= 12x^3 + 3x^2 - 4x^2 - x + 20x + 5$

$= 12x^3 - x^2 + 19x + 5$ ■

Notice that the second step in each part of Example 3 contains all possible products of terms in the first polynomial with terms in the second. This leads to the following rule.

To Multiply Two Polynomials, Neither of Which Is a Monomial

1. Multiply each term in one by each term in the other.
2. Collect and combine like terms.

▶ *The FOIL method for multiplying binomials*

The distributive law guarantees that when two polynomials are multiplied, all products of all terms are found. Now suppose we use the following method to find the product of binomials in Example 3(a).

$$(3x + 2)(x^2 - 5x) = \overset{F}{(3x)(x^2)} + \overset{O}{(3x)(-5x)} + \overset{I}{(2)(x^2)} + \overset{L}{(2)(-5x)}$$

$$= 3x^3 - 15x^2 + 2x^2 - 10x$$

$$= 3x^3 - 13x^2 - 10x$$

Notice that the letters F, O, I, L spell "FOIL" and stand for the **F**irst terms, **O**utside terms, **I**nside terms, and **L**ast terms. Remember this word, and you will not omit terms when multiplying a binomial by a binomial.

FOIL Method

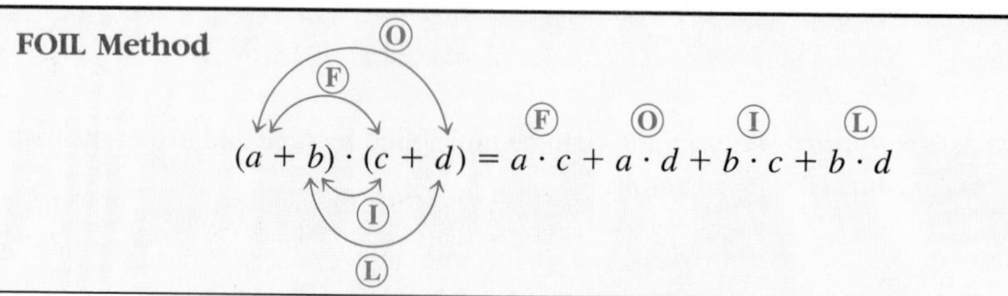

EXAMPLE 4 **Multiplying Binomials Using FOIL**

Use the FOIL method to multiply the binomials.

(a) $(x - 3) \cdot (x + 4) = x^2 + 4x - 3x - 12$ (F O I L)

$= x^2 + x - 12$

(b) $(x + 7)(x + 5) = x^2 + 5x + 7x + 35$ (F O I L)

$= x^2 + 12x + 35$ ■

When we study factoring in Chapter 7, we will start with trinomials such as $x^2 + x - 12$ in Example 4(**a**) and be expected to find the factors $(x - 3)$ and $(x + 4)$. Practicing the FOIL method now will help us understand factoring later.

EXAMPLE 5 **Using the FOIL Method**

Use the FOIL method to multiply the binomials.

(a) $(2x - 3)(3x + 7) = 6x^2 + 14x - 9x - 21$

$= 6x^2 + 5x - 21$

(b) $(2a - 5)(2a + 5) = 4a^2 + 10a - 10a - 25$

$= 4a^2 + 0 \cdot a - 25$

$= 4a^2 - 25$

(c) $(5x + 3)(x + 8) = 5x^2 + 40x + 3x + 24$

$= 5x^2 + 43x + 24$

(d) $(7y - 2)(3y - 8) = 21y^2 - 56y - 6y + 16$

$= 21y^2 - 62y + 16$

(e) $(10a + 5)(3a - 5) = 30a^2 - 50a + 15a - 25$

$= 30a^2 - 35a - 25$ ■

A third way to multiply is to write one polynomial above the other and then arrange like terms in vertical columns.

$$
\begin{array}{rrrl}
& x^2 & -\,5x & \\
& 3x & +\,2 & \\
\hline
3x^3 & -\,15x^2 & & \text{3x multiplied by each term of the top polynomial} \\
& 2x^2 & -\,10x & \text{2 multiplied by each term of the top polynomial} \\
\hline
3x^3 & -\,13x^2 & -\,10x & \text{Sum}
\end{array}
$$

The third method is especially good when trinomials or larger polynomials are part of the multiplication.

EXAMPLE 6

Using Vertical Columns

Multiply.

(a)

$$\begin{array}{rrrrrl}
 & & 5x^3 & -2x & +3 & \\
 & & & -7x^2 & +4x & \\
\hline
-35x^5 & & +14x^3 & -21x^2 & & -7x^2 \text{ multiplied by top polynomial} \\
 & 20x^4 & & -8x^2 & +12x & 4x \text{ multiplied by top polynomial} \\
\hline
-35x^5 & +20x^4 & +14x^3 & -29x^2 & +12x & \text{Sum}
\end{array}$$

We leave spaces for missing terms so we can add like terms in columns.

(b)

$$\begin{array}{rrrrl}
a^2 & +2a & +4 & & \\
a & -2 & & & \\
\hline
a^3 & +2a^2 & +4a & & a \text{ multiplied by top polynomial} \\
 & -2a^2 & -4a & -8 & -2 \text{ multiplied by top polynomial} \\
\hline
a^3 & & & -8 = a^3 - 8 & \text{Sum}
\end{array}$$

(c)

$$\begin{array}{rrrrrl}
 & & 5x^2 & -3x & +7 & \\
 & & -4x^2 & +x & +8 & \\
\hline
-20x^4 & +12x^3 & -28x^2 & & & -4x^2 \text{ multiplied by top polynomial} \\
 & 5x^3 & -3x^2 & +7x & & x \text{ multiplied by top polynomial} \\
 & & 40x^2 & -24x & +56 & 8 \text{ multiplied by top polynomial} \\
\hline
-20x^4 & +17x^3 & +9x^2 & -17x & +56 & \text{Sum} \quad \blacksquare
\end{array}$$

All the procedures used above can be applied to the multiplication of polynomials in several variables.

EXAMPLE 7

Multiplying Polynomials in Two Variables

Use the FOIL method to multiply the binomials in two variables.

(a) $(2x + y)(x - 3y) = 2x^2 - 6xy + xy - 3y^2$
$= 2x^2 - 5xy - 3y^2$

(b) $(2a - 5b)(2a + 5b) = 4a^2 + 10ab - 10ab - 25b^2$
$= 4a^2 + 0 \cdot ab - 25b^2$
$= 4a^2 - 25b^2$

(c) $(5x + 3y)(x + 8y) = 5x^2 + 40xy + 3xy + 24y^2$
$= 5x^2 + 43xy + 24y^2$ ■

EXAMPLE 8 **Using Vertical Columns**

Use vertical columns to multiply.

$$\begin{array}{rll} & 3x^2 - 4xy + 5y^2 & \\ & \underline{6x \quad - 7y \qquad\quad} & \\ & 18x^3 - 24x^2y + 30xy^2 \qquad\qquad & 6x \text{ multiplied by top polynomial} \\ & \underline{\qquad - 21x^2y + 28xy^2 - 35y^3} & -7y \text{ multiplied by top polynomial} \\ & 18x^3 - 45x^2y + 58xy^2 - 35y^3 & \text{Sum} \end{array}$$

■

We conclude this section by solving the applied problem given in the introduction to this chapter.

EXAMPLE 9 **Working with a Sales Application**

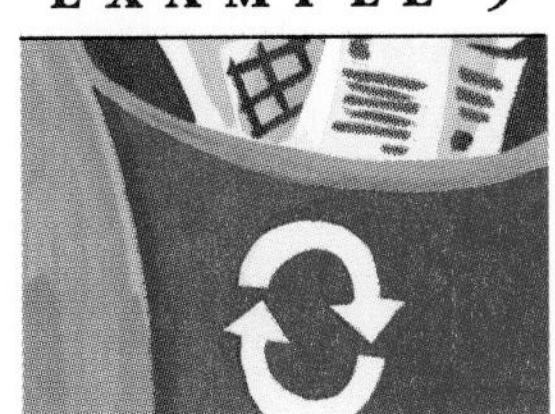

Angelica would like to begin publishing a small environmental magazine which she will call EnviroLife. She has determined that the number n of new magazine subscriptions that can be sold during each month is related to the price in dollars p of a subscription by the equation $n = 200 - 10p$. Find an equation that gives the monthly revenue R in terms of p and use it to find R when p is \$15, \$10, and \$8.

The **revenue** R produced by selling n subscriptions for p dollars is given by $R = np$. In this case the number of subscriptions sold per month is related to the price by $n = 200 - 10p$. Notice that when p is \$15, $n = 200 - 10(15) = 50$, and when p is reduced to \$10, $n = 200 - 10(10) = 100$. This tells us that as the price is lowered more magazines can be sold. The formula for the monthly revenue from new subscriptions is

$$R = np = (200 - 10p)p = 200p - 10p^2.$$

When p is \$15,

$$\begin{aligned} R &= 200(15) - 10(15)^2 \\ &= 3000 - 2250 \\ &= 750, \end{aligned}$$

so the revenue is \$750. When the price is \$10,

$$\begin{aligned} R &= 200(10) - 10(10)^2 \\ &= 2000 - 1000 \\ &= 1000 \end{aligned}$$

so the revenue is \$1000. Finally, when the price is \$8,

$$\begin{aligned} R &= 200(8) - 10(8)^2 \\ &= 1600 - 640 \\ &= 960 \end{aligned}$$

so the revenue is \$960. Notice that of the three prices used, the \$10 price gives the most revenue. ■

6.5 EXERCISES

Multiply the monomials in Exercises 1–4.

1. $(2)(6x)$

2. $(4y^2)(2y^2)$

3. $(8y^3)(-9y^2)$

4. $(-8y^6)(-7y^5)$

Multiply using the distributive law in Exercises 5–16.

5. $2(x + 3)$

6. $3x(x - 4)$

7. $-4y(y + 8)$

8. $3(2x^2 - 3x + 1)$

9. $-10x^2(x^5 - 6x^3 + 7x^2)$

10. $-9a^3(4a^4 - 3a^2 + 2)$

11. $(x + 8)(x + 4)$

12. $(2a - 3)(3a - 2)$

13. $(x - 5)(x^2 - 3x + 2)$

14. $(2y + 7)(3y^2 + y - 1)$

15. $(a^2 + 1)(a^4 - a^2 + 1)$

16. $(x^2 + 4x - 2)(2x^2 - x + 3)$

Use the FOIL method to multiply the binomials in Exercises 17–31.

17. $(x + 10)(x + 2)$

18. $(a - 6)(a + 6)$

19. $(y + 5)(y - 3)$

20. $(x - 7)(x - 3)$

21. $(x - 12)(x + 4)$

22. $(a - 8)(a - 8)$

23. $(5a - 3)(a - 7)$

24. $(2y - 7)(y + 10)$

25. $(2a + 3)(3a + 5)$

26. $(4y - 3)(2y - 5)$

27. $(5x - 2)(3x + 4)$

28. $(9a + 2)(2a - 7)$

29. $(10y - 1)(4y + 5)$

30. $(7x + 5)(3x - 8)$

31. $(2z^2 + 1)(z^2 - 2)$

Multiply the polynomials in Exercises 32–43.

32. $\begin{array}{r} 3a^2 + 5 \\ \underline{a - 4} \end{array}$

33. $\begin{array}{r} 2a^3 - 3a \\ \underline{7a^2 - 5} \end{array}$

34. $\begin{array}{r} 3a^2 - 5 \\ \underline{3a^2 - 5} \end{array}$

35. $\begin{array}{r} 7y^3 - 2 \\ \underline{7y^3 + 2} \end{array}$

36. $\begin{array}{r} 5x^4 + 3x^2 \\ \underline{8x^2 - 7} \end{array}$

37. $\begin{array}{r} 3x^2 - 5x + 2 \\ \underline{x + 4} \end{array}$

38. $\begin{array}{r} 12a^3 - 3a + 8 \\ \underline{4a^2 + 7a} \end{array}$

39. $\begin{array}{r} 12a^3 - 6a + 4 \\ \underline{7a^2 - 3} \end{array}$

40. $\begin{array}{r} 0.3x^2 + 0.2 \\ \underline{0.5x - 0.7} \end{array}$

41. $\begin{array}{r} \frac{2}{3}y^2 - \frac{3}{4} \\ \underline{\frac{1}{2}y + 5} \end{array}$

42. $\begin{array}{r} 3y^2 + 5y - 6 \\ \underline{y^2 - 3y + 2} \end{array}$

43. $\begin{array}{r} -4x^3 + 2x - 5 \\ \underline{6x^2 - x + 1} \end{array}$

In Exercises 44–49, multiply the polynomials in two variables.

44. $2xy(x^2 + 2xy)$

45. $3a^2b(a^2b + 2ab - ab^2)$

46. $(2a - 3b)(5a + b)$

47. $(7a - 2b)(2a - 5b)$

48. $\begin{array}{r} 3x^2 - 2xy + 4y^2 \\ \underline{2x + y} \end{array}$

49. $\begin{array}{r} a^2b^2 + ab - 3 \\ \underline{a^2 - b^2} \end{array}$

In Exercises 50–51, perform the following operations.

50. $(x - 1)(x + 1)(x + 2)$

51. $(y + 3)(y - 2)(y + 2)$

52. GEOMETRY The length of a rectangle measures $(2x + 1)$ feet and the width is $(3x - 2)$ feet. Find the area of the rectangle in terms of x.

53. GEOMETRY The dimensions of a box, given in centimeters, are y, $y + 1$, and $2y + 3$. Find the volume of the box in terms of y.

54. SALES A wholesale distributor who sells clocks knows that the number n of clocks she can sell each month is related to the price in dollars p of each clock by the equation $n = 5000 - 100p$. Find an equation for the monthly revenue R in terms of p and use it to find R when p is \$10, \$30, and \$45.

55. GEOMETRY The length l of a rectangular pasture is to be 300 m longer than the width w. Find an equation that gives the area in terms of the width and use it to give the area when the width is 40 m, 100 m, and 500 m.

FOR REVIEW

In Exercises 56–57, perform the indicated operations.

56. $(-4y^2 + 2y) + (y^3 - 2y) - (y^2 + 3y - 5)$

57. $(x^2 - y^2) - (2x^2 - 3y^2) - (5x^2 - y^2)$

In Exercises 58–60, find the special products using the FOIL method. This will help you prepare for the next section.

58. $(x - 5)(x - 5)$

59. $(3x + 2y)(3x - 2y)$

60. $(3x + 2y)(3x + 2y)$

6.5 PARALLEL EXERCISES

Multiply the following monomials in Exercises 1–4.

1. $(3)(5x)$

2. $(-3a^3)(5a^2)$

3. $(a^7)(a^7)$

4. $(-10y^7)(-20y^8)$

Multiply using the distributive law in Exercises 5–16.

5. $5x(x - 6)$

6. $2x(-3x + 5)$

7. $-9a(2a^2 - 3)$

8. $5(3x^2 - 2x - 3)$

9. $6y^2(-8y^2 + 5y - 3)$

10. $-10a^5(-2a^5 + 2a^4 - 8a^2)$

11. $(x + 5)(x + 10)$

12. $(5a - 2)(2a - 7)$

13. $(x - 3)(x^2 + 5x - 4)$

14. $(3y + 8)(2y^2 - 2y + 3)$

15. $(a^2 - 1)(a^4 + a^2 + 1)$

16. $(2x^2 + 3x - 2)(x^2 - 5x + 1)$

Use the FOIL method to multiply the binomials in Exercises 17–31.

17. $(x + 3)(x - 9)$

18. $(a + 8)(a - 8)$

19. $(x - 4)(x - 5)$

20. $(y - 12)(y + 3)$

21. $(a - 9)(a - 9)$

22. $(y - 9)(y + 4)$

23. $(4a - 5)(a - 6)$

24. $(7y - 2)(y + 5)$

25. $(4a + 5)(5a + 4)$

26. $(3y - 5)(4y - 7)$

27. $(2x - 9)(5x + 3)$

28. $(10a + 3)(5a - 9)$

29. $(7y - 3)(8y + 3)$

30. $(9x + 7)(2x - 1)$

31. $(3z^2 - 1)(z^2 + 1)$

Multiply the polynomials in Exercises 32–43.

32. $\begin{array}{l} 3x + 4 \\ \underline{5x - 8} \end{array}$

33. $\begin{array}{l} 3a^3 - 5a \\ \underline{4a^2 - 7} \end{array}$

34. $\begin{array}{l} 4x^2 + 9 \\ \underline{4x^2 + 9} \end{array}$

35. $\begin{array}{l} 8y^3 + 5 \\ \underline{8y^3 - 5} \end{array}$

36. $\begin{array}{l} 10x^4 + 7x \\ \underline{5x^2 - 2x} \end{array}$

37. $\begin{array}{l} 2x^2 - 8x + 3 \\ \underline{x + 3} \end{array}$

38. $\begin{array}{l} 8a^4 - 5a + 1 \\ \underline{3a^2 + 5} \end{array}$

39. $\begin{array}{l} 15a^3 + 5a^2 - 3 \\ \underline{6a^2 - 7} \end{array}$

40. $\begin{array}{l} 1.2x^2 + 4.5 \\ \underline{0.1x - 1.2} \end{array}$

41. $\begin{array}{l} \frac{1}{2}y^2 - \frac{5}{4} \\ \underline{\frac{4}{3}y + 7} \end{array}$

42. $\begin{array}{l} a^2 + 3a - 1 \\ \underline{a^2 - 3a + 1} \end{array}$

43. $\begin{array}{l} -2x^4 + 5x^2 - 3 \\ \underline{8x^2 - 3x + 2} \end{array}$

In Exercises 44–49, multiply the polynomials in two variables.

44. $5xy(3xy + y^2)$

45. $6a^3b^2(2a^4b - 3a^2b^2 + ab)$

46. $(3a - 5b)(7a + 8b)$

47. $(3a - 8b)(10a - 3b)$

48. $\begin{array}{l} 5x^2 - 5xy + 6y^2 \\ \underline{4x \quad + 3y \qquad} \end{array}$

49. $\begin{array}{l} 2a^2b^2 - 3ab + 9 \\ \underline{\quad ab - 2 \qquad} \end{array}$

In Exercises 50–51, perform the following operations.

50. $(y - 3)(y + 3)(y - 2)$

51. $(x + 4)(x + 2)(x - 4)$

---

52. **GEOMETRY** The base of a triangle measures $(3y + 2)$ inches and the height is $(2y - 1)$ inches. Find the area of the triangle in terms of y.

53. **GEOMETRY** The dimensions of a box, given in feet, are x, $x + 2$, and $3x + 5$. Find the volume of the box in terms of x.

54. **SALES** The Valley Video Center sells blank video cassettes. From past experience it has been shown that the number n of cassettes that can be sold each week depends on the price p in dollars charged for each according to the equation $n = 1000 - 100p$. Find a formula for the weekly revenue R in terms of p. Use this formula to find the revenue when the price of a cassette is \$5, \$8, and \$10.

55. **GEOMETRY** A rectangular metal plate is to be constructed in such a way that the length is 10 cm more than twice the width. Find an equation that gives the area of the top of the plate and use it to find the area when the width is 30 cm, 70 cm, and 120 cm.

FOR REVIEW

In Exercises 56–57, perform the indicated operations.

56. $(9y^2 - 6) + (y^4 - 5y^2) - (2y^2 - 5y + 7)$

57. $(x^2y^2 - xy + 2) - (5x^2y^2 - 3) - (4xy - 11)$

In Exercises 58–60, find the special products using the FOIL method. This will help you prepare for the next section.

58. $(y + 9)(y + 9)$

59. $(5x - 4y)(5x + 4y)$

60. $(5x - 4y)(5x - 4y)$

6.5 ENRICHMENT EXERCISES

In Exercises 1–12, perform the indicated operations and collect like terms.

△ **1.** $(x + y)(x^2 - xy + y^2)$

2. $(x - y)(x^2 + xy + y^2)$

3. $(a - 5b)(2a + b)(2a - 3b)$

△ **4.** $(a - b)[3a^2 - (a + b)(a - 2b)]$

5. $4x^2(-2x + 1) - 3x(x^2 - 5)$

6. $-7x(2x^2 + x) - 5x^2(-x + 3)$

7. $3x^2(3x^2 + 2x - 4) - 2x(4x^2 - x + 3)$

8. $2x^3(-5x^2 + 2x + 3) - 8x(x^3 + 2x^2 - 5)$

9. $(x + 2)(x - 3) + (2x - 3)(-x + 1)$

10. $(2x + 3)(x - 1) + (3x - 2)(-x + 3)$

11. $(2x - 5)(x - 3) - (3x + 1)(-2x - 1)$

12. $(3x + 5)(2x - 3) - (x + 5)(-x - 1)$

13. Can you explain how Burford got the wrong answer of $2x^2 + 3y^2$ when he multiplied $2x + y$ by $x + 3y$?

14. The FOIL method is used on what type of problem? Write a paragraph answering this question and discussing the advantages of FOIL over the distributive law.

SECTION 6.6 Special Products

Student guideposts

- *Difference of squares*
- *Perfect square trinomials*

Difference of squares

In Section 6.5 we learned how to multiply binomials using the FOIL method. Certain products of binomials occur often enough to merit special consideration. For example, suppose we use the FOIL method to multiply the two binomials $x + 6$ and $x - 6$.

$$\begin{aligned}(x + 6)(x - 6) &= x^2 - 6x + 6x - 6^2\\ &= x^2 - 36\end{aligned}$$

Notice that the sum of the middle terms is zero. This always happens when two binomials of the form $a + b$ and $a - b$ are multiplied.

Difference of Two Squares

The product of a sum and a difference is the square of the first minus the square of the second.

$$(a + b)(a - b) = a^2 - b^2$$

Since the order of multiplication can be changed, we also know that $(a - b)(a + b) = a^2 - b^2$.

EXAMPLE 1 **Working with a Difference of Two Squares**

Find each product using both FOIL and the difference of squares formula.

(a) $(x - 7)(x + 7)$.

FOIL method

$$\begin{aligned}(x - 7)(x + 7) &= x^2 + 7x - 7x - 49\\ &= x^2 - 49\end{aligned}$$

Using $(a - b)(a + b) = a^2 - b^2$

$$\begin{aligned}(x - 7)(x + 7) &= x^2 - 7^2\\ &= x^2 - 49\end{aligned}$$

(b) $(3z + 4)(3z - 4)$.

FOIL method

$$\begin{aligned}&(3z + 4)(3z - 4)\\ &= 9z^2 - 12z + 12z - 16\\ &= 9z^2 - 16\end{aligned}$$

Using $(a + b)(a - b) = a^2 - b^2$

$$\begin{aligned}(3z + 4)(3z - 4) &= (3z)^2 - 4^2\\ &= 9z^2 - 16\end{aligned}$$

(c) $(7x^2 - 2x)(7x^2 + 2x)$.

FOIL method

$$\begin{aligned}&(7x^2 - 2x)(7x^2 + 2x)\\ &= 49x^4 + 14x^3 - 14x^3 - 4x^2\\ &= 49x^4 - 4x^2\end{aligned}$$

Using $(a - b)(a + b) = a^2 - b^2$

$$\begin{aligned}(7x^2 - 2x)(7x^2 + 2x) &= (7x^2)^2 - (2x)^2\\ &= 49x^4 - 4x^2\end{aligned}$$

■

▶ *Perfect square trinomials*

Squaring a binomial also takes a special form. For example, suppose we square $x + 6$.

$$\begin{aligned}(x+6)^2 = (x+6)(x+6) &= x^2 + 6x + 6x + 36 \quad \text{FOIL method}\\ &= x^2 + 2(6x) + 36\\ &= x^2 + 12x + 36\end{aligned}$$

This illustrates one of the perfect square formulas.

Perfect Square Trinomial

The square of a binomial of the form $a + b$ is the square of the first plus twice the product of first and second plus the square of the second.

$$(a+b)^2 = (a+b)(a+b) = a^2 + 2ab + b^2$$

EXAMPLE 2

Squaring $a + b$

Find each product using both FOIL and the perfect square formula.

(a) $(y + 3)(y + 3)$.

FOIL method

$$\begin{aligned}(y+3)(y+3) &= y^2 + 3y + 3y + 9\\ &= y^2 + 6y + 9\end{aligned}$$

Using $(a+b)^2 = a^2 + 2ab + b^2$

$$\begin{aligned}(y+3)^2 &= y^2 + 2(y)(3) + 3^2\\ &= y^2 + 6y + 9\end{aligned}$$

(b) $(5x + 4)(5x + 4)$.

FOIL method

$$\begin{aligned}&(5x+4)(5x+4)\\ &= 25x^2 + 20x + 20x + 16\\ &= 25x^2 + 40x + 16\end{aligned}$$

Using $(a+b)^2 = a^2 + 2ab + b^2$

$$\begin{aligned}(5x+4)^2 &= (5x)^2 + 2(5x)(4) + 4^2\\ &= 25x^2 + 40x + 16\end{aligned}$$

■

To illustrate the second perfect square formula, look at the square of the binomial $x - 6$.

$$\begin{aligned}(x-6)^2 = (x-6)(x-6) &= x^2 - 6x - 6x + 36 \quad \text{FOIL method}\\ &= x^2 - 2(6x) + 36\\ &= x^2 - 12x + 36\end{aligned}$$

Perfect Square Trinomial

The square of a binomial of the form $a - b$ is the square of the first minus twice the product of first and second plus the square of the second.

$$(a-b)^2 = (a-b)(a-b) = a^2 - 2ab + b^2$$

EXAMPLE 3

Squaring $a - b$

Find each product using both FOIL and the perfect square formula.

(a) $(y - 2)(y - 2)$

FOIL method

$$(y - 2)(y - 2)$$
$$= y^2 - 2y - 2y + 4$$
$$= y^2 - 4y + 4$$

Using $(a - b)^2 = a^2 - 2ab + b^2$

$$(y - 2)^2 = y^2 - 2(y)(2) + 2^2$$
$$= y^2 - 4y + 4$$

(b) $(5x - 4)(5x - 4)$.

FOIL method

$$(5x - 4)(5x - 4)$$
$$= 25x^2 - 20x - 20x + 16$$
$$= 25x^2 - 40x + 16$$

Using $(a - b)^2 = a^2 - 2ab + b^2$

$$(5x - 4)^2 = (5x)^2 - 2(5x)(4) + 4^2$$
$$= 25x^2 - 40x + 16$$ ■

CAUTION A common mistake students make when squaring a binomial is to write

$(a - b)^2 = a^2 - b^2$ THIS IS WRONG

or $(a + b)^2 = a^2 + b^2$. THIS IS WRONG

To see that $(a + b)^2 \neq a^2 + b^2$, substitute 1 for a and 2 for b. Then,

$$(a + b)^2 = (1 + 2)^2 = 3^2 = 9.$$

However, $a^2 + b^2 = (1)^2 + (2)^2 = 1 + 4 = 5.$

Don't forget the middle term $2ab$ when finding $(a + b)^2$, or $-2ab$ when finding $(a - b)^2$.

EXAMPLE 4

Multiplying Binomials with Two Variables

Use the special formulas in this section to find the following products involving two variables.

(a) $(2x - 3y)(2x + 3y) = (2x)^2 - (3y)^2$ $\quad (a - b)(a + b) = a^2 - b^2$
$= 4x^2 - 9y^2$

(b) $(2x + 3y)^2 = (2x)^2 + 2(2x)(3y) + (3y)^2$ $\quad (a + b)^2 = a^2 + 2ab + b^2$
$= 4x^2 + 12xy + 9y^2$

(c) $(2x - 3y)^2 = (2x)^2 - 2(2x)(3y) + (3y)^2$ $\quad (a - b)^2 = a^2 - 2ab + b^2$
$= 4x^2 - 12xy + 9y^2$

(d) $\left(\frac{1}{3}x - \frac{1}{2}y\right)^2 = \left(\frac{1}{3}x\right)^2 - 2\left(\frac{1}{3}x\right)\left(\frac{1}{2}y\right) + \left(\frac{1}{2}y\right)^2$ $\quad (a - b)^2 = a^2 - 2ab + b^2$

$= \frac{1}{9}x^2 - \frac{1}{3}xy + \frac{1}{4}y^2$ ■

6.6 EXERCISES

In Exercises 1–27, multiply using special formulas.

1. $(x - 3)(x + 3)$ **2.** $(x + 5)^2$ **3.** $(x - 5)^2$

4. $(y - 8)(y + 8)$ **5.** $(7a - 1)(7a + 1)$ **6.** $(2x - 7)^2$

7. $(4y - 9)(4y + 9)$ **8.** $(5a + 7)(5a - 7)$ **9.** $(3a - 1)^2$

10. $(5x - 3)(5x + 3)$ **11.** $(6a + 7)^2$ **12.** $(4x + 8)^2$

13. $(3y - 9)^2$ **14.** $(5a - 10)(5a + 10)$ **15.** $(5y^2 - 1)^2$

16. $(2x^2 - 3x)(2x^2 + 3x)$ **17.** $(2y^2 + 3y)^2$ **18.** $(2y^2 - 3y)^2$

19. $(0.7y - 3)^2$ **20.** $\left(\frac{1}{2}a - \frac{1}{3}\right)\left(\frac{1}{2}a + \frac{1}{3}\right)$ **21.** $(5x - 2y)(5x + 2y)$

22. $(5x + 2y)^2$ **23.** $(5x - 2y)^2$ **24.** $(x^2 + y^2)(x^2 - y^2)$

25. $(2x^2 - y)^2$ **26.** $(8x + 3y)^2$ **27.** $(a^2 + 2b)^2$

Perform the following operations in Exercises 28–30.

28. $(x + 1)^2 - (x - 1)^2$ **29.** $(a - 2b)^2 + (a + 2b)^2$ **30.** $(z - 4)(z + 4) - (z + 4)^2$

31. **GEOMETRY** A field that is rectangular in shape is $(2a + 7)$ miles long and $(a - 1)$ miles wide. Find the area of the field in terms of a.

To multiply the polynomials in Exercises 32–37, use the formulas

$$(a + b)(a^2 - ab + b^2) = a^3 + b^3 \quad \text{and} \quad (a - b)(a^2 + ab + b^2) = a^3 - b^3.$$

32. $(x + 2)(x^2 - 2x + 4)$ **33.** $(x - 2)(x^2 + 2x + 4)$ **34.** $(y - 5)(y^2 + 5y + 25)$

35. $(y + 5)(y^2 - 5y + 25)$ **36.** $(3x + y)(9x^2 - 3xy + y^2)$ **37.** $(3x - y)(9x^2 + 3xy + y^2)$

FOR REVIEW

Multiply the polynomials in Exercises 38–40.

38. $-3a^2(ab^2 - ab + 7)$ **39.** $(5a + 7)(3a - 8)$ **40.** $\begin{array}{r} 2x^2 - xy + y^2 \\ \underline{x - y} \end{array}$

Exercises 41–43 review material from Section 6.1 to help you prepare for the next section. Simplify each expression using the quotient rule for exponents.

41. $\frac{15x^2}{3x}$ **42.** $\frac{26x^2y}{13xy}$ **43.** $\frac{-33x^3y^5}{33x^4y^2}$

6.6 PARALLEL EXERCISES

In Exercises 1–27, multiply using special formulas.

1. $(x-4)(x+4)$
2. $(x+10)^2$
3. $(x-10)^2$
4. $(y-9)(y+9)$
5. $(3y-7)(3y+7)$
6. $(3x+4)^2$
7. $(8y-1)(8y+1)$
8. $(6a-5)(6a+5)$
9. $(9a-1)^2$
10. $(10x-3)(10x+3)$
11. $(4a+5)^2$
12. $(2x+10)^2$
13. $(6y-3)^2$
14. $(6x+3)(6x-3)$
15. $(3y^2+2)^2$
16. $(2a^2-5)(2a^2+5)$
17. $(3y^2+4y)^2$
18. $(3y^2-4y)^2$
19. $(0.4y-5)^2$
20. $\left(\frac{2}{3}a-\frac{1}{4}\right)\left(\frac{2}{3}a+\frac{1}{4}\right)$
21. $(7x-3y)(7x+3y)$
22. $(7x+3y)^2$
23. $(7x-3y)^2$
24. $(x^3+y^3)(x^3-y^3)$
25. $(3x-y^2)^2$
26. $(8x-3y)^2$
27. $(a^2-2b)^2$

Perform the following operations in Exercises 28–30.

28. $(x-1)^2-(x+1)^2$
29. $(a+3b)^2+(a-3b)^2$
30. $(y-2)(y+2)-(y-2)^2$
31. **GEOMETRY** A picture frame is in the shape of a square with sides $(3z+2)$ feet in length. Find the area of the frame in terms of z.

To multiply the polynomials in Exercises 32–37, use the formulas

$$(a+b)(a^2-ab+b^2)=a^3+b^3 \quad \text{and} \quad (a-b)(a^2+ab+b^2)=a^3-b^3.$$

32. $(x+3)(x^2-3x+9)$
33. $(x-3)(x^2+3x+9)$
34. $(y-4)(y^2+4y+16)$
35. $(y+4)(y^2-4y+16)$
36. $(2x+3y)(4x^2-6xy+9y^2)$
37. $(2x-3y)(4x^2+6xy+9y^2)$

FOR REVIEW

Multiply the polynomials in Exercises 38–40.

38. $4ab(-2a^2b-6a+9b)$
39. $(2a-5)(4a-3)$
40. $\begin{array}{r} 5x^2y^2-2xy+3 \\ \underline{2xy\quad -1} \end{array}$

Exercises 41–43 review material from Section 6.1 to help you prepare for the next section. Simplify each expression using the quotient rule for exponents.

41. $\dfrac{-24a^3}{8a^2}$
42. $\dfrac{64a^3b^2}{16ab^5}$
43. $\dfrac{12a^7b}{24a^3b}$

6.6 ENRICHMENT EXERCISES

Perform the indicated operations in Exercises 1–4. Assume all exponents are positive integers.

1. $[2x^2-(x-2y)][2x^2+(x-2y)]$
   [*Hint:* Multiply before removing parentheses.]
2. $(2x+y-z)^2$
3. $(a^n+b^n)(a^n-b^n)$
4. △ $(a^n-b^n)^2$
5. Evaluate **(a)** $(x+2)^2$, **(b)** $(x-2)^2$, **(c)** $(x+2)(x-2)$, **(d)** x^2+4x+4, **(e)** x^2-4x+4, and **(f)** x^2-4 when $x=3$, and notice which of the values are the same.
6. Evaluate **(a)** $(y+3)^2$, **(b)** $(y-3)^2$, **(c)** $(y+3)(y-3)$, **(d)** y^2+6y+9, **(e)** y^2-6y+9, and **(f)** y^2-9 when $y=4$, and notice which of the values are the same.

In Exercises 7–14, give the method that you would use to multiply. Do not find the product.

7. $(x - 5)(x + 5)$ **8.** $3a^2(4a + b)$ **9.** $(3x^2 - 5)(4x + 3)$ **10.** $(y + 5)(3y^2 - 6y + 4)$

11. $(x - 2y)(x - 2y)$ **12.** $(2a + 3b)(2a + 3b)$ **13.** $(6y + z)(6y - z)$ **14.** $[(a + b) + c]^2$

15. Burford thought that $a^2 - b^2$ and $(a - b)^2$ were the same. Can you tell him why he is wrong?

16. Explain when the vertical-column method might be appropriate when multiplying polynomials.

SECTION 6.7 Division of Polynomials

Student guideposts

▶ ***Dividing a polynomial by a monomial***
▶ ***Dividing a polynomial by a binomial***

▶ ***Dividing a polynomial by a monomial***

To illustrate the rule for dividing a polynomial by a monomial, look at the following example.

$$\frac{3x^3 - x^2}{x} = \frac{1}{x}[3x^3 - x^2] \quad \text{Dividing by } x \text{ is the same as multiplying by } \frac{1}{x}$$

$$= \frac{1}{x}(3x^3) - \frac{1}{x}(x^2) \quad \text{Distributive law}$$

$$= \frac{3x^3}{x} - \frac{x^2}{x} \quad \text{Multiplication by } \frac{1}{x} \text{ is the same as dividing by } x$$

$$= 3x^{3-1} - x^{2-1} \quad \frac{a^m}{a^n} = a^{m-n}$$

$$= 3x^2 - x$$

In general, we omit the first two steps, write

$$\frac{3x^3 - x^2}{x} = \frac{3x^3}{x} - \frac{x^2}{x},$$

and use the quotient rule for exponents.

To Divide a Polynomial by a Monomial

1. Divide each term of the polynomial by the monomial.
2. Use the rule

$$\frac{x^m}{x^n} = x^{m-n}$$

to divide the variables.

EXAMPLE 1 **Dividing by a Monomial**

Divide.

(a) $$\frac{14x^3 - 7x^2 + 28x - 7}{7} = \frac{14x^3}{7} - \frac{7x^2}{7} + \frac{28x}{7} - \frac{7}{7}$$

$$= 2x^3 - x^2 + 4x - 1$$

(b) $$\frac{8x^4 - 6x^2 + 12x}{-2x} = \frac{8x^4}{-2x} - \frac{6x^2}{-2x} + \frac{12x}{-2x}$$
$$= -4x^3 + 3x - 6$$

$\frac{x^4}{x} = x^{4-1} = x^3$, $\frac{x^2}{x} = x^{2-1} = x$,
$\frac{x}{x} = x^{1-1} = x^0 = 1$

(c) $$\frac{7x^5 - 35x^4 + 40x}{5x^2} = \frac{7x^5}{5x^2} - \frac{35x^4}{5x^2} + \frac{40x}{5x^2}$$
$$= \frac{7}{5}x^3 - 7x^2 + \frac{8}{x}$$

$\frac{x}{x^2} = \frac{1}{x}$ ■

CAUTION Is $\frac{x+5}{5}$ equal to $x + 1$? The answer is no. Every number in the numerator must be divided by 5. The correct quotient is

$$\frac{x+5}{5} = \frac{x}{5} + \frac{5}{5} = \frac{x}{5} + 1.$$

If a division problem is expressed using the sign ÷, change to the notation used in the examples above. To find $(3a^3b^3 - 9a^2b + 27ab) \div 9ab$ we write

$$\frac{3a^3b^3 - 9a^2b + 27ab}{9ab} = \frac{3a^3b^3}{9ab} - \frac{9a^2b}{9ab} + \frac{27ab}{9ab}$$
$$= \frac{1}{3}a^2b^2 - a + 3.$$

▶ ***Dividing a polynomial by a binomial***

The procedure for dividing a polynomial by a binomial closely follows long division of one whole number by another. It might help to refer to the following numerical problem as you read through the rules given below.

```
43 ÷ 37
 61 ÷ 37
  247 ÷ 37
   252 ÷ 37
     1166     Remainder 30
 37)43172
    37 <--- First digit of quotient times divisor 37
     61     Subtract and bring down next digit of dividend, 43172
     37 <--- Second digit of quotient times 37
     247    Subtract and bring down next digit of dividend
     222 <-- Third digit of quotient times 37
      252   Subtract and bring down next digit
      222 <- Fourth digit of quotient times 37
       30   Subtract; no more digits in dividend
```

The answer is 1166 with a remainder of 30, or $1166 + \frac{30}{37}$.

To Divide a Polynomial by a Binomial

1. Arrange the terms of both polynomial and binomial in descending order and set up as in long division.
2. Divide the first term of the polynomial (the dividend) by the first term of the binomial (the divisor) to obtain the first term of the quotient.
3. Multiply the first term of the quotient by the binomial and subtract the result from the dividend. Bring down the next terms to obtain a new polynomial which becomes the new dividend.
4. Divide the new dividend polynomial by the binomial. Continue the process until the variable in the first term of the remainder dividend is raised to a lower power than the variable in the first term of the divisor.

EXAMPLE 2

Dividing by a Binomial

Divide $6 - 5x + x^2$ by $x - 2$.

1. Arrange terms in descending order.

$$x - 2\overline{)x^2 - 5x + 6}$$

2. Divide the first term of the polynomial by the first term of the binomial.

Equals

$$\begin{array}{r} x \\ x - 2\overline{)x^2 - 5x + 6} \end{array} \qquad x^2 \div x = x$$

Divided by

3. Multiply the first term of the quotient by the binomial and subtract the results from the dividend. Bring down the next terms to obtain a new dividend.

Times

Equals

$$\begin{array}{r} x \\ x - 2\overline{)x^2 - 5x + 6} \\ \ominus x^2 \oplus 2x \\ \hline - 3x + 6 \end{array}$$

$x(x - 2) = x^2 - 2x$

Subtract $x^2 - 2x$ from $x^2 - 5x$ (change signs and add) and bring down $+6$

4. Divide the new dividend polynomial by the binomial, using Steps 2 and 3.

$$\begin{array}{r} x - 3 \\ x - 2\overline{)x^2 - 5x + 6} \\ \ominus x^2 \oplus 2x \\ \hline -3x + 6 \\ \oplus 3x \ominus 6 \\ \hline 0 \end{array}$$

Divide $-3x + 6$ by $x - 2$

Multiply $x - 2$ by -3

No variable in the new dividend; the process terminates ■

EXAMPLE 3 **Dividing by a Binomial**

Divide $a^3 + 27$ by $a + 3$.

Work	Explanation
	The quotient of a^3 and a
	The quotient of $-3a^2$ and a
$a^2 - 3a + 9$	The quotient of $9a$ and a
$a + 3\overline{)a^3 \qquad\qquad + 27}$	Leave space for missing terms
$\ominus a^3 \ominus 3a^2$	The quotient a^2 times the divisor $a + 3$
$-3a^2 \qquad + 27$	Subtract $a^3 + 3a^2$ from a^3 and bring down 27
$\oplus -3a^2 \oplus -9a$	The quotient $-3a$ times $a + 3$
$9a + 27$	Subtract $-3a^2 - 9a$ from $3a^2 + 27$
$\ominus 9a \ominus 27$	The quotient 9 times $a + 3$
0	Subtract; no variable in new dividend

The answer is $a^2 - 3a + 9$ with a remainder of 0. ■

Note that we can check our work in any division problem by multiplying the divisor by the quotient to obtain the dividend. We can check the work in Example 3 as follows.

$$(a + 3)(a^2 - 3a + 9) = a^3 - 3a^2 + 9a + 3a^2 - 9a + 27$$
$$= a^3 + 27$$

EXAMPLE 4 **Dividing by a Binomial**

Divide $3x^4 - 19x^3 + 27x^2 - 41x + 32$ by $x - 5$.

Work	Explanation
$3x^3 - 4x^2 + 7x - 6$	
$x - 5\overline{)3x^4 - 19x^3 + 27x^2 - 41x + 32}$	Divide $3x^4$ by x
$\ominus 3x^4 \oplus -15x^3$	
$-4x^3 + 27x^2 - 41x + 32$	
$\oplus -4x^3 \ominus +20x^2$	
$7x^2 - 41x + 32$	
$\ominus 7x^2 \oplus -35x$	
$-6x + 32$	
$\oplus -6x \ominus +30$	
2	No variable in new dividend; process ends

The answer is $3x^3 - 4x^2 + 7x - 6$ with remainder 2, or $3x^3 - 4x^2 + 7x - 6 + \frac{2}{x - 5}$. ■

EXAMPLE 5 **Dividing by a Binomial**

Divide $20x^3 + 18x^2 + 21x + 40$ by $5x + 7$.

$$
\begin{array}{r}
4x^2 - 2x + 7 \phantom{{}+40} \\
5x + 7\,\overline{)\,20x^3 + 18x^2 + 21x + 40} \\
\ominus 20x^3 \overset{\ominus}{+} 28x^2 \phantom{{}+21x+40} \\
\hline
-10x^2 + 21x + 40 \\
\overset{\oplus}{-} 10x^2 \overset{\oplus}{-} 14x \phantom{{}+40} \\
\hline
35x + 40 \\
\ominus 35x \overset{\ominus}{+} 49 \\
\hline
-9
\end{array}
$$

No variable in new dividend

The answer is $4x^2 - 2x + 7$ with remainder -9, or $4x^2 - 2x + 7 - \frac{9}{5x + 7}$. ■

EXAMPLE 6 **Dividing by a Binomial**

Divide $4x^4 - 8x^3 - 12x^2 + 44x - 15$ by $4x^2 - 8$.

$$
\begin{array}{r}
x^2 - 2x - 1 \phantom{{}+44x-15} \\
4x^2 - 8\,\overline{)\,4x^4 - 8x^3 - 12x^2 + 44x - 15} \\
\ominus 4x^4 \phantom{{}-8x^3} \overset{\oplus}{-} 8x^2 \phantom{{}+44x-15} \\
\hline
-8x^3 - 4x^2 + 44x - 15 \\
\overset{\oplus}{-} 8x^3 \phantom{{}-4x^2} \overset{\ominus}{+} 16x \phantom{{}-15} \\
\hline
-4x^2 + 28x - 15 \\
\overset{\oplus}{-} 4x^2 \phantom{{}+28x} \overset{\ominus}{+} 8 \\
\hline
28x - 23
\end{array}
$$

Keep like terms in same column

x is raised to first power; process ends

The answer is $x^2 - 2x - 1 + \frac{28x - 23}{4x^2 - 8}$. ■

6.7 EXERCISES

Divide the polynomials in Exercises 1–24.

1. $\dfrac{3x^3 - 9x^2 + 27x + 3}{3}$
2. $\dfrac{14x^4 - 7x^2 + 28}{7}$
3. $(25a^5 - 20a^4 + 15a^3) \div (5a^3)$
4. $(y^8 - y^6 + y^5) \div (y^3)$
5. $\dfrac{7x^5 - 35x^4 + 14x^2}{14x^2}$
6. $\dfrac{8x^3 - 64x^2}{8x^2}$
7. $\dfrac{-8x^3 + 6x^2 - 4x}{-2x}$
8. $\dfrac{-8x^3 + 6x^2 - 4x}{0.2x}$
9. $\dfrac{-8y^4 + 16y^3 - 4y}{2y^2}$
10. $\dfrac{-6x^2y^3 + 9x^2y}{3xy}$
11. $\dfrac{27x^2y^4 - 18xy^6 + 36xy^3}{9xy^3}$
12. $\dfrac{12x^4y^4 - 42x^2y^2}{6x^3y^3}$
13. $(x^2 - 5x + 6) \div (x - 3)$
14. $(a^2 + 5a + 6) \div (a + 3)$
15. $(3y + 2 + y^2) \div (y + 2)$
16. $(6 + 8y - y^2) \div (4 - y)$
17. $(3a^2 - 23a + 40) \div (a - 5)$
18. $(14y - 6y^2 + 80) \div (3y + 8)$

19. $4x + 6\overline{)28x^3 + 26x^2 - 44x - 36}$ **20.** $2x - 3\overline{)10x^4 - 15x^3 - 8x + 12}$ **21.** $3a - 12\overline{)6a^3 - 18a^2 + 33a - 80}$

22. $y + 2\overline{)y^5 \qquad + 32}$ **23.** $3x^2 + 2\overline{)9x^3 + 30x^2 + x - 10}$ **24.** $x^2 - 1\overline{)x^4 \qquad - 1}$

25. **GEOMETRY** The area of a rectangle is $6x^2 - 11x - 35$. Find the length if the width is $2x - 7$.

26. **GEOMETRY** The volume of a room is $x^3 - x^2 - 24x - 36$. Find the height if the length is $x + 3$ and the width is $x + 2$.

FOR REVIEW

In Exercises 27–32, multiply using special formulas.

27. $(4x - 1)(4x + 1)$ **28.** $(6x - 5)^2$ **29.** $(2a + 13)^2$

30. $(a^2 - 5)(a^2 + 5)$ **31.** $(y^3 - 2)^2$ **32.** $(2y^2 + 7)^2$

To prepare for factoring polynomials in the next chapter, factor each integer in Exercises 33–36 into a product of primes. (See Section 1.1.)

33. 45 **34.** 210 **35.** 748 **36.** 1625

6.7 PARALLEL EXERCISES

Divide the polynomials in Exercises 1–24.

1. $\dfrac{5x^4 - 25x^2 + 45x - 20}{5}$ **2.** $\dfrac{26x^3 - 16x^2 + 10}{-2}$ **3.** $(55a^6 - 22a^4 + 33a^2) \div (11a^2)$

4. $(-y^{12} + y^7 - y^5) \div (y^4)$ **5.** $\dfrac{-100x^7 + 50x^5 - 20x^3}{10x^2}$ **6.** $\dfrac{15x^3 - 30x^2 + 5x}{30x}$

7. $\dfrac{54x^6 + 81x^4 - 36x^3}{9x^3}$ **8.** $\dfrac{54x^6 + 81x^4 - 36x^3}{0.9x^3}$ **9.** $\dfrac{-3y^6 + 12y^4 - 6y^2}{3y^4}$

10. $\dfrac{4a^2b^2 - 5a^2b + 7ab^2}{ab}$ **11.** $\dfrac{44x^6y^6 + 20x^4y^2 - 28x^2y^4}{4x^2y}$ **12.** $\dfrac{-5x^6y^4 + 10x^4y^6}{5x^6y^6}$

13. $(x^2 - 6x + 8) \div (x - 4)$ **14.** $(a^2 + 6a + 8) \div (a + 2)$ **15.** $(7y + 12 + y^2) \div (y + 4)$

16. $(3 - 5y - y^2) \div (3 - y)$ **17.** $(3a^2 + 13a - 30) \div (a + 6)$ **18.** $(7a - 12 + 12a^2) \div (4a - 3)$

19. $(2y^3 + y^2 - y + 1) \div (2y + 3)$ **20.** $(6x^3 + x^2 - 7x + 2) \div (3x - 1)$ **21.** $(a^4 - 1) \div (a^2 + 1)$

22. $(x^5 - 32) \div (x - 2)$ **23.** $(21x^4 - 7x^3 - 6x + 2) \div (3x - 1)$

24. $(2x^5 - x^3 + 16x^2 - 8) \div (2x^2 - 1)$

25. **GEOMETRY** The area of a rectangle is $8x^2 - 10x - 3$. Find the width if the length is $4x + 1$.

26. **GEOMETRY** The volume of a room is $x^3 - 21x - 20$. Find the width if the length is $x + 4$ and the height is $x - 5$.

FOR REVIEW

In Exercises 27–32, multiply using special formulas.

27. $(3x - 5)(3x + 5)$ **28.** $(3x + 7)^2$ **29.** $(2x - 11)^2$

30. $(a^2 + 7)(a^2 - 7)$ **31.** $(y^3 + 5)^2$ **32.** $(3y^2 - 4)^2$

To prepare for factoring polynomials in the next chapter, factor each integer into a product of primes in Exercises 33–36. (See Section 1.1.)

33. 42 **34.** 462 **35.** 910 **36.** 2805

6.7 ENRICHMENT EXERCISES

Divide in Exercises 1–10.

1. $(2x^6 - 7x^3 - 30) \div (2x^3 + 5)$

△ **2.** $(6x^6 + x^3 - 12) \div (3x^3 - 4)$

3. $(5x^5 + 21 - 26x + x^2 + 10x^4 - 11x^3) \div (x^2 + 2x - 3)$

△ **4.** $(-34x^4 - 5x^3 + 3x^5 + 6x^6 + 54x^2 - 56 + 7x) \div (2x^2 + x - 8)$

5. $(2x^3 - x^2y - 2xy^2 + y^3) \div (x + y)$

6. $(3x^3 + 2x^2y - 7xy^2 + 2y^3) \div (x - y)$

7. $(x^4 - 3x^3 + x^2 + 3x - 2) \div (x^2 - x - 2)$

8. $(2x^4 + 5x^3 - 5x^2 - 11x + 5) \div (x^2 + 2x - 1)$

9. $(x^3 - y^3) \div (x^2 + xy + y^2)$

10. $(x^3 + y^3) \div (x^2 - xy + y^2)$

In Exercises 11–16, divide and multiply the polynomials and combine like terms.

11. $\dfrac{x^4 - 3x^3 + 5x^2}{x^2} - (2x + 1)(2x - 1)$

12. $\dfrac{2y^4 + 3y^3 - 7y^2}{y^2} - (3y + 2)(3y - 2)$

13. $\dfrac{6x^5y^2 - 8x^4y^2 + 4x^3y^2}{2y^2} - 3x(x^3 - x^2)$

14. $\dfrac{14x^3y^5 + 21x^3y^4 - 7x^3y^3}{7x^3} - 5y(y^3 - 3y^2)$

15. $\dfrac{12x^6y^3 - 4x^5y^3 - 8x^4y^3}{4x^4y^3} - (5x - 1)(x + 2)$

16. $\dfrac{15x^2y^7 - 10x^2y^6 - 5x^2y^5}{5x^2y^5} - (y + 3)(3y - 4)$

17. Evaluate $\dfrac{2x + 8}{2}$ and $x + 4$ when $x = 3$. Why are the two values equal?

18. Evaluate $\dfrac{x^2 + 3x}{x}$ and $x + 3$ when $x = 2$. Why are the two values equal?

19. Evaluate $\dfrac{x + 7}{7}$ and $x + 1$ when $x = 2$. Are the two values equal?

20. Evaluate $\dfrac{x^2 - 2}{2}$ and $x^2 - 1$ when $x = 1$. Are the two values equal?

CHAPTER 6 REVIEW

KEY WORDS

6.1 An **exponential expression** is of the form a^n where a is the **base** and n is the **exponent.**

6.2 A number is written in **scientific notation** if it is the product of a power of 10 and a number that is greater than or equal to 1 and less than 10.

6.3 A **polynomial** is an algebraic expression having as terms products of numbers and variables with whole-number exponents.

The **numerical coefficient** is the numerical multiplier of the term.

A **monomial** is a polynomial with one term.

A **binomial** is a polynomial with two terms.

A **trinomial** is a polynomial with three terms.

For a polynomial in one variable, the **degree of a term** is the exponent on the variable.

The **degree of a polynomial** is the degree of the term of highest degree.

KEY CONCEPTS

6.1 1. If a and b are any numbers, and m and n are natural numbers, the following rules for exponents hold.

(a) $a^m a^n = a^{m+n}$

(b) $\dfrac{a^m}{a^n} = a^{m-n}$, if $a \neq 0$

(c) $(a^m)^n = a^{mn}$

(d) $(ab)^n = a^n b^n$

(e) $\left(\dfrac{a}{b}\right)^n = \dfrac{a^n}{b^n}$, if $b \neq 0$

(f) $a^0 = 1$, if $a \neq 0$ and 0^0 is undefined.

2. In an expression such as $2y^3$, only y is cubed, not $2y$. That is, $2y^3$ is not the same as $(2y)^3$, which is equal to $8y^3$.

6.3 Only like terms can be collected. For example, $5x + 3 \neq 8x$ since $5x$ and 3 are *not* like terms. Similarly, $x^2 - 2x + 1$ has no like terms to combine.

6.4 Change all signs when removing parentheses preceded by a minus sign. For example, $3x - (2x^2 - 4x - 2) = 3x - 2x^2 + 4x + 2$.

6.5 1. Use the distributive law or vertical method to multiply polynomials.

2. The FOIL method can be used to multiply binomials.

6.6 1. $(a + b)(a - b) = a^2 - b^2$

2. $(a + b)^2 = a^2 + 2ab + b^2$ (not $a^2 + b^2$)

3. $(a - b)^2 = a^2 - 2ab + b^2$ (not $a^2 - b^2$)

6.7 Write polynomials in descending order before dividing.

CHAPTER 6 REVIEW EXERCISES

PART I

6.1 *Write in exponential notation in Exercises 1–3.*

1. *aaaaa*
2. $(3z)(3z)(3z)$
3. $(a + b)(a + b)$

Write without using exponents in Exercises 4–6.

4. b^7
5. $-2x^3$
6. $(-2x)^3$

In Exercises 7–15, simplify and write without negative exponents.

7. $2y^7y^2$
8. $(3x^2)^3$
9. $(2a)^0 \quad (a \neq 0)$
10. $5a^{-1}$
11. $(5a)^{-1}$
12. $\dfrac{a^{-1}}{b^{-1}}$
13. $(a^2b^{-3})^{-2}$
14. $\dfrac{3^0a^{-5}b^7}{a^4b^{-1}}$
15. $\left(\dfrac{2^{-1}x^2y^{-4}}{x^{-2}y^{-2}}\right)^{-1}$

6.2 *Write in scientific notation in Exercises 16–17.*

16. 0.000000411

17. 549,000,000,000

Write without using scientific notation in Exercises 18–19.

18. 6.15×10^{12}

19. 4×10^{-8}

6.3 *Tell whether the polynomials are monomials, binomials, or trinomials in Exercises 20–22.*

20. $3x^2$

21. $5y^4 + y^2$

22. $-7y^3 + y - 5$

Give the degree of each polynomial in Exercises 23–25.

23. $15x^2 - 14x + 6x^7 - 4x^3$

24. $-x^3 + 14x^4 - x^{10} + 8x^2$

25. $2x^8 - 4x^4 - 16$

In Exercises 26–29, collect and combine like terms and write in descending order.

26. $5x + 2 - 6x$

27. $6y^2 - 2y + 8y^2 + 5 - 3y^2 + y$

28. $4a^3 - 6a + 7a^2 - 4a^3 + a - a^2$

29. $-7x^2 - 30x^4 + x^5 - 3x + 5x^5 - 4x + 22x^4 - 5$

In Exercises 30–31, collect and combine like terms.

30. $8xy + 5 - 4xy - 8$

31. $-a^2b^3 - a^2b^2 - 5a^2b^2 - ab^2 + 5a^2b^3$

32. **SALES** The profit in dollars when x refrigerators are sold is given by the expression $4x^3 - 140$. Find the profit when 5 refrigerators are sold.

6.4

33. Add $5x^2 - 4x + 5$ and $-7x^2 + 4x - 8$.

34. Subtract $-2x^2 - 1$ from $x^3 - 5x^2 + 14$.

Perform the indicated operations in Exercises 35–36.

35. $(16x - 2x^4 + 3x^2 - 5) - (-6 + x^4 - 3x^3 - 3x^2 + 2x)$

36. $(6x^2y^2 - 5xy) + (-4xy + 3) - (3x^2y^2 - 8xy + 5)$

Add in Exercises 37–38.

37.
$$\begin{array}{rrrrr} x^4 & -\ 2x^3 & +\ 7x^2 & & -\ 20 \\ -8x^4 & & -\ 5x^2 & +\ 3x & +\ 7 \\ 36x^4 & -\ 18x^3 & & +\ 5x & -\ 31 \\ \hline \end{array}$$

38.
$$\begin{array}{rrrr} 6.1x^3 & -\ 0.2x^2 & +\ 1.1x & +\ 5 \\ -5.7x^3 & & +\ 2.3x & -\ 7 \\ & 1.1x^2 & -\ 2.3x & +\ 8 \\ \hline \end{array}$$

Multiply in Exercises 39–50.

6.5, 6.6

39. $(x + 8)(x - 10)$

40. $(2x + 1)(3x - 4)$

41. $(4a - 3)^2$

42. $(5y - 6)(4y - 7)$

43. $\left(\frac{3}{4} + 2y^3\right)\left(\frac{3}{4} - 2y^3\right)$

44. $(x + 4)(2x^2 + x - 3)$

45.
$$\begin{array}{rrr} 3x^2 & -\ 2x & +\ 1 \\ x^2 & +\ x & -\ 2 \\ \hline \end{array}$$

46.
$$\begin{array}{rrr} 2x^2 & +\ xy & -\ 3y^2 \\ & x & +\ 4y \\ \hline \end{array}$$

47.
$$\begin{array}{rrr} 6x^2y^2 & -\ xy & +\ 5 \\ & 2xy & -\ 3 \\ \hline \end{array}$$

48. $(7a - b)(4a + 3b)$

49. $(4x - y)(4x + y)$

50. $(8x + y)^2$

6.7 *Divide in Exercises 51–56.*

51. $\dfrac{6x^4y^4 - 2x^3y^3 + 10x^2y^2}{2x^2y^2}$

52. $\dfrac{-14a^4b^2 + 21a^2b^4 - 35ab^2}{-7a^2b^2}$

53. $(x^2 + 3x - 28) \div (x - 4)$

54. $(8x^2 + 10x + 3) \div (2x + 1)$

55. $2x + 3\overline{)14x^4 + 27x^3 + 5x^2 - 16x - 15}$

56. $x - 5\overline{)x^3 \qquad\qquad - 100}$

PART II

57. **BUSINESS** The number n of records that can be sold during each week is related to the price in dollars p of each record by the equation $n = 1200 - 100p$. Find an equation that gives the weekly revenue R in terms of p and use it to find R when p is \$10.

58. **SCIENCE** Light travels at the rate of 186,000 mi per sec. Write this number in scientific notation.

Perform the indicated operation in Exercises 59–64.

59. $(2x + 1)(5x - 2)$
60. $(6x^2y^2 - 3xy) - (-2x^2y^2 + 1)$
61. $(x^2 + 10x + 21) \div (x + 7)$
62. $(5a - b)^2$
63. Subtract $-x^3 - 2$ from $x^3 - 2$.
64. $3a^2b(4a^3b^4 - 5a^2b - 2ab)$

Simplify and write without negative exponents in Exercises 65–67.

65. $\left(\frac{x^3}{y^2}\right)^{-2}$
66. $\frac{2^0x^{-4}y^3}{x^2y^{-3}}$
67. $\left(\frac{ab^{-2}}{a^{-3}b^{-3}}\right)^{-1}$

Give the degree of each polynomial in Exercises 68–69.

68. $6x^3 - 4x^2 + 2x^5 - 1$
69. $-7y + 6y^3 - 2 + y^2$

Tell whether the following are monomials, binomials, or trinomials in Exercises 70–71.

70. $3x + 2$
71. $x^2 - 6x + 7$

Answer true *or* false *in Exercises 72–80. If the statement is false, tell why.*

72. When multiplying two powers with the same base, we add exponents.
73. -3^2 and $(-3)^2$ are the same.
74. Every binomial has degree 2.
75. The product of two binomials can be a binomial.
76. For every $a \neq 0$, $a^0 = 1$.
77. If the sum of two numbers is squared, it is the same as adding the squares of the individual numbers.
78. The FOIL method is used when multiplying two trinomials.
79. Some binomials have degree 6.
80. x^{-1} is positive if x is positive.

CHAPTER 6 TEST

1. Write in exponential notation. $5 \cdot 5 \cdot a \cdot a \cdot a$

Simplify and write without negative exponents.

2. $2y^5y^2$
3. $\frac{a^7}{a^3}$
4. $(-2x^2)^3$
5. z^{-3}
6. $\frac{x^{-6}y^3}{x^2y^{-4}}$
7. Evaluate y^{-3} when $y = -4$.
8. Evaluate. $\frac{3.9 \times 10^{-4}}{1.3 \times 10^{-2}}$
9. Is $3x^2 + 5$ a monomial, binomial, or trinomial?
10. Give the degree of $x^3 - 7x^2 + 10x^4 - 8$.

11. Collect and combine like terms and write in descending order. $3y^3 - 7y^5 + y^3 - 4y + 6 + y^5 - 2y$
12. Collect and combine like terms. $3x^2y^2 - 4x^2 + 3x^2y - 7x^2y^2 + 2x^2y$
13. The cost in dollars of making x pairs of shoes is given by the expression $20x + 45$. Find the cost when 12 pairs of shoes are made.

Add.

14. $(3x + 2) + (-5x + 8)$
15. $(6x^3 + 5x^2 - 3x^4 + 2) + (-8x^2 + 4x^3 + 6x^4 + 5)$
16. $(3a^2b^2 - 2ab + 5) + (4a^2b^2 + 8ab - 3)$

Subtract.

17. $(-5x + 4) - (2x - 3)$
18. $(4x^2 - 6x^4 + 2) - (-2x^2 + x^3 - 2x^4 + 1)$
19. $(8a^2b - 3ab^2 - 2ab) - (4a^2b + ab^2 - ab)$

Multiply.

20. $-4x^2(3x^2 - 4x + 1)$
21. $(x + 5)(x - 8)$
22. $(4a - 3)(2a + 7)$
23. $(y + 8)(3y^2 - 2y + 1)$
24. $(2x + y)(2x - y)$
25. $(3x - 4y)^2$
26. $(2x + 5)^2$
27. $(3x + 2)(2x^2 - 3x + 4)$
28. $(x^2 - 3)(x^2 + 3)$

Divide.

29. $\dfrac{25x^4 - 10x^3 - 15x^2}{5x^2}$
30. $(3x^3 - 11x^2 + 10x - 12) \div (x - 3)$

Answer true *or* false. *If false explain why.*

31. $(x + y)^2$ is the same as $x^2 + y^2$.
32. If w is any real number, $-w^2$ is the same as $(-w)^2$.

CHAPTER 7

Factoring Polynomials

IN CHAPTER 6 WE learned how to multiply polynomials to obtain their product. In this chapter we reverse the procedure. That is, when we are given a polynomial, we will attempt to write it as a product of simpler polynomials. This process is called *factoring*.

Your work will be easier if you are thoroughly familiar with the distributive property and with the special products presented in Section 6.6.

Some applied problems can be solved by first factoring a particular polynomial. One example is presented below and solved in Example 4 of Section 7.6.

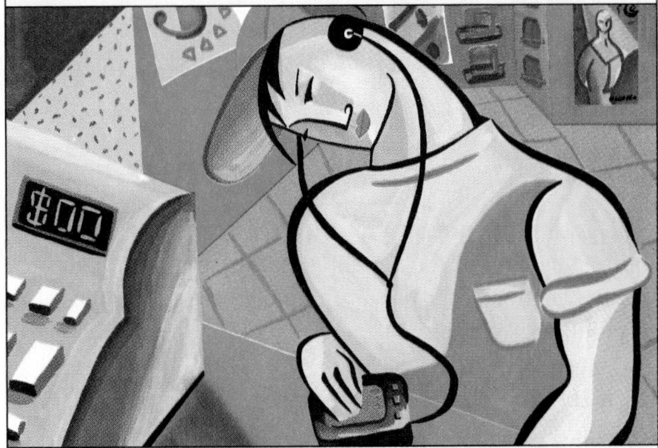

PRODUCTION The production research department at Disc Incorporated has determined that the number n of compact discs that can be sold each week is related to the price p of the disc by the equation $n = 1100 - 100p$. Find the price that the company should set on each disc to produce a weekly revenue of $2800.

We begin with common factors and factoring by grouping using the distributive law. Next we factor general trinomials and consider special cases of perfect squares, difference of squares, and the sum and difference of cubes. Finally, we use factoring to solve equations and examine applied problems that translate to equations solvable by factoring.

SECTION 7.1 Common Factors and Grouping

Student guideposts

- ▶ *Greatest common factor*
- ▶ *Factoring by removing the GCF*
- ▶ *Factoring by grouping*

Factoring is the reverse of multiplying. In Chapter 1 we factored integers such as 28 by writing

$$28 = 4 \cdot 7 = 2 \cdot 2 \cdot 7 = 2^2 \cdot 7.$$

In this form, we see that 4 and 7 are two **factors** of 28, (as are 1, 2, 14, and 28), while 2 and 7 are also **prime factors** (2 and 7 are prime numbers). Algebraic expressions can also be factored into prime factors. For example,

$$28x^3 = 2 \cdot 2 \cdot 7 \cdot x \cdot x \cdot x = 2^2 \cdot 7 \cdot x^3,$$

has 2, 7, and x as its prime factors. A **common factor** of two expressions is a factor that occurs in each of them. For instance, a common factor of 14 and 28 is 7 since

$$14 = 2 \cdot 7 \quad \text{and} \quad 28 = 2^2 \cdot 7.$$

Other common factors of 14 and 28 are 2 and 14.

▶ *Greatest common factor*

The **greatest common factor (GCF)** of two integers is the largest factor common to both integers. Thus, 14 is the greatest common factor of 14 and 28. As shown in the next example, it is easier to find the greatest common factor if integers are expressed as a product of primes.

EXAMPLE 1 Finding the Greatest Common Factor (GCF)

Find the greatest common factor of the integers.

(a) 35 and 75

$$35 = 5 \cdot 7 \quad \text{and} \quad 75 = 3 \cdot 5 \cdot 5$$

GCF: 5

(b) 54 and 90

$$54 = 2 \cdot 3 \cdot 3 \cdot 3 \quad \text{and} \quad 90 = 2 \cdot 3 \cdot 3 \cdot 5$$

GCF: $2 \cdot 3 \cdot 3 = 18$ ∎

We can also find common factors of monomials such as $14x^3$ and $28x^2$. First we write the monomials in factored form.

$$14x^3 = 2 \cdot 7 \cdot x^3 = 2 \cdot 7 \cdot x^2 \cdot x$$
$$28x^2 = 2^2 \cdot 7 \cdot x^2 = 2 \cdot 2 \cdot 7 \cdot x^2$$

Factors common to both are in color

Each blue factor is a common factor of $14x^3$ and $28x^2$, and the product, $2 \cdot 7 \cdot x^2 = 14x^2$, is the greatest common factor of the two monomials. Usually we are interested in finding the greatest common factor of the terms of a polynomial. For instance, $14x^2$ is the greatest common factor of the terms of the polynomial $14x^3 + 28x^2$. The following rule summarizes the technique.

To Find the Greatest Common Factor

1. Write each term as a product of prime factors, expressing repeated factors as powers.
2. Select the factors that are common to all terms and raise each to the *lowest* power that it occurs in any one term.
3. The product of these factors is the greatest common factor (GCF).

EXAMPLE 2

Finding the GCF of a Polynomial

Find the greatest common factor of the terms of each polynomial.

(a) $12x - 9 = 2^2 \cdot 3 \cdot x - 3 \cdot 3$
Common factors: 3
Lowest power of each: 3^1
GCF: 3

(b) $18x^2 + 30x = 2 \cdot 3 \cdot 3 \cdot x \cdot x + 2 \cdot 3 \cdot 5 \cdot x$
Common factors: 2, 3, x
Lowest power of each: $2^1, 3^1, x^1$
GCF: $2 \cdot 3 \cdot x = 6x$

(c) $3x^4 + 12x^2 = 3 \cdot x^2 \cdot x^2 + 2^2 \cdot 3 \cdot x^2$
Common factors: 3, x
Lowest power of each: $3^1, x^2$
GCF: $3 \cdot x^2 = 3x^2$

(d) $7y + 3 = 1 \cdot 7 \cdot y + 1 \cdot 3$
Common factors: 1
Lowest power of each: 1^1
GCF: 1

(e) $14x^4 - 28x^3 + 21x^2 = 2 \cdot 7 \cdot x^2 \cdot x^2 - 2^2 \cdot 7 \cdot x^2 \cdot x + 3 \cdot 7 \cdot x^2$
Common factors: 7, x
Lowest power of each: $7^1, x^2$
GCF: $7 \cdot x^2 = 7x^2$

(f) $5x^2y^3 - 15xy^2 = 5 \cdot x \cdot x \cdot y^2 \cdot y - 3 \cdot 5 \cdot x \cdot y^2$
Common factors: $5, x, y$
Lowest power of each: $5^1, x^1, y^2$
GCF: $5 \cdot x \cdot y^2 = 5xy^2$ ■

Factoring by removing the GCF

A polynomial is said to be **factored by removing common factors** when the greatest common factor is removed using the distributive law. For example, since

$$14x^3 + 28x^2 = 14x^2(x + 2)$$

we have factored $14x^3 + 28x^2$ using the distributive law by removing the greatest common factor $14x^2$. Example 3 illustrates the technique summarized below.

To Factor by Removing the Greatest Common Factor

1. Write each term as a product of primes.
2. Find the greatest common factor.
3. Write each term in the form

   GCF · remaining factors.

4. Use the distributive property to remove the GCF. The factors left in each term are the remaining factors.
5. To check, multiply the GCF by the polynomial factor.

EXAMPLE 3

Removing the GCF

Factor the polynomials given in Example 2.

(a) $12x - 9 = 2^2 \cdot 3 \cdot x - 3 \cdot 3$ — GCF is 3
$= 3(2^2 \cdot x - 3)$ — Remove the GCF using the distributive property
$= 3(4x - 3)$ — Keep the GCF as a multiplier

(b) $18x^2 + 30x = 2 \cdot 3 \cdot 3 \cdot x \cdot x + 2 \cdot 3 \cdot 5 \cdot x$ — GCF is $6x$
$= 2 \cdot 3 \cdot x(3x + 5)$ — Distributive property
$= 6x(3x + 5)$ — Keep the GCF, $6x$, as a multiplier

(c) $3x^4 + 12x^2 = 3x^2 \cdot x^2 + 3x^2 \cdot 4$ — GCF is $3x^2$
$= 3x^2(x^2 + 4)$ — Distributive property

(d) $7y + 3 = 1 \cdot 7y + 1 \cdot 3$ — GCF is 1
$= 7y + 3$ — Cannot be factored

(e) $14x^4 - 28x^3 + 21x^2 = 7x^2 \cdot 2x^2 - 7x^2 \cdot 4x + 7x^2 \cdot 3$ — GCF is $7x^2$
$= 7x^2(2x^2 - 4x + 3)$

(f) $5x^2y^3 - 15xy^2 = 5 \cdot x^2 \cdot y^3 - 3 \cdot 5 \cdot x \cdot y^2$

$= 5xy^2 \cdot xy - 5xy^2 \cdot 3$ GCF is $5xy^2$

$= 5xy^2(xy - 3)$ ■

When the greatest common factor is 1, we say the polynomial cannot be factored by removing the common factor. Polynomials like $7y + 3$ in Example 3(d), which cannot be factored, are called **prime polynomials.**

CAUTION When told to factor a polynomial such as $18x^2 + 30x$, a common error is to give

$$2 \cdot 3 \cdot 3 \cdot x \cdot x + 2 \cdot 3 \cdot 5 \cdot x$$

for the answer. Here the terms of the polynomial have been factored, but the polynomial itself has not. The correct factorization is $6x(3x + 5)$ as shown in Example 3(b).

Often when a polynomial consists of many negative terms, or when its leading coefficient is negative, we factor out the negative of the greatest common factor of its terms, as shown in the next example.

EXAMPLE 4

Factoring Out A Negative Factor

Factor $-6x^5 - 12x^4 - 15x$.

$$-6x^5 - 12x^4 - 15x = (-3x)2x^4 + (-3x)4x^3 + (-3x)5$$
$$= -3x(2x^4 + 4x^3 + 5)$$

In this example the greatest common factor is $3x$; thus, another way to factor is $3x(-2x^4 - 4x^3 - 5)$. Either answer is considered correct, but the first is sometimes preferred. ■

EXAMPLE 5

Factoring with 1 Left in Term

Factor $3x^2y^3 - xy$.

$3x^2y^3 - xy = xy \cdot 3xy^2 - xy \cdot 1$ GCF is xy

$= xy(3xy^2 - 1)$ Distributive property ■

CAUTION When we factored xy out of $xy \cdot 1$ in Example 5, we were left with a 1 in the term. Do not leave this term out and write $xy(3xy^2)$ as the factors of $3x^2y^3 - xy$. If we multiply $xy(3xy^2)$ we get $3x^2y^3$ which is just the first term of the given polynomial.

Sometimes a polynomial contains grouping symbols. For example, the polynomial

$$3x(x + 2) + 5(x + 2)$$

is really a binomial made of the two terms $3x(x + 2)$ and $5(x + 2)$. These terms have a greatest common factor $(x + 2)$.

$$3x(x + 2) + 5(x + 2) = 3x \cdot (x + 2) + 5 \cdot (x + 2) \qquad \text{GCF is } (x + 2)$$
$$= (3x + 5)(x + 2) \qquad \text{Distributive property}$$

Here the $(x + 2)$ is a single factor of each term and is removed using the distributive property.

EXAMPLE 6 **Working with Grouping Symbols**

Factor $3x(a + b) + y(a + b)$.

$$3x(a + b) + y(a + b) = 3x \cdot (a + b) + y \cdot (a + b) \qquad \text{GCF is } (a + b)$$
$$= (3x + y)(a + b) \qquad \text{Distributive property}$$ ■

Factoring by grouping

Notice that if we clear the parentheses in the polynomial in Example 6, we obtain

$$3x(a + b) + y(a + b) = 3xa + 3xb + ya + yb.$$

Suppose we are given the polynomial on the right to factor. We may do so by grouping the first two terms and the last two terms. Then we factor as in Example 6. This process is called **factoring by grouping** and is illustrated in the next example.

EXAMPLE 7 **Factoring by Grouping**

Factor each polynomial by grouping.

(a) $3xa + 3xb + ya + yb$

$$= (3xa + 3xb) + (ya + yb) \qquad \text{Group the first two terms and the last two terms}$$
$$= 3x(a + b) + y(a + b) \qquad \text{Use the distributive law on each group}$$
$$= (3x + y)(a + b) \qquad \text{Use the distributive law to factor out } (a + b)$$

(b) $5ay - 5ax + 3by - 3bx = (5ay - 5ax) + (3by - 3bx)$

$$= 5a(y - x) + 3b(y - x)$$
$$= (5a + 3b)(y - x)$$

(c) $6ax - 8bx - 3ay + 4by = 2x(3a - 4b) - y(3a - 4b)$ Factor $2x$ from first two terms and $-y$ from the last two terms

$$= (2x - y)(3a - 4b)$$ ■

Factoring by grouping should be tried when the polynomial has four terms. We conclude this section with an application of factoring.

EXAMPLE 8 **Solving an Application in Aeronautics**

If a rocket is fired straight up with a velocity of 128 feet per second, the equation $h = -16t^2 + 128t$ gives the height h of the rocket at any time t. Factor the right side of the equation and use this factored form to find the height of the rocket after 6 seconds.

Factoring, we obtain

$$h = -16t^2 + 128t = -16t^2 + 16 \cdot 8t$$
$$= -16t(t - 8). \quad \text{Notice the minus sign}$$

Substitute 6 for t to find h.

$$h = -16t(t - 8)$$
$$= -16(6)(6 - 8)$$
$$= -16(6)(-2) = 192$$

The rocket will be 192 ft high after 6 sec. ∎

> NOTE You never need to make a mistake in a factoring problem since you can always check your work by multiplying the factors and comparing the product with the given polynomial.

7.1 EXERCISES

Find the greatest common factor in Exercises 1–15.

1. 10, 15
2. 28, 42
3. 17, 23
4. $10x^2, 15x$
5. $28y^3, 42y$
6. $17y^2, 23y^4$
7. 28, 42, 12
8. 17, 23, 16
9. $28y^3, 42y^2, 12y^5$
10. $6x^3, 12x^2, 18x^2$
11. $36y^4, 6y^3, 42y^5$
12. $8y^2, 9x, 12y^5$
13. $5x^2y, 40xy^2$
14. $16x^2y^2, 12x^3y^4, 8xy^5$
15. x^4y^3, x^5y^2, x^3

Find the greatest common factor of the terms of the polynomials in Exercises 16–24.

16. $4x + 8$
17. $8y^2 - 16y$
18. $3a^3 - 9a^2$
19. $9y^4 + 18y^2$
20. $4x^3 + 2x^2 - 6x$
21. $3a(a + 2) + 5(a + 2)$
22. $6x^2y^2 - 4x^2y$
23. $5a^3b^3 - 15a^2b^2 + 10ab^2$
24. $x(a + b) + y(a + b)$

Factor each polynomial in Exercises 25–39 by removing the greatest common factor.

25. $3x + 9$
26. $21x - 14$
27. $18y^2 + 11y$
28. $23a^2 - 5$
29. $x^{10} - x^8 + x^6$
30. $6y^4 - 24y^2 + 12y$
31. $60x^3 + 50x^2 - 25x$
32. $-6y^{10} - 8y^8 - 4y^5$
33. $a^2 + 2a + 2$
34. $x^2y^2 + xy$
35. $6a^2b - 2ab^2$
36. $27x^3y^2 + 45xy^2$
37. $15x^3y^3 + 5x^2y^2 + 10xy$
38. $a^2(a + 2) + 3(a + 2)$
39. $x^2(a + b) + y^2(a + b)$

In Exercises 40–47, factor by grouping.

40. $a^3 + 2a^2 + 3a + 6$
41. $x^2a + x^2b + y^2a + y^2b$
42. $a^2b - a^2 + 5b - 5$
43. $x^3 + 2x^2 - 7x - 14$
44. $a^3b^2 + a^3 + 2b^2 + 2$
45. $x^2y - 3x^2 + y - 3$
46. $a^4b + a^3 - ab^3 - b^2$
47. $-x^2y - x^2 - 3y - 3$

48. **INVESTMENT** If a principal of P dollars is invested in an account with an annual interest rate of 9% compounded annually, the amount A in the account after one year is given by the equation $A = P + 0.09P$. Factor the right side of the equation and use this factored form to find the amount in the account in one year when P is **(a)** \$100, **(b)** \$1000, and **(c)** \$4537.35.

49. When asked to factor $4x^3 + 8x^2$, Burford gave $2x(2x^2 + 4x)$ for the answer. What is wrong with Burford's work? What is the correct answer?

50. What is wrong with the following factoring problem?

$$-3x^2y^2 + 6x^2y = -3x^2y(y + 2)$$

51. What is the GCF of the terms of the binomial $2xy + 4x^2$? What is the GCF of the terms of the binomial $5xy - 10y$? Find the product of $2xy + 4x^2$ and $5xy - 10y$ and give the GCF of the terms of this polynomial. What can you conclude?

FOR REVIEW

Exercises 52–55 review material covered in Chapter 6 to help you prepare for the next section. Use the FOIL method to find each product.

52. $(x + 3)(x - 7)$
53. $(x - 3)(x - 7)$
54. $(x + 4y)(x + 3y)$
55. $(x + 4y)(x - 3y)$

7.1 PARALLEL EXERCISES

Find the greatest common factor in Exercises 1–15.

1. 12, 18
2. 32, 48
3. 11, 29
4. $12x, 18x^3$
5. $32y^4, 48y^2$
6. $11y^3, 29y^2$
7. 32, 48, 64
8. 11, 29, 30
9. $32y^3, 48y^5, 64y^4$
10. $15x^2, 20x^3, 5x^4$
11. $22y^5, 33y^4, 44y^3$
12. $36y^4, 15x^2, 5xy$
13. $6x^2y^3, 24x^2y$
14. $30x^5y^5, 2x^2y^4, 12x^4y^3$
15. x^8y^7, x^4y^6, y^5

Find the greatest common factor of the terms of the polynomials in Exercises 16–24.

16. $9x + 3$
17. $22y^2 - 11y$
18. $16x^4 - 24x^2$
19. $100a^{16} + 200a^{14}$
20. $48y^6 - 24y^5 + 12y^2$
21. $7a(a - 5) + 6(a - 5)$
22. $9x^3y^3 - 12xy^4$
23. $4a^3b^3 + 6a^2b^2 - 6ab^2$
24. $2a(x + y) + b(x + y)$

Factor each polynomial in Exercises 25–39 by removing the greatest common factor.

25. $5y - 20$
26. $54y + 12$
27. $25x^4 - 15x^3$
28. $16a^2 - 7$
29. $x^{12} - x^6 + x^4$
30. $8a^6 - 18a^3 + 12$
31. $90x^4 - 45x^3 + 180x^2$
32. $-5y^8 - 10y^6 - 15y^4$
33. $a^2 + a + 5$

34. $x^4y^4 - x^2y$
35. $11a^3b^3 - 22a^2b^2$
36. $24x^4y^3 + 36x^3y^4$
37. $28x^4y^4 + 14x^3y^3 + 35x^2y^2$
38. $2a^3(a - 5) + 5(a - 5)$
39. $a^2(x + y) + 2b(x + y)$

In Exercises 40–47, factor by grouping.

40. $a^3 + 7a^2 + 2a + 14$
41. $a^2x + a^2y + b^2x + b^2y$
42. $a^3b - 2a^3 + 4b - 8$
43. $x^3 + 5x^2 - 2x - 10$
44. $a^5b^3 + 2a^5 + 6b^3 + 12$
45. $xy - 2y + x - 2$
46. $ab^2 + ab - 5b - 5$
47. $-x^3y^2 - 3x^3y - 7y - 21$

48. **PHYSICS** If a bullet is fired straight up with a velocity of 256 feet per second, the equation $h = -16t^2 + 256t$ gives the height h of the bullet at any time t. Factor the right side of the equation and use this factored form to find the height of the bullet after **(a)** 6 sec, **(b)** 8 sec, **(c)** 10 sec, and **(d)** 16 sec.

49. When Burford was told to factor $12x^2 - 8x$ he gave $2 \cdot 2 \cdot 3 \cdot x \cdot x - 2 \cdot 2 \cdot 2 \cdot x$ for the answer. What is wrong with Burford's work? What is the correct answer?

50. What is wrong with the following factoring problem?

$$4x^2y^3 - 2xy = 2xy(2xy^2)$$

51. What is the GCF of the terms of the binomial $2x - 4$? What is the GCF of the terms of the binomial $3x + 6$? Find the product of $2x - 4$ and $3x + 6$ and give the GCF of the terms of this trinomial. What can you conclude?

FOR REVIEW

Exercises 52–55 review material covered in Chapter 6 to help you prepare for the next section. Use the FOIL method to find each product.

52. $(x + 2)(x - 3)$
53. $(x - 2)(x + 3)$
54. $(x - 2y)(x - 2y)$
55. $(x + 2y)(x + 2y)$

7.1 ENRICHMENT EXERCISES

In Exercises 1–6, find the greatest common factor of the expressions.

1. $x + 1,\ 2(x - 3)$
2. $(x - 1),\ (x - 1)(x + 1)$
3. $(x + 1)^2,\ (x + 1)(x + 2)$
4. $9(x + 1),\ 3(x + 1)^2$
5. $12(y + 4)^3,\ 10(y + 4)(y - 4)$
6. $25(y - 5),\ 40(y + 1)(y - 5)^2$

In Exercises 7–10, factor by removing the greatest common factor.

7. $x(b - 1) - y(1 - b)$
8. $3a(x - y) - b(y - x)$
9. $3u(2x - y) - 2v(y - 2x)$
10. $5x(2a - 3b) - 3y(-2a + 3b)$

In Exercises 11–14, factor by grouping. Do not combine like terms first.

11. $6x^2 + 21x - 10x - 35$
12. $10x^2 - 15xy - 2xy + 3y^2$
13. $a^2b^2c^2 - 5abc + 3abc - 15$
△ **14.** $6a^2b^2c - 15ab - 4abc^2 + 10c$

15. Explain what it means to factor completely.

SECTION 7.2 Factoring Trinomials of the Form $x^2 + bx + c$

Student guideposts

- *Review of FOIL*
- *Factoring $x^2 + bx + c$*
- *Factoring $x^2 + bxy + cy^2$*

Review of FOIL

To factor a trinomial into the product of two binomials, we need to recognize the pattern for multiplying binomials in reverse. Consider the following multiplication.

$$\begin{aligned}(x+3)(x+7) &= \overset{F}{x\cdot x} + \overset{O}{x\cdot 7} + \overset{I}{3\cdot x} + \overset{L}{3\cdot 7}\\ &= x^2 + 7x + 3x + 21\\ &= \underset{F}{x^2} + \underset{O+I}{10x} + \underset{L}{21}\end{aligned}$$

Notice that x^2 is the product of the first terms Ⓕ, 21 is the product of the last terms Ⓛ, and $10x$ is the sum of the product Ⓞ and Ⓘ.

If we are given the trinomial $x^2 + 10x + 21$ to factor, we need to reverse the FOIL method above to find $(x + 3)(x + 7)$. That is, we must fill in the blanks in

$$x^2 + 10x + 21 = (x + \_\_)(x + \_\_).$$

The numbers in the blanks must have a product of 21 and a sum of 10.

$$x^2 + 10x + 21 = (x + \underline{3})(x + \underline{7})$$

Sum

Product

Factoring $x^2 + bx + c$

In general, to factor $x^2 + bx + c$ we look for a pair of integers whose product is c and whose sum is b.

$$x^2 + bx + c = (x + \_\_)(x + \_\_)$$

Sum

Product

To Factor $x^2 + bx + c$

1. Write $x^2 + bx + c = (x + \_\_)(x + \_\_)$.
2. List all pairs of integers whose product is c.
3. Find the pair from this list whose sum is b (if there is one).
4. Fill in the blanks with this pair.

EXAMPLE 1 **Factoring Trinomials**

Factor $x^2 + 6x + 8$. $(b = 6$ and $c = 8)$

$$x^2 + 6x + 8 = (x + \_\_)(x + \_\_)$$

Factors of $c = 8$	*Sum of factors*
1, 8	$1 + 8 = 9$
2, 4	$2 + 4 = 6$
−1, −8	$-1 + (-8) = -9$
−2, −4	$-2 + (-4) = -6$

Since the product of 2 and 4 is 8, which equals c, and the sum of 2 and 4 is 6, which equals b, we write

$$x^2 + 6x + 8 = (x + \underline{2})(x + \underline{4}).$$

That is, the blanks are filled in with the shaded pair above. To check, we multiply using the FOIL method.

$$(x + 2)(x + 4) = x^2 + 4x + 2x + 8 = x^2 + 6x + 8 \quad ■$$

EXAMPLE 2 **Factoring Trinomials in One Variable**

Factor each trinomial.

(a) $x^2 + 5x + 6$ $(b = 5$ and $c = 6)$

$$x^2 + 5x + 6 = (x + \_\_)(x + \_\_)$$

Factors of $c = 6$	*Sum of factors*
6, 1	$6 + 1 = 7$
2, 3	$2 + 3 = 5$
−6, −1	$-6 + (-1) = -7$
−2, −3	$-2 + (-3) = -5$

We fill in the blanks with the shaded pair obtaining

$$x^2 + 5x + 6 = (x + \underline{2})(x + \underline{3}). \qquad 2 \cdot 3 = 6 \text{ and } 2 + 3 = 5$$

Note in the table that since $c = 6 > 0$, the factors in each pair must have the same sign. Also, since $b = 5 > 0$, we know that the negative factors will not work. We check by using FOIL.

$$(x + 2)(x + 3) = x^2 + 3x + 2x + 6 = x^2 + 5x + 6$$

(b) $x^2 - 5x + 6 \quad (b = -5 \text{ and } c = 6)$

$$x^2 - 5x + 6 = (x + \_\_)(x + \_\_)$$

Factors of $c = 6$	*Sum of factors*
6, 1	$6 + 1 = 7$
2, 3	$2 + 3 = 5$
−6, −1	$-6 + (-1) = -7$
−2, −3	$-2 + (-3) = -5$

$$x^2 - 5x + 6 = (x - 2)(x - 3) \qquad (-2)(-3) = 6 \text{ and } -2 + (-3) = -5$$

With $c > 0$ the factors in each pair must have the same sign. Since $b = -5$, positive factors will not work. Check the factors by using FOIL.

(c) $x^2 + x - 6 \quad (b = 1 \text{ and } c = -6)$

$$x^2 + x - 6 = (x + \_\_)(x + \_\_)$$

Factors of $c = -6$	*Sum of factors*
6, −1	$6 + (-1) = 5$
−6, 1	$-6 + 1 = -5$
2, −3	$2 + (-3) = -1$
−2, 3	$-2 + 3 = 1$

$$x^2 + x - 6 = (x - 2)(x + 3) \qquad -2 \cdot 3 = -6 \text{ and } -2 + 3 = 1$$

Since $c = -6 < 0$, the factors of c must have opposite signs.

(d) $x^2 - x - 6 \quad (b = -1 \text{ and } c = -6)$

$$x^2 - x - 6 = (x + \_\_)(x + \_\_)$$

Factors of $c = -6$	*Sum of factors*
6, −1	$6 + (-1) = 5$
−6, 1	$-6 + 1 = -5$
2, −3	$2 + (-3) = -1$
−2, 3	$-2 + 3 = 1$

$$x^2 - x - 6 = (x + 2)(x - 3) \qquad 2 \cdot (-3) = -6 \text{ and } 2 + (-3) = -1$$ ■

▶ *Factoring* $x^2 + bxy + cy^2$

To factor trinomials in two variables such as $x^2 + bxy + cy^2$, we use the same procedures as above. But we now fill in the blanks in

$$x^2 + 5xy + 6y^2 = (x + \_\_y)(x + \_\_y).$$

The following table compares factoring trinomials in two variables with factoring similar trinomials in one variable.

One variable	*Two variables*
$x^2 + 5x + 6 = (x + 2)(x + 3)$	$x^2 + 5xy + 6y^2 = (x + 2y)(x + 3y)$
$x^2 - 5x + 6 = (x - 2)(x - 3)$	$x^2 - 5xy + 6y^2 = (x - 2y)(x - 3y)$
$x^2 + x - 6 = (x - 2)(x + 3)$	$x^2 + xy - 6y^2 = (x - 2y)(x + 3y)$
$x^2 - x - 6 = (x + 2)(x - 3)$	$x^2 - xy - 6y^2 = (x + 2y)(x - 3y)$

EXAMPLE 3 **Factoring Trinomials in Two Variables**

Factor each trinomial.

(a) $x^2 + 7xy + 10y^2$ $(b = 7 \text{ and } c = 10)$

$$x^2 + 7xy + 10y^2 = (x + \_\_y)(x + \_\_y)$$

Factors of $c = 10$	*Sum of factors*
10, 1	$10 + 1 = 11$
5, 2	$5 + 2 = 7$
−10, −1	$-10 + (-1) = -11$
−5, −2	$-5 + (-2) = -7$

$$x^2 + 7xy + 10y^2 = (x + 5y)(x + 2y) \qquad 5 \cdot 2 = 10 \text{ and } 5 + 2 = 7$$

(b) $x^2 - xy - 12y^2$ $(b = -1 \text{ and } c = -12)$

$$x^2 - xy - 12y^2 = (x + \_\_y)(x + \_\_y)$$

Factors of $c = -12$	*Sum of factors*
12, −1	$12 + (-1) = 11$
−12, 1	$-12 + 1 = -11$
6, −2	$6 + (-2) = 4$
−6, 2	$-6 + 2 = -4$
4, −3	$4 + (-3) = 1$
−4, 3	$-4 + 3 = -1$

$$x^2 - xy - 12y^2 = (x - 4y)(x + 3y) \qquad (-4) \cdot 3 = -12 \text{ and } -4 + 3 = -1$$ ■

With practice you will be able to find the factors of c that are more likely to sum to b without constructing the complete table.

> CAUTION Not every polynomial can be factored. For example, $x^2 + x + 1$ cannot be written as a product of binomial factors with integers as coefficients.

Some trinomials are not in the form $x^2 + bxy + cy^2$ but can be put into this form by removing a common factor.

EXAMPLE 4 **Factoring Trinomials with a Common Factor**

Factor $3x^2 - 12xy + 12y^2$.

$$3x^2 - 12xy + 12y^2 = 3 \cdot x^2 - 3 \cdot 4xy + 3 \cdot 4y^2$$
$$= 3(x^2 - 4xy + 4y^2)$$

We can now factor $x^2 - 4xy + 4y^2$ where $b = -4$ and $c = 4$.

$$x^2 - 4xy + 4y^2 = (x + \_\_y)(x + \_\_y)$$

Factors of $c = 4$	*Sum of factors*
4, 1	$4 + 1 = 5$
2, 2	$2 + 2 = 4$
$-4, -1$	$-4 + (-1) = -5$
$-2, -2$	$-2 + (-2) = -4$

$$x^2 - 4xy + 4y^2 = (x - 2y)(x - 2y) \qquad (-2)(-2) = 4 \text{ and } -2 + (-2) = -4$$

Thus, $3x^2 - 12xy + 12y^2 = 3(x - 2y)(x - 2y)$. ■

NOTE Always include the common factor as part of the answer. In Example 4 we included the factor 3 in the final product.

Not all trinomials can be factored. One example is $x^2 + 5x + 2$. The only factors of $c = 2$ are 2 and 1, but $2 + 1$ is 3 and not $b = 5$.

Factoring, just like any other skill, is learned by practice. The more time spent and the more problems worked, the more proficient we become.

EXAMPLE 5 **Solving an Application in Business**

A small company manufactures wood-burning stoves. The total cost c of producing n stoves is given by the equation $c = -200n^2 + 1200n + 1400$. Factor the right side of this equation and use this factored form to find the cost of producing 4 stoves.

Factoring gives the following.

$$c = -200n^2 + 1200n + 1400$$
$$= -200(n^2 - 6n - 7) \qquad \text{The GCF is } -200$$
$$= -200(n - 7)(n + 1)$$

Substitute 4 for n to find c.

$$c = -200(4 - 7)(4 + 1)$$
$$= -200(-3)(5) = 3000$$

It would cost \$3000 to produce 4 stoves. ■

7.2 EXERCISES

In Exercises 1–30, factor and check by multiplying.

1. $x^2 + 4x + 3$
2. $x^2 + 2x - 3$
3. $x^2 - 2x - 3$
4. $x^2 - 4x + 3$
5. $u^2 - 12u + 35$
6. $u^2 - 2u - 35$
7. $y^2 + 10y + 21$
8. $y^2 + 5y + 24$
9. $x^2 - 12x + 27$
10. $y^2 - y - 56$
11. $x^2 - 2x - 63$
12. $x^2 - 2x - 120$
13. $x^2 + 4x - 77$
14. $x^2 + 4xy + 3y^2$
15. $x^2 + 2xy - 3y^2$
16. $x^2 - 2xy - 3y^2$
17. $x^2 - 4xy + 3y^2$
18. $u^2 + uv - 20v^2$
19. $x^2 + 13xy - 30y^2$
20. $x^2 + 11xy + 24y^2$
21. $u^2 - 8uv + 15v^2$
22. $u^2 - 3uv - 40v^2$
23. $x^2 - 10xy + 24y^2$
24. $x^2 + 11xy + 30y^2$
25. $2u^2 + 24uv + 72v^2$
26. $-2u^2 + 2uv + 84v^2$
27. $x^2y + xy^2 - 90y^3$
28. $3x^2 - 12xy - 96y^2$
29. $u^2v^2 - 22uv^3 + 121v^4$
30. $-5u^2 - 90uv - 385v^2$

31. PHYSICS A child standing on a bridge 48 ft above the surface of the water throws a rock upward with a velocity of 32 ft per second. The equation that gives the height h in feet of the rock above the water in terms of time t in seconds is $h = -16t^2 + 32t + 48$. Factor the right side of this equation and use this factored form to find the height of the rock after **(a)** 1 sec, **(b)** 2 sec, and **(c)** 3 sec.

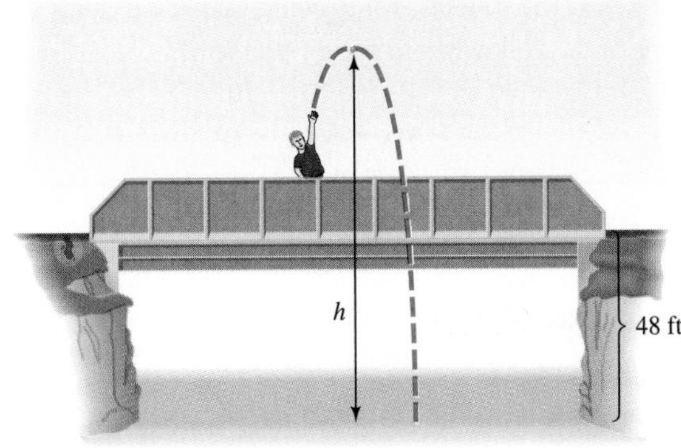

32. What is wrong with Burford's work in the following factoring problem?

$$2x^2 + 10x - 48 = 2(x^2 + 5x - 24)$$
$$= (x - 3)(x + 8)$$

FOR REVIEW

Find the GCF and factor in Exercises 33–35.

33. $35x - 70$
34. $28a^4b^4 - 14a^3b^3 - 21a^2b^2$
35. $2a(x + y) - 3b(x + y)$

Factor by grouping in Exercises 36–37.

36. $x^3 - 6x^2 + 5x - 30$
37. $5ax^2 + 2bx^2 + 5ay^2 + 2by^2$

Exercises 38–40 review material from Chapter 6 that will help you prepare for the next section. Use the FOIL method to multiply.

38. $(2x + 1)(x + 3)$ **39.** $(3x - 5)(2x - 1)$ **40.** $(5x - 2)(2x + 1)$

7.2 PARALLEL EXERCISES

In Exercises 1–30, factor and check by multiplying.

1. $x^2 + 6x + 5$ **2.** $x^2 + 4x - 5$ **3.** $x^2 - 4x - 5$ **4.** $x^2 - 6x + 5$
5. $u^2 + 8u + 15$ **6.** $u^2 + 2u - 15$ **7.** $y^2 - 10y + 21$ **8.** $x^2 - 5x + 24$
9. $u^2 + 12u + 27$ **10.** $x^2 - 4x - 32$ **11.** $u^2 - 2u - 48$ **12.** $y^2 + 16y + 60$
13. $x^2 + 8x - 33$ **14.** $x^2 + 6xy + 5y^2$ **15.** $x^2 + 4xy - 5y^2$ **16.** $x^2 - 4xy - 5y^2$
17. $u^2 - 9uv + 18v^2$ **18.** $u^2 + 3uv - 18v^2$ **19.** $x^2 + 6xy - 27y^2$ **20.** $x^2 + 12xy + 20y^2$
21. $u^2 - 11uv + 28v^2$ **22.** $u^2 + uv - 30v^2$ **23.** $x^2 - 13xy + 40y^2$ **24.** $x^2 + 16xy + 63y^2$
25. $2u^2 + 16uv + 32v^2$ **26.** $-2u^2 + 6uv + 80v^2$ **27.** $x^2y + 6xy^2 - 72y^3$ **28.** $3x^2 - 15xy - 150y^2$
29. $u^4 - 26u^3v + 169u^2v^2$ **30.** $-4u^2 - 76uv - 352v^2$

31. **PRODUCTION** A company can produce n items at a total cost of c dollars where c is given by $c = -100n^2 + 600n + 1600$. Factor the right side of this equation and use this factored form to find the cost of producing **(a)** 0 items, **(b)** 2 items, **(c)** 3 items, and **(d)** 6 items.

32. What is wrong with Burford's work in the following factoring problem?

$$-4x^2 + 12x + 40 = -4(x^2 + 3x - 10)$$
$$= -4(x + 5)(x - 2)$$

FOR REVIEW

Find the GCF and factor in Exercises 33–35.

33. $35y^4 - 21y^2$ **34.** $8a^5b^5 + 20a^3b^4 - 32a^2b^5$ **35.** $6u(x^2 + y^2) + 7(x^2 + y^2)$

Factor by grouping in Exercises 36–37.

36. $x^3 + 3x^2 - 7x - 21$ **37.** $2a^2x - 2a^2y + b^2x - b^2y$

Exercises 38–40 review material from Chapter 6 that will help you prepare for the next section. Use the FOIL method to multiply.

38. $(3x + 1)(x + 7)$ **39.** $(3x + 5)(2x - 1)$ **40.** $(5x - 3)(x + 6)$

7.2 ENRICHMENT EXERCISES

Factor in Exercises 1–6.

1. $x^2 + \frac{1}{3}x - \frac{2}{9}$ **2.** $x^2 - 0.04x + 0.0003$
△ **3.** $(x + 2)^2 - 10(x + 2) + 16$ **4.** $x^4 + 5x^2 + 6$
5. $-12xy + 2x^2 + 16y^2$ **6.** $-2x^3y - 15x^2y^2 + x^4$

Suppose $x^2 + bx + c$ *is factored as* $(x \pm h)(x \pm k)$ *with the two signs to be determined. Answer* true *or* false *in Exercises 7–10. If the statement is false, tell why.*

7. If b is positive and c is positive, then both signs are positive.

8. If b is negative and c is positive, then both signs are positive.

9. If b is positive and c is negative, then one sign is positive and one is negative.

10. If b is negative and c is negative, then one sign is positive and one is negative.

11. Describe in your own words the procedure you follow in factoring a trinomial of the form $x^2 + bx + c$.

SECTION 7.3 Factoring Trinomials of the Form $ax^2 + bx + c$

Student guideposts

- ▶ *Factoring* $ax^2 + bx + c$
- ▶ *Factoring* $ax^2 + bxy + cy^2$
- ▶ *Factoring* $ax^2 + bx + c$ *by grouping*

▶ *Factoring* $ax^2 + bx + c$

In Section 7.2 we concentrated on factoring trinomials for which the coefficient of the squared term is 1. Now we consider trinomials of the form $ax^2 + bx + c$, with $a \neq 1$. As before, it helps to look at the pattern in multiplication.

$$
\begin{aligned}
(5x + 2)(2x + 3) &= \underset{\text{Ⓕ}}{5x \cdot 2x} + \underset{\text{Ⓞ}}{5x \cdot 3} + \underset{\text{Ⓘ}}{2 \cdot 2x} + \underset{\text{Ⓛ}}{2 \cdot 3} \\
&= 10x^2 + 15x + 4x + 6 \\
&= \underset{\text{Ⓕ}}{10x^2} + \underset{\text{Ⓞ + Ⓘ}}{19x} + \underset{\text{Ⓛ}}{6}
\end{aligned}
$$

The term $10x^2$ is the product of the first terms Ⓕ, the 6 is the product of the last terms Ⓛ, and $19x$ is the sum of the products Ⓞ and Ⓘ. With $a \neq 1$ we can use the following trial and error method to factor. (Another method is presented later.)

To Factor $ax^2 + bx + c$

1. Write $ax^2 + bx + c = (\_\_x + \_\_)(\_\_x + \_\_)$.
2. List all pairs of integers whose product is a and try each of these in the first blanks in each binomial factor.
3. List all pairs of integers whose product is c and try each of these in the second blanks.
4. Use trial and error to determine which pair (if one exists) gives Ⓞ + Ⓘ $= b$.

EXAMPLE 1 **Factoring $ax^2 + bx + c$**

Factor $2x^2 + 7x + 3$. $(a = 2, b = 7, c = 3)$

Factors of 3

$$2x^2 + 7x + 3 = (\_\_x + \_\_)(\_\_x + \_\_)$$

Factors of 2

Since all terms of the trinomial are positive, we need only list the positive factors of a and c. We list the factors of c in both orders as a reminder to try all possibilities.

Factors of $a = 2$	*Factors of* $c = 3$
2, 1	3, 1
	1, 3

$2x^2 + 7x + 3 = (\_\_x + \_\_)(\_\_x + \_\_)$

$= (2x + \_\_)(x + \_\_)$ The only factors of a are 2 and 1

$\stackrel{?}{=} (2x + 3)(x + 1)$ Does not work because $2x + 3x = 5x \neq 7x$

$\stackrel{?}{=} (2x + 1)(x + 3)$ This works because $6x + x = 7x$

$2x^2 + 7x + 3 = (2x + 1)(x + 3)$

To check we multiply.

$$(2x + 1)(x + 3) = 2x^2 + 6x + x + 3 = 2x^2 + 7x + 3 \quad \blacksquare$$

NOTE In Example 1 we listed only the factors of c (1 and 3) in both orders and not the factors of a (1 and 2). It is not necessary to list both pairs in both orders. For example, $(2x + 1)(x + 3)$ and $(x + 3)(2x + 1)$ are two factorizations that are the same by the commutative law of multiplication.

EXAMPLE 2 **Factoring $ax^2 + bx + c$**

Factor $6x^2 - 13x + 5$. $(a = 6, b = -13, c = 5)$

Factors of 5

$$6x^2 - 13x + 5 = (\_\_x + \_\_)(\_\_x + \_\_)$$

Factors of 6

Here the factors of $c = 5 > 0$ must both be negative to obtain the term $-13x$. As before we list them in both orders.

Factors of $a = 6$	*Factors of* $c = 5$	
6, 1	−5, −1	Try 6, 1 with both −5, −1 and −1, −5
3, 2	−1, −5	Try 3, 2 with both −5, −1 and −1, −5

$$6x^2 - 13x + 5 = (\_\_x + \_\_)(\_\_x + \_\_)$$

$\stackrel{?}{=} (6x - 5)(x - 1)$ Does not work because $-6x - 5x = -11x \neq -13x$

$\stackrel{?}{=} (6x - 1)(x - 5)$ Does not work because $-30x - x = -31x \neq -13x$

$\stackrel{?}{=} (3x - 5)(2x - 1)$ This works because $-3x - 10x = -13x$

$$6x^2 - 13x + 5 = (3x - 5)(2x - 1)$$

To check we multiply.

$$(3x - 5)(2x - 1) = 6x^2 - 3x - 10x + 5 = 6x^2 - 13x + 5 \quad \blacksquare$$

EXAMPLE 3

Factoring $ax^2 + bx + c$

Factor $8y^2 - 10y - 7$. $(a = 8, b = -10, c = -7)$

The factors of $c = -7$ will have opposite signs.

Factors of $a = 8$	*Factors of $c = -7$*
8, 1	7, −1
4, 2	−7, 1
	1, −7
	−1, 7

With this many cases to test, we try to minimize the number of trials. If 8 and 1 are used, the middle term will be either too big, because $8 \cdot 7y - 1 \cdot 1y = 55y$, or too small, because $8 \cdot 1y - 7 \cdot 1y = y$. Thus, we try 4 and 2 as factors of 8.

$$8y^2 - 10y - 7 = (\_\_y + \_\_)(\_\_y + \_\_)$$

$= (4y + \_\_)(2y + \_\_)$ Try 4, 2

$\stackrel{?}{=} (4y + 7)(2y - 1)$ Does not work

$\stackrel{?}{=} (4y - 7)(2y + 1)$ This works

$$8y^2 - 10y - 7 = (4y - 7)(2y + 1)$$

Check this by multiplying. ■

EXAMPLE 4

Factoring Out a Common Factor

Factor $-4x^2 - 2x + 20$.

Unlike Examples 1, 2, and 3 this trinomial has a common factor. First we factor out the common factor including -1 to make a positive. If a is positive we only have to consider positive factors of a.

$$-4x^2 - 2x + 20 = -2\ (2x^2 + x - 10)$$

Now we factor $2x^2 + x - 10$ where $a = 2$, $b = 1$, and $c = -10$.

Factors of $a = 2$	*Factors of* $c = -10$
2, 1	10, −1 and −10, 1
	−1, 10 and 1, −10
	5, −2 and −5, 2
	−2, 5 and 2, −5

$$-4x^2 - 2x + 20 = -2(2x^2 + x - 10)$$
$$= -2(2x + \_\_)(x + \_\_)$$
$$\stackrel{?}{=} -2(2x + 10)(x - 1) \quad \text{Factors of 10 give too large a middle term}$$
$$\stackrel{?}{=} -2(2x + 5)(x - 2) \quad \text{This works}$$
$$-4x^2 - 2x + 20 = -2(2x + 5)(x - 2) \quad \blacksquare$$

CAUTION Do not forget to include the common factor in the answer. The common factor −2 was included in Example 4.

▶ ***Factoring*** $ax^2 + bxy + cy^2$

Trinomials of the form $ax^2 + bxy + cy^2$ can be factored by filling in the blanks as indicated below.

$$ax^2 + bxy + cy^2 = (\_\_x + \_\_y)(\_\_x + \_\_y)$$

EXAMPLE 5

Factoring $ax^2 + bxy + cy^2$

Factor $3x^2 - 14xy + 8y^2$. ($a = 3$, $b = -14$, $c = 8$)

Both factors of $c = 8$ must be negative since $b = -14$.

Factors of $a = 3$	*Factors of* $c = 8$
3, 1	−8, −1
	−1, −8
	−4, −2
	−2, −4

$$3x^2 - 14xy + 8y^2 = (3x + \_\_y)(x + \_\_y)$$
$$\stackrel{?}{=} (3x - 8y)(x - y) \quad \text{Does not work}$$
$$\stackrel{?}{=} (3x - y)(x - 8y) \quad \text{Does not work}$$
$$\stackrel{?}{=} (3x - 4y)(x - 2y) \quad \text{Does not work}$$
$$\stackrel{?}{=} (3x - 2y)(x - 4y) \quad \text{This works}$$
$$3x^2 - 14xy + 8y^2 = (3x - 2y)(x - 4y) \quad \blacksquare$$

EXAMPLE 6 **Factoring $ax^2 + bxy + cy^2$**

Factor $10u^2 + 7uv - 3v^2$. $(a = 10, b = 7, c = -3)$

Factors of a = 10	*Factors of c* = −3
10, 1	3, −1
5, 2	−3, 1
	1, −3
	−1, 3

$10u^2 + 7uv - 3v^2 = (\_\_u + \_\_v)(\_\_u + \_\_v)$

$\stackrel{?}{=} (10u + 3v)(u - v)$ Does not work since $-10uv + 3uv = -7uv$

$\stackrel{?}{=} (10u - 3v)(u + v)$ We know this works from the first trial

$10u^2 + 7uv - 3v^2 = (10u - 3v)(u + v)$ ■

▶ *Factoring $ax^2 + bx + c$ by grouping*

There is another method for factoring trinomials. Consider the following procedure.

$2x^2 + 13x + 15 = 2x^2 + 10x + 3x + 15$ Rewrite middle term, $13x = 10x + 3x$

$= (2x^2 + 10x) + (3x + 15)$ Group terms in pairs

$= 2x(x + 5) + 3(x + 5)$ Factor the groups separately

$= (2x + 3)(x + 5)$ Factor out the common factor $x + 5$

We have factored $2x^2 + 13x + 15$ by grouping the appropriate terms. But how did we decide to write $13x = 10x + 3x$? Notice that 10 and 3 are factors of $2 \cdot 15 = 30$. That is, 10 and 3 are factors of the product ac in $ax^2 + bx + c$.

To Factor $ax^2 + bx + c$ by Grouping

1. Find the product ac.
2. List the factors of ac until a pair is found with sum b.
3. Write bx as a sum using these factors as coefficients of x.
4. Factor the result by grouping.

EXAMPLE 7 **Factoring by Grouping**

Factor $3x^2 - 10x + 7$ by grouping. The product $ac = 3 \cdot 7 = 21$.

Factors of ac = 21	*Sum of factors*
21, 1	$21 + 1 = 22$
−21, −1	$-21 + (-1) = -22$
7, 3	$7 + 3 = 10$
−7, −3	$-7 + (-3) = -10$

The factors −7 and −3 will work so we write $-10x = -7x - 3x$.

$$3x^2 - 10x + 7 = 3x^2 - 7x - 3x + 7$$
$$= x(3x - 7) - 1 \cdot (3x - 7) \quad \text{Factor out } x \text{ and } -1$$
$$= (x - 1)(3x - 7) \quad \text{The common factor is } 3x - 7$$ ■

EXAMPLE 8 **Factoring $ax^2 + bxy + cy^2$ by Grouping**

Factor $5x^2 + 6xy - 8y^2$ by grouping.

For two variables the procedure is the same. $ac = 5(-8) = -40$. We try factors that seem most likely to have a sum of 6.

Factors of ac = −40	*Sum of factors*
8, −5	8 + (−5) = 3
−8, 5	−8 + 5 = −3
−10, 4	−10 + 4 = −6
10, −4	10 + (−4) = 6

Write $6xy$ as $10xy - 4xy$.

$$5x^2 + 6xy - 8y^2 = 5x^2 + 10xy - 4xy - 8y^2$$
$$= 5x(x + 2y) - 4y(x + 2y) \quad \text{Factor groups}$$
$$= (5x - 4y)(x + 2y) \quad \text{Common factor is } x + 2y$$ ■

7.3 EXERCISES

Factor and check by multiplying in Exercises 1–30.

1. $2x^2 + 7x + 5$
2. $2x^2 - 5x + 3$
3. $2u^2 - 5u - 3$
4. $2u^2 + 13u - 7$
5. $2y^2 + 13y - 24$
6. $2y^2 + 19y + 24$
7. $6z^2 - 13z - 28$
8. $5x^2 - 33x + 40$
9. $-6x^2 - 39x - 54$
10. $7u^2 - 14u + 7$
11. $16u^2 - 16u + 4$
12. $2y^2 + y - 7$
13. $3y^3 + 11y^2 + 10y$
14. $-45x^2 + 150x - 125$
15. $6x^2 - 3x + 21$
16. $6u^2 - 23u + 20$
17. $2x^2 + 7xy + 5y^2$
18. $2u^2 - 5uv - 3v^2$
19. $2u^2 + 13uv - 7v^2$
20. $3x^2 - 10xy + 3y^2$
21. $3x^2 + 13xy + 14y^2$
22. $6u^2 + uv - v^2$
23. $-3x^2 + 18xy - 24y^2$
24. $x^2 + xy + y^2$
25. $4u^2 - v^2$
26. $3u^3v + 14u^2v^2 - 5uv^3$
27. $6x^2 - 35xy - 6y^2$
28. $6x^2 + 29xy + 30y^2$
29. $14x^2 + 30xy + 16y^2$
30. $3x^3y - 2x^2y^2 - xy^3$

FOR REVIEW

Factor in Exercises 31–33.

31. $x^2 + 6xy - 27y^2$
32. $x^2 - 18xy + 81y^2$
33. $-3x^2 + 9x + 120$

Exercises 34–36 review material from Section 6.6 to help you prepare for the next section. Find the following special products.

34. $(4u + 5)^2$
35. $(4u - 5)^2$
36. $(4u + 5)(4u - 5)$

7.3 PARALLEL EXERCISES

Factor and check by multiplying in Exercises 1–30.

1. $2x^2 + 5x + 3$
2. $2x^2 - 7x + 5$
3. $2u^2 + 3u - 14$
4. $2u^2 - 9u - 5$
5. $2u^2 + 9u - 5$
6. $2y^2 + 17y + 30$
7. $6x^2 + x - 15$
8. $5u^2 - 33u + 18$
9. $-4y^2 - 22y - 28$
10. $5x^2 - 20x + 20$
11. $27u^2 + 18u + 3$
12. $3y^2 - y + 5$
13. $2x^4 + 7x^3 + 3x^2$
14. $-16u^2 + 80u - 100$
15. $6y^2 + 36y + 36$
16. $20x^2 - 13x + 2$
17. $2x^2 - 7xy + 5y^2$
18. $2u^2 + 3uv - 14v^2$
19. $2u^2 - 9uv - 5v^2$
20. $3x^2 - 7xy + 2y^2$
21. $3x^2 + 22xy + 7y^2$
22. $6u^2 - uv - 2v^2$
23. $-5x^2 + 25xy - 30y^2$
24. $x^2 - 2xy + 2y^2$
25. $9u^2 - v^2$
26. $3u^4 - 4u^3v - 4u^2v^2$
27. $8x^2 - 7xy - y^2$
28. $6x^2 + 25xy + 11y^2$
29. $14x^2 - 30xy + 16y^2$
30. $3x^3y + 2x^2y^2 - xy^3$

FOR REVIEW

Factor in Exercises 31–33.

31. $x^2 - 5xy - 66y^2$
32. $x^2 + 24xy + 144y^2$
33. $-5x^2 - 20x + 105$

Exercises 34–36 review material from Section 6.6 to help you prepare for the next section. Find the following special products.

34. $(3u + 7)^2$
35. $(3u - 7)^2$
36. $(3u + 7)(3u - 7)$

7.3 ENRICHMENT EXERCISES

Factor in Exercises 1–4.

1. $2x^2 - \frac{1}{5}x - \frac{1}{25}$
2. $0.02x^2 - 0.9x + 4$
3. $2(3x - 1)^2 - (3x - 1) - 1$
[*Hint:* Substitute u for $3x - 1$.]
4. $3x^4 + 10x^2 - 8$

5. Evaluate $3x^2 - 5x - 2$ when $x = 2$. Evaluate $(x - 2)(3x + 1)$ when $x = 2$. Why are the two values the same?

6. Evaluate $10x^2 + x - 3$ when $x = -2$. Evaluate $(2x - 1)(5x + 3)$ when $x = -2$. Why are the two values the same?

7. The factors of a trinomial are 2, $x + 3$, and $2x - 1$. Find the trinomial.

8. The factors of a trinomial are 3, $x - 1$, and $2x + 5$. Find the trinomial.

9. In your own words give the method that you use and the exact procedure for factoring $ax^2 + bxy + cy^2$.

SECTION 7.4 Factoring Perfect Square Trinomials and Difference of Squares

Student guideposts

- ▶ *Perfect square trinomials*
- ▶ *Difference of two squares*
- ▶ *Sum and difference of cubes (optional)*

▶ ***Perfect square trinomials***

We could factor trinomials such as

$$x^2 + 6x + 9 = (x + 3)(x + 3)$$

$$\text{and} \quad 4y^2 - 4y + 1 = (2y - 1)(2y - 1)$$

with the methods of the previous two sections. However, by recognizing these as *perfect square trinomials,* we can save some of the time used in trial-and-error methods. In Section 6.6 we used the formulas

$$(a + b)^2 = a^2 + 2ab + b^2$$

$$(a - b)^2 = a^2 - 2ab + b^2$$

to square binomials. Now we consider the reverse operation, factoring trinomials like those on the right into the square of a binomial. To factor $x^2 + 6x + 9$, we first observe that it fits the appropriate formula.

$$x^2 + 6x + 9 = x^2 + 6x + 3^2 \qquad x^2 \text{ and } 3^2 \text{ are perfect squares}$$

$$= x^2 + 2 \cdot x \cdot 3 + 3^2 \qquad x = a \text{ and } 3 = b \text{ in } a^2 + 2ab + b^2$$

$$= (x + 3)^2 \qquad a^2 + 2ab + b^2 = (a + b)^2$$

From the formula and this example, it is easy to see that a **perfect square trinomial** must contain two terms that are perfect squares (x^2 and 9 in the example). The remaining term must be plus or minus twice the product of the numbers whose squares form the other terms ($2 \cdot x \cdot 3 = 6x$ in the example). Notice that $x^2 + 10x + 9 = (x + 1)(x + 9)$ is *not* a perfect square trinomial because of its middle term, even though both x^2 and 9 are perfect squares.

EXAMPLE 1 Factoring Perfect Square Trinomials

Factor the trinomials.

(a) $x^2 + 8x + 16 = x^2 + 8x + 4^2 \qquad x^2 \text{ and } 16 \text{ are perfect squares}$

$$= x^2 + 2 \cdot x \cdot 4 + 4^2 \qquad x = a \text{ and } 4 = b \text{ in } a^2 + 2ab + b^2$$

$$= (x + 4)^2 \qquad a^2 + 2ab + b^2 = (a + b)^2$$

Notice that we have $(x + 4)^2$ instead of $(x - 4)^2$ since $8x$ is positive.

(b) $x^2 - 8x + 16 = x^2 - 2 \cdot x \cdot 4 + 4^2 \qquad x = a \text{ and } 4 = b$

$$= (x - 4)^2 \qquad \text{Note the minus sign in this case}$$

(c) $16u^2 + 40u + 25 = (4u)^2 + 40u + 5^2$ — $4u = a$ and $5 = b$

$= (4u)^2 + 2(4u)(5) + 5^2$ — $2ab = 2(4u)(5) = 40u$

$= (4u + 5)^2$

(d) $16u^2 - 40u + 25 = (4u)^2 - 2(4u)(5) + 5^2$

$= (4u - 5)^2$ ■

To Factor Perfect Square Trinomials

1. Determine if two terms are perfect squares and the remaining one is twice the product of the numbers whose squares are the other terms.
2. Use the formulas

$$a^2 + 2ab + b^2 = (a + b)^2$$
$$a^2 - 2ab + b^2 = (a - b)^2.$$

EXAMPLE 2

Factoring Perfect Squares

Factor the trinomials in two variables.

(a) $x^2 + 18xy + 81y^2 = x^2 + 18xy + (9y)^2$ — x^2 and $(9y)^2$ are perfect squares

$= x^2 + 2 \cdot x \cdot 9y + (9y)^2$ — $x = a$ and $9y = b$

$= (x + 9y)^2$ — Use the formula

(b) $2u^2 - 40uv + 200v^2 = 2(u^2 - 20uv + 100v^2)$ — Factor out common factor

$= 2(u^2 - 2 \cdot u \cdot 10v + (10v)^2)$ — $u = a$ and $10v = b$

$= 2(u - 10v)^2$

▶*Difference of two squares*

Another special formula can be used whenever we factor the difference of two squares.

$$a^2 - b^2 = (a + b)(a - b)$$

Observe that we are factoring a binomial in this case.

EXAMPLE 3

Factoring a Difference of Squares

Factor the binomials.

(a) $x^2 - 9 = x^2 - 3^2$ — x^2 and 3^2 are perfect squares

$= (x + 3)(x - 3)$ — $x = a$ and $3 = b$

(b) $y^2 - 121 = y^2 - 11^2$ — y^2 and 11^2 are perfect squares

$= (y + 11)(y - 11)$ — $y = a$ and $11 = b$

(c) $16u^2 - 25 = (4u)^2 - 5^2$ — $(4u)^2$ and 5^2 are perfect squares

$= (4u + 5)(4u - 5)$ — $4u = a$ and $5 = b$

(d) $5x^3 - 500x = 5x(x^2 - 100)$ — Factor out common factor
$= 5x(x^2 - 10^2)$
$= 5x(x + 10)(x - 10)$

(e) $y^6 - 49 = (y^3)^2 - 7^2$ — $(y^3)^2$ and 7^2 are perfect squares
$= (y^3 + 7)(y^3 - 7)$ — $y^3 = a$ and $7 = b$

(f) $x^2 + 9 = x^2 + 3^2$ — Cannot be factored ■

CAUTION Notice in Example 3(f) that the sum of two squares cannot be factored. Do not make the mistake of giving $(a + b)^2$ as the factors of $a^2 + b^2$.

$$(a + b)^2 = a^2 + 2ab + b^2 \neq a^2 + b^2$$

Also, $(a - b)^2 \neq a^2 - b^2$.

To Factor a Difference of Two Squares

1. Determine if the binomial is the difference of two perfect squares.
2. Use the formula

$$a^2 - b^2 = (a + b)(a - b).$$

EXAMPLE 4 **Factoring a Difference of Squares**

Factor the binomials in two variables.

(a) $25x^2 - 9y^2 = (5x)^2 - (3y)^2$ — $(5x)^2$ and $(3y)^2$ are perfect squares
$= (5x + 3y)(5x - 3y)$ — $5x = a$ and $3y = b$

(b) $27u^3 - 48uv^2 = 3u(9u^2 - 16v^2)$ — Factor out common factor
$= 3u[(3u)^2 - (4v)^2]$ — $3u = a$ and $4v = b$
$= 3u(3u + 4v)(3u - 4v)$

(c) $x^4 - y^4 = (x^2)^2 - (y^2)^2$ — $x^2 = a$ and $y^2 = b$
$= (x^2 + y^2)(x^2 - y^2)$ — Now $x = a$ and $y = b$ in the difference of two squares $x^2 - y^2$
$= (x^2 + y^2)(x + y)(x - y)$ — Factor again ■

▶ *Sum and difference of cubes (optional)*

We conclude this section with two other factoring techniques that allow us to factor a sum or difference of two cubes. Suppose we multiply the following polynomials.

$(a + b)(a^2 - ab + b^2) = (a + b)a^2 - (a + b)ab + (a + b)b^2$ — Distributive law
$= a^3 + ba^2 - a^2b - ab^2 + ab^2 + b^3$ — Distributive law again
$= a^3 + b^3$

In a similar manner we have

$$\begin{aligned}(a-b)(a^2+ab+b^2) &= (a-b)a^2+(a-b)ab+(a-b)b^2\\ &= a^3-ba^2+a^2b-ab^2+ab^2-b^3\\ &= a^3-b^3\end{aligned}$$

These results provide the formulas for factoring the sum of two cubes, a^3+b^3, and the difference of two cubes, a^3-b^3.

To Factor a Sum or Difference of Cubes

1. Determine if the binomial is the sum or difference of two perfect cubes.
2. Use one of the formulas

$$a^3+b^3=(a+b)(a^2-ab+b^2)$$
$$a^3-b^3=(a-b)(a^2+ab+b^2).$$

NOTE a^2-ab+b^2 and a^2+ab+b^2 cannot be factored.

EXAMPLE 5

Factoring a Sum and Difference of Cubes

Factor the binomials.

(a) $x^3+8=x^3+2^3$ — x^3 and $8=2^3$ are perfect cubes

$=(x+2)(x^2-2x+2^2)$ — $x=a$ and $2=b$ in $a^3+b^3=(a+b)(a^2-ab+b^2)$

$=(x+2)(x^2-2x+4)$

(b) $x^3-8=x^3-2^3$

$=(x-2)(x^2+2x+2^2)$ — $x=a$ and $2=b$

$=(x-2)(x^2+2x+4)$

(c) $27x^3-1=(3x)^3-1^3$ — $27x^3=(3x)^3$ and $1=1^3$ are perfect cubes

$=(3x-1)((3x)^2+(3x)(1)+1^2)$

$=(3x-1)(9x^2+3x+1)$

(d) $8x^3+125=(2x)^3+5^3$

$=(2x+5)((2x)^2-(2x)(5)+5^2)$

$=(2x+5)(4x^2-10x+25)$ ■

CAUTION Do not make the common mistake of factoring a^3+b^3 as $(a+b)^3$ and a^3-b^3 as $(a-b)^3$. Neither of these is correct as can easily be verified by multiplying $(a+b)(a+b)(a+b)$ and $(a-b)(a-b)(a-b)$.

The following provides a summary of the methods for factoring polynomials.

To Factor a Polynomial

1. Factor out any common factor, including -1 if a is negative in $ax^2 + bx + c$ or $ax^2 + bxy + cy^2$.
2. To factor the difference of two squares use the formula
$$a^2 - b^2 = (a + b)(a - b).$$
Remember that $a^2 + b^2$ cannot be factored.
3. To factor a trinomial use the techniques of Section 7.2 or Section 7.3, but also consider perfect squares using the formulas
$$a^2 + 2ab + b^2 = (a + b)^2 \quad \text{and} \quad a^2 - 2ab + b^2 = (a - b)^2.$$
4. To factor a polynomial of more than three terms, try to factor by grouping.
5. To factor the sum or difference of two cubes use one of the formulas
$$a^3 + b^3 = (a + b)(a^2 - ab + b^2)$$
$$a^3 - b^3 = (a - b)(a^2 + ab + b^2).$$
Remember that $a^2 - ab + b^2$ and $a^2 + ab + b^2$ cannot be factored.

7.4 EXERCISES

Factor using the special formulas in Exercises 1–24.

1. $x^2 + 10x + 25$
2. $x^2 - 10x + 25$
3. $x^2 - 25$
4. $x^2 + 25$
5. $u^2 - 14u + 49$
6. $x^2 - 24x + 144$
7. $x^2 - 121$
8. $9u^2 + 6u + 1$
9. $9u^2 - 6u + 1$
10. $4y^2 - 12y + 9$
11. $4x^2 + 20x + 25$
12. $9u^2 - 25$
13. $-12y^2 + 60y - 75$
14. $4y^2 - 36y + 81$
15. $9x^2 + 30x + 25$
16. $x^2 + x + 4$
17. $8u^3 - 8u$
18. $u^6 - 16$
19. $5y^3 - 100y^2 + 500y$
20. $7y^4 - 63$
21. $x^2 + 6xy + 9y^2$
22. $25x^2 - 10xy + y^2$
23. $64u^2 - 9v^2$
24. $u^4 - v^4$

In Exercises 25–39, factor using the appropriate method.

25. $x^2 + 9x + 18$
26. $x^2 - 12x + 36$
27. $u^2 + 10u + 16$
28. $4y^2 - 28y + 49$
29. $-6x^2 + 486$
30. $25u^2 - 20u + 4$
31. $16u^2 - 9$
32. $4y^2 - 16y + 15$
33. $40y^2 + 11y - 2$
34. $3x^9 - 147x^3$
35. $98x^6 - 18$
36. $3x^2 - 19xy - 14y^2$
37. $18u^2 - 98v^2$
38. $100x^5 - 60x^4y + 9x^3y^2$
39. $(x + y)^2 - 25$

FOR REVIEW

Exercises 40–42 review material from Chapter 3 to help you prepare for the next section. Solve the following equations.

40. $2x + 5 = 0$

41. $6x - 1 = 0$

42. $4x = 0$

7.4 PARALLEL EXERCISES

Factor using the special formulas in Exercises 1–24.

1. $x^2 + 12x + 36$

2. $x^2 - 12x + 36$

3. $x^2 - 36$

4. $x^2 + 36$

5. $u^2 + 16u + 64$

6. $x^2 - 22x + 121$

7. $x^2 - 169$

8. $4u^2 + 4u + 1$

9. $4u^2 - 4u + 1$

10. $9y^2 - 12y + 4$

11. $9x^2 + 30x + 25$

12. $4u^2 - 25$

13. $-32y^2 + 48y - 18$

14. $9y^2 - 42y + 49$

15. $25x^2 + 30x + 9$

16. $x^2 + 2x + 4$

17. $4u^3 - 16u$

18. $u^6 - 81$

19. $-4y^2 - 64y - 256$

20. $y^4 - 81$

21. $x^2 + 8xy + 16y^2$

22. $36x^2 - 12xy + y^2$

23. $49u^2 - 16v^2$

24. $81u^4 - v^4$

In Exercises 25–39, factor using the appropriate method.

25. $x^2 + 12x + 35$

26. $x^2 + 20x + 100$

27. $u^2 - 14u + 45$

28. $-4y^2 + 400$

29. $9x^2 - 60x + 100$

30. $28x^2 - 41x + 15$

31. $-10u^2 - 21u + 10$

32. $18u^2 - 98$

33. $42y^2 - 3y - 9$

34. $16y^2 + 6y - 27$

35. $25x^2 - 90x + 81$

36. $2x^2 - 52xy + 338y^2$

37. $200u^2 - 242v^2$

38. $9x^4y^2 - 60x^3y^3 + 100x^2y^4$

39. $(x - y)^2 - 16$

FOR REVIEW

Exercises 40–42 review material from Chapter 3 to help you prepare for the next section. Solve the following equations.

40. $x - 9 = 0$

41. $5x + 6 = 0$

42. $\frac{1}{2}x = 0$

7.4 ENRICHMENT EXERCISES

In Exercises 1–15, factor using the appropriate method.

1. $(x + y)^2 + 2(x + y) + 1$

2. $(x + y)^2 - 2(x + y) + 1$

3. $x^2 - (y + 2)^2$

4. $x^2 - (y - 3)^2$

5. $9 - 6(x - y) + (x - y)^2$

6. $u^2 - 2u(v - 2) + (v - 2)^2$

7. $x^4 + 3x^2 - 4$

8. $x^4 + x^2 - 20$

9. $y^4 - 8y^2 + 16$

10. $y^4 - 18y^2 + 81$

11. $4x^4 - 25x^2 + 36$

12. $9x^4 - 37x^2 + 4$

13. $(u + v)^2 - (x + y)^2$

14. $(u - v)^2 - (x - y)^2$

15. $32x^4 - 162$

In Exercises 16–27, factor each sum or difference of cubes.

16. $x^3 - 3^3$
17. $y^3 - 4^3$
18. $u^3 + 3^3$
19. $w^3 + 4^3$
20. $x^3 - 1$
21. $y^3 + 1$
22. $8u^3 + 27$
23. $8w^3 - 27$
24. $27x^3 - 8y^3$
25. $27x^3 + 8y^3$
26. $125a^3 + 64b^3$
27. $125a^3 - 64b^3$
28. Show that $a^3 + b^3$ is not the same as $(a + b)^3$.
29. Show that $a^3 - b^3$ is not the same as $(a - b)^3$.
30. Describe your method of solving a factoring problem. Tell how you decide on the method and how you proceed to the final check.

SECTION 7.5 Factoring to Solve Equations

Student guideposts

- *Zero-product rule*
- *Solving quadratic equations*

Zero-product rule

A property of the number zero is used to solve certain types of equations. We know that any number times zero yields a zero product. For example,

$$4 \cdot 0 = 0 \quad \text{and} \quad 0 \cdot \frac{2}{3} = 0.$$

Moreover, if a product of two or more numbers is zero, then at least one of the factors must be zero. This property, called the zero-product rule, gives us a useful method for solving equations.

Solving Equations Using the Zero-Product Rule

If an equation has a product of two or more factors on one side of the equation and 0 on the other, the solutions to the equation are found by setting each factor equal to 0.

If $ab = 0$, then $a = 0$ or $b = 0$.

The zero-product rule can be used to solve for x in equations of the form

$$(x - 3)(x + 5) = 0.$$

That is, when $x - 3$ and $x + 5$ are multiplied to give zero, the rule says either $x - 3 = 0$ or $x + 5 = 0$. Thus, one solution of

$$(x - 3)(x + 5) = 0$$

is found by solving

$$x - 3 = 0$$

$$x = 3. \quad \text{One solution is 3}$$

Another solution comes by solving

$$x + 5 = 0$$
$$x = -5. \quad \text{Another solution is } -5$$

There are two solutions to the equation, 3 and -5. To check the solutions we substitute back into the original equations.

Check of 3	*Check of* -5
$(x - 3)(x + 5) = 0$	$(x - 3)(x + 5) = 0$
$(3 - 3)(3 + 5) \stackrel{?}{=} 0$	$(-5 - 3)(-5 + 5) \stackrel{?}{=} 0$
$0 \cdot 8 = 0$	$(-8) \cdot 0 = 0$
So 3 checks.	And -5 checks.

EXAMPLE 1

Using the Zero-Product Rule

Solve $(2x + 1)(x - 1) = 0$.

$$2x + 1 = 0 \quad \text{or} \quad x - 1 = 0$$
$$2x + 1 - 1 = 0 - 1 \qquad x - 1 + 1 = 0 + 1$$
$$2x = -1 \qquad x = 1$$
$$\frac{1}{2} \cdot 2x = \frac{1}{2} \cdot (-1)$$
$$x = -\frac{1}{2}$$

The solutions are $-\frac{1}{2}$ and 1. ∎

EXAMPLE 2

Using the Zero-Product Rule

Solve $x(3x + 1) = 0$.

$$x = 0 \quad \text{or} \quad 3x + 1 = 0$$
$$3x + 1 - 1 = 0 - 1$$
$$3x = -1$$
$$\frac{1}{3} \cdot 3x = \frac{1}{3}(-1)$$
$$x = -\frac{1}{3}$$

The solutions are 0 and $-\frac{1}{3}$. ∎

NOTE When one of the factors has only one term, say x, as in Example 2, one of the solutions will always be zero. Be sure that you give this solution, and do not divide both sides of the equation by x.

▶ *Solving quadratic equations*

Suppose we solve $(x - 2)(x + 3) = 0$.

$$x - 2 = 0 \quad \text{or} \quad x + 3 = 0$$
$$x = 2 \qquad\qquad x = -3$$

The solutions are 2 and -3. The equation $(x - 2)(x + 3) = 0$ is the factored form of $x^2 + x - 6 = 0$, which is a *quadratic equation.* A **quadratic equation** has the form

$$ax^2 + bx + c = 0.$$

Thus, the zero-product rule can sometimes be used to solve quadratic equations, a subject that we will study in more detail in Chapter 10.

To Solve an Equation by Factoring

1. Write all terms on one side of the equation leaving zero on the other side.
2. Factor the expression.
3. Using the zero-product rule, set each factor equal to zero, and solve the resulting equations.
4. Check possible solutions in the original equation.

EXAMPLE 3 **Solving a Quadratic Equation**

Solve $x^2 + 4x = 21$.

$x^2 + 4x - 21 = 0$ Rewrite with all terms on the left

$(x + 7)(x - 3) = 0$ Factor the trinomial

$x + 7 = 0$ or $x - 3 = 0$ Use zero-product rule

$x = -7$ $\qquad x = 3$

Check of -7	Check of 3
$(-7)^2 + 4(-7) \stackrel{?}{=} 21$	$(3)^2 + 4(3) \stackrel{?}{=} 21$
$49 - 28 \stackrel{?}{=} 21$	$9 + 12 \stackrel{?}{=} 21$
$21 = 21$	$21 = 21$

The solutions are -7 and 3. ■

CAUTION Using the zero-product rule, we can only solve equations in the form $ab = 0$. If $ab = 5$, we cannot conclude that $a = 5$ or $b = 5$. Nor can we apply this rule to $a + b = 0$ or $a - b = 0$.

EXAMPLE 4 **Solving a Quadratic Equation**

Solve $x(x - 4) = 5$.

The zero-product rule does not apply immediately because this product does *not* equal zero. When this happens, try to rewrite it as a product that does equal zero. Begin by clearing the parentheses.

$$x^2 - 4x = 5$$

$$x^2 - 4x - 5 = 0 \quad \text{Write all terms on the left}$$

$$(x - 5)(x + 1) = 0 \quad \text{Factor}$$

$$x - 5 = 0 \quad \text{or} \quad x + 1 = 0 \quad \text{Zero-product rule}$$

$$x = 5 \qquad x = -1$$

The solutions are 5 and -1. ■

EXAMPLE 5 **Solving a Linear Equation**

Solve $(2x + 1) - (x + 5) = 0$.

The zero-product rule does not apply because the left side of the equation is a difference, *not* a product. In this case, the equation is linear, not quadratic. To solve, we remove parentheses and then combine like terms.

$$2x + 1 - x - 5 = 0$$

$$x - 4 = 0$$

$$x = 4$$

The solution is 4. Notice that this time after clearing parentheses, the result is a linear equation, not a quadratic equation which would require the zero-product rule. Also, it cannot be solved by setting $2x + 1$ and $x + 5$ equal to zero. ■

The zero-product rule can be extended to include products of three or more factors. That is, if $abc = 0$ then $a = 0$ or $b = 0$ or $c = 0$. We use this fact in the next example.

EXAMPLE 6 **Solving with a Product of Three Factors**

Solve $x^3 + 2x^2 = 15x$.

$$x^3 + 2x^2 - 15x = 0 \quad \text{Subtract } 15x \text{ from both sides}$$

$$x(x^2 + 2x - 15) = 0 \quad \text{Factor out the GCF } x$$

$$x(x - 3)(x + 5) = 0 \quad \text{Factor the trinomial}$$

$$x = 0 \quad \text{or} \quad x - 3 = 0 \quad \text{or} \quad x + 5 = 0 \quad \text{Set each factor equal to 0}$$

$$x = 3 \qquad x = -5$$

The solutions are 0, 3, and -5. Check these in the original equation. ■

7.5 EXERCISES

Solve each equation in Exercises 1–30.

1. $(x - 5)(x + 7) = 0$ **2.** $(x + 6)(x + 1) = 0$ **3.** $(u + 2)(u - 2) = 0$

4. $(u - 0.5)(u + 0.2) = 0$ **5.** $\left(x - \frac{1}{2}\right)\left(x + \frac{2}{5}\right) = 0$ **6.** $(x - 8)^2 = 0$

7. $(3y + 2)(y - 6) = 0$
8. $(5u + 1)(2u - 3) = 0$
9. $(8u - 5)(3u - 8) = 0$
10. $x(3x + 7) = 0$
11. $(2x - 5)(x + 12) = 0$
12. $y^2 - 5y + 6 = 0$
13. $y^2 - y - 6 = 0$
14. $u^2 - 8u + 7 = 0$
15. $u^2 + u - 20 = 0$
16. $x^2 + 10x + 25 = 0$
17. $x^2 - 13x + 40 = 0$
18. $y^2 - y - 42 = 0$
19. $y^2 - 16 = 0$
20. $4u^2 - 8u = 0$
21. $4u^2 + 12u + 9 = 0$
22. $9x^2 - 49 = 0$
23. $(3x - 5) - (x + 7) = 0$
24. $y(y + 3) = 10$
25. $y^2 - 2y = 35$
26. $u^2 = -2u + 35$
27. $16u^2 - 42u + 5 = 0$
28. $(x - 3)(x - 2)(x + 1) = 0$
29. $(2y)(y + 1)(y + 5) = 0$
30. $2x^3 - 4x^2 - 6x = 0$

FOR REVIEW

Factor each expression in Exercises 31–33.

31. $7y^2 - 70y + 175$
32. $2x^2 + 9xy - 5y^2$
33. $45x^2 - 80y^2$

Exercise 34 reviews material from Chapter 3 to help you prepare for the next section. Solve the applied problem.

34. **SALARY** After receiving a 9% raise Lynn Harris now makes \$34,880 per year. What was her salary before the raise?

7.5 PARALLEL EXERCISES

Solve each equation in Exercises 1–30.

1. $(x + 2)(x - 6) = 0$
2. $(x + 8)(x + 3) = 0$
3. $(u + 4)(u - 4) = 0$
4. $(x - 0.7)(x + 0.3) = 0$
5. $\left(x + \frac{1}{3}\right)\left(x + \frac{2}{3}\right) = 0$
6. $(2y - 3)(y + 8) = 0$
7. $(y - 5)^2 = 0$
8. $(5u - 6)(2u + 1) = 0$
9. $(3u + 14)(2u - 5) = 0$
10. $x(4x + 3) = 0$
11. $(2x - 7)(2x + 9) = 0$
12. $y^2 + 8y + 15 = 0$
13. $y^2 - 2y - 15 = 0$
14. $u^2 - 11u + 18 = 0$
15. $u^2 - 3u - 40 = 0$
16. $x^2 - 18x + 81 = 0$
17. $x^2 + 14x + 40 = 0$
18. $2y^2 - 13y + 6 = 0$
19. $49y^2 - 1 = 0$
20. $3u^2 - 27u = 0$
21. $9u^2 - 18u + 9 = 0$
22. $25y^2 - 16 = 0$
23. $(5x + 1) - (x - 7) = 0$
24. $y(y - 8) = -16$
25. $-63 = y^2 - 16y$
26. $63 - u^2 = 2u$
27. $6u^2 - 29u - 5 = 0$
28. $(x - 2)(x + 3)(x - 1) = 0$
29. $4y(y - 1)(y + 3) = 0$
30. $2x^3 - 4x^2 - 6x = 0$

FOR REVIEW

Factor each expression in Exercises 31–33.

31. $-6y^2 - 72y - 216$
32. $15x^2 + xy - 2y^2$
33. $40x^2 - 1210y^2$

Exercise 34 reviews material from Chapter 3 to help you prepare for the next section. Solve the applied problem.

34. **GEOMETRY** The perimeter of a rectangle is 38 m. Find the dimensions if the width is 3 m less than the length.

7.5 ENRICHMENT EXERCISES

Solve each equation in Exercises 1–10.

1. $(x + 3)(2x - 5)(x - 4) = 0$
2. $(x - 3)^2 - 3(x - 3) = 4$
3. $x^4 - 16 = 0$
4. $9(x + 2)^2 - 6(x + 2) = -1$
5. $16x^4 - 8x^2 + 1 = 0$
6. $5(x + 4)^2 = -9(x + 4) + 2$
7. $(x^2 - 25)(x^2 - x - 6) = 0$
8. $(x^2 + x - 20)(x^2 - 9) = 0$
9. $(2x^2 - 9x - 5)(3x^2 + 5x - 2) = 0$
10. $(2x^2 - 5x + 2)(3x^2 + 10x + 3) = 0$

11. When Burford solved the equation $x(x + 1) = 6$, he wrote $x = 6$ or $x + 1 = 6$. What did he do wrong? What are the correct answers?

12. Explain how to solve a quadratic equation using factoring and the zero-product rule.

SECTION 7.6 Problem Solving Using Factoring

Student guideposts

- ▶ *Factoring to solve applied problems*
- ▶ *Geometry applications*
- ▶ *Business applications*

▶ *Factoring to solve applied problems*

Sometimes an applied problem can be translated into an equation that is solvable using the technique in Section 7.5.

EXAMPLE 1 Solving a Number Problem

If two times the square of a number minus three times the number is 27, find the number.

Let $x =$ the number.

Two times the square of the number	minus	three times the number	is	27.
↓	↓	↓	↓	↓
$2x^2$	$-$	$3x$	$=$	27

$$2x^2 - 3x = 27$$

$$2x^2 - 3x - 27 = 0 \quad \text{Subtract 27 from both sides}$$

$$(2x - 9)(x + 3) = 0 \quad \text{Factor}$$

$$2x - 9 = 0 \quad \text{or} \quad x + 3 = 0 \quad \text{Zero-product rule}$$

$$2x = 9 \qquad x = -3$$

$$x = \frac{9}{2}$$

The solutions are $\frac{9}{2}$ and -3. ■

▶ *Geometry applications*

Some geometry problems may also require factoring. It always helps to make a sketch for a geometry problem. Also, be sure that you answer the stated question and that your answer is reasonable. Geometry formulas are found on the inside covers, and the Geometry Appendix gives a discussion of geometric figures.

EXAMPLE 2 **Solving a Geometry Application**

If the area of a rectangle is 48 m^2 and the length is three times the width, find the dimensions of the rectangle.

Make a sketch, as in Figure 7.1.

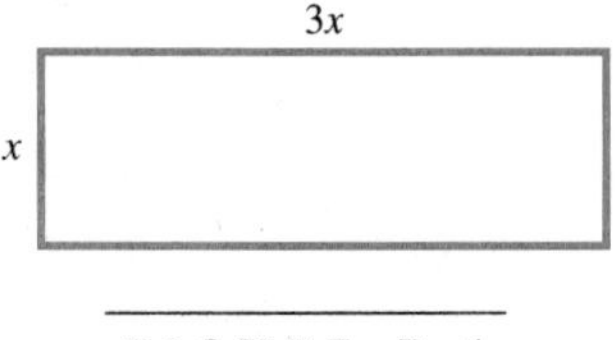

FIGURE 7.1

Let x = width of rectangle in meters,
$3x$ = length of rectangle in meters.
For a rectangle.

$$\text{Width} \cdot \text{length} = \text{area.}$$

$$x \cdot 3x = 48$$

$$3x^2 = 48$$

$$3x^2 - 48 = 0$$

$$3(x^2 - 16) = 0$$

$$x^2 - 16 = 0 \qquad \text{Divide both sides by 3. } \tfrac{0}{3} = 0$$

$$(x - 4)(x + 4) = 0$$

$$x - 4 = 0 \quad \text{or} \quad x + 4 = 0$$

$$x = 4 \qquad x = -4 \qquad \text{Rule out } x = -4 \text{ since we want the width of a rectangle}$$

Thus, since $x = 4$ and $3x = 12$, the rectangle is 4 m by 12 m. ■

▶ *Business applications*

There are numerous applications to business.

EXAMPLE 3 **Solving a Retail Application**

A clothing store owner finds that her daily profit on jeans is given by $P = n^2 - 6n - 20$, where n is the number of jeans sold. How many jeans must be sold for a profit of \$260?

Since P = \$260, we need to solve the following equation.

$$P = n^2 - 6n - 20 = 260 \qquad \text{Profit is to be \$260}$$

$$n^2 - 6n - 280 = 0 \qquad \text{Set equal to zero}$$

$$(n + 14)(n - 20) = 0 \qquad \text{Factor}$$

$$n + 14 = 0 \quad \text{or} \quad n - 20 = 0$$

$$n = -14 \qquad n = 20$$

Since n is the number of jeans sold, the -14 answer is discarded. Thus, 20 jeans must be sold to make \$260. To check we evaluate P for $n = 20$.

$$\begin{aligned} P &= n^2 - 6n - 20 \\ &= (20)^2 - 6(20) - 20 && \text{Substitute 20 for } n \\ &= 400 - 120 - 20 \\ &= 260 && \text{This checks} \end{aligned}$$
■

We conclude this section by solving the applied problem given in the introduction to this chapter.

EXAMPLE 4

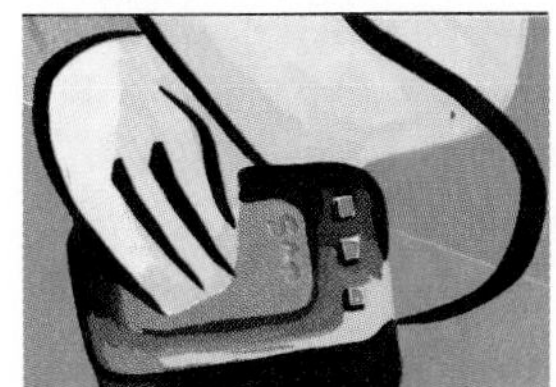

Solving a Production Application

The production research department at Disk Incorporated has determined that the number n of compact disks that can be sold each week is related to the price p of the disk by the equation $n = 1100 - 100p$. Find the price that the company should set on each disk to produce a weekly revenue of \$2800.

The revenue equation is $R = np$ where n is the number of disks sold and p is the price of each disk. Since $n = 1100 - 100p$, substituting we have

$$\begin{aligned} R &= np \\ &= (1100 - 100p)p \\ &= 1100p - 100p^2. \end{aligned}$$

We want to find p when R is 2800.

$$2800 = 1100p - 100p^2$$

Add $100p^2$ and subtract $1100p$ from both sides.

$$\begin{aligned} 100p^2 - 1100p + 2800 &= 0 \\ 100(p^2 - 11p + 28) &= 0 && \text{Factor out 100} \\ 100(p - 4)(p - 7) &= 0 && \text{Factor} \\ p - 4 = 0 \quad \text{or} \quad p - 7 &= 0 && \text{Zero-product rule} \\ p = 4 \qquad\quad p &= 7 \end{aligned}$$

If disks are sold for \$4 or for \$7, the weekly revenue will be \$2800. ■

7.6 EXERCISES

Solve each applied problem in Exercises 1–14.

1. **NUMBER** The product of 5 more than a number and 3 less than the number is zero. Find the number.

2. **NUMBER** If the square of a number plus seven times the number is 44, what is the number?

3. **GEOMETRY** The length of a rectangle is 5 cm more than the width. If the area is 24 cm^2, find the dimensions.

4. **GEOMETRY** The area of a rectangle is 84 ft^2 and the length is 5 feet more than the width. Find the dimensions of the rectangle.

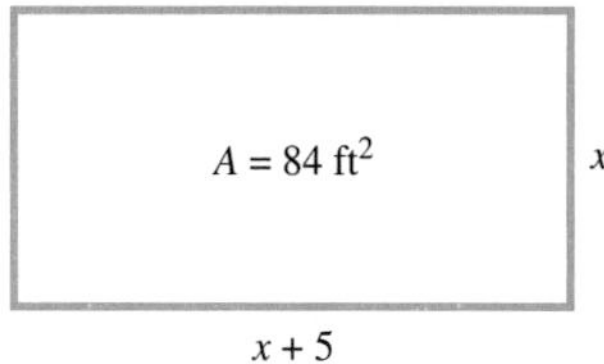

5. **GEOMETRY** The area of a square is numerically 4 less than the perimeter. Find the length of the side in cm.

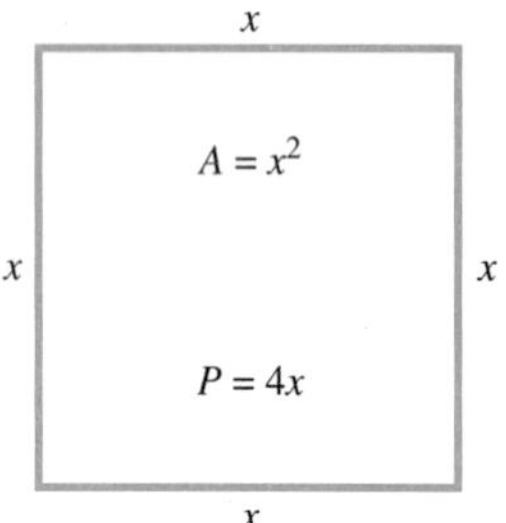

6. **GEOMETRY** A toy box is 20 in high. The length is 3 in longer than the width. If the volume is 80 in^3, find the length and width.

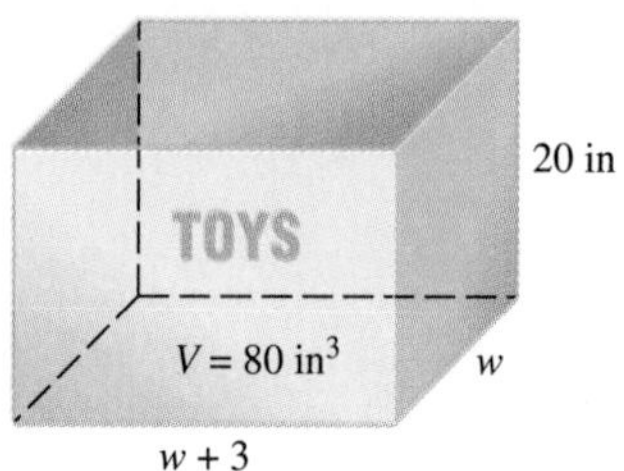

7. **GEOMETRY** The area of a triangle is 56 in^2. If the base is 6 in less than the height, find the base and height.

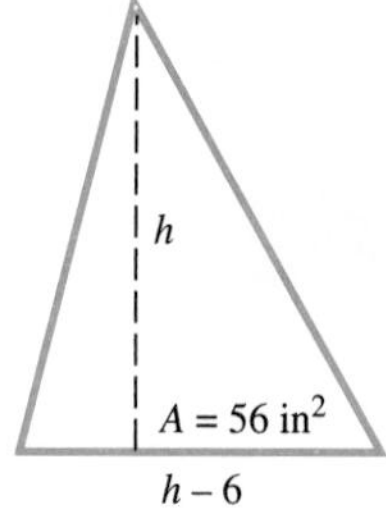

8. **GEOMETRY** The area of a triangle is 98 cm^2. If the base is four times the height, find the base and height.

BUSINESS *The profit on a small appliance is given by the equation $P = n^2 - 3n - 60$ where n is the number of appliances sold per day. Use this equation in Exercises 9–10.*

9. What is the profit when 30 appliances are sold?
10. How many appliances were sold on a day when there was a \$20 loss?

COUNTING *The number of ways of choosing two people from an organization to serve on a committee is given by $N = \frac{1}{2}n(n - 1)$, where n is the number of people in the organization. Use this equation to do Exercises 11–12.*

11. How many committees of two can be formed from a group with 7 members?
12. If 28 different committees of two can be formed from the members of a sorority, how many women are in the sorority?
13. **CHEMISTRY** A chemical reaction is described by the equation $C = 2n^2 - 7n + 1$. Find n when $C = 16$ if n is positive.
14. **BUSINESS** The relationship between the number n of radios a company can sell per month and the price of each radio p is given by the equation $n = 1700 - 100p$. Find the price at which a radio should be sold to produce a monthly revenue of \$7000.

FOR REVIEW

Solve each equation in Exercises 15–17.

15. $9x^2 + 6x + 1 = 0$

16. $50y^2 - 32 = 0$

17. $3y^2 = 13y + 10$

The following exercises review material that we covered in Chapter 1. They will help you prepare for the next section. Perform the indicated operations in Exercises 18–20.

18. $\frac{0}{4}$

19. $\frac{4}{0}$

20. $\frac{-4}{4}$

Supply the missing numerator in Exercises 21–23.

21. $\frac{1}{2} = \frac{?}{6}$

22. $\frac{-3}{7} = \frac{?}{42}$

23. $-\frac{10}{21} = \frac{?}{105}$

Reduce each fraction to lowest terms in Exercises 24–26.

24. $\frac{20}{50}$

25. $\frac{72}{96}$

26. $\frac{144}{252}$

7.6 PARALLEL EXERCISES

Solve each applied problem in Exercises 1–14.

1. **NUMBER** The product of 4 more than a number and 6 less than the number is 0. Find the number.
2. **NUMBER** The square of a number, plus 15, is the same as 8 times the number. Find the number.
3. **GEOMETRY** The length of a rectangle is 10 m more than the width. If the area is 144 m^2, find the dimensions.
4. **GEOMETRY** The area of a rectangle is 40 cm^2 and the length is 3 cm more than the width. Find the dimensions of the rectangle.
5. **GEOMETRY** The area of a square is numerically 12 more than the perimeter. Find the length of a side in ft.
6. **GEOMETRY** A shipping box is 6 in high. The length must be 2 in more than the width and the volume is 210 in^3. Find the length and width.
7. **GEOMETRY** The area of a triangle is 30 in^2. If the base is 4 in more than the height, find the base and height.
8. **GEOMETRY** The area of a triangle is 150 cm^2. If the base is three times the height, find the base and height.

BUSINESS *The profit on one type of shoe is given by the equation* $P = n^2 - 5n - 200$, *where* n *is the number of shoes sold per day. Use this equation to do Exercises 9–10.*

9. What is the profit if 10 pairs of shoes are sold?
10. How many pairs of shoes were sold on a day when the profit was $550?

COUNTING *In a basketball league containing n teams, the number of different ways that the league champion and second place team can be chosen is given by* $N = n(n - 1)$. *Use this equation to do Exercises 11–12.*

11. How many different first and second place finishers are possible in the NBA, which has 26 teams?
12. If it is known that there are 240 different ways for two teams to finish first and second in a league, how many teams are in the league?

13. **ENGINEERING** An engineer found that $E = 3u^2 - 16u + 6$ where u is positive. Find u when $E = 18$.

14. **BUSINESS** The relationship between the number n of tables a furniture store can sell per month and the price of each table p is given by the equation $n = 3000 - 200p$. At what price should the store sell each table to produce a monthly revenue of \$10,800?

FOR REVIEW

Solve each equation in Exercises 15–17.

15. $x^2 - 14x + 49 = 0$
16. $-45y^2 + 245 = 0$
17. $5y^2 = 18y + 8$

The following exercises review material that we covered in Chapter 1. They will help you prepare for the next section. Perform the indicated operations in Exercises 18–20.

18. $\frac{0}{9}$
19. $\frac{9}{0}$
20. $\frac{9}{-9}$

Supply the missing numerator in Exercises 21–23.

21. $\frac{1}{3} = \frac{?}{9}$
22. $\frac{6}{-11} = \frac{?}{55}$
23. $\frac{8}{25} = -\frac{?}{150}$

Reduce each fraction to lowest terms in Exercises 24–26.

24. $\frac{55}{22}$
25. $\frac{450}{750}$
26. $\frac{169}{39}$

7.6 ENRICHMENT EXERCISES

Solve each applied problem in Exercises 1–2.

1. **CHEMISTRY** A chemical reaction is described by the equation $C = 6n^2 - 17n - 4$. Find n when $C = 10$ if n is a positive integer.
2. **BANKING** A banker uses the equation $M = (n + 2)(n - 7)$. Find n when $M = -20$.
3. List the steps in the ATTACK method for solving applied problems giving a brief description of each.
4. Discuss how you applied the ATTACK method to the problems of this section.

CHAPTER 7 REVIEW

KEY WORDS

7.1 A **common factor** of two expressions is a factor that occurs in both of them.
The **greatest common factor (GCF)** of two terms is the largest factor common to both terms.
A **prime polynomial** cannot be factored.

7.4 A **perfect square trinomial** is one that can be factored into the form $(a + b)^2$ or $(a - b)^2$.

KEY CONCEPTS

7.1 Always factor completely. For example, factor $20x + 30$ as $10(2x + 3)$, not $5(4x + 6)$.

7.2 To factor $x^2 + bx + c = (x + \_\_)(x + \_\_)$, list all pairs of integers whose product is c and fill the blanks with the pair from this list whose sum is b.

7.3 To factor $ax^2 + bx + c = (\_\_x + \_\_)(\_\_x + \_\_)$, list all pairs of integers whose product is a for the first blanks in each binomial factor. Do the same for c using these in the second blanks. By trial and error, select the correct pairs that give the middle term bx. Factoring by grouping may also be used.

7.4 **(1)** $a^2 - b^2 = (a + b)(a - b)$, not $(a - b)^2$
(2) $a^2 + 2ab + b^2 = (a + b)^2$
(3) $a^2 - 2ab + b^2 = (a - b)^2$

7.5 **1.** The zero-product rule,

$$\text{if } ab = 0, \quad \text{then } a = 0 \text{ or } b = 0,$$

applies only when one side of the equation is zero. For example, if $ab = 7$, we *cannot* conclude that $a = 7$ or $b = 7$.

2. Do not use the zero-product rule on a zero-sum or zero-difference equation. For example, $(2x + 1) - (x + 5) = 0$ is *not* a zero-product equation. To solve it, clear parentheses and combine terms. *Do not* set $2x + 1$ and $x + 5$ equal to zero.

CHAPTER 7 REVIEW EXERCISES

PART I

7.1 *Factor by removing the greatest common factor in Exercises 1–3.*

1. $8x + 2$ **2.** $3y^4 - 9y^2$ **3.** $a^2(a + b) + 5(a + b)$

Factor by grouping in Exercises 4–5.

4. $x^3 - 3x^2 + 2x - 6$ **5.** $x^2y^2 + x^2 + 6y^2 + 6$

7.2, 7.3, 7.4 *Factor each polynomial in Exercises 6–23.*

6. $x^2 + 3x - 10$ **7.** $9y^2 + 6y + 1$ **8.** $y^2 - 8y + 7$
9. $4x^2 - 9$ **10.** $4y^2 - 12y + 9$ **11.** $y^2 + 12y - 45$
12. $5x^2 + 12x - 9$ **13.** $2y^2 - 50$ **14.** $x^4 - 25$
15. $y^4 - 81$ **16.** $6x^2 + 13x - 5$ **17.** $6y^2 - 13y - 63$
18. $x^2 - 10xy + 25y^2$ **19.** $x^2 - 13xy + 42y^2$ **20.** $81x^2 - 64y^2$
21. $81x^2 + 64y^2$ **22.** $5x^2 - 90xy + 405y^2$ **23.** $6x^2 + 13xy - 28y^2$

7.5 *Solve each equation in Exercises 24–29.*

24. $(2x - 1)(12x + 5) = 0$ **25.** $81y^2 - 9 = 0$ **26.** $4x^2 + 5x + 1 = 0$
27. $y^2 - 4y + 4 = 0$ **28.** $12x^2 + 6x = 0$ **29.** $y(y - 5) = 84$

7.6

30. **NUMBER** The product of a number and 5 less than the number is -6. Find the number.

31. **GEOMETRY** The area of a rectangular garden is 224 m^2. Find the dimensions of the garden if the length is 2 meters more than the width.

32. **GEOMETRY** The length of a rectangle is 5 times the width. If the area is 180 cm^2, find the dimensions.

33. **BUSINESS** The profit on the sale of sport coats is given by the equation $P = n^2 - 6n - 27$, where n is the number of coats sold per day.

    (a) What is the profit when 12 coats are sold?

    (b) How many coats were sold on a day when the profit was $160?

PART II

Solve each equation in Exercises 34–36.

34. $x(x - 3)(x + 8) = 0$ **35.** $4x^2 + 4x - 15 = 0$ **36.** $3x^2 = 11x + 4$

37. **BUSINESS** The equation $n = 2400 - 120p$ gives the relationship between the number n of balls sold and the price p of each ball. What price should be set to have a monthly revenue of $12,000?

Factor each polynomial in Exercises 38–40.

38. $9x^2 + 30x + 25$ **39.** $(x + 1)^2 - 25$ **40.** $2x^2 + ax - 10x - 5a$

Answer true *or* false *for each statement in Exercises 41–45. If the statement is false, tell why.*

41. In any factoring problem, first try to remove the greatest common factor.

42. A polynomial with four terms can sometimes be factored by grouping.

43. The binomial $a^2 + b^2$ can be factored as $(a + b)^2$.

44. There are many trinomials that cannot be factored.

45. One or more of the solutions to an equation that came from an applied problem may not be an actual solution to the applied problem.

CHAPTER 7 TEST

Factor by removing the greatest common factor.

1. $20x + 12$ **2.** $35y - 7$

3. $24x^4 - 12x^3 + 18x^2$ **4.** $5x^3y^3 + 40x^3y^2$

5. Factor $7x^2y^2 - y^2 + 14x^2 - 2$ by grouping.

Factor.

6. $x^2 + 15x + 56$ **7.** $x^2 - 16x + 64$

8. $3y^2 - 75$ **9.** $x^2 - 8x - 20$

10. $2x^2 + 13x - 24$ **11.** $3x^2 + 16xy + 5y^2$

Solve.

12. $(4y - 5)(2y + 3) = 0$ **13.** $x^2 - x - 30 = 0$

14. The product of a number and 3 more than the number is 4. Find the number.

15. The area of a triangle is 12 cm^2. If the base is 2 cm less than the height, find the base and height.

16. The profit on the sale of one type of dress is $P = n^2 - 3n - 8$, where n is the number of dresses sold per day.

(a) What is the profit when 20 dresses are sold?

(b) How many dresses were sold on a day when the profit was $100?

17. If $x(x + 2) = 8$, is $x = 8$ or $x + 2 = 8$? Explain. What is the solution to the equation?

CHAPTER 8

Rational Expressions

Division of one integer by another integer (excluding zero) results in a rational number. In a similar way, dividing one polynomial by another polynomial (making sure that the second is not zero) results in a rational expression. As we will see, many problems involving rational expressions are similar to problems using rational numbers. Since factoring plays an important role when working with rational expressions, a thorough understanding of factoring, presented in Chapter 7, is necessary for success in this chapter.

Numerous applied problems use rational expressions. One such application, presented below, is solved in Example 8 of Section 8.5.

RECREATION Because he had better road conditions Sam was able to drive 260 miles in the same time that it took Carolyn to drive 220 miles for a long weekend at a Colorado ski area. If Sam's average rate of speed was 10 mph faster than Carolyn's, what was Carolyn's average speed?

We begin our study of rational expressions with some of their basic properties and the four major operations (multiplication, division, addition, and subtraction) on such expressions. Next we solve fractional equations and consider a variety of applications that result in fractional equations, including ratio, proportion, and variation problems. We conclude the chapter by simplifying complex fractions.

SECTION 8.1 Algebraic Fractions and Rational Expressions

Student guideposts

- ▶ ***Algebraic fractions and rational expressions***
- ▶ ***Excluding values that make the denominator zero***
- ▶ ***Equivalent fractions***
- ▶ ***Reducing to lowest terms***
- ▶ ***Fractions equivalent to*** -1

▶ ***Algebraic fractions and rational expressions***

In Chapter 1 we reviewed some of the properties of numerical fractions. Now we define an **algebraic fraction** as a fraction that contains a variable in the numerator or denominator or both. The following are algebraic fractions.

$$\frac{xy}{x+1}, \quad \frac{y^2+1}{y-1}, \quad \frac{\sqrt{a}+5}{2}, \quad \frac{7}{(x-2)(x+1)}, \quad \frac{x+y}{x-y}$$

If an algebraic fraction is the quotient of two polynomials it is called a **rational expression.** Of the algebraic fractions listed above only $\frac{\sqrt{a}+5}{2}$ is *not* a rational expression ($\sqrt{a} + 5$ is not a polynomial because a is not raised to a whole number power). The algebraic fractions that we study in this chapter will all be rational expressions.

▶ ***Excluding values that make the denominator zero***

With rational expressions, we need to avoid division by zero, which is undefined. Any value of the variable that makes the denominator zero must be excluded from consideration. The expression is defined for all other values of the variable.

To Find the Values Which Must Be Excluded in a Rational Expression

1. Set the denominator equal to zero.
2. Solve this equation; any solution must be excluded.

EXAMPLE 1 Finding Excluded Values

Find the value of the variable that must be excluded in each rational expression.

(a) $\dfrac{2x}{x+7}$

Set the denominator equal to zero and solve.

$$x + 7 = 0$$
$$x = -7$$

Check: $\dfrac{2(-7)}{-7+7} = \dfrac{-14}{0}$

Since division by zero is not defined, -7 must be excluded. The expression is defined for all x except -7.

(b) $\dfrac{(a-1)(a+1)}{2}$

Set the denominator equal to zero and solve.

$$2 = 0$$

Since there is no solution to this equation, there are no values to exclude. The expression is defined for all values of a.

(c) $\dfrac{3y}{(y-1)(y+4)}$

We need to solve $(y-1)(y+4) = 0$, so we use the zero-product rule.

$$y - 1 = 0 \quad \text{or} \quad y + 4 = 0$$
$$y = 1 \qquad\qquad y = -4$$

The values to exclude are 1 and -4. The expression is defined for all values of y except 1 and -4.

(d) $\dfrac{x^2+1}{x^2+5x+6}$

We need to solve $x^2 + 5x + 6 = 0$. First factor and then use the zero-product rule.

$$x^2 + 5x + 6 = 0$$
$$(x+2)(x+3) = 0$$
$$x + 2 = 0 \quad \text{or} \quad x + 3 = 0$$
$$x = -2 \qquad\qquad x = -3$$

The values to exclude are -2 and -3. The expression is defined for all values of x except -2 and -3. ■

▶ *Equivalent fractions*

In Chapter 1 we saw that multiplying or dividing the numerator and denominator of a fraction by the same nonzero number gives us an equivalent fraction.

$$\frac{4}{6} = \frac{4 \cdot 3}{6 \cdot 3} = \frac{12}{18} \qquad \tfrac{4}{6} \text{ is equivalent to } \tfrac{12}{18}$$

$$\frac{4}{6} = \frac{4 \div 2}{6 \div 2} = \frac{2}{3} \qquad \tfrac{4}{6} \text{ is equivalent to } \tfrac{2}{3}$$

We can generalize the idea of equivalent fractions to include algebraic fractions.

Fundamental Principle of Fractions

If the numerator and denominator of an algebraic fraction are multiplied or divided by the same nonzero expression, the resulting fraction is **equivalent** to the original. That is, if $\frac{P}{Q}$ is an algebraic fraction, $Q \neq 0$, and R is a nonzero expression, then

$$\frac{P}{Q} \text{ is equivalent to } \frac{P \cdot R}{Q \cdot R} \text{ and to } \frac{P \div R}{Q \div R}.$$

NOTE The Fundamental Principle of Fractions results from multiplying a fraction by 1, the multiplicative identity, written in the form $\frac{R}{R}$ or $\frac{\frac{1}{R}}{\frac{1}{R}}$, where $R \neq 0$.

$$\frac{P}{Q} = \frac{P}{Q} \cdot 1 = \frac{P}{Q} \cdot \frac{R}{R} = \frac{P \cdot R}{Q \cdot R}$$

$$\frac{P}{Q} = \frac{P}{Q} \cdot 1 = \frac{P}{Q} \cdot \frac{\frac{1}{R}}{\frac{1}{R}} = \frac{\frac{P}{R}}{\frac{Q}{R}} = \frac{P \div R}{Q \div R}$$

EXAMPLE 2

Equivalent Fractions

Are the given fractions equivalent?

(a) $\dfrac{3}{x+2}$ and $\dfrac{3(x+1)}{(x+2)(x+1)}$

$$\frac{3 \cdot (x+1)}{(x+2) \cdot (x+1)} = \frac{3(x+1)}{(x+2)(x+1)}$$

Numerator and denominator are both multiplied by $x + 1$

The fractions are equivalent since the first becomes the second when both numerator and denominator are multiplied by $x + 1$.

We may also divide numerator and denominator of the second fraction by $x + 1$ to obtain the first.

$$\frac{3(x+1) \div (x+1)}{(x+2)(x+1) \div (x+1)} = \frac{\frac{3(x+1)}{(x+1)}}{\frac{(x+2)(x+1)}{(x+1)}} = \frac{3}{x+2}$$

This division can be abbreviated by showing the expression is equivalent to $\frac{3}{x+2}$ times 1.

$$\frac{3(x+1)}{(x+2)(x+1)} = \frac{3}{x+2} \cdot \frac{x+1}{x+1}$$
$$= \frac{3}{x+2}\, 1 = \frac{3}{x+2}$$

We usually accomplish this by dividing out the factor common to both numerator and denominator.

$$\frac{3(x+1)}{(x+2)(x+1)} = \frac{3\cancel{(x+1)}}{(x+2)\cancel{(x+1)}} = \frac{3}{x+2}$$

The word ''cancel'' is often used to describe this process, but we will use ''divide out.''

(b) $\frac{3}{x+2}$ and $\frac{7}{x+1}$

These are not equivalent since there is no expression that one can be multiplied by, in both numerator and denominator, to give the other. ■

▶ *Reducing to lowest terms*

A fraction is **reduced to lowest terms** when 1 (or -1) is the only number or expression that divides both numerator and denominator. For example, we reduce $\frac{30}{12}$ to lowest terms as follows.

$$\frac{30}{12} = \frac{\cancel{2} \cdot \cancel{3} \cdot 5}{\cancel{2} \cdot 2 \cdot \cancel{3}} = \frac{5}{2}$$ Factor completely and divide out or cancel common factors

CAUTION Divide out or cancel *factors* only, never cancel *terms.* The only expressions that can be divided out are those that are multiplied (never added or subtracted) by every other expression in the numerator or denominator. For example,

$$\frac{5 \cdot 6}{5} = \frac{\cancel{5} \cdot 6}{\cancel{5}} \quad \text{but} \quad \frac{5+6}{5} \neq \frac{\cancel{5}+6}{\cancel{5}}.$$

We can generalize this procedure to reduce rational expressions.

To Reduce a Rational Expression to Lowest Terms

1. Factor numerator and denominator completely.
2. Divide out all common factors.
3. Multiply the remaining factors in the numerator and multiply the remaining factors in the denominator.

EXAMPLE 3 **Reducing Fractions**

Reduce each fraction to lowest terms.

(a) $\dfrac{12x^2}{18x^3} = \dfrac{\not{2} \cdot 2 \cdot \not{3} \cdot \not{x} \cdot \not{x}}{\not{2} \cdot \not{3} \cdot 3 \cdot \not{x} \cdot \not{x} \cdot x} = \dfrac{2}{3x}$ Factor completely and divide out common factors

With practice you can avoid factoring completely to prime factors. For example, the above might take the form

$$\frac{12x^2}{18x^3} = \frac{\not{6} \cdot 2 \cdot \not{x^2}}{\not{6} \cdot 3 \cdot \not{x^2} \cdot x} = \frac{2}{3x}.$$

(b) $\dfrac{x}{2x^2} = \dfrac{\overset{1}{\not{x}}}{2 \cdot \underset{1}{\not{x}} \cdot x} = \dfrac{1}{2x}$

Notice that when the factors x are divided out, 1 is left in the numerator, not 0. The small reminder numbers "1" may help you remember this.

(c) $\dfrac{2x^2 + x}{3x^3 + 3x} = \dfrac{\not{x}(2x + 1)}{3\not{x}(x^2 + 1)} = \dfrac{2x + 1}{3(x^2 + 1)}$

(d) $\dfrac{7a + 14}{7} = \dfrac{\not{7}(a + 2)}{\not{7}} = \dfrac{a + 2}{1} = a + 2$

(e) $\dfrac{2 + 2y}{2y} = \dfrac{\not{2}(1 + y)}{\not{2}y} = \dfrac{1 + y}{y}$

We cannot divide out the y's. The y in the numerator is a term, not a factor. If we replace y with the number 2, it is easy to see that

$$\frac{1 + y}{y} \textit{ is not equal to } \frac{1 + \not{y}}{\not{y}}.$$

(f) $\dfrac{x^2 + 3xy + 2y^2}{x^2 - 4y^2} = \dfrac{(x + y)\not{(x + 2y)}}{(x - 2y)\not{(x + 2y)}} = \dfrac{x + y}{x - 2y}$

Why can't we divide out the x and the y in the answer to obtain $-\frac{1}{2}$? ■

▶ *Fractions equivalent to −1*

Consider the fraction $\frac{5 - x}{x - 5}$. Our first impression might be that it is reduced to lowest terms. However, if we factor -1 from the numerator, we obtain

$$\frac{5 - x}{x - 5} = \frac{(-1)(-5 + x)}{x - 5}$$

$$= \frac{(-1)\not{(x - 5)}}{\not{(x - 5)}} \qquad -5 + x = x - 5$$

$$= -1.$$

This is a Special Case of the Following Rule.
In general, if $a \neq b$,

$$\frac{a-b}{b-a} = -1.$$

For example, if $a = 5$ and $b = 2$,

$$\frac{a-b}{b-a} = \frac{5-2}{2-5} = \frac{3}{-3} = -1.$$

Whenever a fraction of this type results, simply replace it with -1.

CAUTION Remember that $a + b = b + a$ so that $\frac{a+b}{b+a} = 1$, not -1.

EXAMPLE 4 **Reducing a Fraction to −1**

Reduce $\frac{x^2 - xy}{3y - 3x}$ to lowest terms.

$$\frac{x^2 - xy}{3y - 3x} = \frac{x(x-y)}{3(y-x)} = \frac{x}{3} \cdot \frac{x-y}{y-x}$$

$$= \frac{x}{3} \cdot (-1) \qquad \frac{x-y}{y-x} = -1$$

$$= -\frac{x}{3} \quad \blacksquare$$

8.1 EXERCISES

In Exercises 1–6, find the values of the variable that must be excluded in each rational expression.

1. $\frac{3}{x+1}$
2. $\frac{y+1}{y(y+3)}$
3. $\frac{z+2}{2(z+4)}$
4. $\frac{x+2}{(x-1)(x+4)}$
5. $\frac{2x+7}{x^2+2x+1}$
6. $\frac{(x-1)(x+1)}{7}$

Are the fractions given in Exercises 7–12 equivalent? Explain.

7. $\frac{3}{y}, \frac{-3}{-y}$
8. $\frac{a^2}{3}, \frac{-2a^2}{-6}$
9. $\frac{x+1}{9}, \frac{(x+1)(x-1)}{9(x-1)}$
10. $\frac{2}{x^2}, \frac{2+x}{x^2+x}$
11. $\frac{x-1}{3x-1}, \frac{x}{3x}$
12. $\frac{z-2}{z^2-4}, \frac{1}{z+2}$

Reduce each expression in Exercises 13–24 to lowest terms.

13. $\frac{21}{30}$
14. $\frac{2y^2}{10y^3}$
15. $\frac{4x^3y}{2xy^2}$

16. $\frac{3x^2z}{21x^6z^2}$

17. $\frac{z+9}{z^2+9}$

18. $\frac{w^2+7w}{w^2-49}$

19. $\frac{x^2-3x-10}{x^2-6x+5}$

20. $\frac{2a(a+5)}{10a+2a^2}$

21. $\frac{x^2-9}{3-x}$

22. $\frac{y+4}{y-4}$

23. $\frac{a^2+2ab+b^2}{a+b}$

24. $\frac{x^2-7xy+6y^2}{x^2-4xy-12y^2}$

25. Burford reduced the fraction as shown below. What is wrong with his work?

$$\frac{1+2x}{1+5x} = \frac{\cancel{1}+\cancel{2x}}{\cancel{1}+\cancel{5x}} = \frac{2}{5}$$

26. Reduce the fraction $\frac{x+y}{x^2-y^2}$ to lowest terms, and substitute 3 for x and 2 for y in both fractions to show that the two are equivalent.

27. Reduce $\frac{1-a}{a-1}$ to lowest terms.

28. Reduce $\frac{1+a}{a+1}$ to lowest terms.

FOR REVIEW

The following exercises review material from Chapter 1 to help you prepare for the next section. Perform the indicated operations in Exercises 29–31.

29. $\frac{5}{8} \cdot \frac{2}{15}$

30. $\frac{2}{3} \div \frac{4}{9}$

31. $\frac{4}{5} \div 2$

32. Factor 300 into a product of primes.

8.1 PARALLEL EXERCISES

In Exercises 1–6, find the values of the variable that must be excluded in each rational expression.

1. $\frac{x^2+8}{x+5}$

2. $\frac{y-3}{y(y-4)}$

3. $\frac{z-8}{2(z+10)}$

4. $\frac{a+5}{(a-3)(a+3)}$

5. $\frac{3x-1}{x^2-2x+1}$

6. $\frac{z+5}{z^2+9}$

Are the fractions given in Exercises 7–12 equivalent? Explain.

7. $\frac{3}{5}, \frac{6}{10}$

8. $\frac{a^3}{4}, \frac{-2a^3}{-8}$

9. $\frac{x+3}{8}, \frac{(x+3)(x-4)}{8(x-4)}$

10. $\frac{3}{x^3}, \frac{3-x}{x^3-x}$

11. $\frac{z+3}{z^2-9}, \frac{1}{z-3}$

12. $\frac{x^2+2}{3x^2+2}, \frac{x^2}{3x^2}$

Reduce each expression in Exercises 13–24 to lowest terms.

13. $\frac{22}{55}$

14. $\frac{45x^6}{15x^2}$

15. $\frac{9a^4b}{3ab^3}$

16. $\dfrac{6ay}{18a^2y^3}$

17. $\dfrac{z + 16}{z^2 + 16}$

18. $\dfrac{x^3 + 5x^2}{x(x^2 - 25)}$

19. $\dfrac{x^2 - 3x - 10}{x^2 - 8x + 15}$

20. $\dfrac{3a^2(a + 4)}{9a + 6a^2}$

21. $\dfrac{16 - x^2}{x - 4}$

22. $\dfrac{2y + 3}{2y - 3}$

23. $\dfrac{a^2 + 7ab + 10b^2}{a + 5b}$

24. $\dfrac{x^2 - 10xy + 25y^2}{x^2 - 4xy - 5y^2}$

25. Burford reduced the fraction as shown below. What is wrong with his work?

$$\frac{3 - 2y}{3 + 7y} = \frac{\cancel{3} - 2\cancel{y}}{\cancel{3} + 7\cancel{y}} = \frac{-2}{7} = -\frac{2}{7}$$

26. Substitute 2 for a in $\dfrac{a^2 - 12a + 36}{a - 6}$ and in $a - 6$. Why are both results equal to -4?

27. Reduce $\dfrac{2 - z}{z - 2}$ to lowest terms.

28. Reduce $\dfrac{2 + z}{z + 2}$ to lowest terms.

FOR REVIEW

The following exercises review material from Chapter 1 to help you prepare for the next section. Perform the indicated operations in Exercises 29–31.

29. $\dfrac{7}{10} \cdot \dfrac{5}{14}$

30. $\dfrac{3}{4} \div \dfrac{9}{16}$

31. $7 \div \dfrac{14}{3}$

32. Factor 420 into a product of primes.

8.1 ENRICHMENT EXERCISES

Reduce to lowest terms in Exercises 1–6. The factoring formulas in Section 7.4 are used in some of these exercises.

1. $\dfrac{5x^2 - 25xy + 30y^2}{10x^2 - 40y^2}$

△ 2. $\dfrac{27x^3 - y^3}{18x^2 + 6xy + 2y^2}$

3. $\dfrac{x^4 + 8xy^3}{x^4 - 16y^4}$

4. $\dfrac{3a^2 + 5ab - 2b^2}{6a^2 + ab - b^2}$

5. $\dfrac{x^2 - 2x + ax - 2a}{x^2 + 3x + ax + 3a}$

△ 6. $\dfrac{y^2 + 2y - ay - 2a}{y^2 - 2y - ay + 2a}$

7. When Burford tried to reduce $\dfrac{a^2 + b^2}{a + b}$ he gave an answer of $a + b$. What kind of error do you suppose he made to come up with this answer? What is the correct answer?

In Exercises 8–11, find a rational expression that answers each question.

△ 8. If the area of a rectangle is 20 ft^2 and the width is w, what is the length?

9. If 3 pounds of steak cost c dollars, what is the price per pound?

10. If Marvin drove 200 miles at a rate of $r + 5$ mph, how long did he drive?

11. If a complete order can be filled in x hours, how much of the order can be filled in 1 hour?

12. Write a sentence or two explaining why it is important to be aware of values for the variable that must be excluded when considering a rational expression.

SECTION 8.2 Multiplication and Division of Fractions

Student guideposts

▶ *Multiplying fractions*
▶ *Dividing fractions*

▶ *Multiplying fractions*

In Chapter 1 we saw that the product of two or more fractions is equal to the product of all numerators divided by the product of all denominators. The resulting fraction should be reduced to lowest terms. For example,

$$\frac{3}{4} \cdot \frac{2}{9} = \frac{3 \cdot 2}{4 \cdot 9} = \frac{6}{36}.$$

To reduce $\frac{6}{36}$ to lowest terms, factor the numerator and denominator.

$$\frac{6}{36} = \frac{\cancel{2} \cdot \cancel{3}}{\cancel{2} \cdot \cancel{3} \cdot 2 \cdot 3} = \frac{1}{6}$$

To accomplish multiplication and reduction in one process we factor numerators and denominators first, divide out common factors, and then multiply. The resulting fraction is the product.

$$\frac{3}{4} \cdot \frac{2}{9} = \frac{3}{2 \cdot 2} \cdot \frac{2}{3 \cdot 3} = \frac{\cancel{3} \cdot \cancel{2}}{\cancel{2} \cdot 2 \cdot \cancel{3} \cdot 3} = \frac{1}{2 \cdot 3} = \frac{1}{6}$$

We can generalize this procedure to multiply algebraic fractions.

To Multiply Algebraic Fractions

1. Factor all numerators and denominators completely.
2. Place the factored product of all numerators over the factored product of all denominators.
3. Divide out common factors before multiplying the remaining numerator factors and multiplying the remaining denominator factors.

EXAMPLE 1 Multiplying Fractions

Multiply.

$$\frac{x}{6} \cdot \frac{3}{2x^2} = \frac{x}{2 \cdot 3} \cdot \frac{3}{2 \cdot x \cdot x}$$ Factor

$$= \frac{\cancel{x} \cdot \cancel{3}}{2 \cdot \cancel{3} \cdot 2 \cdot \cancel{x} \cdot x}$$ Indicate product and divide out common factors

$$= \frac{1}{2 \cdot 2 \cdot x}$$ The numerator is 1, *not* 0

$$= \frac{1}{4x}$$ Multiply ■

EXAMPLE 2 **Multiplying Fractions**

Multiply.

$$\frac{a^2 - 9}{a^2 - 4a + 4} \cdot \frac{a - 2}{a + 3}$$

$$= \frac{(a - 3)(a + 3)}{(a - 2)(a - 2)} \cdot \frac{(a - 2)}{(a + 3)} \qquad \text{Factor}$$

$$= \frac{(a - 3)\cancel{(a + 3)}\cancel{(a - 2)}}{(a - 2)\cancel{(a - 2)}\cancel{(a + 3)}} \qquad \text{Divide out common factors}$$

$$= \frac{a - 3}{a - 2} \qquad \textit{Do not} \text{ divide out the term } a\text{; it is not a factor}$$

■

CAUTION A common mistake made when told to multiply two expressions such as in Example 2 is to write

$$\frac{a^2 - 9}{a^2 - 4a + 4} \cdot \frac{a - 2}{a + 3} = \frac{a^3 - 2a^2 - 9a + 18}{a^3 - a^2 - 8a + 12}.$$

Now to reduce the product, we would have to factor the numerator and denominator, that is, turn right around and undo what we just did. *Never multiply rational expressions without first factoring and dividing out common factors.*

EXAMPLE 3 **Multiplying Fractions**

Multiply.

$$\frac{x^2 - y^2}{xy} \cdot \frac{xy - x^2}{x^2 - 2xy + y^2}$$

$$= \frac{(x - y)(x + y)}{xy} \cdot \frac{x(y - x)}{(x - y)(x - y)} \qquad \text{Factor}$$

$$= \frac{\cancel{(x - y)}(x + y) \cdot \cancel{x} \cdot (y - x)}{\cancel{x} \cdot y \cdot \cancel{(x - y)}(x - y)} \qquad \text{Divide out common factors}$$

$$= \frac{x + y}{y} \cdot \frac{(y - x)}{(x - y)}$$

$$= \frac{x + y}{y} \cdot (-1) \qquad \frac{y - x}{x - y} = -1$$

$$= -\frac{x + y}{y}$$

■

▶ *Dividing fractions* In Chapter 1 we divided one numerical fraction by another. In

$$\frac{2}{3} \div \frac{3}{5},$$

we divide the dividend $\frac{2}{3}$ by the divisor $\frac{3}{5}$. To find the quotient, we multiply the dividend by the **reciprocal** of the divisor. That is,

$$\frac{2}{3} \div \frac{3}{5} = \frac{2}{3} \cdot \frac{5}{3} = \frac{2 \cdot 5}{3 \cdot 3} = \frac{10}{9}. \qquad \frac{5}{3} \text{ is the reciprocal of } \frac{3}{5}$$

We use exactly the same process when dividing algebraic fractions.

To Divide Algebraic Fractions

Multiply the dividend by the reciprocal of the divisor.

$$\frac{P}{Q} \div \frac{R}{S} = \frac{P}{Q} \cdot \frac{S}{R}$$

The following table lists several algebraic fractions and their reciprocals.

Fraction	*Reciprocal*	
$\frac{2}{x}$	$\frac{x}{2}$	
$\frac{x+1}{(x-5)^2}$	$\frac{(x-5)^2}{x+1}$	
5	$\frac{1}{5}$	5 can be thought of as $\frac{5}{1}$
x	$\frac{1}{x}$	x is $\frac{x}{1}$
$\frac{1}{3}$	3	3 is $\frac{3}{1}$
$x + y$	$\frac{1}{x+y}$	Not $\frac{1}{x} + \frac{1}{y}$. For example, $\frac{1}{2+3} = \frac{1}{5} \neq \frac{1}{2} + \frac{1}{3} = \frac{5}{6}$

EXAMPLE 4 **Dividing Fractions**

Divide.

(a)
$$\frac{x}{x+1} \div \frac{x}{2} = \frac{x}{x+1} \cdot \frac{2}{x} \qquad \frac{2}{x} \text{ is the reciprocal of } \frac{x}{2}$$

$$= \frac{\cancel{x} \cdot 2}{(x+1) \cdot \cancel{x}} \qquad \text{Divide out common factor}$$

$$= \frac{2}{x+1}$$

(b) $\dfrac{y+3}{y} \div y = \dfrac{y+3}{y} \cdot \dfrac{1}{y}$ $\frac{1}{y}$ is the reciprocal of y

$= \dfrac{y+3}{y^2}$

(c) $\dfrac{a^2-4a+4}{a^2-9} \div \dfrac{a-2}{a+3} = \dfrac{a^2-4a+4}{a^2-9} \cdot \dfrac{a+3}{a-2}$

$= \dfrac{(a-2)(a-2)}{(a-3)(a+3)} \cdot \dfrac{(a+3)}{(a-2)}$

$= \dfrac{\cancel{(a-2)}(a-2)\cancel{(a+3)}}{(a-3)\cancel{(a+3)}\cancel{(a-2)}}$

$= \dfrac{a-2}{a-3}$ Do not divide out a ■

EXAMPLE 5 **Dividing Fractions**

Divide.

$\dfrac{x^2-3xy+2y^2}{x^2-4y^2} \div (x^2+xy-2y^2)$

$= \dfrac{x^2-3xy+2y^2}{x^2-4y^2} \cdot \dfrac{1}{x^2+xy-2y^2}$ Find reciprocal and multiply

$= \dfrac{(x-y)(x-2y)}{(x+2y)(x-2y)} \cdot \dfrac{1}{(x-y)(x+2y)}$ Factor

$= \dfrac{1\cancel{(x-y)}\cancel{(x-2y)}}{(x+2y)\cancel{(x-2y)}\cancel{(x-y)}(x+2y)}$ Divide out common factors

$= \dfrac{1}{(x+2y)^2}$ Remember the numerator is 1; also, the answer is NOT $(x+2y)^2$ ■

8.2 EXERCISES

Multiply in Exercises 1–13.

1. $\dfrac{1}{x^2} \cdot \dfrac{x}{3}$
2. $\dfrac{2y}{5} \cdot \dfrac{25}{4y^3}$
3. $\dfrac{2x}{(x+1)^2} \cdot \dfrac{x+1}{4x^2}$
4. $\dfrac{x^2-36}{x^2-6x} \cdot \dfrac{x}{x+6}$
5. $\dfrac{5x+5}{x-2} \cdot \dfrac{x^2-4x+4}{x^2-1}$
6. $\dfrac{y^2-3y-10}{y^2-4y+4} \cdot \dfrac{y-2}{y-5}$
7. $\dfrac{z^2-z-20}{z^2+7z+12} \cdot \dfrac{z+3}{z^2-25}$
8. $\dfrac{y^2+6y+5}{7y^2-63} \cdot \dfrac{7y+21}{(y+5)^2}$
9. $\dfrac{16-x^2}{5x-1} \cdot \dfrac{5x^2-x}{16-8x+x^2}$
10. $\dfrac{a^2-4}{a^2-4a+4} \cdot \dfrac{a^2-9a+14}{a^3+2a^2}$
11. $\dfrac{2x^2-5xy+3y^2}{x^2-y^2} \cdot (x^2+2xy+y^2)$

12. $\dfrac{x^2 - y^2}{(x+y)^2} \cdot \dfrac{x+y}{x-y}$

13. $\dfrac{x^2 - 7xy + 6y^2}{x^2 - xy - 2y^2} \cdot \dfrac{x+y}{x-6y}$

Find the reciprocal of each expression in Exercises 14–16.

14. $\dfrac{3}{7}$

15. $\dfrac{1}{x+1}$

16. $\dfrac{2x-3}{x+5}$

Divide in Exercises 17–27.

17. $\dfrac{x}{x+2} \div \dfrac{x}{3}$

18. $\dfrac{2(a+3)}{7} \div \dfrac{4(a+3)}{21}$

19. $\dfrac{3(x^2+5)}{4(x^2-3)} \div \dfrac{x^2+5}{4(x^2-3)}$

20. $\dfrac{5y^4}{y^2-1} \div \dfrac{5y^3}{y^2+2y+1}$

21. $(x+6) \div \dfrac{x^2-36}{x^2-6x}$

22. $\dfrac{z^2-4z+4}{z^2-1} \div \dfrac{z-2}{5z+5}$

23. $\dfrac{a^2+10a+21}{a^2-2a-15} \div \dfrac{a+7}{a^2-25}$

24. $\dfrac{y^3-64y}{2y^2+16} \div \dfrac{y^2-9y+8}{y^2+4y-5}$

25. $\dfrac{x^2+16x+64}{2x^2-128} \div \dfrac{3x^2+30x+48}{x^2-6x-16}$

26. $\dfrac{x^2-5xy+6y^2}{x^2-4y^2} \div (x^2-2xy-3y^2)$

27. $\dfrac{x+2y}{x^2-y^2} \div \dfrac{x+2y}{x+y}$

Perform the indicated operations in Exercise 28–29.

28. $\dfrac{x^2-25}{x+2} \cdot \dfrac{x^2+4x+4}{x-5} \div \dfrac{x+2}{x+5}$

29. $\dfrac{a^2-y^2}{a^2-ay} \cdot \dfrac{2a^2+ay}{a^2-4y^2} \div \dfrac{a+y}{a+2y}$

FOR REVIEW

In Exercises 30–32, find the values of the variable that must be excluded in each rational expression.

30. $\dfrac{y-1}{y^2+2y}$

31. $\dfrac{a}{a^2+5}$

32. $\dfrac{(x+1)(x-5)}{3x}$

Are the fractions given in Exercises 33–35 equivalent?

33. $\dfrac{x+5}{2x^2+5}, \dfrac{x}{2x^2}$

34. $\dfrac{x}{3}, \dfrac{x^2+2x}{3(x+2)}$

35. $\dfrac{1}{x+1}, \dfrac{x+1}{1}$

36. Change $\frac{x}{2}$ to an equivalent fraction with the given denominator.

(a) 10 **(b)** $2x$ **(c)** $2x^2$

(d) $2(x+1)$ **(e)** $2(2x-1)$ **(f)** $2(x^2-1)$

37. Burford reduced the rational expression $\dfrac{a-5}{a^2-4a-5}$ in the following way:

$$\frac{a-5}{a^2-4a-5} = \frac{\cancel{a-5}}{(\cancel{a-5})(a+1)} = \frac{0}{a+1} = 0$$

What is wrong with Burford's work? What is the correct reduction?

Exercises 38–40 review material from Section 1.2 to help you prepare for the next two sections. Perform the indicated operations.

38. $\dfrac{3}{4} - \dfrac{1}{4}$

39. $\dfrac{5}{6} - \dfrac{4}{21}$

40. $5 + \dfrac{2}{3}$

8.2 PARALLEL EXERCISES

Multiply in Exercises 1–13.

1. $\frac{2}{x^3} \cdot \frac{x^2}{6}$

2. $\frac{5a^2}{8} \cdot \frac{4a}{10a^3}$

3. $\frac{3x^2}{x+5} \cdot \frac{(x+5)^2}{9x}$

4. $\frac{z^3}{z+3} \cdot \frac{z^2-9}{z^2-3z}$

5. $\frac{4x+4}{4x-4} \cdot \frac{x^2-2x+1}{x^2-1}$

6. $\frac{y^2-5y+6}{y^2-9} \cdot \frac{y+2}{y-2}$

7. $\frac{z^2+z-20}{z^2-7x+12} \cdot \frac{z-3}{z^2-25}$

8. $\frac{y^2+8y+7}{5y^2-125} \cdot \frac{5y-25}{(y+1)^2}$

9. $\frac{9-x^2}{3x-2} \cdot \frac{3x^2-2x}{9-6x+x^2}$

10. $\frac{a^2-25}{a^2-10a+25} \cdot \frac{a^2-8a+15}{a^3-3a^2}$

11. $\frac{2x^2+xy-10y^2}{x^2-4y^2} \cdot (x^2+4xy+4y^2)$

12. $\frac{x^2-2xy+y^2}{x+y} \cdot \frac{(x+y)^2}{x-y}$

13. $\frac{x^2-7xy+10y^2}{x^2-3xy-10y^2} \cdot \frac{x+2y}{x-2y}$

Find the reciprocal of each expression in Exercises 14–16.

14. $\frac{6}{y}$

15. $\frac{3x-2}{x-2}$

16. $5a-1$

Divide in Exercises 17–27.

17. $\frac{x+3}{x} \div \frac{4}{x}$

18. $\frac{6(a+4)}{5} \div \frac{4(a+4)}{35}$

19. $\frac{8(x^2+x+1)}{6(x^2-2)} \div \frac{x^2+x+1}{3(x^2-2)}$

20. $\frac{y^2+4y+4}{8y^3} \div \frac{y^2-4}{2y^2}$

21. $\frac{z^2+4z+4}{z^2-4} \div \frac{z+2}{3z-6}$

22. $\frac{x^2-49}{x^2+7x} \div (x-7)$

23. $\frac{a^2-10a+21}{a^2+2a-15} \div (5a-35)$

24. $\frac{x^2-16x+64}{3x^2-192} \div \frac{3x^2-30x+48}{x^2+6x-16}$

25. $\frac{5y^2+10y}{2y^3-8y} \div \frac{y^2+5y-6}{y^2-3y+2}$

26. $\frac{x^2+8xy+15y^2}{x^2-25y^2} \div (x^2+2xy-3y^2)$

27. $\frac{x^2-y^2}{x-3y} \div \frac{x-y}{x-3y}$

Perform the indicated operations in Exercises 28–29.

28. $\frac{x-4}{x^2-16} \cdot \frac{x^2+5x+4}{x-3} \div \frac{x+1}{x+3}$

29. $\frac{u^2-4v^2}{u^2+uv-2v^2} \cdot \frac{4u^2-4uv-3v^2}{2u^2-3uv-2v^2} \div \frac{3u+v}{u-v}$

FOR REVIEW

In Exercises 30–32, find the values of the variable that must be excluded in each rational expression.

30. $\frac{x-3}{x^2-8x}$

31. $\frac{a^2+1}{a^2-9}$

32. $\frac{y^2+3y}{6}$

Are the fractions given in Exercises 33–35 equivalent?

33. $\frac{6x^3-7}{7x-7}, \frac{6x^3}{7x}$

34. $\frac{x^2-5x}{3x-15}, \frac{x^2}{3x}$

35. $\frac{2x+y}{1}, \frac{1}{2x+y}$

36. Change $\frac{x^2}{5}$ to an equivalent fraction with the given denominator.

(a) 35

(b) $5x^3$

(c) $5(x-2)$

(d) $5(x+3)$

(e) $5(5x+1)$

(f) $5(x^3+2x)$

37. Burford reduced the rational expression $\frac{a-5}{a^2-4a-5}$ in the following way:

$$\frac{a-5}{a^2-4a-5} = \frac{\cancel{a-5}}{\cancel{(a-5)}(a+1)} = a+1$$

What is wrong with Burford's work? What is the correct reduction?

Exercises 38–40 review material from Section 1.2 to help you prepare for the next two sections. Perform the indicated operations.

38. $\frac{7}{9} - \frac{4}{9}$ **39.** $\frac{5}{6} + \frac{5}{18}$ **40.** $3 - \frac{15}{2}$

8.2 ENRICHMENT EXERCISES

Perform the indicated operations in Exercises 1–4.

1. $\frac{x^2-5x-6}{x+1} \div \frac{x^2-12x+36}{x^2-1} \cdot \frac{x}{x-1}$

2. $\frac{y^2-3y-4}{y^2-1} \div \frac{y+3}{y^2-9} \cdot \frac{y-1}{y^2-6y+9}$

3. $\frac{a^2-b^2}{2a+b} \div \left[\frac{a-b}{2a^2+3ab+b^2} \cdot \frac{a-b}{a+b}\right]$

4. $\frac{a+2b}{a^2-4b^2} \div \left[\frac{a-b}{a^2-3ab+2b^2} \cdot \frac{a+2b}{a-2b}\right]$

5. Perform the indicated operation: $(a-2) \div (2-a)$

6. Perform the indicated operation: $(a+2) \div (2+a)$

7. Explain why you should never multiply numerators and place the result over the product of the denominators in the first step of multiplying rational expressions.

8. Outline the method used to multiply rational expressions.

9. Outline the method used to divide rational expressions.

SECTION 8.3 Addition and Subtraction of Like Fractions

Student guideposts

- ▶ *Adding and subtracting like fractions*
- ▶ *Denominators differing in sign only*

▶ *Adding and subtracting like fractions*

Fractions that have the same denominators are called **like fractions.** For example,

$$\frac{3}{5x} \quad \text{and} \quad \frac{x+2}{5x} \qquad \text{Like fractions}$$

are like fractions, while

$$\frac{1}{2x+1} \quad \text{and} \quad \frac{1}{2x} \qquad \text{Unlike fractions}$$

are called **unlike fractions.**

To Add or Subtract Like Fractions

1. Add or subtract the numerators to find the numerator of the answer.
2. Use the common denominator as the denominator of the answer.
3. Reduce the sum or difference to lowest terms.

Symbolically, if P, Q, and R are fractions, with $R \neq 0$, then

$$\frac{P}{R} + \frac{Q}{R} = \frac{P+Q}{R} \quad \text{and} \quad \frac{P}{R} - \frac{Q}{R} = \frac{P-Q}{R}.$$

EXAMPLE 1

Operating on Like Fractions

Perform the indicated operation.

(a) $\frac{3}{7} + \frac{2}{7} = \frac{3+2}{7}$ Add numerators and place sum over the common denominator 7

$= \frac{5}{7}$

(b) $\frac{2+x}{x} + \frac{x^2+1}{x} = \frac{(2+x)+(x^2+1)}{x}$ Add numerators and place sum over common denominator x

$= \frac{x^2+x+3}{x}$

(c) $\frac{1}{4} - \frac{3}{4} = \frac{1-3}{4} = \frac{-2}{4} = \frac{-\cancel{2}}{\cancel{2} \cdot 2} = -\frac{1}{2}$

Always reduce the answer to lowest terms.

(d) $\frac{2x+1}{x-5} - \frac{x-3}{x-5} = \frac{(2x+1)-(x-3)}{x-5}$ Use parentheses in subtraction to avoid making a sign error

$= \frac{2x+1-x+3}{x-5}$ Be sure to change the sign to $+3$

$= \frac{x+4}{x-5}$ ■

CAUTION When subtracting rational expressions, if you enclose the numerators in parentheses, you will eliminate sign errors when the distributive property is used. Notice how this happens in Example 1(d) when $-(x-3)$ becomes $-x+3$.

▶ *Denominators differing in sign only*

Some fractions have denominators that are negatives of each other. These can be made into like fractions by changing the sign of both the numerator and the denominator of *one* of the fractions. To do this, multiply both numerator and denominator by -1. Since you are multiplying the fraction by $\frac{-1}{-1} = 1$, the result is equivalent to the original fraction. This is illustrated in the next example.

EXAMPLE 2 **Working with Denominators Differing in Sign**

Perform the indicated operations.

(a)
$$\frac{x}{5} + \frac{2x+1}{-5} = \frac{x}{5} + \frac{(-1)(2x+1)}{(-1)(-5)} \quad \text{Multiply numerator and denominator by } -1$$
$$= \frac{x}{5} + \frac{(-2x-1)}{5} \quad \text{The fractions are now like fractions}$$
$$= \frac{x + (-2x-1)}{5} \quad \text{Add numerators}$$
$$= \frac{-x-1}{5}$$

(b)
$$\frac{2x}{x-3} - \frac{x+3}{3-x} = \frac{2x}{x-3} - \frac{(-1)(x+3)}{(-1)(3-x)} \quad x-3 \text{ and } 3-x \text{ are negatives of each other}$$
$$= \frac{2x}{x-3} - \frac{(-x-3)}{-3+x}$$
$$= \frac{2x}{x-3} - \frac{(-x-3)}{x-3}$$
$$= \frac{2x-(-x-3)}{x-3}$$
$$= \frac{2x+x+3}{x-3} \quad \text{Watch all signs}$$
$$= \frac{3x+3}{x-3} \quad \blacksquare$$

8.3 EXERCISES

Perform the indicated operations in Exercises 1–20.

1. $\frac{3}{5} + \frac{7}{5}$
2. $\frac{2}{x} + \frac{7}{x}$
3. $\frac{2x+1}{x-7} + \frac{-1-2x}{x-7}$
4. $\frac{2y}{y+2} - \frac{y+1}{y+2}$
5. $\frac{z-1}{z+1} - \frac{2z-1}{z+1}$
6. $\frac{7x^2}{3x^2-1} - \frac{4x^2}{3x^2-1}$
7. $\frac{a}{(a+1)^2} + \frac{1}{(a+1)^2}$
8. $\frac{4}{a} + \frac{2a-3}{-a}$
9. $\frac{2x}{-3} + \frac{3x+7}{3}$
10. $\frac{7}{2z} - \frac{3z+1}{-2z}$
11. $\frac{2a}{a-1} + \frac{3a}{1-a}$
12. $\frac{3x}{1-x} + \frac{x+1}{x-1}$
13. $\frac{3}{a^2+2a+1} - \frac{2-a}{a^2+2a+1}$
14. $\frac{x}{6x-12} - \frac{4}{3(4-2x)}$

15. $\dfrac{2z-3}{z^2+3z-4} - \dfrac{z-7}{z^2+3z-4}$

16. $\dfrac{2x}{x^2+x-6} + \dfrac{x-3}{6-x-x^2}$

17. $\dfrac{x^2-15}{x^2+4x+3} - \dfrac{2x}{x^2+4x+3}$

18. $\dfrac{x+y}{x-y} - \dfrac{x+y}{y-x}$

19. $\dfrac{5x}{x+1} + \dfrac{2x-1}{x+1} - \dfrac{3x}{x+1}$

20. $\dfrac{x+2y}{2x-y} - \dfrac{3x-2y}{2x-y} - \dfrac{4y}{2x-y}$

FOR REVIEW

Perform the indicated operations in Exercises 21–22.

21. $\dfrac{a^2-9}{4a+12} \div \dfrac{a-3}{6}$

22. $\dfrac{x^2-5xy+6y^2}{x^2+3xy-10y^2} \cdot \dfrac{x^2+5xy}{x^2-3xy}$

8.3 PARALLEL EXERCISES

Perform the indicated operations in Exercises 1–20.

1. $\dfrac{4}{5} - \dfrac{9}{5}$

2. $\dfrac{5}{3x} - \dfrac{8}{3x}$

3. $\dfrac{3x-2}{x-4} + \dfrac{2-3x}{x-4}$

4. $\dfrac{8y}{y-5} - \dfrac{4y+3}{y-5}$

5. $\dfrac{a+2}{a+2} + \dfrac{3a-2}{a+2}$

6. $\dfrac{6x^2}{5x^2+2} - \dfrac{9x^2}{5x^2+2}$

7. $\dfrac{a^2}{a^2+1} - \dfrac{-1}{a^2+1}$

8. $\dfrac{z}{3} + \dfrac{2z-3}{-3}$

9. $\dfrac{9}{a} + \dfrac{5a-2}{-a}$

10. $\dfrac{10}{5z} - \dfrac{5z+4}{-5z}$

11. $\dfrac{5a}{a-4} + \dfrac{7a}{4-a}$

12. $\dfrac{4x}{7-x} - \dfrac{2x+5}{x-7}$

13. $\dfrac{5}{a^2+4a+4} - \dfrac{3-a}{a^2+4a+4}$

14. $\dfrac{2x}{5(x-2)} - \dfrac{3}{10-5x}$

15. $\dfrac{3z+2}{z^2+4z-12} - \dfrac{2z-4}{z^2+4z-12}$

16. $\dfrac{2x}{x^2-2x-15} + \dfrac{x+5}{15+2x-x^2}$

17. $\dfrac{x^2-8}{x^2-4x+3} - \dfrac{-7x}{x^2-4x+3}$

18. $\dfrac{x-y}{2x-y} - \dfrac{x-y}{y-2x}$

19. $\dfrac{3x-1}{x+2} + \dfrac{4x-2}{x+2} - \dfrac{5x-3}{x+1}$

20. $\dfrac{x+3y}{x-2y} - \dfrac{4x+y}{x-2y} - \dfrac{2y}{x-2y}$

FOR REVIEW

Perform the indicated operations in Exercises 21–22.

21. $\dfrac{y^2-11y+28}{y^2-2y-35} \div (y^2+y-20)$

22. $\dfrac{2x^2+9xy+4y^2}{x^2+xy-12y^2} \cdot \dfrac{3xy-x^2}{2x^2+xy}$

8.3 ENRICHMENT EXERCISES

Perform the indicated operations in Exercises 1–4.

1. $\frac{2x}{x-5} - \frac{2}{5-x} + \frac{3x}{5-x}$
2. $\frac{5y}{x^2-y^2} + \frac{5y}{y^2-x^2} - \frac{x-y}{y^2-x^2}$
3. $\frac{a+5}{(a-2)(a-3)} - \frac{2a-1}{(2-a)(3-a)} + \frac{3a-2}{(a-2)(3-a)}$
4. $\frac{a+b}{2a-b} - \frac{2b-a}{b-2a} - \frac{a-b}{2a-b} + \frac{3b-a}{b-2a}$

Burford's work on two subtraction problems is shown in Exercises 5–6. What is he doing wrong? What is the correct answer?

5. $\frac{x}{x+1} - \frac{x-2}{x+1} = \frac{x-x-2}{x+1} = \frac{-2}{x+1} = -\frac{2}{x+1}$
6. $\frac{a+2}{a} - \frac{a+4}{-a} = \frac{(a+2)-(a+4)}{a-(-a)} = \frac{a+2-a-4}{a+a} = \frac{-2}{2a} = -\frac{1}{a}$
7. Suppose you obtain $\frac{-1}{b-a}$ as the answer to a problem but the book gives $\frac{1}{a-b}$ for the answer. Did you do anything wrong? Explain.
8. Outline the method used to add like fractions.
9. Outline the method used to subtract like fractions.

SECTION 8.4 Addition and Subtraction of Unlike Fractions

Student guideposts

- *Least common denominator (LCD)*
- *Adding and subtracting fractions*

Before we can add or subtract unlike fractions, we need to convert them to equivalent like fractions. Recall from Chapter 1 that to add $\frac{2}{15}$ and $\frac{1}{6}$ we must first find a common denominator. One such denominator is $15 \cdot 6 = 90$. Since

$$\frac{2}{15} = \frac{2 \cdot 6}{15 \cdot 6} = \frac{12}{90} \quad \text{and} \quad \frac{1}{6} = \frac{1 \cdot 15}{6 \cdot 15} = \frac{15}{90}$$

we could add as follows.

$$\begin{aligned}\frac{2}{15} + \frac{1}{6} &= \frac{12}{90} + \frac{15}{90}\\ &= \frac{12+15}{90}\\ &= \frac{27}{90} = \frac{\cancel{9} \cdot 3}{\cancel{9} \cdot 10} = \frac{3}{10}\end{aligned}$$

Least common denominator (LCD) Often it is wiser to try to find a common denominator smaller than the product of denominators. If we use the *least common denominator,* we shorten the computation needed to reduce the final sum or difference to lowest terms. In the example above, we could have used the least common denominator, 30.

$$\frac{2}{15}+\frac{1}{6}=\frac{2\cdot 2}{15\cdot 2}+\frac{1\cdot 5}{6\cdot 5}=\frac{4}{30}+\frac{5}{30}=\frac{9}{30}=\frac{3}{10}$$

In the same way, with algebraic fractions we will be concerned with finding the **least common denominator (LCD)** of all fractions.

To Find the LCD of Two or More Fractions

1. Factor the denominators completely.
2. Identify each different factor.
3. Put each different factor in the LCD as many times as it appears in the denominator where it is found the greatest number of times.

EXAMPLE 1

Finding the LCD

Find the LCD of the given fractions.

(a) $\frac{7}{90}$ and $\frac{5}{24}$

One 2 Two 3's One 5 | Three 2's One 3

$$90 = 2 \cdot 3 \cdot 3 \cdot 5 \quad \text{and} \quad 24 = 2 \cdot 2 \cdot 2 \cdot 3.$$

The LCD must consist of three 2's, two 3's, and one 5.

$$\text{LCD} = 2 \cdot 2 \cdot 2 \cdot 3 \cdot 3 \cdot 5 = 360$$

(b) $\frac{3}{x}$ and $\frac{2}{x+1}$

Since x and $x + 1$ are already completely factored, and since there are no common factors in the two denominators, the LCD $= x(x + 1)$.

(c) $\frac{3}{2y}$ and $\frac{y+1}{y^2}$

The denominators are essentially factored already. We see that the LCD has one 2 and two y's. Thus, the LCD is $2y^2$.

(d) $\frac{2x-3}{x^2-25}$ and $\frac{7x}{2x-10}$

$$x^2 - 25 = (x-5)(x+5) \quad \text{and} \quad 2x - 10 = 2(x-5)$$

We need one $(x - 5)$, one $(x + 5)$, and one 2 for the LCD. That is, the LCD $= 2(x - 5)(x + 5)$.

(e) $\dfrac{y}{y^2-4}$ and $\dfrac{4}{y^2-4y+4}$

$$y^2-4=(y-2)(y+2) \quad \text{and} \quad y^2-4y+4=(y-2)(y-2)$$

The LCD must consist of two $(y-2)$'s and one $(y+2)$. Thus, the LCD = $(y-2)^2(y+2)$. ■

▶ *Adding and subtracting fractions*

To add or subtract unlike fractions, we first find their LCD and then use the fundamental principle of fractions to transform each fraction into an equivalent fraction having the LCD as its denominator. We illustrate this method in the following numerical example.

$$\frac{2}{15}+\frac{3}{35}$$

$$=\frac{2}{3\cdot 5}+\frac{3}{5\cdot 7}$$ Since $15=3\cdot 5$ and $35=5\cdot 7$, the LCD is $3\cdot 5\cdot 7=105$

$$=\frac{2\cdot 7}{3\cdot 5\cdot 7}+\frac{3\cdot 3}{5\cdot 7\cdot 3}$$ Multiply numerator and denominator of $\frac{2}{15}$ by 7 and of $\frac{3}{35}$ by 3 so the denominators are the same

$$=\frac{2\cdot 7+3\cdot 3}{3\cdot 5\cdot 7}$$ Since denominators are now the same, add numerators and place the sum over the LCD

$$=\frac{14+9}{3\cdot 5\cdot 7}$$ Leave the denominator in factored form and simplify the numerator

$$=\frac{23}{3\cdot 5\cdot 7}=\frac{23}{105}$$ Since 23 has no factor of 3, 5, or 7, the resulting fraction is in lowest terms

We use exactly the same procedure for rational expressions except we now have polynomials for numerators and denominators.

To Add or Subtract Rational Expressions

1. Rewrite the indicated sum or difference with all denominators expressed in factored form.
2. Find the LCD.
3. Multiply the numerator and denominator of each fraction by all factors present in the LCD but missing in the denominator of the particular fraction.
4. Write out the sum or difference of all numerators, using parentheses if needed, and place the result over the LCD.
5. Simplify and factor (if possible) the resulting numerator and divide any factors common to the LCD.

EXAMPLE 2 **Adding Fractions**

Add.

$$\frac{5}{6x} + \frac{3}{10x^2}$$

$$= \frac{5}{2 \cdot 3 \cdot x} + \frac{3}{2 \cdot 5 \cdot x \cdot x}$$ Factor denominators; LCD $= 2 \cdot 3 \cdot 5 \cdot x \cdot x$

$$= \frac{5 \cdot 5 \cdot x}{2 \cdot 3 \cdot x \cdot 5 \cdot x} + \frac{3 \cdot 3}{2 \cdot 5 \cdot x \cdot x \cdot 3}$$ Supply missing factors in both the numerator and denominator

$$= \frac{5 \cdot 5 \cdot x + 3 \cdot 3}{2 \cdot 3 \cdot 5 \cdot x \cdot x}$$ Add numerators over LCD

$$= \frac{25x + 9}{30x^2}$$ No common factors exist, so this is in lowest terms

EXAMPLE 3 **Subtracting Fractions**

Subtract.

$$\frac{2}{y+2} - \frac{2}{y+3}$$ Denominators already factored; LCD $= (y+2)(y+3)$

$$= \frac{2(y+3)}{(y+2)(y+3)} - \frac{2(y+2)}{(y+2)(y+3)}$$ Supply missing factors

$$= \frac{2(y+3) - 2(y+2)}{(y+2)(y+3)}$$ Subtract numerators over LCD

$$= \frac{2y + 6 - 2y - 4}{(y+2)(y+3)}$$ Simplify the numerator and watch signs when using the distributive law

$$= \frac{2}{(y+2)(y+3)}$$ Collect like terms; since no common factors exist, this is in lowest terms ■

CAUTION We can use Example 3 to illustrate a very common mistake. In the second step when we have

$$\frac{2(y+3) - 2(y+2)}{(y+2)(y+3)}$$

students will often try to cancel (divide out) as shown below

$$\frac{2\cancel{(y+3)} - 2\cancel{(y+2)}}{\cancel{(y+2)}\cancel{(y+3)}}.$$ THIS IS WRONG

Since $(y + 3)$ and $(y + 2)$ are not factors of the entire numerator, just factors of terms of the numerator, we cannot divide them out at this step. Remember, we can only cancel (divide out) factors, never cancel terms.

EXAMPLE 4 **Adding Fractions**

Add.

(a) $\dfrac{5}{x^2 - 4} + \dfrac{7}{x^2 + 2x}$

$= \dfrac{5}{(x - 2)(x + 2)} + \dfrac{7}{x(x + 2)}$ — Factor denominators; LCD $= x(x - 2)(x + 2)$

$= \dfrac{5(x)}{(x - 2)(x + 2)(x)} + \dfrac{7(x - 2)}{x(x + 2)(x - 2)}$ — Supply missing factors

$= \dfrac{5x + 7(x - 2)}{x(x + 2)(x - 2)}$ — Add numerators

$= \dfrac{5x + 7x - 14}{x(x + 2)(x - 2)}$ — Simplify the numerator by clearing parentheses using the distributive law

$= \dfrac{12x - 14}{x(x + 2)(x - 2)}$ — Collect like terms in the numerator

$= \dfrac{2(6x - 7)}{x(x + 2)(x - 2)}$ — Factor; no common factors exist, so this is in lowest terms

(b) $\dfrac{5}{x^2 + x - 6} + \dfrac{3x}{x^2 - 4x + 4}$

$= \dfrac{5}{(x - 2)(x + 3)} + \dfrac{3x}{(x - 2)(x - 2)}$ — LCD $= (x + 3)(x - 2)^2$

$= \dfrac{5(x - 2)}{(x - 2)(x + 3)(x - 2)} + \dfrac{3x(x + 3)}{(x - 2)(x - 2)(x + 3)}$

$= \dfrac{5(x - 2) + 3x(x + 3)}{(x + 3)(x - 2)^2}$ — Add numerators

$= \dfrac{5x - 10 + 3x^2 + 9x}{(x + 3)(x - 2)^2}$ — Clear parentheses

$= \dfrac{3x^2 + 14x - 10}{(x + 3)(x - 2)^2}$ — Collect like terms; this is in lowest terms ■

We use the same procedures even if there are two variables and more than two fractions.

EXAMPLE 5 **Subtracting Fractions with Two Variables**

Perform the indicated operations.

$$\frac{2x}{x+y} - \frac{y}{x-y} - \frac{-4xy}{x^2-y^2}$$

$$= \frac{2x}{x+y} - \frac{y}{x-y} - \frac{-4xy}{(x+y)(x-y)} \qquad \text{LCD} = (x+y)(x-y)$$

$$= \frac{2x(x-y)}{(x+y)(x-y)} - \frac{y(x+y)}{(x-y)(x+y)} - \frac{-4xy}{(x+y)(x-y)} \qquad \text{Supply missing factors}$$

$$= \frac{2x(x-y) - y(x+y) + 4xy}{(x+y)(x-y)} \qquad \text{Perform operations in the numerator}$$

$$= \frac{2x^2 - 2xy - xy - y^2 + 4xy}{(x+y)(x-y)} \qquad \text{Clear parentheses}$$

$$= \frac{2x^2 + xy - y^2}{(x+y)(x-y)} \qquad \text{The numerator will factor}$$

$$= \frac{(2x-y)\cancel{(x+y)}}{\cancel{(x+y)}(x-y)} \qquad \text{Divide out } (x+y)$$

$$= \frac{2x-y}{x-y} \qquad \text{This is in lowest terms} \quad \blacksquare$$

8.4 EXERCISES

Find the LCD of the fractions given in Exercises 1–12.

1. $\frac{1}{20}$ and $\frac{7}{30}$
2. $\frac{2}{39}$ and $\frac{4}{35}$
3. $\frac{y+1}{y^2}$ and $\frac{1}{3y}$
4. $\frac{2}{3x}$ and $\frac{x+2}{3x+3}$
5. $\frac{2a+1}{a^2-25}$ and $\frac{3}{a+5}$
6. $\frac{3x+2}{3x+6}$ and $\frac{x}{x^2-4}$
7. $\frac{1}{x^2+2x+1}$ and $\frac{2}{x^2-1}$
8. $\frac{3}{z^2-9}$ and $\frac{2}{z^2+z-6}$
9. $\frac{2}{a^2-9}$ and $\frac{2}{a^2+2a-3}$
10. $\frac{1}{x^2-y^2}$ and $\frac{3xy}{x-y}$
11. $\frac{5x}{x+y}$, $\frac{7y}{2x+2y}$, and $\frac{2xy}{3x+3y}$
12. $\frac{16}{5x}$, $\frac{5}{3y}$, and $\frac{xy}{2x-7}$

Perform the indicated operations in Exercises 13–30.

13. $\frac{4}{21} + \frac{5}{14}$
14. $\frac{5}{12} - \frac{11}{30}$
15. $\frac{2}{9x} + \frac{4}{15x^2}$
16. $\frac{5}{y+5} - \frac{3}{y-5}$
17. $\frac{2}{3x+21} - \frac{3}{5x+35}$
18. $\frac{8}{7-a} - \frac{8a}{49-a^2}$
19. $\frac{3}{2x^2-2x} - \frac{5}{2x-2}$
20. $\frac{3z+2}{3z+6} + \frac{z-2}{z^2-4}$
21. $\frac{2}{y^2-1} + \frac{1}{y^2+2y-3}$

22. $\frac{2}{z^2 - 9} - \frac{2}{z^2 + 2z - 3}$

23. $\frac{3}{a^2 - a - 12} + \frac{2}{a^2 - 9}$

24. $\frac{5}{x^2 - 4x + 3} + \frac{7}{x^2 + x - 2}$

25. $\frac{y + 1}{y + 4} + \frac{4 - y^2}{y^2 - 16}$

26. $\frac{2}{a - 1} + \frac{a}{a^2 - 1}$

27. $\frac{3}{x + 1} + \frac{5}{x - 1} - \frac{10}{x^2 - 1}$

28. $\frac{5x}{x + y} + \frac{6y - 2x}{x - y}$

29. $\frac{2y}{y + 5} - \frac{3y}{y - 2} - \frac{2y^2}{y^2 + 3y - 10}$

30. $\frac{1}{x(x - y)} - \frac{2}{y(x + y)}$

FOR REVIEW

Perform the indicated operations in Exercises 31–33.

31. $\frac{3}{z^2 + 2z + 1} - \frac{2 - z}{z^2 + 2z + 1}$

32. $\frac{2a - 1}{a - 5} - \frac{6 - a}{5 - a}$

33. $\frac{x^2}{x - y} + \frac{x^2}{x - y} - \frac{y^2}{y - x}$

Exercises 34–36 review material that we covered in Chapters 3 and 7. They will help you prepare for the next section. Solve.

34. $y - 4(2y + 1) = y + 4$

35. $x^2 - x - 6 = 0$

36. $x^2 + 5x = 0$

37. **INTEREST** Eric Wade receives 11% simple interest on his savings. How much interest will he earn at the end of one year if he deposits $875?

38. **MOTION** Two families leave their homes at the same time planning to meet for a reunion at a point between them. If one travels at a rate of 55 mph, the other travels at 50 mph, and they live 273 miles apart, how long will it take for them to meet?

8.4 PARALLEL EXERCISES

Find the LCD of the fractions given in Exercises 1–12.

1. $\frac{1}{40}$ and $\frac{1}{30}$

2. $\frac{4}{39}$ and $\frac{2}{15}$

3. $\frac{3}{x}$ and $\frac{8}{7x}$

4. $\frac{3}{5x}$ and $\frac{x + 5}{5x + 5}$

5. $\frac{2z + 3}{z^2 - 9}$ and $\frac{12}{z + 3}$

6. $\frac{4x - 1}{2x + 6}$ and $\frac{5x + 1}{x^2 - 9}$

7. $\frac{4}{y^2 - 1}$ and $\frac{y}{y^2 - 2y + 1}$

8. $\frac{a}{a^2 - 4}$ and $\frac{2a + 5}{a^2 - a - 6}$

9. $\frac{6y^2}{y^2 - 25}$ and $\frac{3y}{y^2 + y - 20}$

10. $\frac{1}{4x^2 - y^2}$ and $\frac{x^2}{2x + y}$

11. $\frac{2}{4x - 4y}$, $\frac{3x}{2x - 2y}$, and $\frac{3xy}{5x - 5y}$

12. $\frac{21y}{8x}$, $\frac{15x}{7y}$, and $\frac{x^2y^2}{x + 3y}$

Perform the indicated operations in Exercises 13–30.

13. $\frac{2}{15} + \frac{3}{25}$

14. $\frac{11}{20} - \frac{8}{35}$

15. $\frac{3}{4y} + \frac{5}{8y^2}$

16. $\frac{6}{x - 6} - \frac{4}{x + 6}$

17. $\frac{7}{4x + 8} - \frac{5}{7x + 14}$

18. $\frac{14}{49 - a^2} - \frac{7}{7 - a}$

19. $\dfrac{5}{3x^2 - 3x} - \dfrac{7}{3x - 3}$

20. $\dfrac{10}{x^2 - 25} - \dfrac{3}{x - 5}$

21. $\dfrac{2}{a^2 - a - 2} + \dfrac{a}{a^2 - 1}$

22. $\dfrac{y}{y^2 - 1} - \dfrac{y + 2}{y^2 + y - 2}$

23. $\dfrac{4}{x^2 - 9} - \dfrac{4}{x^2 - 2x - 3}$

24. $\dfrac{8}{x^2 + 4x + 3} + \dfrac{3}{x^2 - x - 2}$

25. $\dfrac{y - 3}{y + 5} + \dfrac{9 - y^2}{y^2 - 25}$

26. $\dfrac{4}{a - 2} + \dfrac{2a}{a^2 - 4}$

27. $\dfrac{2}{x + 5} + \dfrac{3}{x - 5} - \dfrac{7}{x^2 - 25}$

28. $\dfrac{2y}{x - y} + \dfrac{3x - y}{x + y}$

29. $\dfrac{3y}{y + 4} - \dfrac{2y}{y - 3} - \dfrac{y^2}{y^2 + y - 12}$

30. $\dfrac{3}{x(x + y)} - \dfrac{2}{y(x - y)}$

FOR REVIEW

Perform the indicated operations in Exercises 31–33.

31. $\dfrac{z}{z^2 + 2z + 1} + \dfrac{2 + z}{z^2 + 2z + 1}$

32. $\dfrac{y + 2}{y - 2} - \dfrac{y^2 - 2}{2 - y}$

33. $\dfrac{2x^2}{2x - y} + \dfrac{3y^2}{2x - y} - \dfrac{x^2 + y^2}{y - 2x}$

Exercises 34–36 review material that we covered in Chapters 3 and 7. They will help you prepare for the next section. Solve.

34. $2y - 3(3y - 2) = -y - 6$

35. $x^2 - 5x + 6 = 0$

36. $2x^2 - 6x = x^2$

37. **TAX** If \$16.80 is charged as tax on the sale of a washing machine priced at \$420, what is the tax rate?

38. **MOTION** Mary hiked to a gold mine at a rate of 3 mph and returned at a rate of 5 mph. If the total time of the trip was 8 hours, how long did it take to reach the mine? What was the total distance hiked?

8.4 ENRICHMENT EXERCISES

Perform the indicated operations in Exercises 1–4.

△ 1. $\dfrac{2}{x^2 - y^2} - \dfrac{3}{x^2 + 2xy + y^2} - \dfrac{3}{x^2 - 2xy + y^2}$

2. $\dfrac{3}{x^2 - 7xy + 10y^2} + \dfrac{2}{x^2 + 2xy - 8y^2} - \dfrac{2}{x^2 - xy - 20y^2}$

3. $\dfrac{1}{x + 5y} \div \dfrac{1}{x - 5y} - \dfrac{1}{x + 5y} \cdot \dfrac{-6xy}{x - y}$

△ 4. $\dfrac{2x - y}{x^2 - y^2} \div \dfrac{2x - y}{x + y} - \dfrac{x + y}{(x - y)^2} \div \dfrac{x + y}{2y}$

In Exercises 5–6, be sure to reduce each fraction to lowest terms before finding the sum.

△ 5. $\dfrac{y - 6}{y^2 - 5y - 6} + \dfrac{2y + 1}{2y^2 - 5y - 3}$

6. $\dfrac{y + 2}{y^2 + 6y + 8} + \dfrac{3y - 1}{3y^2 + 8y - 3}$

7. Write an expression for the sum of a number and its reciprocal. Simplify the expression by adding. What numbers must be excluded from the sum?

8. If one number is five times another, write an expression for the sum of their reciprocals. Simplify the expression by adding. What numbers must be excluded from the sum?

9. Find the error in Burford's work. Explain.

$$\frac{x+1}{x-1} - \frac{x-3}{x(x+2)} = \frac{x(x+1)(x+2)}{x(x-1)(x+2)} - \frac{(x-3)(x-1)}{x(x-1)(x+2)}$$
$$= \frac{x(x+1)\cancel{(x+2)} - (x-3)\cancel{(x-1)}}{x\cancel{(x-1)}\cancel{(x+2)}}$$
$$= \frac{x(x+1) - (x-3)}{x}$$
$$= \frac{x^2 + x - x + 3}{x}$$
$$= \frac{x^2 + 3}{x}$$

10. Outline the method used to add and subtract factions.

SECTION 8.5 Fractional Equations and Problem Solving

Student guideposts

- ▶ *Fractional equations*
- ▶ *Applications of fractional equations*
- ▶ *Work problems*
- ▶ *Motion problems*

▶ *Fractional equations*

An equation that has one or more algebraic fractions or rational expressions is called a **fractional equation.** Once all the fractions have been eliminated (called **clearing the fractions**) by multiplying both sides by the LCD of the denominators in the equation, the resulting equation can often be solved by the techniques of Chapter 3 or Section 7.5. Every solution to this new equation must be checked in the original equation to be sure that it does not make one of the denominators equal to zero. If this occurs it must be discarded.

To Solve a Fractional Equation

1. Find the LCD of all fractions in the equation.
2. Multiply both sides of the equation by the LCD, making sure that *all* terms are multiplied. Once simplified, the resulting equation will be free of fractions.
3. Solve this equation.
4. Check your solutions in the original equation to be certain your answers do not make one of the denominators zero.

EXAMPLE 1 **Solving a Fractional Equation**

Solve $\frac{2}{5} + \frac{x}{15} = \frac{1}{3}$.

$$15\left(\frac{2}{5} + \frac{x}{15}\right) = 15 \cdot \frac{1}{3}$$ Multiply both sides by the LCD, 15

$$15 \cdot \frac{2}{5} + 15 \cdot \frac{x}{15} = 5$$ Clear the parentheses using the distributive law

$$6 + x = 5$$

$$6 - 6 + x = 5 - 6$$ Subtract 6 from both sides

$$x = -1$$

Check: $\frac{2}{5} + \frac{-1}{15} \stackrel{?}{=} \frac{1}{3}$

$$\frac{2 \cdot 3}{5 \cdot 3} + \frac{-1}{15} \stackrel{?}{=} \frac{1 \cdot 5}{3 \cdot 5}$$

$$\frac{6}{15} + \frac{-1}{15} \stackrel{?}{=} \frac{5}{15}$$

$$\frac{5}{15} = \frac{5}{15}$$

The solution is -1. ■

CAUTION A common mistake is to confuse addition or subtraction of fractions with solving a fractional equation. Compare the two problems:

Solve: $\frac{2}{5} + \frac{x}{15} = \frac{1}{3}$ Add: $\frac{2}{5} + \frac{x}{15} + \frac{1}{3}$

At first glance they appear quite similar. However, in the first case, we are solving an equation so the answer will be a number. In fact, in Example 1 we found the answer to be -1. In the second case, the answer will be the rational expression $\frac{x+11}{15}$ (verify this). In both cases, the LCD of the fractions must be found, but it is used in two different ways. In an equation, we multiply both sides by the LCD to clear the fractions and eventually find a numerical solution. In an addition or subtraction problem, each fraction is changed to an equivalent fraction with the LCD as the denominator, then we add or subtract to obtain an algebraic expression.

EXAMPLE 2 **Solving a Fractional Equation**

Solve:

(a) $\frac{1}{y} = \frac{1}{8 - y}$.

$$y(8 - y)\left(\frac{1}{y}\right) = y(8 - y)\left(\frac{1}{8 - y}\right)$$ Multiply both sides by the LCD, $y(8 - y)$

$$8 - y = y$$

$$8 = 2y$$ Add y to both sides

$$4 = y$$

Check: $\frac{1}{4} \stackrel{?}{=} \frac{1}{8-4}$

$$\frac{1}{4} = \frac{1}{4}$$

The solution is 4.

(b) $\frac{3x}{x-3} - 3 = \frac{1}{x}$.

$$x(x-3)\left[\frac{3x}{x-3} - 3\right] = x(x-3)\left[\frac{1}{x}\right] \qquad \text{The LCD} = x(x-3)$$

$$x(3x) - 3x(x-3) = x - 3 \qquad \text{Be sure to multiply 3 by LCD}$$

$$3x^2 - 3x^2 + 9x = x - 3$$

$$8x = -3$$

$$x = -\frac{3}{8}$$

Substituting $-\frac{3}{8}$ into the original equation to check would require much calculation. Instead, we might note that the only two numbers that make a denominator zero are 0 and 3, neither of which is our answer, $-\frac{3}{8}$. After checking our work for mistakes, we conclude that the solution is $-\frac{3}{8}$. ■

EXAMPLE 3 **Working with an Equation Having No Solution**

Solve $\frac{x}{x+4} - \frac{4}{x-4} = \frac{x^2+16}{x^2-16}$.

The LCD $= (x-4)(x+4)$.

$$(x-4)(x+4)\left(\frac{x}{x+4} - \frac{4}{x-4}\right) = (x-4)(x+4)\left(\frac{x^2+16}{x^2-16}\right)$$

$$x(x-4) - 4(x+4) = x^2 + 16$$

$$x^2 - 4x - 4x - 16 = x^2 + 16$$

$$-8x - 16 = 16$$

$$-8x = 32$$

$$x = -4$$

Check: $\frac{-4}{-4+4} - \frac{4}{-4-4} \stackrel{?}{=} \frac{(-4)^2+16}{(-4)^2-16}$.

But $\frac{-4}{-4+4} = \frac{-4}{0}$, which is undefined. Thus, -4 *does not check*. There are no solutions. ■

> CAUTION Be sure to check your answers in the *original* equation. Example 4 shows that sometimes a possible solution may have to be excluded because it makes one or more denominators equal to zero.

In some fractional equations, when the fractions are cleared the resulting equation must be solved by the factoring method that we studied in Chapter 7.

EXAMPLE 4

Using the Zero-Product Rule

Solve $\dfrac{2}{x+2} + \dfrac{3}{x-2} = 1.$

$$(x+2)(x-2)\left[\frac{2}{x+2} + \frac{3}{x-2}\right] = (x+2)(x-2)(1) \qquad \text{LCD} = (x+2)(x-2)$$

$$2(x-2) + 3(x+2) = x^2 - 4$$

$$2x - 4 + 3x + 6 = x^2 - 4$$

$$5x + 2 = x^2 - 4$$

$$-x^2 + 5x + 6 = 0 \qquad \text{We obtain a quadratic equation}$$

$$x^2 - 5x - 6 = 0 \qquad \text{Multiply by } -1$$

$$(x-6)(x+1) = 0 \qquad \text{Factor}$$

$$x - 6 = 0 \quad \text{or} \quad x + 1 = 0 \qquad \text{Zero-product Rule}$$

$$x = 6 \qquad\qquad x = -1$$

Check:

$$\frac{2}{6+2} + \frac{3}{6-2} \stackrel{?}{=} 1 \qquad \frac{2}{-1+2} + \frac{3}{-1-2} \stackrel{?}{=} 1$$

$$\frac{2}{8} + \frac{3}{4} \stackrel{?}{=} 1 \qquad \frac{2}{1} + \frac{3}{-3} \stackrel{?}{=} 1$$

$$\frac{1}{4} + \frac{3}{4} = 1 \qquad 2 - 1 = 1$$

The solutions are 6 and -1. ■

▶ *Applications of fractional equations*

In Chapter 3 we looked at applied problems that resulted in simple linear equations. We now consider similar problems that result in fractional equations. We begin with a simple number problem and use it to review the ATTACK method of problem solving.

EXAMPLE 5

Solving a Number Problem

The reciprocal of 2 more than a number is three times the reciprocal of the number. Find the number.

Analysis: We are looking for a particular number with properties described in the problem.

Tabulation: Let n = the desired number.

$n + 2$ = 2 more than the number.

$\frac{1}{n+2}$ = the reciprocal of 2 more than the number.

$\frac{1}{n}$ = the reciprocal of the number.

Since $3 \cdot \frac{1}{n} = \frac{3}{1} \cdot \frac{1}{n} = \frac{3}{n}$, we have that

$\frac{3}{n}$ = three times the reciprocal of the number.

Translation: The equation to solve is:

$$\frac{1}{n+2} = \frac{3}{n}$$

Multiply both sides by the LCD, $n(n + 2)$.

$$\begin{aligned} n(n+2)\left(\frac{1}{n+2}\right) &= n(n+2)\left(\frac{3}{n}\right) \\ n &= (n+2)(3) \\ n &= 3n + 6 \\ -2n &= 6 \\ n &= -3 \end{aligned}$$

Approximation: In problems such as this, the approximation step is really not of much help. We did obtain a value for n, so we should go on and check to see if n satisfies the words of the problem.

Check: 2 more than -3 is $2 + (-3) = -1$, and the reciprocal of this is $\frac{1}{-1} = -1$. The reciprocal of -3 is $\frac{1}{-3} = -\frac{1}{3}$, and three times this reciprocal is $3\left(-\frac{1}{3}\right) = -1$. So -3 does satisfy the words of the problem.

Thus, the desired number is -3. ■

EXAMPLE 6

Solving a Geometry Problem

The width of the top of a rectangular table is 20 inches less than the length, and the length divided by the width is $\frac{12}{7}$. Find the dimensions of the table top.

Analysis: We are really asked to find the length and width of a rectangle. Make a sketch as shown in Figure 8.1.

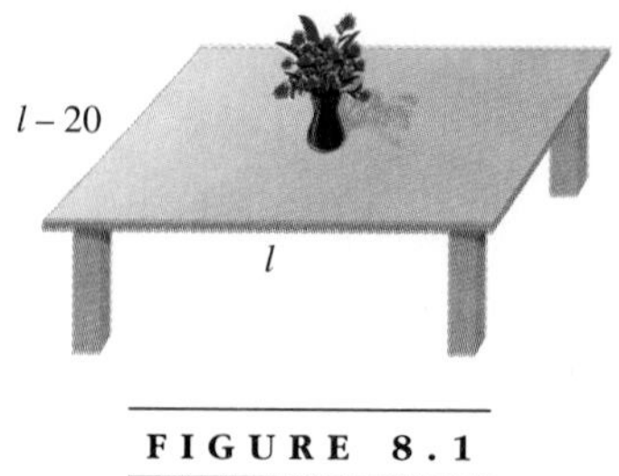

FIGURE 8.1

Tabulation: Let $l =$ the length of the table top.

Since the width is 20 inches less than the length, we have

$l - 20 =$ the width of the table top.

Translation: Since the length divided by the width is $\frac{12}{7}$, we must solve:

$$\frac{l}{l - 20} = \frac{12}{7}$$

$$7(l - 20)\left(\frac{l}{l - 20}\right) = 7(l - 20)\left(\frac{12}{7}\right)$$

$$7l = (l - 20)(12)$$

$$7l = 12l - 240$$

$$-5l = -240$$

$$l = 48$$

$$l - 20 = 48 - 20 = 28$$

Approximation: Since 48 in and 28 in are reasonable values for the length and width of a table, we can assume that we have made no major mistakes.

Check: Since 48 divided by 28 is $\frac{48}{28} = \frac{4 \cdot 12}{4 \cdot 7} = \frac{12}{7}$, our answers check.
Thus, the table top is 48 inches long by 28 inches wide. ■

> NOTE As we move on to other applications, we will begin to present the solution more in the form you should use without specifically mentioning all the steps in the method. However, be sure to write complete descriptions of the variable.

▶ *Work problems* Consider the following problem: Bob can do a job in 2 hours and Pete can do the same job in 4 hours. How long would it take them to do the job if they worked together?

To solve this type of problem, usually called a *work problem,* three principles must be kept in mind:

1. The time it takes to do a job when the individuals work together must be less than the time it takes for the faster worker to complete the job alone.

Thus, the time together is *not* the average of the two times (which would be 3 hours in this case). Since Bob can do the job alone in 2 hr, with help the time must clearly be less than 2 hr.

2. If a job can be done in t hr, in 1 hour $\frac{1}{t}$ of the job would be completed. For example, since Bob can do the job in 2 hours, in 1 hour he would do $\frac{1}{2}$ the job. Similarly, Pete would do $\frac{1}{4}$ the job in 1 hr since he does it all in 4 hr.
3. The amount of work done by Bob in 1 hr added to the amount of work done by Pete in 1 hr equals the amount of work done together in 1 hr. So if t is the time it takes to do the job working together,

(amount Bob does in 1 hr) + (amount Pete does in 1 hr)
= (amount done together in 1 hr)

translates to the equation

$$\frac{1}{2} + \frac{1}{4} = \frac{1}{t}.$$

We see that a work problem translates to a fractional equation that may result in either a first-degree equation or a second-degree (quadratic) equation. In our example, we obtain a first-degree equation after we multiply both sides by the LCD, $4t$. We will work only with first-degree equations in this section.

$$\begin{aligned} 4t\left(\frac{1}{2} + \frac{1}{4}\right) &= 4t\left(\frac{1}{t}\right) \\ 4t \cdot \frac{1}{2} + 4t \cdot \frac{1}{4} &= 4 \\ 2t + t &= 4 \\ 3t &= 4 \\ t &= \frac{4}{3} \end{aligned}$$

Thus, it would take $\frac{4}{3}$ hr (1 hr 20 min) for Bob and Pete to do the job working together. This is reasonable since Bob can do the whole job in 2 hr; so with help from Pete, the time should be a little less than 2 hr.

The next example is a variation of a work problem. It asks for the time it takes for one working unit to do a job when the time for the other and the time together are given.

EXAMPLE 7

Solving An Engineering Work Problem

When the valves on a 6-inch pipe and a 2-inch pipe are opened together, it takes 5 hr to fill an oil storage tank. If the 6-inch pipe can fill the tank in 7 hr, how long would it take the 2-inch pipe to fill the tank by itself?

$$5 = \text{number of hr to fill the tank together,}$$

$$\frac{1}{5} = \text{portion filled together in 1 hr,}$$

$$7 = \text{number of hr for 6-inch pipe to fill the tank,}$$

$$\frac{1}{7} = \text{portion filled by the 6-inch pipe in 1 hr.}$$

$$\text{Let } t = \text{number of hr for 2-inch pipe to fill the tank,}$$

$$\frac{1}{t} = \text{portion filled by the 2-inch pipe in 1 hr.}$$

We have the following equation.

$$\text{(portion by 6-inch pipe)} + \text{(portion by 2-inch pipe)} = \text{(portion together)}$$

$$\frac{1}{7} + \frac{1}{t} = \frac{1}{5}$$

$$\mathbf{35t}\left(\frac{1}{7} + \frac{1}{t}\right) = \mathbf{35t}\left(\frac{1}{5}\right) \qquad \text{The LCD is } 35t$$

$$35t\left(\frac{1}{7}\right) + 35t\left(\frac{1}{t}\right) = 35t \cdot \frac{1}{5}$$

$$5t + 35 = 7t$$

$$35 = 2t$$

$$\frac{35}{2} = t$$

The 2-inch pipe would take $\frac{35}{2}$ hours or $17\frac{1}{2}$ hours to fill the tank alone. (Does this make sense in view of principle (1) of work problems?) Notice that the 6 inches and 2 inches only describe the size of the pipes and do not enter into the calculations. ■

▶ *Motion problems*

Recall that most motion problems use the formula $d = rt$, where d is the distance traveled at a uniform rate r over a period of time t. When two alternative forms of this equation, solved for r and t,

$$r = \frac{d}{t} \quad \text{and} \quad t = \frac{d}{r},$$

are used in an applied problem, we often obtain a fractional equation. Most motion problems involve two distances, two rates, and two times. It is helpful if we precisely describe each of these six quantities. We illustrate this in the next example, which solves the applied problem in the chapter introduction.

EXAMPLE 8

Solving a Recreation Application

Because he had better road conditions Sam was able to drive 260 miles in the same time that it took Carolyn to drive 220 miles for a long weekend at a Colorado ski area. If Sam's average rate of speed was 10 mph faster than Carolyn's, what was Carolyn's average speed?

Let r = Carolyn's average speed.

Since Sam's speed was 10 mph faster than Carolyn's, we have

$r + 10$ = Sam's average speed.

We also have

220 = distance Carolyn traveled,

260 = distance Sam traveled.

Using the formula $t = \frac{d}{r}$ we can find expressions for the time each traveled.

$\frac{220}{r}$ = time Carolyn traveled,

$\frac{260}{r + 10}$ = time Sam traveled.

Sometimes it is convenient to organize this information in a table rather than making the six individual statements.

	Distance (miles)	*Rate*	*Time*
Carolyn	220	r	$\frac{220}{r}$
Sam	260	$r + 10$	$\frac{260}{r + 10}$

Since we are told that the two times are the same, we identify the equation to solve:

$$\frac{220}{r} = \frac{260}{r + 10}$$

Multiply both sides by the LCD, $r(r + 10)$.

$$r(r + 10)\left(\frac{220}{r}\right) = r(r + 10)\left(\frac{260}{r + 10}\right)$$

$$(r + 10)(220) = r(260)$$

$$220r + 2200 = 260r$$

$$2200 = 40r$$

$$55 = r$$

Thus, Carolyn averaged 55 mph. Is this reasonable? Check by finding Sam's rate. ■

8.5 EXERCISES

Solve each fractional equation in Exercises 1–12.

1. $\dfrac{3x+5}{6} = \dfrac{4+3x}{5}$

2. $\dfrac{1}{x} - \dfrac{2}{x} = 6$

3. $\dfrac{1}{z-3} + \dfrac{3}{z-5} = 0$

4. $\dfrac{2y+1}{3y-2} = \dfrac{2y-3}{3y+1}$

5. $\dfrac{2x}{x+2} - 2 = \dfrac{1}{x}$

6. $\dfrac{4}{z-3} + \dfrac{2z}{z^2-9} = \dfrac{1}{z+3}$

7. $\dfrac{3}{x+3} + \dfrac{1}{x-3} = \dfrac{10}{x^2-9}$

8. $\dfrac{y}{y+3} - \dfrac{3}{y-3} = \dfrac{y^2+9}{y^2-9}$

9. $\dfrac{y}{y-4} - 1 = \dfrac{8}{y^2-16}$

10. $\dfrac{3}{x-3} + \dfrac{2}{x+3} = -1$

11. $\dfrac{4}{y-4} + \dfrac{6}{y+4} = -1$

12. $\dfrac{2z}{z-2} - 1 = \dfrac{1}{z^2-4}$

Solve each problem in Exercises 13–28.

13. **NUMBER** Find the number which when added to both the numerator and denominator of $\frac{5}{7}$ will produce a fraction equivalent to $\frac{4}{5}$.

14. **NUMBER** The reciprocal of 3 less than a number is four times the reciprocal of the number. Find the number.

15. **NUMBER** The numerator of a fraction is 4 less than its denominator. If both the numerator and denominator are increased by 1, the value of the fraction is $\frac{2}{3}$. Find the fraction.

16. **AGE** Mary's age is 4 years more than Ruth's age, and the quotient of their ages is $\frac{7}{5}$. How old is each?

17. **NUMBER** The denominator of a fraction exceeds the numerator by 6, and the value of the fraction is $\frac{5}{6}$. Find the fraction.

18. **NUMBER** The reciprocal of 4 less than a number is three times the reciprocal of the number. Find the number.

19. **WORK** If Jerry can mow a lawn in 7 hours and Hilda can mow the same lawn in 3 hours, how long would it take them to mow it if they worked together?

20. **WORK** Bob can paint a house alone in 12 days. When he and his father work together it takes only 9 days. How long would it take his father to paint the house if he worked alone?

21. **WORK** A 6-inch pipe can fill a reservoir in 3 weeks. When this pipe and a second pipe are both turned on, it takes only 2 weeks to fill the reservoir. How long would it take the second pipe to fill it by itself?

22. **WORK** If Irv takes 4 times longer to repair a car than Max, and together they can repair it in 8 hours, how long does it take each working alone?

23. **WORK** If a 1-inch pipe takes 40 minutes to drain a pond and a 2-inch pipe takes 10 minutes to drain the same pond, how long would it take them to drain it together?

24. **CONSTRUCTION** If Art can frame a shed in 4 days, and together Art and Clyde can frame the same shed in 3 days, how long would it take Clyde to frame it working by himself?

25. **MANUFACTURING** An older machine requires twice as much time to do a job as a modern one. Together they accomplish the job in 8 minutes. How long would it take each to do the job alone?

26. **MANUFACTURING** Susan can make 100 widgets in 3 hours. It takes Harry 5 hours to produce 100 widgets. How long would it take them to produce 100 widgets if they worked together?

27. **MOTION** Jess hiked 24 mi in the same time that Ernie hiked 30 mi. If Jess's average rate was 1 mph slower than Ernie's rate, how fast was each hiking?

28. **NAVIGATION** A stream has a current of 3 mph. If a boat can travel 50 miles downstream in the same time it takes to travel 38 miles upstream, what is the speed of the boat in still water? [*Hint:* If r is the speed of the boat, the speed with the current is $r + 3$, and the speed against the current is $r - 3$.]

FOR REVIEW

Perform the indicated operations in Exercises 29–31.

29. $\dfrac{5}{y^2 - 25} + \dfrac{5}{y^2 - 3y - 10}$

30. $\dfrac{3}{x^2 - x - 2} - \dfrac{2}{x^2 + 6x + 5}$

31. $\dfrac{x + y}{x - y} - \dfrac{x - y}{x + y}$

8.5 PARALLEL EXERCISES

Solve each fractional equation in Exercises 1–12.

1. $\dfrac{5x - 2}{3} = \dfrac{2 + 7x}{4}$

2. $\dfrac{3}{x} - \dfrac{4}{x} = 3$

3. $\dfrac{2}{3x - 1} - \dfrac{1}{4x - 5} = 0$

4. $\dfrac{2y - 3}{4y - 1} = \dfrac{y - 6}{2y - 1}$

5. $\dfrac{x + 1}{x} = 1 + \dfrac{1}{x + 1}$

6. $\dfrac{5}{z + 2} + \dfrac{3z}{z^2 - 4} = \dfrac{2}{z - 2}$

7. $\dfrac{-2}{x + 5} + \dfrac{1}{x - 5} = \dfrac{4}{x^2 - 25}$

8. $\dfrac{y}{y + 5} - \dfrac{5}{y - 5} = \dfrac{y^2 + 25}{y^2 - 25}$

9. $\dfrac{y}{y + 6} - 1 = \dfrac{6}{y^2 - 36}$

10. $\dfrac{6}{x + 5} + \dfrac{1}{x - 5} = 1$

11. $\dfrac{1}{y - 6} - \dfrac{6}{y + 6} = -1$

12. $\dfrac{3z}{z - 3} - 2 = \dfrac{10}{z^2 - 9}$

Solve each problem in Exercises 13–28.

13. **NUMBER** Find the number which when added to both the numerator and denominator of $\frac{3}{11}$ will produce a fraction equivalent to $\frac{1}{2}$.

14. **NUMBER** The reciprocal of 6 less than a number is four times the reciprocal of the number. Find the number.

15. **NUMBER** The numerator of a fraction is 5 less than the denominator. If both the numerator and the denominator are decreased by 2, the value of the fraction is $\frac{1}{6}$. Find the fraction.

16. **AGE** Cindy is 4 years younger than Becky and the quotient of their ages is $\frac{7}{9}$. How old is each?

17. **NUMBER** The numerator of a fraction exceeds the denominator by 10, and the value of the fraction is $\frac{7}{5}$. Find the fraction.

18. **NUMBER** The reciprocal of 6 more than a number is four times the reciprocal of the number. Find the number.

19. **WORK** Alfonse can paint a garage in 20 hours and Heidi can do the same job in 10 hours. How long would it take them if they worked together?

20. **WORK** Walter can dig a well in 8 days. When he and Sean work together they can dig the same size well in 6 days. How long would it take Sean to do the job working alone?

21. **WORK** If Andy takes 3 times as long to put new brakes on a car as Hortense does, and together they can do the job in 4 hours, how long does it take each working alone?

22. **WORK** There are two drains to a water tank. If one is used, the tank is drained in 24 minutes. The other requires 32 minutes. How long will it take if both are opened?

23. **BUSINESS** If Nancy can process an order of 1000 appliances in 20 minutes and together she and Hans can process the order in 12 minutes, how long will it take Hans to process the order by himself?

24. MANUFACTURING Using old equipment it requires 5 times as long to make 100 sportcoats as with new equipment. If together the equipment can accomplish the job in $7\frac{1}{2}$ hours, how long would it take each working alone?

25. MANUFACTURING Charles can make 200 dolls in 3 weeks and Wilma can make 200 dolls in $2\frac{1}{2}$ weeks. How long will it take to make 200 dolls if they work together?

26. WORK Bertha can clean the stable in 4 hours. If Bertha and Jose work together they can do the same job in 1 hour. How long would Jose take to do the job working alone?

27. MOTION It took Sue the same time to drive 225 miles as it took Ben to drive 250 miles. If Sue's average speed was 5 mph slower than Ben's, how fast was Ben driving?

28. AERONAUTICS An airplane can fly 1320 miles with a tailwind in the same time it can fly 1080 miles with a headwind. If the speed of the wind is 20 mph, what is the speed of the airplane in still air? [*Hint:* If r is the speed of the airplane, then $r + 20$ is the speed with the wind, and $r - 20$ is the speed against the wind.]

FOR REVIEW

Perform the indicated operations in Exercises 29–31.

29. $\dfrac{3}{y^2 - 6y + 8} + \dfrac{7}{y^2 - 16}$

30. $\dfrac{5}{x^2 + x - 12} - \dfrac{3}{x^2 + 10x + 24}$

31. $\dfrac{x - y}{x + y} - \dfrac{x + y}{x - y}$

8.5 ENRICHMENT EXERCISES

Solve each equation or applied problem in Exercises 1–5.

1. $\dfrac{3}{x^2 - 6x + 5} - \dfrac{2}{x^2 - 25} = \dfrac{4}{x^2 + 4x - 5}$

△ **2.** $\dfrac{2x}{x^2 - 3x - 4} - \dfrac{x - 1}{x^2 + 2x + 1} = \dfrac{x + 4}{x^2 + 5x + 4}$

3. RECREATION A man walks a distance of 12 mi at a rate 8 mph slower than the rate he rides a bicycle for a distance of 24 mi. If the total time of the trip is 5 hr, how fast does he walk? How fast does he ride?

△ **4. WORK** A swimming pool can be filled by an inlet pipe in 6 hr. It can be drained by an outlet in 9 hr. If the inlet and outlet are both opened, how long will it take to fill the empty pool?

5. MOTION Bill Ewing drove 1320 miles to Mount Rushmore for a vacation. On the return trip his speed averaged 5 mph slower. If the total time that he spent driving was 46 hours, what was his average rate going and returning?

In Exercises 6–9, solve each equation or perform the indicated operations.

6. $\frac{x}{3} - \frac{1}{x} = -\frac{11}{6}$

7. $\frac{x}{3} - \frac{1}{x} - \frac{11}{6}$

8. $\frac{1}{x} + \frac{1}{6} = \frac{1}{x-1}$

9. $\frac{1}{x} + \frac{1}{6} - \frac{1}{x-1}$

Solve each literal equation for the indicated variable in Exercises 10–12.

10. $\frac{y-2}{x+1} = \frac{2}{3}$ for y

11. $\frac{b+1}{a} = \frac{1}{2}$ for b

12. $\frac{1}{a} + \frac{1}{3} = c$ for a

13. Explain how the LCD is used to solve a fractional equation.

SECTION 8.6 Ratio, Proportion, and Variation

Student guideposts

- ▶ *Ratios*
- ▶ *Proportions*
- ▶ *Means-extremes property*
- ▶ *Applying proportions*
- ▶ *Direct variation*
- ▶ *Inverse variation*

▶ *Ratios*

The **ratio** of one number x to another number y is the quotient

$$x \div y \quad \text{or} \quad \frac{x}{y}.$$

We sometimes express the ratio $\frac{x}{y}$ with the notation $x:y$, which is read "the ratio of x to y." Ratios occur in applications such as percent, rate of speed, gas mileage, unit cost, and number comparisons. Consider the following examples.

Applications	*Ratio*
5% sales tax	$\frac{\$5}{\$100} = \$5$ per $100
200 miles in 4 hours	$\frac{200 \text{ mi}}{4 \text{ hr}} = 50\frac{\text{mi}}{\text{hr}} = 50$ mi per hr
200 miles on 10 gallons of gas	$\frac{200 \text{ mi}}{10 \text{ gal}} = 20\frac{\text{mi}}{\text{gal}} = 20$ mi per gal
$12 for 2 kg of meat	$\frac{\$12}{2 \text{ kg}} = \$6$ per kg
30 children and 6 adults	$\frac{30 \text{ children}}{6 \text{ adults}} = 5$ children per adult

Proportions Ratios are used to define *proportions* which can describe many practical problems.

Proportions

An equation which states that two ratios are equal is called a **proportion.** That is, if $\frac{a}{b}$ and $\frac{c}{d}$ are two ratios, the equation

$$\frac{a}{b} = \frac{c}{d}$$

is a proportion. It can be read "a is to b as c is to d."

Means-extremes property Consider the following proportion.

$$\frac{2}{3} = \frac{4}{6}$$

The numbers 2 and 6 are the **extremes** of the proportion, and the numbers 3 and 4 are the **means.**

2 is to 3 as 4 is to 6

Means (3 and 4)

Extremes (2 and 6)

In the proportion

$$\frac{a}{b} = \frac{c}{d},$$

the extremes are a and d and the means are b and c. If we multiply both sides by the LCD of the two fractions, bd, we obtain

$$bd\frac{a}{b} = \frac{c}{d}bd$$

$$\text{or} \quad ad = bc.$$

We have just verified the following property of proportions.

Means-Extremes Property of Proportions

In any proportion, the product of the extremes is equal to the product of the means. That is, if

$$\frac{a}{b} = \frac{c}{d} \quad \text{then} \quad ad = bc.$$

This property of proportions allows us to solve for an unknown term. We call this **solving the proportion.** For example, suppose we solve the proportion

$$\frac{15}{25} = \frac{x}{5}.$$

$$15 \cdot 5 = 25 \cdot x \qquad \text{The product of the extremes equals the product of the means}$$

$$75 = 25x \qquad \text{Simplify}$$

$$\frac{75}{25} = x \qquad \text{Divide both sides by 25}$$

$$3 = x \qquad \text{Reduce the fraction}$$

▶ *Applying proportions*

We now show how proportions can be used to solve applied problems. Consider the following: If it takes 3 hours to travel 150 miles, how many hours would it take to travel 250 miles? The simple proportion

$$\begin{matrix} \text{First time} \rightarrow \\ \text{First distance} \rightarrow \end{matrix} \frac{3}{150} = \frac{x}{250} \begin{matrix} \leftarrow \text{Second time} \\ \leftarrow \text{Second distance} \end{matrix}$$

where x is the number of hours it takes to travel 250 miles, completely describes this problem. That is, the ratio of the first time to the first distance must equal the ratio of the second time to the second distance. Setting the product of the extremes equal to the product of the means, we have

$$\begin{pmatrix}\text{First}\\\text{time}\end{pmatrix} \cdot \begin{pmatrix}\text{Second}\\\text{distance}\end{pmatrix} = \begin{pmatrix}\text{First}\\\text{distance}\end{pmatrix} \cdot \begin{pmatrix}\text{Second}\\\text{time}\end{pmatrix}$$

$$3 \cdot 250 = 150 \cdot x$$

or

$$5 = x.$$

It would take 5 hours to go 250 miles.

EXAMPLE 1

Solving a Proportion Application

If a secretary spends 37 minutes typing 3 pages of a report, how long will it take her to type the remaining 10 pages?

Let x be the number of minutes it takes to complete the typing. We set up the following proportion.

$$\begin{matrix} \text{Minutes to} \\ \text{type 3 pages} \rightarrow \end{matrix} \frac{3}{37} = \frac{10}{x}. \begin{matrix} \text{Minutes to} \\ \leftarrow \text{type 10 pages} \end{matrix}$$

$$3x = 370 \qquad \text{Product of the extremes equals product of the means}$$

$$x = 123\frac{1}{3}.$$

It will take another $123\frac{1}{3}$ minutes. ■

Another application of proportions can be found in geometry. Two triangles are **similar** if they have the same shape but not necessarily the same size. More formally, two triangles are similar if the angles of one are equal, respectively, to the angles of the other. An important property of similar triangles is that their corresponding sides (sides opposite equal angles) are proportional. In Figure 8.2, the two triangles are similar and have corresponding sides a and a', b and b', and c and c'. The fact that these corresponding sides are proportional can be stated using the equations

$$\frac{a}{a'} = \frac{b}{b'} = \frac{c}{c'}.$$

Notice that this does represent three different equations, $\frac{a}{a'} = \frac{b}{b'}$, $\frac{a}{a'} = \frac{c}{c'}$, and $\frac{b}{b'} = \frac{c}{c'}$. For more about similar triangles see Appendix A.

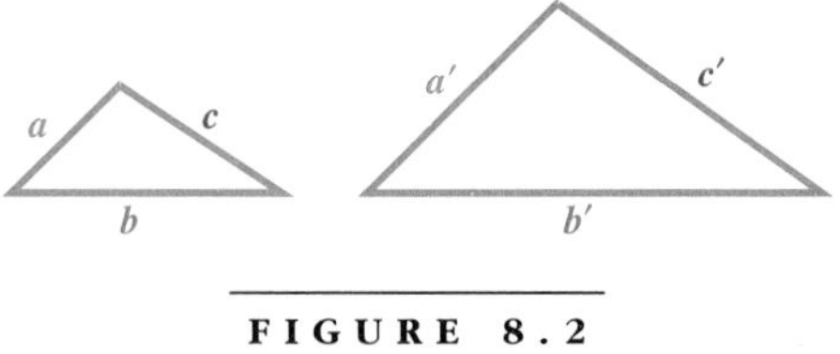

FIGURE 8.2

EXAMPLE 2

Solving a Similar Triangle Application

If the sides of a triangle are of lengths 10 ft, 15 ft, and 21 ft, what is the length of the shortest side of a similar triangle whose longest side is 63 ft?

Let x = the length of the shortest side of a similar triangle. Make a sketch of the triangles as shown in Figure 8.3.

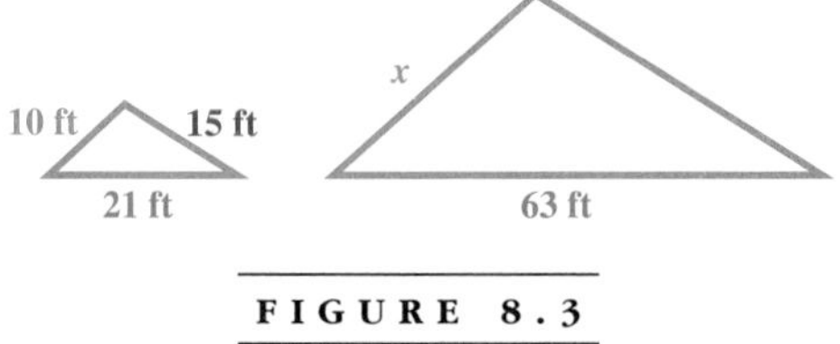

FIGURE 8.3

The proportion

$$\frac{\text{shortest side of first triangle}}{\text{shortest side of second triangle}} = \frac{\text{longest side of first triangle}}{\text{longest side of second triangle}}$$

can be used to solve this problem. Substituting we have:

$$\frac{10}{x} = \frac{21}{63}$$

$$(10)(63) = 21x \quad \text{Means-extremes property}$$

$$\frac{(10)(63)}{21} = x$$

$$(10)(3) = x$$

$$30 = x$$

Thus, the length of the shortest side is 30 ft. ■

▶ *Direct variation*

Another way of looking at proportion problems is in terms of **variation.** For example, the distance that a car travels varies (or changes) as we vary or change the speed. Also, the total cost of a roast will vary as the price per pound varies. The equation in each of these examples can be written as a ratio equal to a constant. This type of variation is called **direct variation.**

Direct Variation

If two variables have a constant ratio k,

$$\frac{y}{x} = k \quad \text{or} \quad y = kx,$$

we say that y **varies directly** as x and call k the **constant of variation.**

One common example of this is the fact that the ratio of the circumference to the diameter of any circle is π.

$$\frac{c}{d} = \pi \quad \text{or} \quad c = \pi d \qquad k = \pi$$

In a variation problem if we know the value of y for one value of x, we can find k. With k known we can find y for any x.

EXAMPLE 3

Using Direct Variation

Find the equation of variation if y varies directly as x and we know that $y = 30$ when $x = 6$. Also, find y when $x = 10$.

First, write an equation stating that *y varies directly as x*. Then substitute $y = 30$ and $x = 6$ to find k.

$$\begin{aligned} y &= kx && y \text{ varies directly as } x \\ 30 &= k \cdot 6 && y = 30 \text{ and } x = 6 \\ \frac{30}{6} &= k && k \text{ is a ratio} \\ 5 &= k \end{aligned}$$

The equation of variation is

$$y = 5x.$$

To find y when $x = 10$, substitute 10 for x in the equation of variation.

$$\begin{aligned} y &= 5x && \text{Equation of variation} \\ y &= 5(10) && \text{Substitute 10 for } x \\ y &= 50 \end{aligned}$$

Thus y is 50 when x is 10. ■

EXAMPLE 4 **Applying Direct Variation**

The cost c of steak varies directly as the weight w of the steak purchased. If 8 kg of steak cost \$36, how much will 30 kg of steak cost?

First write the equation for c varies directly as w. Then substitute $c = \$36$ and $w = 8$ kg to find k.

$$c = kw \qquad c \text{ varies directly as } w$$
$$36 = k \cdot 8 \qquad c = \$36 \text{ and } w = 8 \text{ kg}$$
$$4.5 = k \qquad \frac{36}{8} = 4.5$$

The equation of variation that we can use for any weight of meat is

$$c = 4.5\,w.$$

To find the cost of 30 kg of steak substitute 30 for w.

$$c = 4.5w$$
$$c = 4.5(30)$$
$$= 135$$

Thus 30 kg (about 66 lb) of steak would cost \$135. ■

▶ *Inverse variation* In many applications the product of the variables is a constant. This is called **inverse variation.**

Inverse Variation

If two variables have a constant product k,

$$xy = k \quad \text{or} \quad y = \frac{k}{x}$$

where k is the **constant of variation,** we say that y **varies inversely as** x.

EXAMPLE 5 **Applying Inverse Variation**

The time t it takes to drive a fixed distance d varies inversely as the rate r (or speed) of the car. If it takes 3 hours when the speed is 40 mph, how long will it take when the speed is 50 mph?

The equation of variation in this case is

$$t = \frac{d}{r}.$$

Since the distance is fixed, d is the constant of variation. We are given that $t = 3$ hr when $r = 40$ mph.

$$t = \frac{d}{r}$$

$$3 = \frac{d}{40}$$

$$120 = d$$

Thus $$t = \frac{120}{r} \quad \text{Equation of variation}$$

$$t = \frac{120}{50} \quad r = 50 \text{ mph}$$

$$t = 2.4.$$

It will take 2.4 hours to go the distance at 50 mph. ∎

8.6 EXERCISES

In Exercises 1–3, write as a ratio and simplify.

1. \$10 for 4 lb of meat
2. 420 mi on 12 gal of gas
3. 200 trees on 4 acres

Solve each proportion in Exercises 4–6.

4. $\frac{x}{2} = \frac{9}{27}$
5. $\frac{y+8}{y-2} = \frac{7}{3}$
6. $\frac{z+5}{z-2} = \frac{z-7}{z-3}$

Use a proportion to solve each problem in Exercises 7–20.

7. **POLITICS** In an election the winning candidate won by a 5 to 3 margin. If she received 1025 votes, how many votes did the losing candidate receive?
8. **GAS MILEAGE** If a boat uses 7 gal of gas to go 51 mi, how many gallons would be needed to go 255 mi?
9. **ELECTRICITY** If 50 feet of electrical wire weigh 15 lb, what will 80 feet of the same wire weigh?
10. **MAP READING** If $\frac{3}{4}$ inch on a map represents 10 mi, how many miles will be represented by 9 in?

11. **BUSINESS** A sample of 184 tires contained 6 that were defective. How many defective tires would you expect in a sample of 1288?
12. **CONSTRUCTION** If 2 bricks weigh 9 pounds, how much will 558 bricks weigh?
13. **POLITICS** In an election, the successful candidate won by a 3 to 2 margin. If he received 324 votes, how many did the losing candidate receive?
14. **GAS MILEAGE** If a car uses 8 gallons of gas for a trip of 132 miles, how much gas will be used for a trip of 550 miles?
15. **GEOMETRY** Two triangles are similar. If the sides of one measure 6 cm, 10 cm, and 14 cm, and the longest side of the second measures 63 cm, find the lengths of the remaining sides.
16. **GEOMETRY** Two isosceles triangles are similar with the equal sides of one measuring 15 in and the base measuring 5 in. If the equal sides of the second triangle are 18 in long, how long is the base?
17. **MAP READING** On a map 2 cm represent 14 km. How many centimeters are used to represent 35 km?

18. **BUSINESS** In a sample of 212 light bulbs, 3 were defective. How many defective bulbs would you expect in a shipment of 3240?

19. **COMMISSION** Pat was charged a commission of \$65.00 on the purchase of 400 shares of stock. What commission would be charged on 700 shares of the same stock?

20. **GAME MANAGEMENT** To determine the approximate number of fish in a lake, the State Game and Fish Department caught 100 fish, tagged their fins, and returned them to the water. After a period of time they caught 70 fish and discovered that 14 were tagged. Approximately how many fish are in the lake?

Use direct variation to solve each problem in Exercises 21–28.

21. If y varies directly as x, and $y = 10$ when $x = 15$, find y when $x = 42$.

22. If u varies directly as w, and $u = 24$ when $w = 6$, find w when $u = 80$.

23. If y varies directly as x, and $y = 12$ when $x = 9$, find y when $x = 6$.

24. **CONSUMER** The cost c of peaches varies directly as the total weight w of the peaches. If 12 pounds of peaches cost \$4.80, what would 66 pounds cost?

25. **BUSINESS** The number d of defective tires in a shipment varies directly as the number n of tires in the shipment. If there were 10 defective tires in a shipment of 2200, how many defective tires would you expect in a shipment of 8800 tires?

26. **GAS MILEAGE** The number g of gallons of gas needed varies directly as the number n of miles traveled. If 25 gallons are needed to travel 650 miles, how many gallons will be needed to travel 3900 miles?

27. **SALARY** The size of Maria's paycheck varies directly as the number of hours she works. If she is paid \$334.00 for working 40 hours each week, how much would she be paid for working 2080 hours (1 year)?

28. **CONSUMER** The amount of money a man spends on recreation varies directly as his total income. If he spends \$1920 on recreation when earning \$16,000, how much would he spend if his income is increased by \$5,000?

Use inverse variation to solve each problem in Exercises 29–34.

29. If y varies inversely as x, and $y = 12$ when $x = 9$, find y when $x = 6$.

30. If p varies inversely as q, and $p = 520$ when $q = 80$, find q when $p = 208$.

31. **RATE-MOTION** The time t needed to travel a fixed distance varies inversely as the rate r of travel. If 6 hr are needed when the rate is 500 mph, how long would it take at 1200 mph?

32. **RATE-MOTION** The rate r of travel for a fixed distance varies inversely as the time t. If the rate is 120 km per hour when the time is 4 hr, find the rate when the time is 6 hr.

33. **PHYSICS** The volume V of a given amount of gas varies inversely as the pressure P. If the volume is 24 in^3 when the pressure is 8 lb/in^2, what is the volume when the pressure is 6 lb/in^2?

34. **ELECTRICITY** The current I in an electrical circuit with constant voltage varies inversely as the resistance R of the circuit. If the current is 3 amps when the resistance is 4 ohms, find I when $R = 6$ ohms.

FOR REVIEW

Solve each equation or applied problem in Exercises 35–39.

35. $\dfrac{3x}{x-3} - 3 = \dfrac{1}{x}$

36. $\dfrac{1}{y-5} + \dfrac{1}{y+5} = \dfrac{1}{y^2-25}$

37. $\dfrac{2x}{x-3} - 1 = \dfrac{16}{x^2-9}$

38. **WORK** Phillip can paint a wall in 3 hr and Elizabeth can paint the same size wall in 2 hr. How long would it take to paint the wall if they worked together?

39. **WORK** Steve can type a manuscript 3 times as fast as Randy. Working together they can do the job in 5 hr. How long would it take each working alone?

The following exercises review material from Chapter 1 to help you prepare for the next section. Find the reciprocal of each fraction in Exercises 40–41.

40. $\dfrac{7}{11}$

41. 4

Divide the fractions in Exercises 42–43.

42. $\dfrac{4}{9} \div \dfrac{8}{27}$

43. $8 \div \dfrac{10}{9}$

8.6 PARALLEL EXERCISES

In Exercises 1–3, write as a ratio and simplify.

1. \$6 for 15 lb of apples

2. 2232 mi on 72 gal of gas

3. 600 bushels from 12 acres

Solve each proportion in Exercises 4–6.

4. $\dfrac{x}{18} = \dfrac{12}{20}$

5. $\dfrac{w+8}{5} = \dfrac{w-4}{3}$

6. $\dfrac{y+8}{y-4} = \dfrac{y+1}{y-6}$

Use a proportion to solve each problem in Exercises 7–20.

7. **POLITICS** In an election the winning candidate won by a 6 to 5 margin. If the loser received 1520 votes, how many did the winner receive?

8. **GAS MILEAGE** If a boat uses 12 gallons of gas to go 82 miles, how many gallons would be needed to go 123 miles?

9. **PLUMBING** If 20 m of pipe weighs 6 kg, what will 320 m of the same pipe weigh?

10. **MAP READING** If 3 cm on a map represent 14 km, how many km are represented by 36 cm?

11. **BUSINESS** A sample of 350 bolts contained 5 that were defective. How many defective bolts should be expected in a shipment of 9870 bolts?

12. **CONSTRUCTION** If 5 blocks weigh 14 pounds, how much will 255 blocks weigh?

13. **POLITICS** In an election the losing candidate lost by a 3 to 4 margin. If he received 5280 votes, how many votes did the winner receive?

14. **GAS MILEAGE** A boat uses 12 gal of gas in 4 hr. Under the same conditions how many gallons will be used in 10 hr?

15. **GEOMETRY** Two triangles are similar. If the sides of one measure 15 cm, 18 cm, and 33 cm, and the shortest side of the second measures 5 cm, find the lengths of the remaining sides.

16. **GEOMETRY** Two isosceles triangles are similar with the equal sides of one measuring 40 in and the base measuring 8 in. If the equal sides of the second triangle are 10 in long, how long is the base?

17. **MAP READING** On a map 5 inches represent 24 mi. How many miles are represented by 2 in?

18. **BUSINESS** In a sample of 280 toasters, 8 were defective. How many defective toasters should be expected in a warehouse containing 42,700 toasters?

19. **SALARY** Marvin received a commission of \$1200 on the sale of \$150,000 worth of life insurance. If the same person had bought \$250,000 worth of insurance, what commission would Marvin have earned?

20. **GAME MANAGEMENT** To determine the number of antelope on a game preserve, a ranger caught 50 antelope and tagged their ears. Some time later he captured 18 antelope and discovered that 5 were tagged. Approximately how many antelope are on the preserve?

Use direct variation to solve each problem in Exercises 21–28.

21. If y varies directly as x, and $y = 5$ when $x = 35$, find y when $x = 10$.

22. If u varies directly as w, and $u = 52$ when $w = 13$, find w when $u = 88$.

23. If y varies directly as x, and $y = 7$ when $x = 3$, find y when $x = 39$.

---

24. **CONSUMER** The cost c of carrots varies directly as the total weight w. If 5 kg of carrots cost \$3.20, what would 80 kg of carrots cost?

25. **BUSINESS** The number d of defective bolts in a shipment varies directly as the number n of bolts in the shipment. If there were 16 defective bolts in a shipment of 4800, how many would be expected in a shipment of 8400?

26. **GAS MILEAGE** The number g of gallons of gas needed varies directly as the number n of miles traveled. If 16 gallons are needed to travel 840 miles, how many gallons will be needed to travel 2800 miles?

27. **TAX** The amount of tax paid on real estate varies directly as its assessed value. If the Austins paid \$320.00 in taxes on a home valued at \$90,000, how much tax will the Wilsons pay on their home valued at \$65,000?

28. **CONSUMER** The amount of money a family spends on food varies directly as its income. If the Carpenters spend \$3780 on food and have an income of \$18,000, how much will the Woods spend if their income is \$31,000?

Use inverse variation to solve each problem in Exercises 29–34.

29. If y varies inversely as x, and $y = 7$ when $x = 3$, find y when $x = 39$.

30. If p varies inversely as q, and $p = 580$ when $q = 20$, find q when $p = 232$.

---

31. **RATE-MOTION** The time t it takes to travel a fixed distance varies inversely as the rate r of travel. If it takes 12 hr when the rate is 24 mph, how long would it take at 36 mph?

32. **RATE-MOTION** The rate r of travel for a fixed distance varies inversely as the time t. If the rate is 580 km per hour when the time is 8 hr, find the rate when the time is 20 hr.

33. **PHYSICS** The volume V of a given amount of gas varies inversely as the pressure P. If the volume is 120 ft^3 when the pressure is 15 lb per sq ft, what is the volume when the pressure is 50 lb per sq ft?

34. **ELECTRICITY** The resistance R of an electrical circuit with constant voltage varies inversely as the current I of the circuit. If the resistance is 10 ohms when the current is 5 amps, find the resistance when the current is 25 amps.

FOR REVIEW

Solve each equation or applied problem in Exercises 35–39.

35. $\dfrac{2x}{x+5} - 2 = \dfrac{1}{x}$

36. $\dfrac{1}{y+6} + \dfrac{1}{y-6} = \dfrac{4}{y^2-36}$

37. $\dfrac{3x}{x+4} - 2 = \dfrac{12}{x^2-16}$

38. **CONSTRUCTION** Grady can build a log cabin in 5 weeks and Smitty can build the same type of cabin in 4 weeks. How long would it take to build a cabin if they worked together?

39. **BUSINESS** Lynda can process an order twice as fast as Maria, and working together they can do the job in 3 hours. How long would it take each working alone?

The following exercises review material from Chapter 1 to help you prepare for the next section. Find the reciprocal of each fraction in Exercises 40–41.

40. $-\dfrac{17}{8}$

41. $\dfrac{1}{99}$

Divide the fractions in Exercises 42–43.

42. $-\dfrac{24}{25} \div \dfrac{16}{15}$

43. $\dfrac{49}{36} \div 14$

8.6 ENRICHMENT EXERCISES

Solve each problem in Exercises 1–6.

1. **BUSINESS** In a sample of 120 tires, 4 were defective. Because of manufacturing problems it is estimated that the defective rate will increase by 50% on the next shipment of 480 tires. How many of the new shipment would you predict to be defective?

2. **BUSINESS** A light-bulb manufacturer detected 12 defective bulbs in a sample of 840. After buying new equipment he was able to decrease the number of defective bulbs by 40 percent. How many defective bulbs should now be expected in a shipment of 1400?

3. If z varies directly as x and inversely as y, show that x varies directly as y and z.

4. **PHYSICS** The volume V of a gas varies directly as the temperature T and inversely as the pressure P. If the volume is 50 ft^3 when the temperature is 300° and the pressure is 30 lb per sq ft, find V when $T = 400°$ and $P = 20$ lb/ft^2.

5. **GEOMETRY** Find the values of x and y in the figure below.

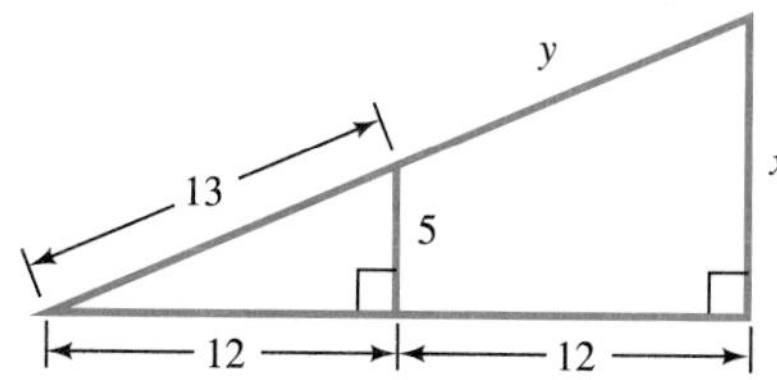

6. **GEOMETRY** A tree casts a shadow 48 ft long at the same time that a man's shadow is 4 ft long. If the man is 6 ft tall, how tall is the tree?

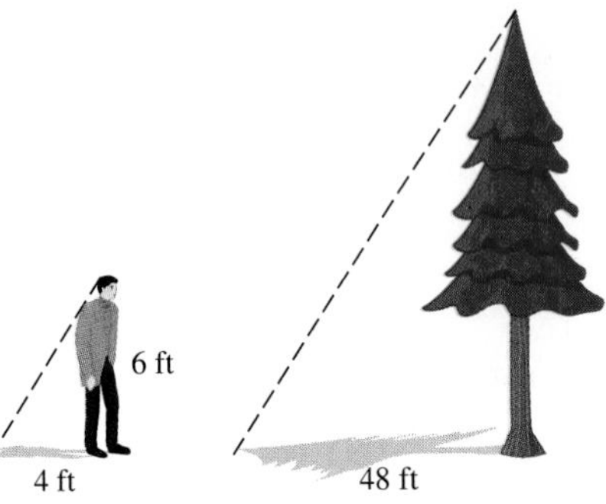

7. When told to solve the equation

$$\frac{x}{x+1} = \frac{2}{x} - \frac{3}{2},$$

Burford tried to use the means-extremes property. Explain to Burford why he cannot do this.

8. If y varies directly as x, what happens to $|y|$ when $|x|$ gets larger and larger?
9. If y varies inversely as x, what happens to $|y|$ as $|x|$ gets larger and larger?
10. If y varies directly as x, explain why we can also say x varies directly as y.
11. Measure the circumference and diameter of several cans of food and consider the ratios of the circumference to the diameter. Write a paragraph discussing the results of your experiment.
12. Look for examples of ratios, proportions, direct variation, and inverse variation in articles in magazines and newspapers. Write a paragraph discussing what you find.

SECTION 8.7 Simplifying Complex Fractions

Student guideposts

▶ *Complex fractions*
▶ *Simplifying complex fractions*

▶ *Complex fractions*

A **complex fraction** is a fraction that contains at least one other fraction within it. The following are complex fractions.

$$\frac{\frac{2}{3}}{5}, \quad \frac{\frac{1}{2}}{\frac{4}{5}}, \quad \frac{\frac{1}{x}}{3}, \quad \frac{1+\frac{1}{x}}{2}, \quad \frac{1+\frac{1}{a}}{1-\frac{1}{a}}$$

▶ *Simplifying complex fractions*

A complex fraction is **simplified** when all its component fractions have been eliminated. There are two basic methods for simplifying a complex fraction. We will present both methods since with some complex fractions one method might be more easily applied than the other. The first method involves writing the numerator and denominator as single fractions and then dividing.

To Simplify a Complex Fraction (Method 1)

1. Change the numerator and denominator to single fractions.
2. Divide the two fractions.
3. Reduce the result to lowest terms.

EXAMPLE 1

Simplifying Complex Fractions (Method 1)

Simplify the complex fractions.

(a) $\dfrac{\dfrac{x}{4}}{\dfrac{x^2}{2}}$

Since the numerator and denominator are already single fractions, all we need to do is divide.

$$\frac{\dfrac{x}{4}}{\dfrac{x^2}{2}} = \frac{x}{4} \div \frac{x^2}{2} = \frac{x}{4} \cdot \frac{2}{x^2} = \frac{\cancel{x} \cdot \cancel{2}}{\cancel{2} \cdot 2 \cdot \cancel{x} \cdot x} = \frac{1}{2x}$$

(b) $\dfrac{1 + \dfrac{1}{2}}{1 - \dfrac{1}{3}}$

$$1 + \frac{1}{2} = \frac{2}{2} + \frac{1}{2} = \frac{3}{2} \qquad \text{Add the numerator fractions}$$

$$1 - \frac{1}{3} = \frac{3}{3} - \frac{1}{3} = \frac{2}{3} \qquad \text{Subtract the denominator fractions}$$

Thus, $\dfrac{1 + \dfrac{1}{2}}{1 - \dfrac{1}{3}} = \dfrac{\dfrac{3}{2}}{\dfrac{2}{3}} = \dfrac{3}{2} \div \dfrac{2}{3} = \dfrac{3}{2} \cdot \dfrac{3}{2} = \dfrac{9}{4}.$

(c) $\dfrac{1 + \dfrac{1}{x}}{2}$

$$1 + \frac{1}{x} = \frac{x}{x} + \frac{1}{x} = \frac{x+1}{x} \qquad \text{Add the numerator fractions}$$

Thus, $\dfrac{1 + \dfrac{1}{x}}{2} = \dfrac{\dfrac{x+1}{x}}{2} = \dfrac{x+1}{x} \div 2 = \dfrac{x+1}{x} \cdot \dfrac{1}{2} = \dfrac{x+1}{2x}.$ ■

The second method involves clearing all fractions within the complex fraction by multiplying numerator and denominator by the LCD of all the internal fractions using the Fundamental Principle of Fractions.

To Simplify a Complex Fraction (Method 2)

1. Find the LCD of **all** fractions within the complex fraction.
2. Multiply numerator and denominator of the complex fraction by the LCD to obtain an equivalent fraction.
3. Reduce the result to lowest terms.

EXAMPLE 2 **Simplifying a Complex Fraction (Method 2)**

Simplify $\dfrac{1 + \dfrac{2}{a}}{1 - \dfrac{4}{a^2}}$.

The denominator in $1 + \frac{2}{a}$ is a, and in $1 - \frac{4}{a^2}$ is a^2. Thus, the LCD $= a^2$.

$$\frac{1 + \dfrac{2}{a}}{1 - \dfrac{4}{a^2}} = \frac{\left(1 + \dfrac{2}{a}\right) \cdot a^2}{\left(1 - \dfrac{4}{a^2}\right) \cdot a^2}$$

Multiply by the LCD $= a^2$ in both the numerator and denominator

$$= \frac{1 \cdot a^2 + \dfrac{2}{a} \cdot a^2}{1 \cdot a^2 - \dfrac{4}{a^2} \cdot a^2}$$

Multiply all terms by a^2 using the distributive law

$$= \frac{a^2 + 2a}{a^2 - 4}$$

$$= \frac{a(a + 2)}{(a + 2)(a - 2)}$$

Factor and reduce to lowest terms

$$= \frac{a}{a - 2} \quad \blacksquare$$

CAUTION Recall that the fundamental principle of fractions states that an equivalent equation is obtained if we multiply the numerator and denominator by the *same* nonzero expression. To simplify a complex fraction such as the one in Example 2 using Method 2, students will often multiply the numerator by a and the denominator by a^2. Doing this certainly clears the fractions, but the result is *not equivalent* to the original complex fraction.

EXAMPLE 3 **Simplifying a Complex Fraction (Method 2)**

Simplify $\dfrac{1 + \dfrac{2}{x - 2}}{\dfrac{2}{x + 2} - 1}$.

The denominator in $1 + \frac{2}{x-2}$ is $x - 2$, and in $\frac{2}{x+2} - 1$ is $x + 2$. Thus, the LCD = $(x - 2)(x + 2)$.

$$\frac{1 + \dfrac{2}{x-2}}{\dfrac{2}{x+2} - 1} = \frac{\left(1 + \dfrac{2}{x-2}\right)(x-2)(x+2)}{\left(\dfrac{2}{x+2} - 1\right)(x-2)(x+2)} \qquad \text{Multiply by LCD}$$

$$= \frac{1 \cdot (x-2)(x+2) + \dfrac{2}{\cancel{x-2}}\cancel{(x-2)}(x+2)}{\dfrac{2}{\cancel{x+2}}(x-2)\cancel{(x+2)} - 1 \cdot (x-2)(x+2)}$$

$$= \frac{(x^2 - 4) + 2(x + 2)}{2(x - 2) - (x^2 - 4)}$$

$$= \frac{x^2 - 4 + 2x + 4}{2x - 4 - x^2 + 4} \qquad \text{Watch signs when clearing parentheses using the distributive law}$$

$$= \frac{x^2 + 2x}{-x^2 + 2x}$$

$$= \frac{\cancel{x}(x + 2)}{\cancel{x}(-x + 2)} = \frac{x + 2}{2 - x} \qquad \text{Factor and reduce to lowest terms} \quad \blacksquare$$

> **NOTE** Students often ask, "Which method should I use?" Unless you are told otherwise by your instructor, use the method with which you feel the most comfortable. However, for some complex fractions one method might be a bit easier to use than the other, so analyze the situation before you start.

8.7 EXERCISES

Simplify each complex fraction in Exercises 1–12.

1. $\dfrac{3 + \dfrac{2}{3}}{1 - \dfrac{1}{3}}$

2. $\dfrac{\dfrac{1}{3} + \dfrac{1}{5}}{\dfrac{2}{3} - \dfrac{3}{5}}$

3. $\dfrac{1 - \dfrac{1}{a}}{3}$

4. $\dfrac{y-1}{y-\dfrac{1}{y}}$

5. $\dfrac{1-\dfrac{4}{y}}{\dfrac{4-y}{y}}$

6. $\dfrac{\dfrac{2}{a}+a}{\dfrac{a}{2}+a}$

7. $\dfrac{\dfrac{2}{y}+3}{2-\dfrac{3}{y}}$

8. $\dfrac{\dfrac{1}{x}+1}{\dfrac{1}{x}-1}$

9. $\dfrac{4-\dfrac{1}{a^2}}{2-\dfrac{1}{a}}$

10. $\dfrac{1-\dfrac{2}{y}-\dfrac{3}{y^2}}{1+\dfrac{1}{y}}$

11. $\dfrac{x-3+\dfrac{2}{x}}{x-4+\dfrac{3}{x}}$

12. $\dfrac{\dfrac{3}{a-3}+1}{\dfrac{3}{a+3}-1}$

13. **PHYSICS** An important formula in physics gives V in terms of S_1 and S_2 by the formula

$$V=\frac{3}{\dfrac{1}{S_1}+\dfrac{1}{S_2}}.$$

Express V as a simple fraction and use the result to find V when S_1 is 2 and S_2 is 5.

14. **ENGINEERING** A transportation engineer uses the formula

$$R=\frac{2}{\dfrac{1}{g}+\dfrac{1}{r}}$$

to calculate average rate of speed on a round trip. Simplify this complex fraction.

FOR REVIEW

Solve each applied problem in Exercises 15–18.

15. **RECREATION** A boat can go 38 mi on 6 gal of gas. How far can it go on 21 gal of gas?

16. If y varies directly as x, and $y=42$ when $x=18$, find y when $x=3$.

17. **CONSUMER** The cost c of fish varies directly as the total weight w of the fish. If 8 lb of fish cost $18.60, what would 60 lb of fish cost?

18. **RECREATION** A recipe calls for 2.5 cups of flour to feed 6 people. How many cups would be needed to feed 18 people?

Exercises 19–24 review material from Chapters 1 and 2 to help you prepare for the first section of the next chapter. Simplify each expression.

19. $(-3)^2$

20. -3^2

21. $2^2 \cdot 5^2$

22. $(2 \cdot 5)^2$

23. $|-4|$

24. $-(4-5)^2$

8.7 PARALLEL EXERCISES

Simplify each complex fraction in Exercises 1–12.

1. $\dfrac{7 + \frac{1}{2}}{2 - \frac{1}{2}}$

2. $\dfrac{\frac{1}{6} + \frac{1}{8}}{\frac{5}{6} - \frac{1}{8}}$

3. $\dfrac{10}{1 - \frac{1}{y}}$

4. $\dfrac{2 - \frac{1}{y}}{\frac{2}{y}}$

5. $\dfrac{a - \frac{1}{a}}{1 - \frac{1}{a}}$

6. $\dfrac{\frac{3}{a} + a}{\frac{a}{3} + a}$

7. $\dfrac{\frac{1}{a} + \frac{2}{a}}{\frac{3}{a} + \frac{4}{a}}$

8. $\dfrac{\frac{2}{x-2} + 1}{\frac{2}{x+2} - 1}$

9. $\dfrac{\frac{1}{y^2} - 4}{\frac{1}{y} - 2}$

10. $\dfrac{1 - \frac{2}{x} - \frac{3}{x^2}}{\frac{1}{x} + 1}$

11. $\dfrac{\frac{5}{y+5} - 1}{\frac{5}{y-5} + 1}$

12. $\dfrac{z - 5 + \frac{6}{z}}{z - 1 - \frac{2}{z}}$

13. **CHEMISTRY** An environmental chemist might use the formula

$$w = \frac{\frac{1}{c}}{1 + \frac{1}{d}}.$$

Express w as a simple fraction and use the result to find w when c is 3 and d is 14.

14. **NAVIGATION** A navigation expert uses the formula

$$V = \frac{v_1 + v_2}{1 + \frac{v_1 v_2}{c^2}}$$

to calculate the velocity of an airplane. Simplify this complex fraction.

FOR REVIEW

Solve each applied problem in Exercises 15–18.

15. **BUSINESS** In a shipment of 200 tires, 6 were defective. How many defective tires would you expect in a shipment of 9000 tires?

16. If y varies directly as x, and $y = 14$ when $x = 5$, find y when $x = 20$.

17. **RATE-MOTION** The distance d traveled varies directly as the rate r of travel. If 280 miles are traveled at a rate of 40 mph, what distance could be traveled at 60 mph?

18. **UNIT CONVERSION** If 1 quart contains 0.95 liters, how many quarts are in 190 liters?

Exercises 19–24 review material from Chapters 1 and 2 to help you prepare for the first section of the next chapter. Simplify each expression.

19. $(-5)^2$ **20.** -5^2 **21.** $4^2 \cdot 3^2$

22. $(4 \cdot 3)^2$ **23.** $|-9|$ **24.** $-(6 - 8)^2$

8.7 ENRICHMENT EXERCISES

Simplify each complex fraction in Exercises 1–3.

1. $\dfrac{\dfrac{a+b}{a-b} - \dfrac{a-b}{a+b}}{\dfrac{a}{a-b} + \dfrac{b}{a+b}}$ ⚠ **2.** $\dfrac{\dfrac{1}{xy} + \dfrac{1}{yz} + \dfrac{1}{xz}}{\dfrac{x+y+z}{xyz}}$ ⚠ **3.** $a - \dfrac{a}{1 - \dfrac{a}{1-a}}$

4. **STATISTICS** A recent survey of college students revealed that $\frac{2}{3}$ of the male students and $\frac{1}{4}$ of the female students drove a car on campus. It was also determined that $\frac{1}{8}$ of the male students and $\frac{1}{2}$ of the female students who drove cars paid their own insurance premiums. There were an equal number n of male students and female students in the survey. Form the ratio

$$\frac{\textit{total number of students who pay their own insurance premiums}}{\textit{total number of students who drive a car on campus}}$$

and simplify the fraction. What percent of the students in the survey pay their own insurance premiums?

5. Burford simplified the complex fraction as shown below. What is wrong with Burford's work? What is the correct simplification?

$$\frac{\frac{1}{x} + 1}{1 - \frac{1}{x^2}} = \frac{\left(\frac{1}{x} + 1\right) \cdot x}{\left(1 - \frac{1}{x^2}\right) \cdot x^2}$$

$$= \frac{\left(\frac{1}{x}\right) \cdot x + 1 \cdot x}{1 \cdot x^2 - \left(\frac{1}{x^2}\right) \cdot x^2}$$

$$= \frac{1 + x}{x^2 - 1}$$

$$= \frac{\cancel{x+1}}{\cancel{(x+1)}(x-1)}$$

$$= \frac{1}{x - 1}$$

6. Describe the two methods used to simplify a complex fraction, and include a discussion of when one might be preferred over the other.

CHAPTER 8 REVIEW

KEY WORDS

8.1 An **algebraic fraction** is a fraction that contains a variable in the numerator or denominator or both.

A **rational expression** is the quotient of two polynomials.

A fraction is **reduced to lowest terms** when 1 (or -1) is the only number or expression that divides both numerator and denominator.

8.2 The **reciprocal** of the fraction $\frac{a}{b}$ is $\frac{b}{a}$.

8.3 **Like fractions** have the same denominator.

Unlike fractions have different denominators.

8.4 The **least common denominator (LCD)** of two or more fractions is the smallest of all common denominators.

8.5 A **fractional equation** is one that contains one or more algebraic fractions.

8.6 The **ratio** of one number x to another number y is the quotient $x \div y$.

A **proportion** is an equation which states that two ratios are equal.

The **extremes** of the proportion $\frac{a}{b} = \frac{c}{d}$ are a and d.

The **means** of the proportion $\frac{a}{b} = \frac{c}{d}$ are b and c.

If $y = kx$ **(direct variation)** or $y = \frac{k}{x}$ **(inverse variation),** k is called the **constant of variation.**

8.7 A **complex fraction** is a fraction that contains at least one other fraction within it.

KEY CONCEPTS

8.1

1. Always be aware of values that must be excluded when working with algebraic fractions. For example, 4 cannot replace x in $\frac{3}{x-4}$.
2. When reducing fractions, divide out factors only, never terms.
3. When reducing fractions by dividing out common factors, do not make the numerator 0 when it is actually 1. For example,

$$\frac{\cancel{(x+1)}}{3\cancel{(x+1)}} = \frac{1}{3}, \quad \textit{not} \quad \frac{0}{3}.$$

8.2 When multiplying or dividing fractions, factor numerators and denominators and divide out common factors. Do not find the LCD.

8.3, 8.4

1. Find the LCD of all fractions when adding or subtracting.
2. When subtracting fractions, use parentheses to avoid sign errors. For example,

$$\frac{2x+1}{x-5} - \frac{x-3}{x-5}$$
$$= \frac{2x+1-(x-3)}{x-5}$$
$$= \frac{2x+1-x+3}{x-5} = \frac{x+4}{x-5}.$$

3. Do not divide out terms when adding or subtracting algebraic fractions. For example,

$$\frac{3(x-2)}{(x+2)(x-2)} - \frac{7(x+2)}{(x-2)(x+2)}$$
$$= \frac{3(x-2)-7(x+2)}{(x+2)(x-2)}$$
$$= \frac{3x-6-7x-14}{(x+2(x-2)},$$

$$\text{not} \quad \frac{3\cancel{(x-2)} - 7\cancel{(x+2)}}{\cancel{(x+2)}\cancel{(x-2)}} \qquad \text{THIS IS WRONG}$$

8.5 1. To solve a fractional equation, multiply both sides by the LCD of all fractions.

2. Check all answers in the *original* fractional equation. Watch for division by zero.

8.6 1. If y varies as x, then $y = kx$ where k is the constant of variation.

2. If y varies inversely as x, then $y = \frac{k}{x}$ where k is the constant of variation.

8.7 One way to simplify a complex fraction is to write the numerator as a single fraction, the denominator as a single fraction, and divide. Another way is to multiply the numerator and denominator of a complex fraction by the LCD of **all** fractions. For example,

$$\frac{1+\frac{1}{x}}{1-\frac{1}{x}} = \frac{\left(1+\frac{1}{x}\right)\cdot x}{\left(1-\frac{1}{x}\right)\cdot x}$$
$$= \frac{1\cdot x + \frac{1}{x}\cdot x}{1\cdot x - \frac{1}{x}\cdot x} = \frac{x+1}{x-1}.$$

CHAPTER 8 REVIEW EXERCISES

PART I

8.1 *In Exercises 1–3, find the values of the variable that must be excluded.*

1. $\frac{x+2}{x(x-1)}$

2. $\frac{a}{a^2+1}$

3. $\frac{y^2}{(y+1)(y-5)}$

Are the fractions given in Exercises 4–6 equivalent?

4. $\frac{x-2}{5x-2}, \frac{x}{5x}$ **5.** $\frac{a-3}{a^2-9}, \frac{1}{a+3}$ **6.** $\frac{x+y}{x}, \frac{x}{x+y}$

Reduce to lowest terms in Exercises 7–9.

7. $\frac{x^2+2x}{x}$ **8.** $\frac{x^2-9}{x+3}$ **9.** $\frac{x^2+2xy+y^2}{x+y}$

8.2 *Perform the indicated operations in Exercises 10–12.*

10. $\frac{y^2-y-2}{y^2-2y-3} \cdot \frac{y^2-3y}{y+2}$ **11.** $\frac{4y^4}{y^2-1} \div \frac{2y^3}{y^2-2y+1}$ **12.** $\frac{9x^2-y^2}{x+y} \div \frac{3x+y}{x^2-y^2}$

8.3, 8.4 *Perform the indicated operations in Exercises 13–18.*

13. $\frac{2x}{x^2-x} + \frac{x}{x^2-1}$ **14.** $\frac{x+1}{x-3} - \frac{x-1}{3-x}$ **15.** $\frac{a}{a^2-1} - \frac{a+2}{a^2+a-2}$

16. $\frac{3}{x-2} + \frac{x+2}{x-2} - \frac{2x}{2-x}$ **17.** $\frac{6x}{x^2-9} - \frac{2}{x-3} - \frac{5}{x+3}$ **18.** $\frac{x}{x+y} + \frac{y}{x-y}$

8.5 *Solve each equation or applied problem in Exercises 19–25.*

19. $\frac{2}{z+5} = \frac{3}{z}$ **20.** $\frac{3}{x+2} + \frac{2}{x-2} = \frac{3}{x^2-4}$ **21.** $\frac{x}{x-1} + 1 = \frac{x^2+1}{x^2-1}$

22. **NUMBER** The denominator of a fraction is 2 less than the numerator. If 2 is added to both the numerator and denominator, the result has value $\frac{4}{3}$. Find the fraction.

23. **RECREATION** Diane Gray rode a bike 90 mi in the same time it took Don Cole to ride 108 mi. If Don's rate was 3 mph faster than Diane's rate, find each rate.

24. **WORK** If Tim can do a job in 3 days and Bob can do the same job in 11 days, how long would it take them to do the job if they worked together?

25. **WORK** If it takes pipe A three times longer to fill a tank than pipe B and together they can fill it in 6 hours, how long would it take pipe B to fill the tank?

8.6 *Give as a ratio and simplify in Exercises 26–28.*

26. 450 mi on 15 gal of gas **27.** 1200 trees on 6 acres **28.** \$12 for 8 lb of meat

Solve each equation in Exercises 29–31.

29. $\frac{x-2}{x+2} = \frac{3}{2}$ **30.** $\frac{y+5}{y-4} = \frac{y+4}{y-5}$ **31.** $\frac{z-8}{z+3} = \frac{z+9}{z-2}$

32. **POLITICS** In an election, the winner won by a 6 to 5 margin. If the winner had 270 votes, how many votes did the loser receive?

33. **ELECTRICITY** If 70 ft of electrical wire weighs 15 lb, how much will 210 ft of the same wire weigh?

34. If y varies directly as x, and $y = 20$ when $x = 4$, find y when $x = 14$.

35. **CONSUMER** The cost c of candy varies directly as the total weight w of the candy. If 4 lb of candy cost \$10.40, what would 6 lb cost?

8.7 *Simplify each complex fraction in Exercises 36–38.*

36. $\dfrac{2 - \dfrac{1}{8}}{3 + \dfrac{3}{4}}$ **37.** $\dfrac{4x - \dfrac{1}{x}}{2 - \dfrac{1}{x}}$ **38.** $\dfrac{y - 2 + \dfrac{1}{y}}{1 - \dfrac{1}{y}}$

PART II

39. **CONSTRUCTION** If Sandy can frame a shed in 4 days and together Sandy and Clyde can frame the same shed in 3 days, how long would it take Clyde to frame it working by himself?

40. If y varies inversely as x, and $y = 45$ when $x = 5$, find x when $y = 15$.

Solve each equation in Exercises 41–43.

41. $\dfrac{3}{x-4} + \dfrac{4}{x+4} = \dfrac{3}{x^2-16}$ **42.** $x + \dfrac{6}{x} = 5$ **43.** $\dfrac{x}{x-2} - 1 = \dfrac{3}{x^2-4}$

Perform the indicated operation and simplify in Exercises 44–46.

44. $\dfrac{x+1}{x-2} - \dfrac{x-1}{x+3}$ **45.** $\dfrac{y^2-3y}{y^2-y-6} \div \dfrac{y}{y+2}$ **46.** $\dfrac{1 + \dfrac{3}{x} - \dfrac{10}{x^2}}{1 - \dfrac{5}{x} + \dfrac{6}{x^2}}$

47. **WORK** Jan can wash the dishes in 20 minutes, and it takes her mother 15 minutes to wash them. How long would it take to wash the dishes if they work together?

48. **MOTION** Arnold Parker can paddle his canoe 30 miles downstream in the same time that he can paddle 18 miles upstream. If the speed of the stream is 2 mph, what is Arnold's rate in still water?

Answer true *or* false *in Exercises 49–60. If the answer is false, explain why.*

49. The rational expression $\dfrac{x+5}{5}$ reduces to x.

50. If $x \neq y$, then $\dfrac{x-y}{y-x} = -1$.

51. When multiplying rational expressions, the very first step should be to factor all polynomials.

52. When multiplying and dividing rational expressions, always find the LCD first.

53. The LCD of the fractions $\dfrac{3}{x^2-1}$ and $\dfrac{2}{x-1}$ is $(x+1)(x-1)$.

54. When adding or subtracting rational expressions, first change each fraction to an equivalent fraction having the LCD as the denominator.

55. To simplify the complex fraction $\dfrac{\dfrac{1}{x} + \dfrac{1}{y}}{\dfrac{2}{x} - \dfrac{2}{y}}$ multiply the numerator and denominator by $2xy$.

56. A statement saying that two ratios are equal is a proportion.

57. To solve a fractional equation, multiply both sides of the equation by the LCD of all fractions.

58. If a varies inversely as b, we can write $a = kb$.

59. If Jonas can do a job in x days, in one day he will do $\frac{1}{x}$ of the job.

60. If two triangles are similar, then their corresponding sides are equal.

CHAPTER 8 TEST

1. What are the values of the variable that must be excluded in $\frac{5}{x(x+5)}$?

2. Are the fractions $\frac{y}{5}$ and $\frac{6y}{30}$ equivalent?

3. Reduce to lowest terms. $\frac{a+2}{a^2+2a}$

4. Multiply. $\frac{x^2-16}{7x^2} \cdot \frac{35x}{x-4}$

5. Divide. $\frac{y}{y^2+y-12} \div \frac{y^2+3y}{y^2+7y+12}$

6. Add. $\frac{3}{a-b} + \frac{2}{b-a}$

7. Add. $\frac{x^2-6x}{x^2-4} + \frac{x}{x-2}$

8. Subtract. $\frac{4}{y^2-1} - \frac{3}{y^2-y-2}$

9. Solve. $\frac{x}{x+1} = \frac{x^2+1}{x^2-1} + \frac{3}{x-1}$

10. John can hike 14 miles in the same time it takes Cindy to hike 21 miles. If Cindy's rate is 1 mph faster than John's, how fast is John hiking?

11. A car needed 16 gal of gas to go 352 mi. How many gallons would be needed to go 814 mi?

12. The cost c of ground beef varies directly as the total weight w of the meat purchased. If 5 lb of ground beef cost $5.75, what would 12 lb cost?

13. Ralph can do a job in 3 days and Harry can do the same job in 5 days. How long would it take them to do the same job if they work together?

14. Simplify. $\dfrac{\frac{1}{y}-1}{\frac{1}{y}-y}$

15. If y varies inversely as x, and $y = 20$ when $x = 4$, find y when $x = 16$.

16. Two triangles are similar and the sides of one measure 6 ft, 9 ft, and 14 ft. If the shortest side of the second triangle is 15 ft, find the length of the longest side.

17. Explain how to reduce the expression $\frac{1-2x}{2x-1}$.

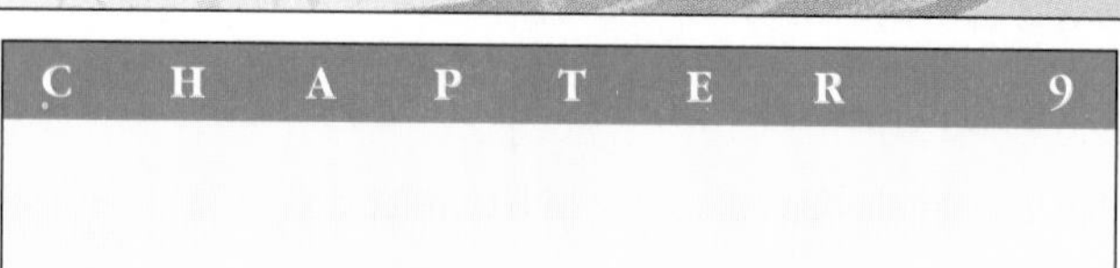

CHAPTER 9

Radicals and Rational Exponents

IN THIS CHAPTER WE will study radical expressions and learn to simplify them. Primarily we will be concerned with expressions involving square roots, although higher order roots are introduced. Since finding a square root of a number is the reverse of squaring a number, exponents and their properties, first discussed in Chapter 6, are important here.

Radicals are used in many applied problems. The example below has its solution in Example 3 of Section 9.7.

CONSTRUCTION Mr. Rodriques is using a 20-ft ladder to aid in building a tree house for his two children. For safety reasons he'll place the foot of the ladder 8 feet from the base of the tree. How far up the side of the tree will the ladder reach?

We begin our study of radicals with basic definitions and methods for simplifying radical expressions. Next we consider the operations of multiplication, division, addition, subtraction, and rationalizing denominators. Following a discussion of radical equations with applications, we conclude with an introduction to higher order radicals and fractional exponents.

SECTION 9.1 Roots and Radicals

Student guideposts

- ▶ *Perfect squares and square roots*
- ▶ *Evaluating $\sqrt{x^2}$*
- ▶ *Using a calculator*
- ▶ *Applications of radicals*

▶ *Perfect squares and square roots*

To introduce our study of radicals we review material from Section 2.6. Consider the following.

$$2^2 = 2 \cdot 2 = 4$$
$$(-2)^2 = (-2)(-2) = 4$$

When an integer is squared, the result is a **perfect square.** Thus 4 is a perfect square, since $4 = 2^2$. Either of the identical factors of a perfect square is a *square root* of the number. From above, 2 is a square root of 4 and since $(-2)^2 = 4$, -2 is also a square root of 4.

In addition to whole number perfect squares, there are also fractional perfect squares. For example,

$$\frac{4}{9} \text{ is a perfect square since } \frac{4}{9} = \left(\frac{2}{3}\right)^2,$$
$$\text{and } \frac{2}{3} \text{ is a square root of } \frac{4}{9}.$$

There are fractional perfect squares that do not have perfect square numerators and perfect square denominators. For example, $\frac{8}{18}$ is a perfect square since

$$\frac{8}{18} = \frac{4 \cdot \cancel{2}}{9 \cdot \cancel{2}} = \frac{4}{9},$$

which is a perfect square.

We saw in Chapter 2 that some square roots are irrational numbers. As we will see later, these numbers are included in the following definition.

Square Root

If a and x are real numbers such that

$$a^2 = x,$$

then a is a square root of x.

In general, every *positive* real number has two square roots. If a is a square root of x, then both a and $-a$ are square roots of x since

$$a^2 = x \quad \text{and} \quad (-a)^2 = x.$$

The nonnegative square root of a positive real number is called its **principal square root,** and is denoted by a **radical,** $\sqrt{}$. For example, if we write $\sqrt{4}$, we call 4 the **radicand** and 2 its principal square root. That is,

$$\sqrt{4} = 2. \qquad \text{2 is the principal (nonnegative) square root of 4}$$

To indicate the other square root of 4, we place a minus sign in front of the radical. Thus,

$$-\sqrt{4} = -2.$$

The positive and negative square roots of a positive real number can be represented together with the symbol $\pm$. For example,

$$\pm\sqrt{4} = \pm 2$$

represents both 2 and -2, and is read "plus or minus 2." Of course 0 has only one square root, namely 0, since $-0 = 0$.

We have seen that every positive real number has two square roots (one positive and one negative), that 0 has only one square root (namely 0 itself), but what about negative numbers? Does -9 have a square root, for example? The obvious choices would be -3 or 3, but

$$(-3)^2 = 9 \quad \text{and} \quad 3^2 = 9.$$

In fact, since $a^2 \geq 0$ for any real number a, a^2 could never be equal to the *negative* number -9. Thus, since no real number squared can be negative, negative numbers have no real square roots. We say that $\sqrt{-9}$, for example, is not a real number. In Section 10.7 we will have more to say about square roots of negative numbers.

EXAMPLE 1 **Evaluating Square Roots**

Evaluate the following radicals.

(a) $\sqrt{100} = 10 \qquad 10^2 = 100$

(b) $-\sqrt{100} = -10$

(c) $\pm\sqrt{100} = \pm 10$ (two numbers, 10 and -10)

(d) $\sqrt{-100}$ is not a real number   No real number times itself can be negative, in particular, -100

(e) $\sqrt{\dfrac{25}{81}} = \dfrac{5}{9}$

(f) $\sqrt{\dfrac{12}{75}} = \sqrt{\dfrac{4 \cdot \cancel{3}}{25 \cdot \cancel{3}}} = \sqrt{\dfrac{4}{25}} = \dfrac{2}{5}$

(g) $\sqrt{1} = 1$

(h) $\sqrt{0} = 0$

(i) $\sqrt{5^2} = \sqrt{25} = 5$

(j) $\sqrt{(-5)^2} = \sqrt{25} = 5$ $\quad (-5)^2 = (-5)(-5) = 25$

(k) $\sqrt{-5^2} = \sqrt{-25}$ is not a real number. $\quad -5^2 = -(5)(5) = -25$ ■

▶ *Evaluating* $\sqrt{x^2}$

In Example 1 we saw that

$$\sqrt{5^2} = 5 \quad \text{and} \quad \sqrt{(-5)^2} = 5.$$

This is also true in general. Thus, if x is a nonnegative number, $\sqrt{x^2} = x$. For example, $\sqrt{5^2} = 5$. However, if x is negative then $\sqrt{x^2} = -x$. For example, $\sqrt{(-5)^2} = -(-5) = 5$. To make it clear that the principal square root of a number is positive, we write

$$\sqrt{x^2} = |x|,$$

where $|x|$ is the absolute value of x. To avoid problems of this nature, we will agree to the following.

Taking Roots from This Point Forward

All variables and algebraic expressions under radicals represent nonnegative real numbers. Thus, for $x \geq 0$, we have

$$\sqrt{x^2} = x.$$

For example, under this agreement,

$$\sqrt{(x-7)^2} = x - 7,$$

since we are assuming that $x - 7 \geq 0$.

EXAMPLE 2

Evaluating Radicals

Evaluate the following radicals assuming all variables and algebraic expressions are nonnegative.

(a) $\sqrt{49} = \sqrt{7^2} = 7$

(b) $\sqrt{y^2} = y$

(c) $\sqrt{25x^2} = \sqrt{5^2x^2} = \sqrt{(5x)^2} = 5x$ $\quad a^nb^n = (ab)^n$

(d) $\sqrt{x^2 + 6x + 9} = \sqrt{(x+3)^2} = x + 3$

(e) $-\sqrt{81} = -\sqrt{9^2} = -9$

(f) $-\sqrt{u^2} = -u$ ■

▶ *Using a calculator*

The square roots we have looked at so far have all resulted in rational numbers. For example, $\sqrt{25}$ is the rational number 5. Many square roots, such as $\sqrt{5}$, do not have this property. Since 5 is not a perfect square, that is, since there is no integer a such that

$a^2 = 5$, $\sqrt{5}$ cannot be simplified further. In fact, $\sqrt{5}$ is an irrational number for which an approximate rational number must be used in a practical situation. There are two ways to find such an approximation, with a table of square roots or with a calculator. Whenever we need to find the approximate value of a square root, we will use a calculator with a $\boxed{\sqrt{\ }}$ key.

To find a rational-number approximation for $\sqrt{5}$, use the following steps on your calculator.

$$5 \ \boxed{\sqrt{\ }} \rightarrow \boxed{2.2360680}$$

To see that 2.2360680 is indeed an approximation of $\sqrt{5}$, enter 2.2360680 on your calculator and square it using the $\boxed{x^2}$ key.

$$2.2360680 \ \boxed{x^2} \rightarrow \boxed{5.0000001}$$

▶ *Applications of radicals*

In applied problems such as the next example, the approximate value of a square root is needed.

EXAMPLE 3

Applying Radicals

If P dollars are invested in an account for two years and at the end of this period the value of the account is A dollars, then the annual rate of return r on the investment can be found by the formula

$$r = \sqrt{\frac{A}{P}} - 1.$$

Suppose Diane purchased a rare book for \$1000 and two years later sold it for \$1500. What was the annual rate of return on Diane's investment?

Since $A = 1500$ and $P = 1000$, we substitute into the formula to find r.

$$r = \sqrt{\frac{A}{P}} - 1 = \sqrt{\frac{1500}{1000}} - 1$$
$$\approx 0.2247449$$

The calculator steps used to find r are:

$$1500 \ \boxed{\div} \ 1000 \ \boxed{=} \ \boxed{\sqrt{\ }} \ \boxed{-} \ 1 \ \boxed{=} \rightarrow \boxed{0.2247449}$$ [1]

Rounded to three decimal places, $r \approx 0.225$, which translates to 22.5%. Thus, Diane realized an approximate annual return of 22.5% on her investment. ■

CAUTION Do not get in the habit of reaching immediately for your calculator when given a radical expression. Using a calculator, for example, to evaluate $\sqrt{4}$ would be as ridiculous as using it to find $2 + 3$. Throughout this chapter you should use a calculator only for approximate values of radicals whose square roots are not integers.

[1] Calculator steps are given using algebraic logic. If you have a calculator that uses Reverse Polish Notation (RPN), consult your operator's manual.

9.1 EXERCISES

Tell whether each number has 0, 1, or 2 square roots in Exercises 1–4.

1. 25 **2.** -25 **3.** 0 **4.** 175

Evaluate each square root in Exercises 5–20. Assume that all variables and algebraic expressions under the radical are nonnegative.

5. $\sqrt{6^2}$ **6.** $\sqrt{(-6)^2}$ **7.** $\sqrt{-6^2}$ **8.** $-\sqrt{121}$

9. $\pm\sqrt{121}$ **10.** $\sqrt{\frac{9}{4}}$ **11.** $\pm\sqrt{\frac{9}{4}}$ **12.** $\sqrt{\frac{1000}{10}}$

13. $\sqrt{\frac{50}{2}}$ **14.** $\sqrt{(x-1)^2}$ **15.** $\sqrt{49a^2}$ **16.** $\sqrt{x^2y^2}$

17. $\sqrt{-x^2y^2}$ **18.** $-\sqrt{x^2y^2}$ **19.** $\sqrt{x^2+10x+25}$ **20.** $\sqrt{y^2-8y+16}$

In a particular manufacturing plant, the productivity, p, is related to the work force, w, by the equation $p = \sqrt{w}$. Use this information in Exercises 21–23.

21. Find p when $w = 25$. **22.** Find w when $p = 12$. **23.** Find p when $w = -4$.

In Exercises 24–27, use a calculator to find each square root correct to three decimal places.

24. $\sqrt{41}$ **25.** $\sqrt{26.5}$ **26.** $\sqrt{627.84}$ **27.** $\sqrt{543.09}$

Use the formula given in Example 3 to solve each investment problem given in Exercises 28–29.

28. **INVESTMENT** Suppose Janet McShane invested \$300 in the stock market and two years later the stocks were worth \$525. Find the approximate annual rate of return on Janet's investment.

29. **INVESTMENT** If Peter Horn purchased an antique car for \$4500 and sold it two years later for \$6700, what was the approximate annual rate of return on his investment?

FOR REVIEW

Exercises 30–32 review material from Section 6.1 to help you prepare for the next section. Simplify each exponential expression.

30. $(2x^3)(18x^7)$ **31.** $\frac{8x^6}{2x^2}$ **32.** $\frac{50x^2y^3}{2x^6y}$

9.1 PARALLEL EXERCISES

Tell whether each number has 0, 1, or 2 square roots in Exercises 1–4.

1. 81 **2.** -81 **3.** 19 **4.** -0

Evaluate each square root in Exercises 5–20. Assume that all variables and algebraic expressions under the radical are nonnegative.

5. $\sqrt{49}$ **6.** $\sqrt{(-7)^2}$ **7.** $\sqrt{-7^2}$ **8.** $-\sqrt{144}$

9. $\pm\sqrt{144}$ **10.** $\sqrt{\frac{121}{16}}$ **11.** $\sqrt{\frac{75}{3}}$ **12.** $\pm\sqrt{\frac{64}{25}}$

13. $\sqrt{-0}$ **14.** $\sqrt{(y+2)^2}$ **15.** $\sqrt{36x^2}$ **16.** $\sqrt{u^2v^2}$

17. $\sqrt{-u^2v^2}$ **18.** $-\sqrt{u^2v^2}$ **19.** $\sqrt{x^2+12x+36}$ **20.** $\sqrt{y^2-14y+49}$

In a particular retail operation, the cost of production, c, is related to the number of items sold, n, by the equation $c = \sqrt{n}$. Use this information in Exercises 21–23.

21. Find c when $n = 49$.
22. Find n when $c = 6$.
23. Find c when $n = -1$.

In Exercises 24–27, use a calculator to find each square root correct to three decimal places.

24. $\sqrt{91}$
25. $\sqrt{63.7}$
26. $\sqrt{340.22}$
27. $\sqrt{992.13}$

Use the formula given in Example 3 to solve each investment problem given in Exercises 28–29.

28. **INVESTMENT** Craig Gagstetter invested \$2150 in savings. At the end of two years the account was worth \$2490. Find the approximate annual rate of return.

29. **INVESTMENT** Jane Gunton bought a painting for \$3200. Two years later it was valued at \$4100. What was the approximate annual rate of return?

FOR REVIEW

Exercises 30–32 review material from Section 6.1 to help you prepare for the next section. Simplify each exponential expression.

30. $(3y^5)(15y^3)$
31. $\dfrac{30y^6}{10y^5}$
32. $\dfrac{99x^3y^7}{11x^7y}$

9.1 ENRICHMENT EXERCISES

Use the definition of cube root, $\sqrt[3]{a^3} = a$, in Exercises 1–4.

1. $\sqrt[3]{5^3}$
2. $\sqrt[3]{27}$
3. $\sqrt[3]{8x^3}$
4. $\sqrt[3]{(2x+1)^6}$

In Exercises 5–8 do not assume that variables or algebraic expressions under radicals necessarily represent nonnegative real numbers. That is, evaluate each root and write answers using absolute value bars when appropriate to make sure that principal square roots are nonnegative.

5. $\sqrt{y^2}$
6. $-\sqrt{y^2}$
7. $\sqrt{(x-1)^2}$
8. $\sqrt{x^2y^2}$

9. If x represents a real number, is x positive or negative?

10. If x represents a real number, is $-x$ positive or negative?

11. If x is a real number, when will $\sqrt{x}$ be a real number?

12. If x is a real number, when will $\sqrt{-x}$ be a real number?

13. Explain why $\sqrt{(-3)^2}$ is 3 and not -3 according to our definition of principal square roots.

14. Enter 5 on your calculator and press the $\boxed{\sqrt{\ }}$ key. Without clearing the display, press the $\boxed{x^2}$ key. What does your display show? Now enter 5 on your calculator and press the $\boxed{\sqrt{\ }}$ key. Write down the number in the display, clear your calculator, and enter the number you wrote. Press the $\boxed{x^2}$ key. Does the display show 5? Explain what is happening.

15. Enter -5 on your calculator, press the $\boxed{x^2}$ key, then press the $\boxed{\sqrt{\ }}$ key. Does your calculator give back the number -5? Explain what this says about your calculator and the way it is programmed to find roots.

SECTION 9.2 Simplifying Radicals

Student guideposts

- *Square roots of products*
- *Square roots of quotients*
- *Rationalizing a denominator*
- *Simplified radicals*

Square roots of products

In the last section we saw that $\sqrt{9} = \sqrt{3^2} = 3$, but what about square roots such as $\sqrt{18}$? We might use a calculator but this would result in only an approximation of $\sqrt{18}$. However, since $18 = 9 \cdot 2$, we can write

$$\sqrt{18} = \sqrt{9 \cdot 2} = \sqrt{9} \cdot \sqrt{2}$$
$$= 3\sqrt{2}.$$

This is an example of the following rule.

Simplifying Rule for Products

If $a \geq 0$ and $b \geq 0$, then

$$\sqrt{ab} = \sqrt{a}\sqrt{b}.$$

The square root of a product is equal to the product of square roots.

What do we look for to take advantage of this rule? In the example

$$\sqrt{18} = \sqrt{9 \cdot 2} = \sqrt{9}\sqrt{2} = 3\sqrt{2},$$

9 is a perfect square. Thus we look for perfect square factors of the radicand (18 in this case). Notice that when there are no perfect square factors the rule does not help us. For example, it does no good in trying to simplify $\sqrt{6} = \sqrt{2 \cdot 3}$ since neither 2 nor 3 is a perfect square. In fact $\sqrt{6}$ is in its simplest form.

NOTE When using the simplifying rule for products, it sometimes helps to factor the radicand into the product of primes to recognize perfect squares. For example, we could write

$$\sqrt{18} = \sqrt{3 \cdot 3 \cdot 2} = \sqrt{3^2 \cdot 2} = \sqrt{3^2}\sqrt{2} = 3\sqrt{2}.$$

This technique would be especially helpful when a perfect square is a larger number.

EXAMPLE 1 Simplifying Square Roots of Products

Simplify the radicals.

(a) $\sqrt{27} = \sqrt{9 \cdot 3}$ 9 is a perfect square

$= \sqrt{9}\sqrt{3}$ $\sqrt{ab} = \sqrt{a}\sqrt{b}$

$= 3\sqrt{3}$ $\sqrt{9} = \sqrt{3^2} = 3$

(b) $\sqrt{52} = \sqrt{4 \cdot 13}$ — 4 is a perfect square
$= \sqrt{4}\sqrt{13}$ — $\sqrt{ab} = \sqrt{a}\sqrt{b}$
$= 2\sqrt{13}$ — $\sqrt{4} = \sqrt{2^2} = 2$

(c) $\sqrt{15} = \sqrt{3 \cdot 5}$ — Cannot be simplified since neither 3 nor 5 is a perfect square
$= \sqrt{15}$

(d) $\sqrt{3^4} = \sqrt{(3^2)^2}$ — $3^4 = 3^{2 \cdot 2} = (3^2)^2$, which is a perfect square
$= 3^2 = 9$ — $\sqrt{(3^2)^2} = 3^2$

(e) $2\sqrt{3^6} = 2\sqrt{(3^3)^2}$ — $3^6 = 3^{3 \cdot 2} = (3^3)^2$
$= 2 \cdot 3^3 = 2 \cdot 27 = 54$

(f) $\sqrt{3^7} = \sqrt{3^6 \cdot 3}$ — $3^7 = 3^{6+1} = 3^6 \cdot 3^1 = 3^6 \cdot 3$
$= \sqrt{(3^3)^2}\sqrt{3}$
$= 3^3\sqrt{3} = 27\sqrt{3}$ ■

As Example 1 illustrates, to simplify radicals we need to recall the rules of exponents such as

$$a^{m+n} = a^m a^n \quad \text{and} \quad a^{mn} = (a^m)^n.$$

Notice in Example 1(d) and (e) when the exponent under the radical is even, the radicand is a perfect square. When the exponent under the radical is odd, we rewrite the radicand as a product with a perfect square factor. For example, in Example 1(f), we rewrite $3^7 = 3^6 \cdot 3$ and then simplify further. This process also works with variables. For example,

$\sqrt{x^7} = \sqrt{x^6 \cdot x}$ — x^6 is a perfect square
$= \sqrt{x^6}\sqrt{x}$ — $\sqrt{ab} = \sqrt{a}\sqrt{b}$
$= \sqrt{(x^3)^2}\sqrt{x}$ — $x^6 = x^{3 \cdot 2} = (x^3)^2$
$= x^3\sqrt{x}.$

Remember our agreement that all variables represent nonnegative real numbers.

EXAMPLE 2 **Finding Square Roots Involving Variables**

Simplify the radicals.

(a) $\sqrt{x^4} = \sqrt{(x^2)^2}$ — $(x^2)^2$ is a perfect square
$= x^2$

(b) $\sqrt{x^5} = \sqrt{x^4 \cdot x}$ — $x^5 = x^{4+1} = x^4 \cdot x$
$= \sqrt{x^4}\sqrt{x}$ — $\sqrt{ab} = \sqrt{a}\sqrt{b}$
$= \sqrt{(x^2)^2}\sqrt{x}$
$= x^2\sqrt{x}$

(c) $\sqrt{27a^3} = \sqrt{9 \cdot 3 \cdot a^2 \cdot a}$ — 9 and a^2 are perfect squares

$= \sqrt{9 \cdot a^2 \cdot 3a}$ — $3a$ will be left under the radical

$= \sqrt{9} \cdot \sqrt{a^2} \cdot \sqrt{3a}$ — The simplifying rule expanded to three factors, $\sqrt{abc} = \sqrt{a}\sqrt{b}\sqrt{c}$

$= 3 \cdot a \cdot \sqrt{3a}$

$= 3a\sqrt{3a}$

(d) $\sqrt{x^4y^7} = \sqrt{x^4y^6 \cdot y}$ — x^4 and y^6 are perfect squares

$= \sqrt{x^4}\sqrt{y^6}\sqrt{y}$ — $\sqrt{abc} = \sqrt{a}\sqrt{b}\sqrt{c}$

$= \sqrt{(x^2)^2}\sqrt{(y^3)^2}\sqrt{y}$

$= x^2y^3\sqrt{y}$

(e) $\sqrt{288ab^2} = \sqrt{2 \cdot 144 \cdot a \cdot b^2}$ — 144 and b^2 are perfect squares

$= \sqrt{144 \cdot b^2 \cdot 2a}$

$= \sqrt{144}\sqrt{b^2}\sqrt{2a}$

$= 12b\sqrt{2a}$

▶ *Square roots of quotients*

We can use the simplifying rule above to simplify

$$\sqrt{\frac{9}{4}} = \sqrt{\left(\frac{3}{2}\right)^2} = \frac{3}{2}.$$

This can also be simplified as

$$\sqrt{\frac{9}{4}} = \frac{\sqrt{9}}{\sqrt{4}} = \frac{3}{2}.$$

This is an example of the following rule which is used for radical expressions involving fractions.

Simplifying Rule for Quotients

If $a \geq 0$ and $b > 0$, then

$$\sqrt{\frac{a}{b}} = \frac{\sqrt{a}}{\sqrt{b}}.$$

The square root of a quotient is equal to the quotient of the square roots.

EXAMPLE 3 **Simplifying Square Roots of Quotients**

Simplify the radicals.

(a) $\sqrt{\frac{27}{4}} = \frac{\sqrt{27}}{\sqrt{4}}$ — $\sqrt{\frac{a}{b}} = \frac{\sqrt{a}}{\sqrt{b}}$

$= \frac{\sqrt{9 \cdot 3}}{2}$ — $\sqrt{4} = 2$

$= \frac{\sqrt{9}\sqrt{3}}{2} = \frac{3\sqrt{3}}{2}$ — $\sqrt{ab} = \sqrt{a}\sqrt{b}$

(b) $\sqrt{\dfrac{4x^3}{y^2}} = \dfrac{\sqrt{4x^3}}{\sqrt{y^2}}$ $\qquad \sqrt{\dfrac{a}{b}} = \dfrac{\sqrt{a}}{\sqrt{b}}$

$= \dfrac{\sqrt{4 \cdot x^2 \cdot x}}{y}$ $\qquad \sqrt{y^2} = y$

$= \dfrac{\sqrt{4}\sqrt{x^2}\sqrt{x}}{y}$ $\qquad \sqrt{abc} = \sqrt{a}\sqrt{b}\sqrt{c}$

$= \dfrac{2x\sqrt{x}}{y}$

(c) $\sqrt{\dfrac{48x^3y^2}{3xy}} = \sqrt{\dfrac{\not{3} \cdot 16 \cdot x^3 \cdot y^2}{\not{3}xy}}$ $\qquad$ Simplify under the radical first

$= \sqrt{16x^2y}$ $\qquad \dfrac{x^3}{x} = x^{3-1} = x^2, \dfrac{y^2}{y} = y^{2-1} = y$

$= \sqrt{16}\sqrt{x^2}\sqrt{y}$

$= 4x\sqrt{y}$ ■

Notice that in Example 3(c) we used

$$\frac{a^m}{a^n} = a^{m-n}.$$

▶ *Rationalizing a denominator*

Consider the following problem.

$$\sqrt{\frac{9}{7}} = \frac{\sqrt{9}}{\sqrt{7}} = \frac{3}{\sqrt{7}} \qquad \sqrt{7} \text{ is in the denominator}$$

When a square root is left in the denominator, the radical expression is not considered completely simplified. The process of removing radicals from the denominator (making the denominator a rational number) is called **rationalizing the denominator.** We do this by making the expression under the radical in the denominator a perfect square.

To rationalize denominators we need the following property. Since $\sqrt{ab} = \sqrt{a}\sqrt{b}$, if we let $a = b$, then

$$\sqrt{aa} = \sqrt{a}\sqrt{a}$$
$$\sqrt{a^2} = \sqrt{a}\sqrt{a}$$
$$a = \sqrt{a}\sqrt{a}.$$

Thus, $\sqrt{7}\sqrt{7} = 7$ and $\sqrt{x^3}\sqrt{x^3} = x^3$.

EXAMPLE 4 **Rationalizing Denominators**

Rationalize the denominators.

(a) $\dfrac{3}{\sqrt{7}} = \dfrac{3\sqrt{7}}{\sqrt{7}\sqrt{7}}$ $\qquad$ Multiply numerator and denominator by $\sqrt{7}$

$= \dfrac{3\sqrt{7}}{7}$ $\qquad$ Since $\sqrt{7}\sqrt{7} = 7$, the denominator is now rational

(b) $\sqrt{\dfrac{25x^2}{y}} = \dfrac{\sqrt{25x^2}}{\sqrt{y}}$ $\qquad \sqrt{\dfrac{a}{b}} = \dfrac{\sqrt{a}}{\sqrt{b}}$

$= \dfrac{\sqrt{25}\,\sqrt{x^2}}{\sqrt{y}}$

$= \dfrac{5x}{\sqrt{y}}$

$= \dfrac{5x\sqrt{y}}{\sqrt{y}\,\sqrt{y}} = \dfrac{5x\sqrt{y}}{y}$ $\qquad$ The denominator is rationalized

(c) $\sqrt{\dfrac{25x^2y}{yz^2}} = \sqrt{\dfrac{25x^2\not{y}}{\not{y}z^2}}$ $\qquad$ Simplify under the radical first

$= \dfrac{\sqrt{25x^2}}{\sqrt{z^2}}$ $\qquad \sqrt{\dfrac{a}{b}} = \dfrac{\sqrt{a}}{\sqrt{b}}$

$= \dfrac{5x}{z}$ $\qquad$ Do not need to rationalize ■

NOTE The phrase ''rationalize the denominator'' refers to making the denominator into a rational number. Historically, denominators were rationalized to make computation of approximate values easier. For example, consider the expression

$$\frac{1}{\sqrt{3}} \text{ which rationalized becomes } \frac{1}{\sqrt{3}} = \frac{1 \cdot \sqrt{3}}{\sqrt{3} \cdot \sqrt{3}} = \frac{\sqrt{3}}{3}.$$

Using 1.732 for an approximation of $\sqrt{3}$, we can calculate an approximate value for $\frac{1}{\sqrt{3}}$, or equivalently, $\frac{\sqrt{3}}{3}$, as follows:

$$\frac{1}{\sqrt{3}} \approx \frac{1}{1.732} \approx 0.577 \quad \text{and} \quad \frac{\sqrt{3}}{3} \approx \frac{1.732}{3} \approx 0.577$$

Clearly without a calculator, the second division is easier than the first. As a result, prior to the availability of calculators, rationalizing denominators made a lot of sense. So why do we rationalize today? There are two reasons. First, the process of rationalizing has other applications in more advanced mathematics; and second, if we rationalize, our answers will always have the same form for easy comparison.

▶ *Simplified radicals* We now summarize what is meant for a radical to be in simplest form.

A Radical Is Considered Simplified

1. When there are no perfect square factors of the radicand.
2. When there are no fractions under the radical.
3. When there are no radicals in the denominator.

EXAMPLE 5 **Solving an Application to Physics**

If an object is dropped from a height of h feet, the time t in seconds it takes the object to reach the ground is given by the formula

$$t = \sqrt{\frac{h}{16}}.$$

Simplify this radical expression and use it to find the time it would take for a rock to reach the ground if dropped from a hot air balloon 144 feet above the ground. See Figure 9.1.

FIGURE 9.1

Simplify t.

$$t = \sqrt{\frac{h}{16}} = \frac{\sqrt{h}}{\sqrt{16}} = \frac{\sqrt{h}}{4}$$

Substitute 144 for h.

$$t = \frac{\sqrt{h}}{4} = \frac{\sqrt{144}}{4} = \frac{12}{4} = 3$$

It would take 3 seconds for the rock to reach the ground. ■

9.2 EXERCISES

Simplify each radical in Exercises 1–28. Assume that all variables are positive.

1. $\sqrt{75}$
2. $\sqrt{10}$
3. $\sqrt{32}$
4. $3\sqrt{200}$
5. $\sqrt{7^3}$
6. $\sqrt{5^5}$
7. $\sqrt{75y^2}$
8. $\sqrt{25x^3}$
9. $\sqrt{75y^3}$
10. $\sqrt{3^3y^3}$
11. $\sqrt{147x^5}$
12. $\sqrt{9x^2y^2}$
13. $\sqrt{27x^3y^2}$
14. $\sqrt{48x^2y^3}$
15. $\sqrt{75x^9y^5}$
16. $\sqrt{\frac{75}{49}}$
17. $\sqrt{\frac{50}{32}}$
18. $\sqrt{\frac{25x^2}{y^2}}$
19. $\sqrt{\frac{16x^4}{y^4}}$
20. $\sqrt{\frac{75x^2}{y^2}}$

21. $\sqrt{\dfrac{75x^2y^4}{3}}$ 22. $\sqrt{\dfrac{x^3y^3}{49}}$ 23. $\dfrac{8}{\sqrt{7}}$ 24. $\sqrt{\dfrac{9}{5}}$

25. $\sqrt{\dfrac{75x^2y^3}{yz^2}}$ 26. $\sqrt{\dfrac{36y^2}{x}}$ 27. $\sqrt{\dfrac{25x^3}{y^3z^4}}$ 28. $\sqrt{\dfrac{48x^2y^2}{3x^4y^4}}$

In a wholesale operation, it has been estimated that the cost, c, is related to the number of items sold, n, by the equation $c = \sqrt{n}$. Use this information in Exercises 29–31.

29. Find c if $n = 8$. **30.** Find c if $n = 75$. **31.** Find c if $n = 2^5$.

PHYSICS *A child drops a coin from the top of a building. Use the formula given in Example 5 to find the time it will take for the coin to reach the ground for each height h given in Exercises 32–35. Use a calculator to give the answer correct to the nearest tenth of a second if appropriate.*

32. 256 ft **33.** 100 ft **34.** 150 ft **35.** 740 ft

FOR REVIEW

Evaluate each radical in Exercises 36–38.

36. $-\sqrt{121}$ **37.** $\sqrt{-121}$ **38.** $\sqrt{x^2 - 10x + 25}$

9.2 PARALLEL EXERCISES

Simplify each radical in Exercises 1–28. Assume that all variables are positive.

1. $\sqrt{98}$ **2.** $\sqrt{35}$ **3.** $\sqrt{50}$ **4.** $2\sqrt{300}$

5. $\sqrt{5^3}$ **6.** $\sqrt{7^5}$ **7.** $\sqrt{98y^2}$ **8.** $\sqrt{49x^3}$

9. $\sqrt{98y^3}$ **10.** $\sqrt{5^3x^3}$ **11.** $\sqrt{125x^5}$ **12.** $\sqrt{16x^2y^2}$

13. $\sqrt{32x^3y^2}$ **14.** $\sqrt{27x^2y^3}$ **15.** $\sqrt{12x^7y^9}$ **16.** $\sqrt{\dfrac{75}{144}}$

17. $\sqrt{\dfrac{45}{20}}$ **18.** $\sqrt{\dfrac{49x^2}{y^2}}$ **19.** $\sqrt{\dfrac{81x^4}{y^4}}$ **20.** $\sqrt{\dfrac{147x^2}{y^2}}$

21. $\sqrt{\dfrac{x^5y^5}{25}}$ **22.** $\sqrt{\dfrac{147x^4y^7}{3}}$ **23.** $\dfrac{3}{\sqrt{5}}$ **24.** $\sqrt{\dfrac{16}{3}}$

25. $\sqrt{\dfrac{4x^4}{y}}$ **26.** $\sqrt{\dfrac{147x^3y^2}{xz^2}}$ **27.** $\sqrt{\dfrac{50x^3y^3}{2x^5y^5}}$ **28.** $\sqrt{\dfrac{16x^5}{y^5z^2}}$

In a manufacturing process, two quantities p and r are related by the equation $p = \sqrt{r}$. Use this information in Exercises 29–31.

29. Find p when $r = 27$. **30.** Find p when $r = 32$. **31.** Find p when $r = 3^5$.

PHYSICS *A child drops a coin from the top of a building. Use the formula given in Example 5 to find the time it will take for the coin to reach the ground for each height h given in Exercises 32–35. Use a calculator to give the answer correct to the nearest tenth of a second if appropriate.*

32. 64 ft **33.** 196 ft **34.** 270 ft **35.** 580 ft

FOR REVIEW

Evaluate each radical in Exercises 36–38.

36. $-\sqrt{144}$ **37.** $\sqrt{-144}$ **38.** $\sqrt{x^2 + 10x + 25}$

9.2 ENRICHMENT EXERCISES

Simplify each radical in Exercises 1–3. Assume all variables are positive.

1. $\sqrt{\dfrac{27x^9y^7}{2x^6}}$ **2.** $\sqrt{\dfrac{243x^5y^4}{8xyz^3}}$ △ **3.** $\sqrt{\dfrac{75xy}{9x^5y^6z^7}}$

Use $\sqrt[3]{a^3} = a$ in Exercises 4–6.

4. $\sqrt[3]{y^5}$ **5.** $\sqrt[3]{\dfrac{81x^5y^4}{8z^3}}$ △ **6.** $\sqrt[3]{\dfrac{24x^4}{y}}$

7. If $\sqrt{xy}$ is the denominator of an expression, explain how you would rationalize the denominator of the expression.

8. When Burford worked a problem he obtained $\sqrt{\frac{4}{3}}$ for his answer. When he checked the answers in the text, the answer given was $\frac{2\sqrt{3}}{3}$. Burford assumed that he had made a major error, thought he didn't understand the material, and decided not to finish the exercise set. Write a sentence or two and explain to Burford that he probably is not as bad off as he might have thought.

9. Discuss what is meant by the phrase *simplified radical.*

10. Write a short paragraph explaining why denominators were rationalized in the past and why we continue to rationalize denominators today.

SECTION 9.3 Multiplication and Division of Radicals

Student guideposts

- ▶ *Product of square roots*
- ▶ *Quotient of square roots*

In algebra we work with the real number system. As a result, it is important for us to be able to multiply, divide, add, and subtract real numbers. In Chapters 1 and 2 we reviewed these operations on the rational numbers, which make up part of the set of real numbers. Up to now, we have not spent any time with the operations on irrational numbers. Since many irrational numbers are defined by radicals, for example, $\sqrt{2}$, $\sqrt{3}$, $\sqrt{5}$, and so forth, we should be able to operate on these kinds of numbers as well. In this section, we consider the operations of multiplication and division by looking at products and quotients of radicals.

▶ *Product of square roots*

The simplifying rule for products, introduced in Section 9.2, allows us to simplify radicals like the following.

$$\sqrt{4 \cdot 9} = \sqrt{4}\sqrt{9} = 2 \cdot 3 = 6$$

The rule can also be used in the reverse order to multiply radicals. For example,

$\sqrt{2}\sqrt{18} = \sqrt{2 \cdot 18}$	Reverse of the simplifying rule
$= \sqrt{2 \cdot 2 \cdot 9}$	Factor 18 into $2 \cdot 9$
$= \sqrt{4 \cdot 9}$	4 and 9 are perfect squares
$= \sqrt{4}\sqrt{9} = 2 \cdot 3 = 6.$	

Here we used the simplifying rule for products from Section 9.2 in reverse order. This gives us the rule for multiplying radicals.

Multiplication Rule

If $a \geq 0$ and $b \geq 0$, then

$$\sqrt{a}\sqrt{b} = \sqrt{ab}.$$

The product of square roots is equal to the square root of the product.

EXAMPLE 1

Multiplying Radicals

Multiply and then simplify.

(a) $\sqrt{7}\sqrt{7} = \sqrt{7 \cdot 7}$	$\sqrt{a}\sqrt{b} = \sqrt{ab}$
$= \sqrt{7^2} = 7$	We did this in Section 9.2
(b) $\sqrt{5}\sqrt{20} = \sqrt{5 \cdot 20}$	$\sqrt{a}\sqrt{b} = \sqrt{ab}$
$= \sqrt{5 \cdot 5 \cdot 4}$	
$= \sqrt{25 \cdot 4}$	25 and 4 are perfect squares
$= \sqrt{25}\sqrt{4}$	$\sqrt{ab} = \sqrt{a}\sqrt{b}$
$= 5 \cdot 2 = 10$	
(c) $\sqrt{6}\sqrt{75} = \sqrt{6 \cdot 75}$	$\sqrt{a}\sqrt{b} = \sqrt{ab}$
$= \sqrt{2 \cdot 3 \cdot 3 \cdot 25}$	Factor to find perfect squares
$= \sqrt{9 \cdot 25 \cdot 2}$	2 will be left under the radical
$= \sqrt{9}\sqrt{25}\sqrt{2}$	
$= 3 \cdot 5 \cdot \sqrt{2} = 15\sqrt{2}$	
(d) $\sqrt{5}\sqrt{7y} = \sqrt{5 \cdot 7 \cdot y}$	$\sqrt{a}\sqrt{b} = \sqrt{ab}$
$= \sqrt{35y}$	This is considered a simpler form than $\sqrt{5}\sqrt{7y}$
(e) $\sqrt{3x}\sqrt{75x} = \sqrt{3x \cdot 75x}$	$\sqrt{a}\sqrt{b} = \sqrt{ab}$
$= \sqrt{3 \cdot 3 \cdot 25 \cdot x^2}$	Look for perfect squares
$= \sqrt{9}\sqrt{25}\sqrt{x^2}$	9, 25, and x^2 are perfect squares
$= 3 \cdot 5 \cdot x = 15x$	

EXAMPLE 2 **Multiplying Radicals**

Multiply and then simplify.

(a) $\sqrt{5x^3}\sqrt{3x^3}\sqrt{5x} = \sqrt{5x^3 \cdot 3x^3 \cdot 5x}$ — $\sqrt{a}\sqrt{b}\sqrt{c} = \sqrt{abc}$

$= \sqrt{5 \cdot 5 \cdot x^3 \cdot x^3 \cdot 3x}$ — Look for perfect squares

$= \sqrt{5^2 \cdot (x^3)^2 \cdot 3x}$ — 5^2 and $(x^3)^2$ are perfect squares

$= \sqrt{5^2}\sqrt{(x^3)^2}\sqrt{3x}$

$= 5x^3\sqrt{3x}$

(b) $\sqrt{2xy}\sqrt{2x^3y^3} = \sqrt{2xy \cdot 2x^3y^3}$ — $\sqrt{a}\sqrt{b} = \sqrt{ab}$

$= \sqrt{2^2x^4y^4}$

$= \sqrt{2^2}\sqrt{(x^2)^2}\sqrt{(y^2)^2}$ — $x^4 = (x^2)^2$ and $y^4 = (y^2)^2$

$= 2x^2y^2$

(c) $7\sqrt{6ab}\sqrt{3a} = 7\sqrt{6ab \cdot 3a}$ — Multiplication rule

$= 7\sqrt{2 \cdot 3 \cdot 3 \cdot a^2 \cdot b}$ — 3^2 and a^2 are perfect squares

$= 7\sqrt{3^2a^2 \cdot 2b}$

$= 7\sqrt{3^2}\sqrt{a^2}\sqrt{2b}$

$= 7 \cdot 3 \cdot a \cdot \sqrt{2b}$

$= 21a\sqrt{2b}$ ■

▶ *Quotient of square roots* The simplifying rule for quotients, presented in Section 9.2, allows us to simplify problems such as

$$\sqrt{\frac{9}{4}} = \frac{\sqrt{9}}{\sqrt{4}} = \frac{3}{2}.$$

Again, we can reverse this rule to simplify quotients of radicals. For example,

$$\frac{\sqrt{45}}{\sqrt{20}} = \sqrt{\frac{45}{20}} = \sqrt{\frac{\cancel{5} \cdot 9}{\cancel{5} \cdot 4}} = \sqrt{\frac{9}{4}} = \frac{\sqrt{9}}{\sqrt{4}} = \frac{3}{2}.$$

We see that a quotient of radicals may be simplified by first considering the radical of the quotient, then reducing the quotient. This technique is summarized in the next rule.

Division Rule

If $a \geq 0$ and $b > 0$, then

$$\frac{\sqrt{a}}{\sqrt{b}} = \sqrt{\frac{a}{b}}.$$

The quotient of square roots is equal to the square root of the quotient.

EXAMPLE 3 **Dividing Radicals**

Divide and then simplify.

(a) $\dfrac{\sqrt{75}}{\sqrt{12}} = \sqrt{\dfrac{75}{12}}$ $\qquad \dfrac{\sqrt{a}}{\sqrt{b}} = \sqrt{\dfrac{a}{b}}$

$= \sqrt{\dfrac{\cancel{3} \cdot 25}{\cancel{3} \cdot 4}}$ $\qquad$ Look for perfect squares and common factors

$= \sqrt{\dfrac{25}{4}}$ $\qquad$ 25 and 4 are perfect squares

$= \dfrac{\sqrt{25}}{\sqrt{4}} = \dfrac{5}{2}$ $\qquad \sqrt{\dfrac{a}{b}} = \dfrac{\sqrt{a}}{\sqrt{b}}$

(b) $\dfrac{\sqrt{15x^3}}{\sqrt{3x}} = \sqrt{\dfrac{15x^3}{3x}}$ $\qquad \dfrac{\sqrt{a}}{\sqrt{b}} = \sqrt{\dfrac{a}{b}}$

$= \sqrt{\dfrac{\cancel{3} \cdot 5 \cdot \cancel{x} \cdot x^2}{\cancel{3}\cancel{x}}}$ $\qquad$ 3 and x are common factors and x^2 is a perfect square

$= \sqrt{5x^2} = x\sqrt{5}$

(c) $\dfrac{\sqrt{12y^5}}{} = \sqrt{\dfrac{12y^5}{}}$ $\qquad$ Division rule

$= \sqrt{\dfrac{\cancel{3} \cdot 4 \cdot \cancel{y^5}}{\cancel{3} \cdot 25 \cdot \cancel{y^5} \cdot y^4}}$ $\qquad$ 3 and y^5 are common factors since $y^9 = y^{5+4} = y^5 \cdot y^4$

$= \sqrt{\dfrac{4}{25y^4}}$

$= \dfrac{\sqrt{4}}{\sqrt{25}\sqrt{y^4}} = \dfrac{2}{5y^2}$ ■

EXAMPLE 4 **Dividing Radicals**

Divide and then simplify.

(a) $\dfrac{\sqrt{3xy^3}}{\sqrt{4x^3y}} = \sqrt{\dfrac{3xy^3}{4x^3y}}$ $\qquad$ Division rule

$= \sqrt{\dfrac{3 \cdot \cancel{x} \cdot y^2 \cdot \cancel{y}}{4 \cdot \cancel{x} \cdot x^2 \cdot \cancel{y}}}$ $\qquad$ x and y are common factors

$= \sqrt{\dfrac{3y^2}{4x^2}}$

$= \dfrac{\sqrt{y^2}\sqrt{3}}{\sqrt{4}\sqrt{x^2}} = \dfrac{y\sqrt{3}}{2x}$

(b) $\dfrac{2\sqrt{3x}}{\sqrt{12x^3}} = 2\sqrt{\dfrac{3x}{12x^3}}$ Division rule

$= 2\sqrt{\dfrac{\cancel{3} \cdot \cancel{x}}{\cancel{3} \cdot 4 \cdot x^2 \cdot \cancel{x}}}$ 3 and x are common factors

$= 2\sqrt{\dfrac{1}{4x^2}}$ 1 is left in the numerator

$= \dfrac{2\sqrt{1}}{\sqrt{4}\sqrt{x^2}}$

$= \dfrac{\cancel{2} \cdot 1}{\cancel{2}x} = \dfrac{1}{x}$ 2 is a common factor and $\sqrt{1} = 1$

(c) $\dfrac{\sqrt{2x^2}}{\sqrt{6y}} = \sqrt{\dfrac{2x^2}{6y}}$ Division rule

$= \sqrt{\dfrac{x^2}{3y}}$ 2 is a common factor

$= \dfrac{\sqrt{x^2}}{\sqrt{3y}}$

$= \dfrac{x}{\sqrt{3y}}$

$= \dfrac{x\sqrt{3y}}{\sqrt{3y}\sqrt{3y}}$ Rationalize the denominator

$= \dfrac{x\sqrt{3y}}{3y}$ ■

9.3 EXERCISES

Multiply and simplify in Exercises 1–16.

1. $\sqrt{2}\sqrt{50}$ **2.** $\sqrt{15}\sqrt{5}$ **3.** $\sqrt{18}\sqrt{98}$ **4.** $\sqrt{6}\sqrt{7}$

5. $\sqrt{6}\sqrt{30}$ **6.** $2\sqrt{24}\sqrt{42}$ **7.** $\sqrt{98}\sqrt{75}$ **8.** $\sqrt{27x}\sqrt{3x}$

9. $\sqrt{15y}\sqrt{5}$ **10.** $\sqrt{3a^2}\sqrt{12a}$ **11.** $\sqrt{3x^3}\sqrt{3x}$ **12.** $\sqrt{2xy}\sqrt{8xy}$

13. $\sqrt{6x^2y}\sqrt{2xy^2}$ **14.** $\sqrt{7x^3y^3}\sqrt{42xy^3}$ **15.** $\sqrt{5x}\sqrt{15xy}\sqrt{3y}$ **16.** $\sqrt{2xy}\sqrt{6xy}\sqrt{9xy}$

Divide and simplify in Exercises 17–32.

17. $\dfrac{\sqrt{50}}{\sqrt{2}}$ **18.** $\dfrac{\sqrt{98}}{\sqrt{18}}$ **19.** $\dfrac{\sqrt{6}}{\sqrt{50}}$ **20.** $\dfrac{\sqrt{54}}{\sqrt{50}}$

21. $\dfrac{\sqrt{4}}{\sqrt{3}}$ **22.** $\dfrac{\sqrt{20}}{\sqrt{35}}$ **23.** $\dfrac{\sqrt{50x^2}}{\sqrt{2x^2}}$ **24.** $\dfrac{\sqrt{3y}}{\sqrt{4y}}$

25. $\dfrac{\sqrt{27x^2}}{\sqrt{3}}$ **26.** $\dfrac{\sqrt{4y}}{\sqrt{y^3}}$ **27.** $\dfrac{\sqrt{9x^2y}}{\sqrt{4y}}$ **28.** $\dfrac{\sqrt{50x^3y^3}}{\sqrt{2xy}}$

29. $\frac{5\sqrt{2xy}}{\sqrt{25x}}$
30. $\frac{\sqrt{18x}}{\sqrt{2y}}$
31. $\frac{\sqrt{25}}{\sqrt{x}}$
32. $\frac{\sqrt{2y^2}}{\sqrt{5x}}$

In an environmental study, three quantities m, p, and q have been found to be related by the equation $m = \sqrt{p}\sqrt{q}$. Use this information in Exercises 33–35.

33. Find m if $p = 4$ and $q = 9$.
34. Find m if $p = 25$ and $q = 8$.
35. Find m if $p = 4$ and $q = -4$.

FOR REVIEW

Simplify each radical in Exercises 36–38.

36. $\sqrt{147x^2y}$
37. $\sqrt{\frac{98x^2}{25}}$
38. $\sqrt{\frac{36x^2}{5y}}$

Exercises 39–41 review material from Section 2.5 to prepare for the next section. Use the distributive law to collect like terms.

39. $4x - x + 6x$
40. $\frac{1}{2}y - \frac{3}{4}y + \frac{1}{8}y$
41. $4x + 3y - 2x - 9y$

9.3 PARALLEL EXERCISES

Multiply and simplify in Exercises 1–16.

1. $\sqrt{5}\sqrt{45}$
2. $\sqrt{6}\sqrt{2}$
3. $\sqrt{20}\sqrt{45}$
4. $\sqrt{7}\sqrt{11}$
5. $\sqrt{10}\sqrt{18}$
6. $3\sqrt{35}\sqrt{45}$
7. $\sqrt{72}\sqrt{48}$
8. $\sqrt{8x}\sqrt{2x}$
9. $\sqrt{12y}\sqrt{4}$
10. $\sqrt{5a^2}\sqrt{20a}$
11. $\sqrt{5x}\sqrt{5x^3}$
12. $\sqrt{3xy}\sqrt{27xy}$
13. $\sqrt{10x^2y}\sqrt{2xy^2}$
14. $\sqrt{5x^3y^3}\sqrt{35xy^3}$
15. $\sqrt{2x}\sqrt{14xy}\sqrt{7y}$
16. $\sqrt{3xy}\sqrt{15xy}\sqrt{xy}$

Divide and simplify in Exercises 17–32.

17. $\frac{\sqrt{3}}{\sqrt{48}}$
18. $\frac{\sqrt{125}}{\sqrt{45}}$
19. $\frac{\sqrt{14}}{\sqrt{72}}$
20. $\frac{\sqrt{150}}{\sqrt{8}}$
21. $\frac{\sqrt{9}}{\sqrt{2}}$
22. $\frac{\sqrt{50}}{\sqrt{14}}$
23. $\frac{\sqrt{98x^2}}{\sqrt{2x^2}}$
24. $\frac{\sqrt{5y}}{\sqrt{9y}}$
25. $\frac{\sqrt{8a^3}}{\sqrt{2}}$
26. $\frac{\sqrt{9y}}{\sqrt{y^3}}$
27. $\frac{\sqrt{25xy^2}}{\sqrt{9x}}$
28. $\frac{\sqrt{98x^3y^3}}{\sqrt{2xy}}$
29. $\frac{7\sqrt{3xy}}{\sqrt{49y}}$
30. $\frac{\sqrt{16}}{\sqrt{x}}$
31. $\frac{\sqrt{75y}}{\sqrt{3x}}$
32. $\frac{\sqrt{3x^2}}{\sqrt{7y}}$

During a scientific experiment, it was found that three quantities v, w, and d are related by the equation $v = \frac{\sqrt{w}}{\sqrt{d}}$. Use this information in Exercises 33–35.

33. Find v if $w = 8$ and $d = 16$.
34. Find v if $w = 0$ and $d = 5$.
35. Find v if $w = -9$ and $d = 7$.

FOR REVIEW

Simplify each radical in Exercises 36–38.

36. $\sqrt{75xy^2}$
37. $\sqrt{\frac{147x^2}{16}}$
38. $\sqrt{\frac{25x^2}{6y}}$

Exercises 39–41 review material from Section 2.5 to prepare for the next section. Use the distributive law to collect like terms.

39. $3x + 7x - 6x$

40. $\frac{2}{3}y - \frac{1}{9}y + \frac{1}{18}y$

41. $-5x + 4y + 2x - 6y$

9.3 ENRICHMENT EXERCISES

Multiply or divide and simplify in Exercises 1–3.

1. $\sqrt{3x^3y^{-3}}\sqrt{6xy^{-1}}$

2. $\frac{\sqrt{125x^{-6}y^{-3}}}{\sqrt{45x^4y^{-6}}}$

3. $\frac{\sqrt{16x^2y^5z^{-1}}}{\sqrt{6x^3y^{-4}z^{-3}}}$

Use $\sqrt[3]{a^3} = a$ in Exercises 4–6.

4. $\sqrt[3]{81x^4y^6}\sqrt[3]{18x^5y^5}$

5. $\frac{\sqrt[3]{9x^4y^7}}{\sqrt[3]{24xy^2}}$

6. $\frac{\sqrt[3]{40x^6y}}{\sqrt[3]{25xy^5}}$

7. GEOMETRY The radius r of a circle inscribed in a triangle with sides a, b, and c (see the figure below) is given by

$$r = \frac{\sqrt{s-a}\sqrt{s-b}\sqrt{s-c}}{\sqrt{s}},$$

where $s = \frac{1}{2}(a + b + c)$. Write the right side of this formula as a single radical, and use the result to find the radius of circle inscribed in a triangle with sides 12.0 in, 14.0 in, and 20.0 in. Give the radius correct to the nearest tenth of an inch.

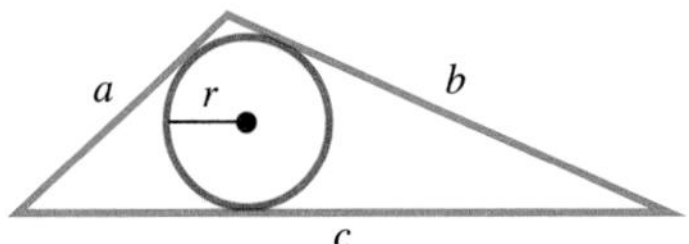

8. Evaluate $\sqrt{a+b}$ when $a = 144$ and $b = 25$. Then evaluate $\sqrt{a} + \sqrt{b}$ when $a = 144$ and $b = 25$. What can you conclude from this?

9. Evaluate $\sqrt{a-b}$ when $a = 169$ and $b = 25$. Then evaluate $\sqrt{a} - \sqrt{b}$ when $a = 169$ and $b = 25$. What can you conclude from this?

10. Explain how you would multiply $\sqrt{30}$ times $\sqrt{15}$, giving complete descriptions of each of your steps.

SECTION 9.4 Addition and Subtraction of Radicals

Student guideposts

- **Like radicals and unlike radicals**
- **Adding and subtracting radicals**

The rules for multiplication and division of radicals,

$$\sqrt{a}\sqrt{b} = \sqrt{ab} \quad \text{and} \quad \frac{\sqrt{a}}{\sqrt{b}} = \sqrt{\frac{a}{b}},$$

do not have counterparts relative to addition and subtraction. For example,

$$\sqrt{9+16} = \sqrt{25} = 5 \quad \text{but} \quad \sqrt{9} + \sqrt{16} = 3 + 4 = 7, \qquad 5 \neq 7$$

so that in general,

$$\sqrt{a+b} \neq \sqrt{a} + \sqrt{b}.$$

Also, since

$$\sqrt{25-9} = \sqrt{16} = 4 \quad \text{but} \quad \sqrt{25} - \sqrt{9} = 5 - 3 = 2, \qquad 4 \neq 2$$

in general,

$$\sqrt{a-b} \neq \sqrt{a} - \sqrt{b}.$$

▶ *Like radicals and unlike radicals*

We may, however, use the distributive law to add or subtract *like radicals.* **Like radicals** have the same radicand. Thus, the terms

$$\sqrt{11}, \quad 3\sqrt{11}, \quad -5\sqrt{11} \qquad \text{Like radicals}$$

have like radicals. Also, terms such as

$$\sqrt{x}, \quad -7\sqrt{x}, \quad 100\sqrt{x} \qquad \text{Like radicals}$$

contain like radicals. However,

$$\sqrt{11}, \quad \sqrt{x}, \quad 3\sqrt{y} \qquad \text{Unlike radicals}$$

do not have like radicals; they are **unlike radicals.**

▶ *Adding and subtracting radicals*

We add or subtract like radicals just as we collect like terms of polynomials. Remember,

$$3x + 5x = (3+5)x = 8x.$$

We collect like radicals in the same way.

$$3\sqrt{x} + 5\sqrt{x} = (3+5)\sqrt{x} = 8\sqrt{x}$$

EXAMPLE 1 **Adding and Subtracting Like Radicals**

Add or subtract.

(a) $9\sqrt{5} + 4\sqrt{5} = (9+4)\sqrt{5}$ Distributive law, $ac + bc = (a+b)c$
$= 13\sqrt{5}$

(b) $9\sqrt{5} - 4\sqrt{5} = (9-4)\sqrt{5}$ Distributive law, $ac - bc = (a-b)c$
$= 5\sqrt{5}$

(c) $3\sqrt{xy} - 10\sqrt{xy} = (3-10)\sqrt{xy}$ Distributive law
$= -7\sqrt{xy}$

(d) $7\sqrt{x} + 5\sqrt{y}$ cannot be simplified since $\sqrt{x}$ and $\sqrt{y}$ are not like radicals. ■

Some unlike radicals can be changed into like radicals if we simplify. For example, $\sqrt{2}$ and $\sqrt{8}$ are not like radicals since they have different radicands. However,

$$\sqrt{8} = \sqrt{4 \cdot 2} = \sqrt{4}\,\sqrt{2} = 2\sqrt{2}.$$

Now the terms $\sqrt{2}$ and $2\sqrt{2}$ do contain like radicals.

To Add or Subtract Radicals

1. Simplify each radical as much as possible.
2. Use the distributive law to collect any like radicals.

EXAMPLE 2 **Simplifying Before Adding or Subtracting**

Add or subtract.

(a) $3\sqrt{2} + 5\sqrt{8} = 3\sqrt{2} + 5\sqrt{4 \cdot 2}$ — 4 is a perfect square

$= 3\sqrt{2} + 5\sqrt{4}\,\sqrt{2}$ — $\sqrt{ab} = \sqrt{a}\,\sqrt{b}$

$= 3\sqrt{2} + 5 \cdot 2\sqrt{2}$ — $\sqrt{4} = 2$

$= 3\sqrt{2} + 10\sqrt{2}$ — Terms now contain like radicals

$= (3 + 10)\sqrt{2} = 13\sqrt{2}$ — Distributive law

(b) $\sqrt{12} + \sqrt{75} = \sqrt{4 \cdot 3} + \sqrt{25 \cdot 3}$ — 4 and 25 are perfect squares

$= \sqrt{4}\,\sqrt{3} + \sqrt{25}\,\sqrt{3}$ — $\sqrt{ab} = \sqrt{a}\,\sqrt{b}$

$= 2\sqrt{3} + 5\sqrt{3}$ — $\sqrt{4} = 2$ and $\sqrt{25} = 5$

$= (2 + 5)\sqrt{3} = 7\sqrt{3}$ — Distributive law

(c) $5\sqrt{12} - 7\sqrt{27} = 5\sqrt{4 \cdot 3} - 7\sqrt{9 \cdot 3}$ — 4 and 9 are perfect squares

$= 5\sqrt{4}\,\sqrt{3} - 7\sqrt{9}\,\sqrt{3}$ — $\sqrt{ab} = \sqrt{a}\,\sqrt{b}$

$= 5 \cdot 2 \cdot \sqrt{3} - 7 \cdot 3 \cdot \sqrt{3}$

$= 10\sqrt{3} - 21\sqrt{3}$ — Terms contain like radicals

$= (10 - 21)\sqrt{3} = -11\sqrt{3}$ — Distributive law

(d) $2\sqrt{25y} - 4\sqrt{36y} = 2\sqrt{25}\,\sqrt{y} - 4\sqrt{36}\,\sqrt{y}$ — 25 and 36 are perfect squares

$= 2 \cdot 5\sqrt{y} - 4 \cdot 6\sqrt{y}$

$= 10\sqrt{y} - 24\sqrt{y}$

$= (10 - 24)\sqrt{y} = -14\sqrt{y}$ — Distributive law ∎

EXAMPLE 3 **Adding Several Radicals**

Perform the indicated operations.

(a) $4\sqrt{18} + 3\sqrt{27} - 6\sqrt{12}$

$= 4\sqrt{9 \cdot 2} + 3\sqrt{9 \cdot 3} - 6\sqrt{4 \cdot 3}$

$= 4\sqrt{9}\,\sqrt{2} + 3\sqrt{9}\,\sqrt{3} - 6\sqrt{4}\,\sqrt{3}$

$= 4 \cdot 3\sqrt{2} + 3 \cdot 3\sqrt{3} - 6 \cdot 2\sqrt{3}$

$= 12\sqrt{2} + 9\sqrt{3} - 12\sqrt{3}$ — Only the last two terms are like terms

$= 12\sqrt{2} + (9 - 12)\sqrt{3}$ — Distributive law

$= 12\sqrt{2} - 3\sqrt{3}$ — As simple as possible

(b) $$\begin{aligned} 3\sqrt{x} - 2\sqrt{4x} - 5\sqrt{9x} &= 3\sqrt{x} - 2\sqrt{4}\sqrt{x} - 5\sqrt{9}\sqrt{x} \\ &= 3\sqrt{x} - 2 \cdot 2\sqrt{x} - 5 \cdot 3\sqrt{x} \\ &= 3\sqrt{x} - 4\sqrt{x} - 15\sqrt{x} \\ &= (3 - 4 - 15)\sqrt{x} = -16\sqrt{x} \quad \blacksquare \end{aligned}$$

To obtain like terms, it may be necessary to rationalize denominators.

EXAMPLE 4 **Rationalizing Before Adding**

Add or subtract.

(a) $$\begin{aligned} 3\sqrt{2} + \frac{5}{\sqrt{2}} &= 3\sqrt{2} + \frac{5\sqrt{2}}{\sqrt{2}\sqrt{2}} && \text{Rationalize denominator} \\ &= 3\sqrt{2} + \frac{5\sqrt{2}}{2} && \sqrt{2}\sqrt{2} = 2 \\ &= 3\sqrt{2} + \frac{5}{2}\sqrt{2} && \frac{5\sqrt{2}}{2} = \frac{5 \cdot \sqrt{2}}{2 \cdot 1} = \frac{5}{2} \cdot \frac{\sqrt{2}}{1} = \frac{5}{2}\sqrt{2} \\ &= \left(3 + \frac{5}{2}\right)\sqrt{2} && \text{Distributive law} \\ &= \left(\frac{6}{2} + \frac{5}{2}\right)\sqrt{2} = \frac{11}{2}\sqrt{2} = \frac{11\sqrt{2}}{2} \end{aligned}$$

(b) $$\begin{aligned} \frac{6}{\sqrt{5}} - 4\sqrt{5} &= \frac{6\sqrt{5}}{\sqrt{5}\sqrt{5}} - 4\sqrt{5} && \text{Rationalize the denominator} \\ &= \frac{6\sqrt{5}}{5} - 4\sqrt{5} \\ &= \frac{6}{5}\sqrt{5} - 4\sqrt{5} && \frac{6\sqrt{5}}{5} = \frac{6 \cdot \sqrt{5}}{5 \cdot 1} = \frac{6}{5} \cdot \frac{\sqrt{5}}{1} = \frac{6}{5}\sqrt{5} \\ &= \left(\frac{6}{5} - 4\right)\sqrt{5} && \text{Distributive law} \\ &= \left(\frac{6}{5} - \frac{20}{5}\right)\sqrt{5} \\ &= -\frac{14}{5}\sqrt{5} = -\frac{14\sqrt{5}}{5} \quad \blacksquare \end{aligned}$$

9.4 EXERCISES

Add or subtract in Exercises 1–15.

1. $9\sqrt{2} + \sqrt{2}$
2. $-4\sqrt{5} + 3\sqrt{5}$
3. $-18\sqrt{xy} - 7\sqrt{xy}$
4. $3\sqrt{2} + 2\sqrt{3}$
5. $\sqrt{50} + \sqrt{98}$
6. $\sqrt{18} - \sqrt{8}$
7. $5\sqrt{3} - \sqrt{27}$
8. $4\sqrt{50} + 7\sqrt{18}$
9. $3\sqrt{18} - 5\sqrt{12}$

10. $\sqrt{147} - 2\sqrt{75}$ **11.** $6\sqrt{44} + 2\sqrt{99}$ **12.** $2\sqrt{75} - 3\sqrt{125}$
13. $2\sqrt{4x} + 7\sqrt{9x}$ **14.** $8\sqrt{50y} + 2\sqrt{18y}$ **15.** $x\sqrt{y^3} + y\sqrt{x^2y}$

Perform the indicated operations in Exercises 16–23.

16. $\sqrt{18} + \sqrt{50} + \sqrt{72}$ **17.** $\sqrt{27} - \sqrt{75} - \sqrt{108}$
18. $-3\sqrt{24} - 5\sqrt{150} - 4\sqrt{54}$ **19.** $4\sqrt{98} - 8\sqrt{72} + 5\sqrt{32}$
20. $\sqrt{4x} + \sqrt{16x} - \sqrt{25x}$ **21.** $3\sqrt{5x} + 2\sqrt{20x} - 8\sqrt{45x}$
22. $9\sqrt{100a^2b^2} - 4\sqrt{36a^2b^2} - 10\sqrt{a^2b^2}$ **23.** $2\sqrt{25ab^3} - b\sqrt{36ab} - 5\sqrt{49ab^3}$

In Exercises 24–29, rationalize the denominator and then add or subtract.

24. $\sqrt{3} + \dfrac{1}{\sqrt{3}}$ **25.** $2\sqrt{5} - \dfrac{3}{\sqrt{5}}$ **26.** $3\sqrt{7} - \sqrt{\dfrac{1}{7}}$

27. $-3\sqrt{5} - \dfrac{9}{\sqrt{5}}$ **28.** $\dfrac{\sqrt{2}}{\sqrt{10}} - \sqrt{5}$ **29.** $\sqrt{\dfrac{2}{3}} - 2\sqrt{6}$

Suppose we are given the formula $F = \sqrt{f} + 2\sqrt{g}$, relating the three quantities, F, f, and g. Use this information in Exercises 30–31.

30. Find F when $f = 60$ and $g = 15$. **31.** Find F when $f = 0$ and $g = 7$.

FOR REVIEW

Perform the indicated operations in Exercises 32–34.

32. $\sqrt{3a^2}\sqrt{15a}$ **33.** $\dfrac{\sqrt{150x}}{\sqrt{3x}}$ **34.** $\dfrac{\sqrt{12x^2}}{\sqrt{5y}}$

Exercises 35–38 review material from Sections 6.5 and 6.6. They will help you prepare for the next section. Multiply the polynomials.

35. $(x - y)(x + 7y)$ **36.** $(x - 3y)^2$ **37.** $(x + 4y)(x - 4y)$ **38.** $(3x - 7y)(3x + 7y)$

9.4 PARALLEL EXERCISES

Add or subtract in Exercises 1–15.

1. $5\sqrt{3} - 9\sqrt{3}$ **2.** $-5\sqrt{7} - 9\sqrt{7}$ **3.** $-9\sqrt{xy} - 3\sqrt{xy}$
4. $5\sqrt{5} + 3\sqrt{3}$ **5.** $\sqrt{48} + \sqrt{75}$ **6.** $\sqrt{45} - \sqrt{20}$
7. $4\sqrt{2} - \sqrt{50}$ **8.** $8\sqrt{32} + 3\sqrt{50}$ **9.** $6\sqrt{27} - 4\sqrt{18}$
10. $3\sqrt{75} - 5\sqrt{147}$ **11.** $-8\sqrt{99} + 8\sqrt{44}$ **12.** $5\sqrt{45} - 2\sqrt{48}$
13. $-4\sqrt{4y} - 9\sqrt{25y}$ **14.** $6\sqrt{8y} + 5\sqrt{32y}$ **15.** $y\sqrt{x^3} + x\sqrt{xy^2}$

Perform the indicated operations in Exercises 16–23.

16. $\sqrt{8} + \sqrt{72} + \sqrt{98}$ **17.** $\sqrt{12} - \sqrt{27} - \sqrt{147}$
18. $-2\sqrt{6} - 2\sqrt{54} - 5\sqrt{150}$ **19.** $5\sqrt{147} - 2\sqrt{108} + 7\sqrt{48}$
20. $\sqrt{25x} + \sqrt{36x} - \sqrt{49x}$ **21.** $5\sqrt{3x} + 6\sqrt{27x} - 7\sqrt{75x}$
22. $5\sqrt{25a^2b^2} - 3\sqrt{16^2b^2} - 20\sqrt{a^2b^2}$ **23.** $2a\sqrt{16ab} + \sqrt{4a^3b} - 3\sqrt{25a^3b}$

In Exercises 24–29, rationalize the denominator and then add or subtract.

24. $3\sqrt{5} - \dfrac{4}{\sqrt{5}}$ **25.** $\dfrac{8}{\sqrt{3}} + 2\sqrt{3}$ **26.** $4\sqrt{5} - \dfrac{1}{\sqrt{5}}$

27. $-4\sqrt{7} - \frac{3}{\sqrt{7}}$ **28.** $\sqrt{\frac{3}{2}} - 5\sqrt{6}$ **29.** $\frac{\sqrt{5}}{\sqrt{10}} - \sqrt{2}$

Suppose we have the formula $P = \sqrt{n} - 3\sqrt{p}$, relating the three quantities, P, n, and p. Use this information in Exercises 30–31.

30. Find P when $n = 49$ and $p = 45$. **31.** Find P when $n = 11$ and $p = 0$.

FOR REVIEW

Perform the indicated operations in Exercises 32–34.

32. $\sqrt{8a^2}\sqrt{10a}$ **33.** $\frac{\sqrt{150x}}{\sqrt{2x}}$ **34.** $\frac{\sqrt{18y^2}}{\sqrt{7x}}$

Exercises 35–38 review material from Sections 6.5 and 6.6. They will help you prepare for the next section. Multiply the polynomials.

35. $(2x - y)(x + 4y)$ **36.** $(4x - y)^2$ **37.** $(2x - y)(2x + y)$ **38.** $(5x + 2y)(5x - 2y)$

9.4 ENRICHMENT EXERCISES

Add or subtract in Exercises 1–4.

1. $\sqrt{12x^4 - 4x^2y^2} - \sqrt{27x^4 - 9x^2y^2}$

△ **2.** $\sqrt{2x^2 - 20xy + 50y^2} + \sqrt{8x^2 - 80xy + 200y^2}$

3. $3\sqrt[3]{40x^4y^4} - 2x\sqrt[3]{5xy^4}$ [*Hint*: $\sqrt[3]{a^3} = a$]

△ **4.** $-6ab\sqrt[3]{27a^5b^3} + 10\sqrt[3]{27a^8b^6}$

Find the error in Burford's work in Exercises 5–7. What is the correct answer?

5. $3\sqrt{x} + 4\sqrt{x} = 7\sqrt{2x}$ **6.** $2\sqrt{y} + 5\sqrt{y} = 10\sqrt{y}$ **7.** $2\sqrt{x} + 3\sqrt{y} = 5\sqrt{x + y}$

8. Write complete sentences describing each step as you add $3\sqrt{2x^3} + x\sqrt{2x}$ to obtain $4x\sqrt{2x}$.

SECTION 9.5 Summary of Techniques and Rationalizing Denominators

Student guideposts

- ▶ *Simplifying radical expressions*
- ▶ *Multiplying binomial radical expressions*
- ▶ *Rationalizing binomial denominators*

▶ *Simplifying radical expressions*

Below is a summary of the simplifying techniques from the previous sections.

To Simplify a Radical Expression

1. Combine all like radicals using the distributive laws.
2. When needed, use the rules of multiplication and division,

$$\sqrt{a}\sqrt{b} = \sqrt{ab} \quad \text{and} \quad \frac{\sqrt{a}}{\sqrt{b}} = \sqrt{\frac{a}{b}}.$$

3. Remove all perfect squares from under the radicals.
4. Rationalize all denominators.

The following table illustrates the various techniques.

Simplification	*Type*
$3\sqrt{2} - \sqrt{2} = 2\sqrt{2}$	Combining like radicals
$\sqrt{2}\sqrt{3} = \sqrt{6}$	Using multiplication rule
$\dfrac{\sqrt{12}}{\sqrt{3}} = \sqrt{\dfrac{12}{3}} = \sqrt{4} = 2$	Using division rule and removing perfect squares
$\sqrt{9x^2y} = 3x\sqrt{y}$	Removing perfect squares
$\dfrac{3}{\sqrt{2}} = \dfrac{3\sqrt{2}}{\sqrt{2}\sqrt{2}} = \dfrac{3\sqrt{2}}{2}$	Rationalizing the denominator

To multiply radical expressions, we often use one or more of the simplifying techniques, as in the next example.

EXAMPLE 1 **Multiplying Using the Distributive Law**

Multiply.

(a)
$$\begin{aligned}\sqrt{5}(\sqrt{15} + \sqrt{5}) &= \sqrt{5}\sqrt{15} + \sqrt{5}\sqrt{5} && \text{Distributive law}\\ &= \sqrt{5 \cdot 15} + \sqrt{5 \cdot 5} && \sqrt{a}\sqrt{b} = \sqrt{ab}\\ &= \sqrt{5 \cdot 5 \cdot 3} + \sqrt{5 \cdot 5} && \text{Factor}\\ &= \sqrt{5^2}\sqrt{3} + \sqrt{5^2} && 5^2 \text{ is a perfect square}\\ &= 5\sqrt{3} + 5\end{aligned}$$

(b)
$$\begin{aligned}\sqrt{3}(\sqrt{27} - \sqrt{12}) &= \sqrt{3}\sqrt{27} - \sqrt{3}\sqrt{12} && \text{Distributive law}\\ &= \sqrt{3 \cdot 3^3} - \sqrt{3 \cdot 3 \cdot 4} && \sqrt{a}\sqrt{b} = \sqrt{ab}\\ &= \sqrt{3^4} - \sqrt{3^2 \cdot 2^2} && 3^4,\ 3^2, \text{ and } 2^2 \text{ are perfect squares}\\ &= 3^2 - 3 \cdot 2\\ &= 9 - 6 = 3\end{aligned}$$

(c)
$$\begin{aligned}\sqrt{7}\left(5\sqrt{7} - \frac{8}{\sqrt{7}}\right) &= \sqrt{7}(5\sqrt{7}) - \sqrt{7}\left(\frac{8}{\sqrt{7}}\right) && \text{Distributive law}\\ &= 5(\sqrt{7})^2 - \frac{\cancel{\sqrt{7}}}{\cancel{\sqrt{7}}} \cdot 8 && \text{Commutative and associative laws}\\ &= 5 \cdot 7 - 1 \cdot 8 && (\sqrt{7})^2 = \sqrt{7}\sqrt{7} = 7\\ &= 35 - 8 = 27 \quad \blacksquare\end{aligned}$$

▶ *Multiplying binomial radical expressions* In Chapter 6 we used the FOIL method (*F*—First terms, *O*—Outside terms, *I*—Inside terms, and *L*—Last terms) to multiply binomials. Recall that, for example, to multiply $x + 2y$ and $2x - y$ we proceed as follows.

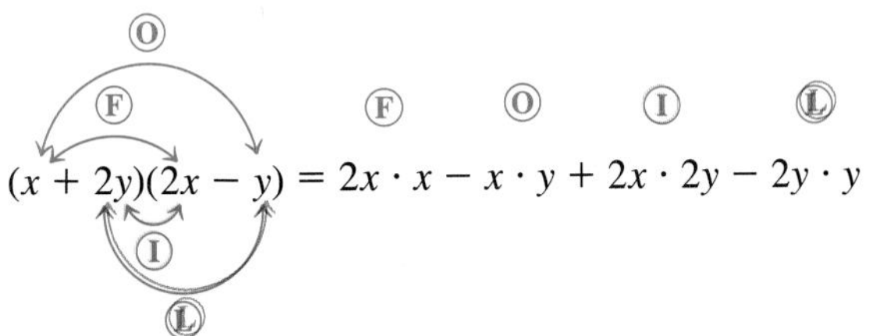

$$(x + 2y)(2x - y) = 2x \cdot x - x \cdot y + 2x \cdot 2y - 2y \cdot y$$

The same rule can be used to multiply binomial radical expressions.

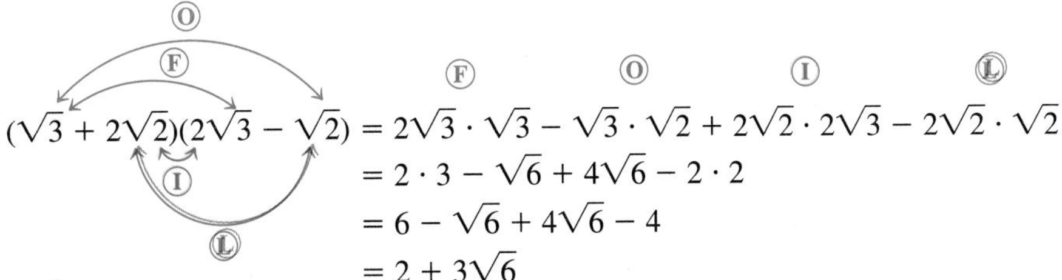

$$
\begin{aligned}
(\sqrt{3} + 2\sqrt{2})(2\sqrt{3} - \sqrt{2}) &= 2\sqrt{3} \cdot \sqrt{3} - \sqrt{3} \cdot \sqrt{2} + 2\sqrt{2} \cdot 2\sqrt{3} - 2\sqrt{2} \cdot \sqrt{2} \\
&= 2 \cdot 3 - \sqrt{6} + 4\sqrt{6} - 2 \cdot 2 \\
&= 6 - \sqrt{6} + 4\sqrt{6} - 4 \\
&= 2 + 3\sqrt{6}
\end{aligned}
$$

We multiplied the first terms Ⓕ, the outside terms Ⓞ, the inside terms Ⓘ, and the last terms Ⓛ, and then used the product rule and collected like terms.

EXAMPLE 2 **Using FOIL**

Multiply.

(a)
$$
\begin{aligned}
(\sqrt{3} - \sqrt{2})(\sqrt{3} + 5\sqrt{2}) &= \sqrt{3}\sqrt{3} + \sqrt{3}(5\sqrt{2}) - \sqrt{2}\sqrt{3} - \sqrt{2}(5\sqrt{2}) \\
&= 3 + 5\sqrt{6} - \sqrt{6} - 5(2) \\
&= 3 - 10 + (5 - 1)\sqrt{6} \\
&= -7 + 4\sqrt{6}
\end{aligned}
$$

(b)
$$
\begin{aligned}
(\sqrt{3} - \sqrt{2})(\sqrt{3} + \sqrt{2}) &= \sqrt{3}\sqrt{3} + \sqrt{3}\sqrt{2} - \sqrt{2}\sqrt{3} - \sqrt{2}\sqrt{2} \\
&= 3 + \sqrt{6} - \sqrt{6} - 2 \\
&= 3 - 2 \\
&= 1 \quad \blacksquare
\end{aligned}
$$

▶ *Rationalizing binomial denominators*

The product in Example 2(b) is the rational number 1. This is a special case of a more general result involving products of expressions of the form

$$(a - b)(a + b) = a^2 - b^2.$$

Notice that

$$
\begin{aligned}
(\sqrt{3} - \sqrt{2})(\sqrt{3} + \sqrt{2}) &= (\sqrt{3})^2 - (\sqrt{2})^2 \qquad \sqrt{3} = a \text{ and } \sqrt{2} = b \\
&= 3 - 2 = 1.
\end{aligned}
$$

Any time that a sum and a difference like those above are multiplied, the result will be a rational number free of radicals. This observation leads to a way to rationalize the denominator of an expression with a binomial in the denominator. For example, we can rationalize the denominator of $\frac{1}{\sqrt{3}-\sqrt{2}}$ by multiplying the numerator and denominator by $\sqrt{3}+\sqrt{2}$.

$$\frac{1}{\sqrt{3}-\sqrt{2}} = \frac{1(\sqrt{3}+\sqrt{2})}{(\sqrt{3}-\sqrt{2})(\sqrt{3}+\sqrt{2})}$$
$$= \frac{\sqrt{3}+\sqrt{2}}{(\sqrt{3})^2-(\sqrt{2})^2} = \frac{\sqrt{3}+\sqrt{2}}{3-2}$$
$$= \frac{\sqrt{3}+\sqrt{2}}{1} = \sqrt{3}+\sqrt{2}$$

Had the denominator been $\sqrt{3}+\sqrt{2}$, we would have rationalized by multiplying both numerator and denominator by $\sqrt{3}-\sqrt{2}$. The binomials $\sqrt{3}+\sqrt{2}$ and $\sqrt{3}-\sqrt{2}$ are called **conjugates** as are binomials of the form $\sqrt{3}+2$ and $\sqrt{3}-2$.

To Rationalize a Binomial Denominator

Multiply both numerator and denominator of the fraction by the conjugate of the denominator and simplify.

EXAMPLE 3

Rationalizing Denominators

Rationalize the denominators.

(a)
$$\frac{2}{\sqrt{7}+\sqrt{5}} = \frac{2(\sqrt{7}-\sqrt{5})}{(\sqrt{7}+\sqrt{5})(\sqrt{7}-\sqrt{5})}$$ Multiply numerator and denominator by $\sqrt{7}-\sqrt{5}$, the conjugate of $\sqrt{7}+\sqrt{5}$

$$= \frac{2(\sqrt{7}-\sqrt{5})}{(\sqrt{7})^2-(\sqrt{5})^2}$$ $(a+b)(a-b) = a^2-b^2$

$$= \frac{2(\sqrt{7}-\sqrt{5})}{7-5}$$ $(\sqrt{7})^2 = 7$ and $(\sqrt{5})^2 = 5$

$$= \frac{\cancel{2}(\sqrt{7}-\sqrt{5})}{\cancel{2}}$$
$$= \sqrt{7}-\sqrt{5}$$

(b)
$$\frac{\sqrt{3}}{\sqrt{3}-2} = \frac{\sqrt{3}(\sqrt{3}+2)}{(\sqrt{3}-2)(\sqrt{3}+2)}$$ Multiply numerator and denominator by $\sqrt{3}+2$, the conjugate of $\sqrt{3}-2$

$$= \frac{\sqrt{3}(\sqrt{3}+2)}{(\sqrt{3})^2-(2)^2}$$ $(a-b)(a+b) = a^2-b^2$

$$= \frac{\sqrt{3}(\sqrt{3}+2)}{3-4}$$ $(\sqrt{3})^2 = 3$ and $(2)^2 = 4$

$$= \frac{\sqrt{3}(\sqrt{3}+2)}{-1}$$
$$= -\sqrt{3}(\sqrt{3}+2)$$ $\frac{a}{-1} = -a$

$$= -\sqrt{3}\cdot\sqrt{3}-\sqrt{3}\cdot 2$$ Distributive law

$$= -3-2\sqrt{3}$$ ■

9.5 EXERCISES

Refer to the summary of techniques and simplify each expression in Exercises 1–12.

1. $\sqrt{20} - \sqrt{45}$

2. $\sqrt{3x}\sqrt{12x}$

3. $\dfrac{\sqrt{25x^2}}{\sqrt{3y}}$

4. $\sqrt{147} - \sqrt{108}$

5. $\sqrt{2}\sqrt{10} - \sqrt{15}\sqrt{3}$

6. $\dfrac{\sqrt{2}}{\sqrt{50}} - \dfrac{\sqrt{3}}{\sqrt{75}}$

7. $\dfrac{\sqrt{3}}{\sqrt{2}} - \dfrac{\sqrt{5}}{\sqrt{2}}$

8. $\sqrt{3x}\sqrt{6x} + \sqrt{5x}\sqrt{10x}$

9. $\sqrt{x}\sqrt{y} + \dfrac{\sqrt{xy^2}}{\sqrt{y}}$

10. $\sqrt{5x} - \dfrac{\sqrt{x}}{\sqrt{5}}$

11. $6\sqrt{2}\sqrt{6} + 2\sqrt{5}\sqrt{15} - 3\sqrt{12}\sqrt{25}$

12. $\sqrt{x^3}\sqrt{y} - 3x\sqrt{x}\sqrt{y} + \dfrac{4x\sqrt{xy^2}}{\sqrt{y}}$

Multiply and simplify in Exercises 13–24.

13. $\sqrt{3}(\sqrt{3} + \sqrt{2})$

14. $\sqrt{5}(\sqrt{125} - \sqrt{45})$

15. $\sqrt{7}(\sqrt{5} - \sqrt{125})$

16. $\sqrt{6}(\sqrt{2} - 1)$

17. $\sqrt{7}\left(\dfrac{1}{\sqrt{7}} + \sqrt{7}\right)$

18. $\sqrt{15}\left(\dfrac{\sqrt{3}}{\sqrt{5}} + \dfrac{1}{\sqrt{15}}\right)$

19. $\sqrt{5}\left(\sqrt{10} - \dfrac{\sqrt{5}}{\sqrt{2}}\right)$

20. $(\sqrt{2} - \sqrt{5})^2$

21. $(\sqrt{2} - \sqrt{5})(\sqrt{2} + \sqrt{5})$

22. $(2\sqrt{3} + 1)(\sqrt{3} + 1)$

23. $(\sqrt{2} - 2)(\sqrt{2} + 1)$

24. $(3\sqrt{3} - \sqrt{2})(2\sqrt{3} + \sqrt{2})$

Rationalize the denominator in Exercises 25–33.

25. $\dfrac{1}{\sqrt{2} - 1}$

26. $\dfrac{2}{\sqrt{7} + \sqrt{5}}$

27. $\dfrac{3}{\sqrt{5} - 2}$

28. $\dfrac{6}{\sqrt{5} + 2}$

29. $\dfrac{-8}{\sqrt{3} - \sqrt{7}}$

30. $\dfrac{2\sqrt{3}}{\sqrt{3} - 1}$

31. $\dfrac{\sqrt{2}}{\sqrt{2} + 1}$

32. $\dfrac{2\sqrt{5}}{\sqrt{5} - \sqrt{3}}$

33. $\dfrac{x - 1}{\sqrt{x} - 1}$

Exercises 34–36 will help you prepare for the next section. Square each expression.

34. $\sqrt{3x}$

35. $3\sqrt{2x - 5}$

36. $\sqrt{2x + 2}$

FOR REVIEW

Perform the indicated operations in Exercises 37–38.

37. $2\sqrt{75} - 6\sqrt{48} + 9\sqrt{12}$

38. $6\sqrt{20x} - 2\sqrt{45x} - \sqrt{5x}$

Exercises 39–41 review material from Chapter 3 and Section 7.5 to help you prepare for the next section. Solve each equation.

39. $x^2 - 1 = x(x + 1) + 2$

40. $x^2 - 3x - 4 = 0$

41. $x^2 + 2x = 0$

9.5 PARALLEL EXERCISES

Refer to the summary of techniques and simplify each expression in Exercises 1–12.

1. $\sqrt{98} + \sqrt{50}$

2. $\sqrt{5y}\sqrt{75y}$

3. $\dfrac{\sqrt{4y^2}}{\sqrt{3x}}$

4. $2\sqrt{175} - 3\sqrt{28}$

5. $\sqrt{5}\sqrt{10} - \sqrt{6}\sqrt{3}$

6. $\dfrac{\sqrt{3}}{\sqrt{75}} + \dfrac{\sqrt{5}}{\sqrt{125}}$

7. $\dfrac{\sqrt{2}}{\sqrt{5}} - \dfrac{\sqrt{3}}{\sqrt{5}}$

8. $\sqrt{2x}\sqrt{6x} + \sqrt{15x}\sqrt{5x}$

9. $\dfrac{\sqrt{x^2y}}{\sqrt{x}} - \sqrt{x}\sqrt{y}$

10. $\dfrac{\sqrt{x}}{\sqrt{7}} + \sqrt{7x}$

11. $3\sqrt{5}\sqrt{15} + 5\sqrt{27} - 6\sqrt{6}\sqrt{8}$

12. $\dfrac{3y\sqrt{x^2y}}{\sqrt{y}} + 3x\sqrt{y^2} - \dfrac{5x\sqrt{y^3}}{\sqrt{y}}$

Multiply and simplify in Exercises 13–24.

13. $\sqrt{2}(\sqrt{3} + \sqrt{2})$

14. $\sqrt{3}(\sqrt{27} - \sqrt{12})$

15. $\sqrt{5}(\sqrt{12} - \sqrt{48})$

16. $\sqrt{10}(\sqrt{5} + 1)$

17. $\sqrt{5}\left(\sqrt{5} - \dfrac{1}{\sqrt{5}}\right)$

18. $\sqrt{18}\left(\sqrt{2} - \dfrac{1}{\sqrt{18}}\right)$

19. $\sqrt{2}\left(\sqrt{10} - \dfrac{\sqrt{2}}{\sqrt{5}}\right)$

20. $(\sqrt{3} - \sqrt{7})^2$

21. $(\sqrt{3} - \sqrt{7})(\sqrt{3} + \sqrt{7})$

22. $(3\sqrt{5} + 1)(\sqrt{5} + 1)$

23. $(\sqrt{3} - 3)(\sqrt{3} + 1)$

24. $(2\sqrt{3} + \sqrt{5})(2\sqrt{3} - \sqrt{5})$

Rationalize the denominator in Exercises 25–33.

25. $\dfrac{2}{\sqrt{3} - 1}$

26. $\dfrac{3}{\sqrt{5} - \sqrt{2}}$

27. $\dfrac{4}{\sqrt{7} + \sqrt{3}}$

28. $\dfrac{6}{\sqrt{5} - \sqrt{7}}$

29. $\dfrac{9}{\sqrt{7} + 2}$

30. $\dfrac{2\sqrt{3}}{\sqrt{3} + 1}$

31. $\dfrac{4\sqrt{5}}{\sqrt{5} - 1}$

32. $\dfrac{3\sqrt{5}}{\sqrt{5} - \sqrt{2}}$

33. $\dfrac{1 - x}{1 - \sqrt{x}}$

Exercises 34–36 will help you prepare for the next section. Square each expression.

34. $\sqrt{5y}$

35. $2\sqrt{4x + 1}$

36. $\sqrt{3x - 3}$

FOR REVIEW

Perform the indicated operations in Exercises 37–38.

37. $5\sqrt{125} + 3\sqrt{5} - 8\sqrt{45}$

38. $7\sqrt{12x} - 3\sqrt{48x} - 2\sqrt{75x}$

Exercises 39–41 review material from Chapter 3 and Section 7.5 to help you prepare for the next section. Solve each equation.

39. $4 - x^2 = x(3 - x) - 2$

40. $x^2 + x - 6 = 0$

41. $2x^2 - x = 0$

9.5 ENRICHMENT EXERCISES

Multiply and simplify in Exercises 1–2.

1. $(\sqrt{ax} - \sqrt{by})(\sqrt{ax} + \sqrt{by})$

▲ **2.** $(\sqrt{x} - \sqrt{y})(x + \sqrt{xy} + y)$

Rationalize the denominator and simplify in Exercises 3–4.

3. $\dfrac{x\sqrt{y} - y\sqrt{x}}{\sqrt{x} - \sqrt{y}}$ △ **4.** $\dfrac{x}{\sqrt{4 - x^2}} + \sqrt{4 - x^2}$

In Exercises 5–7, rationalize the ***numerator*** *of each expression. To do this, multiply the numerator and denominator by the conjugate of the numerator. Rationalizing numerators is an important process in higher mathematics.*

△ **5.** $\dfrac{\sqrt{2} + 1}{\sqrt{2} - 1}$ **6.** $\dfrac{\sqrt{x} - \sqrt{y}}{\sqrt{x} + \sqrt{y}}$ **7.** $\dfrac{\sqrt{x} - \sqrt{y}}{x - y}$

In Exercises 8–10, the given equation is false. Change the right side to make it true.

8. $(2\sqrt{x})^2 = 2x$ △ **9.** $(\sqrt{x} + 1)^2 = x + 1$ **10.** $(2 - \sqrt{x + 1})^2 = 4 - x - 1$

11. Describe the process of *rationalizing a binomial denominator.*

SECTION 9.6 Solving Radical Equations

Student guideposts

▶ *Rule of squaring*
▶ *Solving equations involving radicals*

▶ ***Rule of squaring***

Sometimes an equation contains a radical expression with a variable in the radicand, such as $\sqrt{x} = 5$. We use the following rule to solve such equations.

Rule of Squaring

$$\text{If } a = b, \quad \text{then} \quad a^2 = b^2.$$

▶ ***Solving equations involving radicals***

When $\sqrt{x} = 5$, then the rule of squaring gives $(\sqrt{x})^2 = 5^2$ or $x = 25$. When this rule is applied to an equation with a variable, the resulting equation may have more solutions than the original. For instance, 2 is the only solution to the equation $x = 2$, but the equation formed by squaring both sides, $x^2 = 4$, has two solutions, 2 and -2. We call -2 an **extraneous root** in this case. Thus, when the rule of squaring is used, any possible solutions *must be* checked in the original equation, and extraneous roots must be discarded.

To Solve an Equation Involving Radicals

1. If only one radical is present, isolate this radical on one side of the equation and proceed to 3.
2. If two radicals are present, isolate one of the radicals on one side of the equation with the other radical on the other side.
3. Square both sides to obtain an equation without the isolated radical expression(s).
4. Solve the resulting equation.
5. Check all possible solutions in the original equation.

EXAMPLE 1 **Solving a Radical Equation**

Solve.

$$\sqrt{3x} - 5 = 7$$

$$\sqrt{3x} = 12 \quad \text{Add 5 to both sides to isolate radical on the left}$$

$$(\sqrt{3x})^2 = (12)^2 \quad \text{Use the rule of squaring}$$

$$3x = 144 \quad \text{Squaring}$$

$$x = 48 \quad \text{Divide both sides by 3}$$

Check: $\sqrt{3(48)} - 5 \stackrel{?}{=} 7$

$$\sqrt{144} - 5 \stackrel{?}{=} 7$$

$$12 - 5 \stackrel{?}{=} 7$$

$$7 = 7$$

The solution is 48. ■

EXAMPLE 2 **Solving a Radical Equation**

Solve.

$$\sqrt{x+3} + 4 = 11$$

$$\sqrt{x+3} = 11 - 4 \quad \text{Isolate the radical}$$

$$\sqrt{x+3} = 7$$

$$(\sqrt{x+3})^2 = 7^2 \quad \text{Rule of squaring}$$

$$x + 3 = 49$$

$$x = 46$$

Check: $\sqrt{46 + 3} + 4 \stackrel{?}{=} 11$

$$\sqrt{49} + 4 \stackrel{?}{=} 11$$

$$7 + 4 \stackrel{?}{=} 11$$

$$11 = 11$$

The solution is 46. ■

EXAMPLE 3 **Solving an Equation with Two Radicals**

Solve.

$$3\sqrt{2x-5} - \sqrt{x+23} = 0$$

$$3\sqrt{2x-5} = \sqrt{x+23} \quad \text{Isolate the radicals}$$

$$(3\sqrt{2x-5})^2 = (\sqrt{x+23})^2$$

$$9(2x-5) = x + 23 \quad \text{Be sure to square the 3 on the left}$$

$$18x - 45 = x + 23$$

$$17x = 68$$

$$x = 4$$

$$\text{Check:}\quad 3\sqrt{2\cdot 4-5}-\sqrt{4+23}\stackrel{?}{=}0$$
$$3\sqrt{3}-\sqrt{27}\stackrel{?}{=}0$$
$$3\sqrt{3}-3\sqrt{3}=0$$

The solution is 4. ∎

NOTE When solving any equation, it is a good idea to check possible solutions in the original equation. But when solving a radical equation, *you must check possible solutions in the original equation.* The process of squaring both sides may result in extraneous roots that must be discarded. If all possibilities are discarded, the equation has no solution. This is illustrated in the next example.

EXAMPLE 4

Working with an Equation with No Solution

Solve.

$$\sqrt{x^2-5}-x+5=0$$
$$\sqrt{x^2-5}=x-5 \qquad \text{Isolate the radical}$$
$$(\sqrt{x^2-5})^2=(x-5)^2 \qquad \text{Do } \textit{not} \text{ square the right side as } x^2-25$$
$$x^2-5=x^2-10x+25$$
$$-5=-10x+25 \qquad \text{Subtract } x^2 \text{ from both sides}$$
$$-30=-10x$$
$$x=\frac{-30}{-10}=3$$

$$\text{Check:}\quad \sqrt{3^2-5}-3+5\stackrel{?}{=}0$$
$$\sqrt{9-5}-3+5\stackrel{?}{=}0$$
$$\sqrt{4}-3+5\stackrel{?}{=}0$$
$$2-3+5\stackrel{?}{=}0 \qquad \sqrt{4} \text{ is 2 } \textit{not} -2$$
$$4\neq 0 \qquad \text{3 does not check}$$

The equation has no solution. ∎

CAUTION Remember that the radical represents the principal (nonnegative) root. Thus, in Example 4, we cannot replace $\sqrt{4}$ with -2 in the check.

Sometimes the equation that results when the radical is eliminated must be solved by factoring and using the zero-product rule. We see this in Example 5.

EXAMPLE 5 **Using the Zero-Product Rule**

Solve.

$$\sqrt{2x+2} - x + 3 = 0$$

$\sqrt{2x+2} = x - 3$	Isolate the radical
$(\sqrt{2x+2})^2 = (x-3)^2$	
$2x + 2 = x^2 - 6x + 9$	$(a-b)^2 = a^2 - 2ab + b^2$
$0 = x^2 - 8x + 7$	Subtract $2x$ and 2
$0 = (x-1)(x-7)$	Factor
$x - 1 = 0$ or $x - 7 = 0$	Zero-product rule
$x = 1$ $\quad$ $x = 7$	

Check:

$\sqrt{2(1)+2} - 1 + 3 \stackrel{?}{=} 0$	$\sqrt{2(7)+2} - 7 + 3 \stackrel{?}{=} 0$
$\sqrt{4} - 1 + 3 \stackrel{?}{=} 0$	$\sqrt{16} - 7 + 3 \stackrel{?}{=} 0$
$2 - 1 + 3 \stackrel{?}{=} 0$	$4 - 7 + 3 \stackrel{?}{=} 0$
$4 \neq 0$	$0 = 0$
1 does not check.	7 does check.

The only solution is 7. ■

9.6 EXERCISES

Solve each radical equation in Exercises 1–21.

1. $\sqrt{x} = 4$
2. $3\sqrt{2x} - 9 = 0$
3. $\sqrt{4x-3} = 5$
4. $3\sqrt{a-3} + 6 = 0$
5. $4\sqrt{2a-1} - 2 = 0$
6. $3\sqrt{x} = \sqrt{x+16}$
7. $3\sqrt{y+3} = \sqrt{y+35}$
8. $\sqrt{3a+2} - \sqrt{a+8} = 0$
9. $\sqrt{5a-3} - \sqrt{2a+1} = 0$
10. $3\sqrt{x-1} - \sqrt{x+31} = 0$
11. $3\sqrt{y+7} = 4\sqrt{y}$
12. $2\sqrt{2x+5} - 3\sqrt{3x-2} = 0$
13. $\sqrt{a^2-5} + a - 5 = 0$
14. $\sqrt{a^2+2} - a - 2 = 0$
15. $-\sqrt{x^2-12} + x + 6 = 0$
16. $\sqrt{x^2+16} - x + 8 = 0$
17. $\sqrt{x+1} = 1 - x$
18. $\sqrt{x-3} - x + 5 = 0$
19. $\sqrt{x+4} - x + 2 = 0$
20. $\sqrt{x+15} - x - 3 = 0$
21. $\sqrt{x+10} + x - 2 = 0$

FOR REVIEW

Simplify each expression in Exercises 22–23.

22. $(\sqrt{3} + \sqrt{5})(2\sqrt{3} - \sqrt{5})$
23. $\dfrac{3\sqrt{5}}{\sqrt{5} - \sqrt{2}}$

Exercises 24–25 will help you prepare for the next section.

24. If $c = \sqrt{a^2 + b^2}$, find c when $a = 4$ and $b = 3$.
25. If $b = \sqrt{c^2 - a^2}$, find b when $a = 5$ and $c = 13$.

9.6 PARALLEL EXERCISES

Solve each radical equation in Exercises 1–21.

1. $\sqrt{x} = 9$
2. $5\sqrt{3x} - 10 = 0$
3. $\sqrt{8x + 2} = 2$
4. $5\sqrt{a - 2} + 10 = 0$
5. $3\sqrt{3a + 1} - 6 = 0$
6. $5\sqrt{x} = \sqrt{x + 3}$
7. $3\sqrt{y - 2} = \sqrt{y + 12}$
8. $\sqrt{5a + 3} - \sqrt{a + 4} = 0$
9. $\sqrt{7a - 10} - \sqrt{4a - 5} = 0$
10. $2\sqrt{x - 5} - \sqrt{x + 22} = 0$
11. $3\sqrt{y + 2} = 5\sqrt{y}$
12. $3\sqrt{2x - 4} - 2\sqrt{3x + 3} = 0$
13. $\sqrt{a^2 + 5} - a + 5 = 0$
14. $\sqrt{a^2 - 8} - a - 4 = 0$
15. $-\sqrt{x^2 - 20} + x + 10 = 0$
16. $\sqrt{x^2 - 15} + x = 5$
17. $\sqrt{x + 1} = x - 1$
18. $\sqrt{x + 3} - x + 3 = 0$
19. $\sqrt{x + 6} - x - 4 = 0$
20. $\sqrt{x + 21} + x + 1 = 0$
21. $\sqrt{x + 5} + x - 1 = 0$

FOR REVIEW

Simplify each expression in Exercises 22–23.

22. $(\sqrt{5} - \sqrt{3})(\sqrt{5} - 2\sqrt{3})$
23. $\dfrac{4\sqrt{7}}{\sqrt{7} - \sqrt{5}}$

Exercises 24–25 will help you prepare for the next section.

24. If $c = \sqrt{a^2 + b^2}$, find c if $a = 6$ and $b = 8$.
25. If $a = \sqrt{c^2 - b^2}$, find a when $c = 7$ and $b = 5$.

9.6 ENRICHMENT EXERCISES

1. Square the expression $2 + \sqrt{x - 3}$, then solve the equation $\sqrt{x + 5} - \sqrt{x - 3} = 2$. You will use the first part in your solution, and you will need to isolate and square again.
2. Square the expression $5 - \sqrt{x + 2}$, then solve the equation $\sqrt{x - 3} + \sqrt{x + 2} = 5$. You will use the first part in your solution, and you will need to isolate and square again.

Burford's solutions to two equations are given in Exercises 3–4. What is wrong with Burford's work? What is the correct solution?

3.
$$\begin{aligned} \sqrt{x} + 3 &= 4 \\ (\sqrt{x})^2 + (3)^2 &= (4)^2 \\ x + 9 &= 16 \\ x &= 7 \end{aligned}$$

4.
$$\begin{aligned} \sqrt{a - 1} + 3 &= 0 \\ \sqrt{a - 1} &= -3 \\ (\sqrt{a - 1})^2 &= (-3)^2 \\ a - 1 &= 9 \\ a &= 10 \end{aligned}$$

5. Using the fact that the radical represents the nonnegative root only, can you explain to Burford why the equation in Exercise 4 cannot have a solution without going through all the steps and checking?
6. Explain the method used to solve a radical equation, and include a detailed discussion of why checking is a must when solving radical equations.

SECTION 9.7 Problem Solving Using Radicals

Student guideposts

▶ *Right triangles and the Pythagorean theorem*
▶ *30°—60° and 45°—45° right triangles*

▶ *Right triangles and the Pythagorean theorem*

Many applied problems use radicals. For example, finding one side of a right triangle when the other two sides are given requires taking a square root. Remember that a **right triangle** is a triangle with a 90° (right) angle. The side opposite the 90° angle is the **hypotenuse** of the right triangle and the remaining two sides are its **legs.** We will agree to label the legs a and b and the hypotenuse c as in Figure 9.2. The next well-known theorem is named after the Greek mathematician Pythagoras.

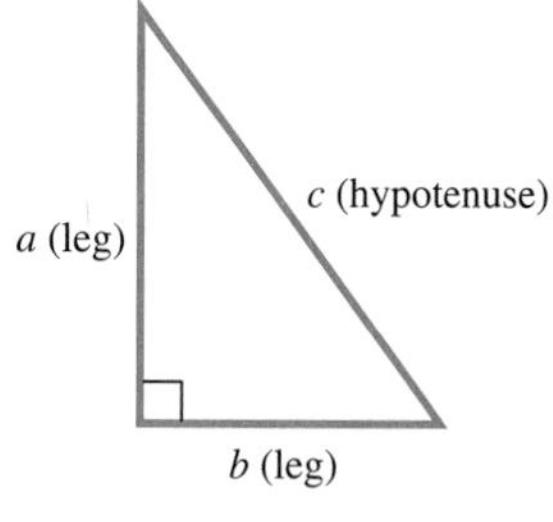

FIGURE 9.2
$a^2 + b^2 = c^2$

Pythagorean Theorem

In a right triangle with legs a and b and hypotenuse c,

$$a^2 + b^2 = c^2.$$

EXAMPLE 1 **Finding the Hypotenuse**

If the legs of a right triangle are 3 and 4, find the hypotenuse. See Figure 9.3.

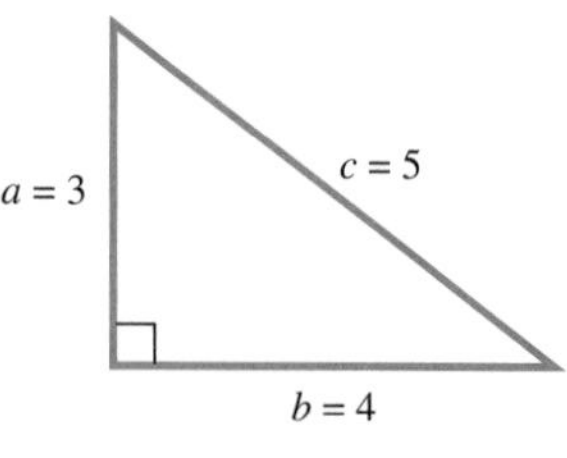

FIGURE 9.3

By the Pythagorean theorem,

$$\begin{aligned} c^2 &= a^2 + b^2 \\ &= 3^2 + 4^2 \qquad a = 3 \text{ and } b = 4 \\ &= 9 + 16 = 25. \end{aligned}$$

We need to solve $c^2 = 25$.

$$
\begin{aligned}
c^2 &= 25 \\
c^2 - 25 &= 0 && \text{Subtract 25} \\
c^2 - 5^2 &= 0 && 25 = 5^2 \\
(c + 5)(c - 5) &= 0 && \text{Factor using } a^2 - b^2 = (a + b)(a - b) \\
c + 5 = 0 \quad &\text{or} \quad c - 5 = 0 \\
c = -5 \quad & \qquad\quad c = 5
\end{aligned}
$$

Since we want the length of the hypotenuse, we discard -5; $c = 5$. ■

> NOTE Consider the following way to solve for c in Exercise 1.
>
> $$c^2 = 25$$
> $$c = \sqrt{25} = 5.$$
>
> That is, if we take the principal square root of both sides of the equation, the result is 5. This technique, useful when the equation cannot be factored, will be studied in more detail in Chapter 10.

EXAMPLE 2 Finding a Leg of the Triangle

If $c = 7$ and $a = 3$, find b. See Figure 9.4.

$$
\begin{aligned}
a^2 + b^2 &= c^2 && \text{Pythagorean theorem} \\
3^2 + b^2 &= 7^2 && a = 3 \text{ and } c = 7 \\
9 + b^2 &= 49 \\
b^2 &= 40 \\
b &= \sqrt{40} && \text{Take the principal square root on both sides} \\
b &= \sqrt{4 \cdot 10} = 2\sqrt{10}
\end{aligned}
$$

■

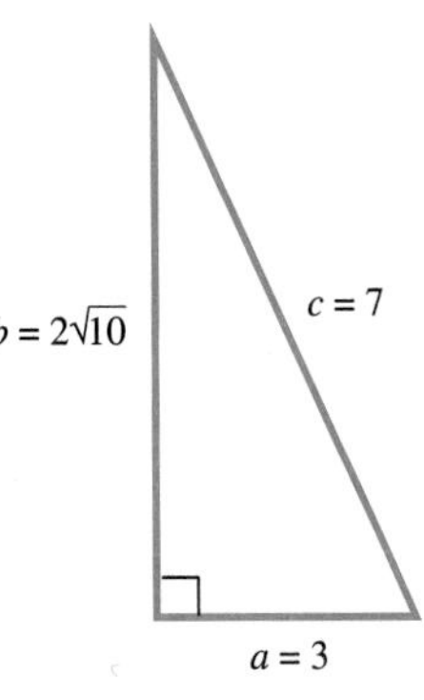

FIGURE 9.4

We now solve the applied problem given in the chapter introduction.

EXAMPLE 3

Working with a Construction Application

Mr. Rodriques is using a 20-ft ladder to aid in building a tree house for his two children. For safety reasons he'll place the foot of the ladder 8 feet from the base of the tree. How far up the side of the tree will the ladder reach? See Figure 9.5.

$$a^2 + b^2 = c^2 \qquad \text{Pythagorean theorem}$$
$$a^2 + 8^2 = 20^2 \qquad b = 8 \text{ and } c = 20$$
$$a^2 + 64 = 400$$
$$a^2 = 336$$
$$a = \sqrt{336} \qquad \text{Take the principal square root on both sides}$$
$$= \sqrt{16 \cdot 21}$$
$$= 4\sqrt{21}$$

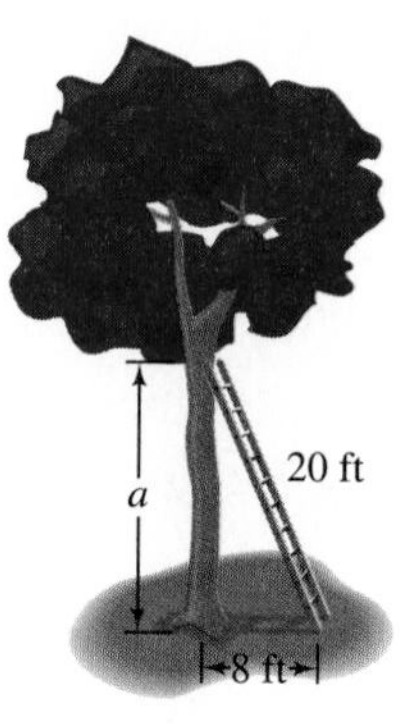

FIGURE 9.5

The top of the ladder is $4\sqrt{21}$ ft from the ground. It is usually practical to give an approximate solution. Using a calculator, we find that $\sqrt{21} \approx 4.58$, so that $4\sqrt{21} \approx 18.3$. Thus, the ladder reaches about 18.3 ft up the tree. ■

NOTE In Example 3 we used an approximate value for the answer, 18.3 ft, rather than $4\sqrt{21}$ ft since we are able to comprehend the height more easily this way. Keep in mind, however, that we only give decimal approximations to roots in applied problems for this reason.

Applications from the business world, such as the next one, use square roots.

EXAMPLE 4

Solving an Application to Business

A manufacturer of novelty items has found that his total daily costs for production are given by the equation

$$c = 10\sqrt{n + 25},$$

where c represents total costs and n is the number of items produced.

(a) Find the total costs when no items are produced. This is called **overhead.**

$$\begin{aligned} c &= 10\sqrt{n + 25} && \text{Cost equation} \\ &= 10\sqrt{0 + 25} && \text{Substitute 0 for } n \\ &= 10\sqrt{25} \\ &= 10 \cdot 5 = 50 \end{aligned}$$

Overhead is \$50 per day.

(b) Find the total costs when 600 items are produced.

$$\begin{aligned} c &= 10\sqrt{n + 25} && \text{Cost equation} \\ &= 10\sqrt{600 + 25} && \text{Substitute 600 for } n \\ &= 10\sqrt{625} \\ &= 10(25) = 250 && (25)^2 = 625 \end{aligned}$$

Total costs are \$250 per day when 600 items are produced.

(c) How many items are made when the cost is \$120 per day?

$$\begin{aligned} c &= 10\sqrt{n + 25} && \text{Cost equation} \\ 120 &= 10\sqrt{n + 25} && \text{We solve for } n \text{ when } c \text{ is 120} \\ 12 &= \sqrt{n + 25} && \text{To simplify, divide both sides by 10} \\ (12)^2 &= (\sqrt{n + 25})^2 && \text{Square both sides} \\ 144 &= n + 25 \\ 119 &= n \end{aligned}$$

Thus, 119 items are made on the day when costs total \$120. ■

EXAMPLE 5 **Solving an Application to Aeronautics**

If an airplane is flying above the earth, an equation that gives the approximate distance to the horizon in terms of the altitude of the plane is

$$d = \sqrt{8000h},$$

where d is the distance to the horizon in miles and h is the altitude (distance above the earth) in miles. See Figure 9.6.

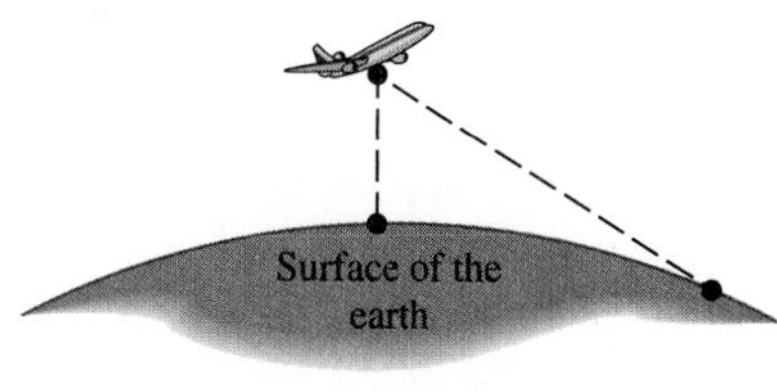

FIGURE 9.6

(a) Give the distance to the horizon when viewed from a plane at an altitude of 5 miles.

$$\begin{aligned} d &= \sqrt{8000h} && \text{Horizon equation} \\ d &= \sqrt{(8000)(5)} && h = 5 \text{ miles} \\ d &= \sqrt{40000} \\ &= \sqrt{(200)^2} && (200)^2 = 40{,}000 \\ &= 200 \end{aligned}$$

The horizon is approximately 200 miles away.

(b) Find the altitude of a plane when the horizon is 50 miles away.

$$\begin{aligned} d &= \sqrt{8000h} && \text{Horizon equation} \\ 50 &= \sqrt{8000h} && d = 50 \text{ miles, solve for } h \\ (50)^2 &= (\sqrt{8000h})^2 && \text{Square both sides} \\ 2500 &= 8000h \\ \frac{2500}{8000} &= h \\ \frac{5}{16} &= h \end{aligned}$$

The plane is about $\frac{5}{16}$ of a mile (about 1650 ft) above the earth. ■

▶ *30°–60° and 45°–45° right triangles*

To conclude this section we look at two special right triangles which have several applications in mathematics. A right triangle in which the two acute angles have measure 30° and 60° is called a **30°–60° right triangle.** The sides in such a triangle satisfy the following property.

Property of 30°–60° Right Triangle

In a 30°–60° right triangle, the length of the leg opposite the 30° angle is one-half the length of the hypotenuse.

Consider the right triangle in Figure 9.7. Since the hypotenuse c is 2, a must be 1 (one-half of c). We can find b using one of the equivalent forms of the Pythagorean theorem.

$$\begin{aligned} b^2 &= c^2 - a^2 \\ &= 2^2 - 1^2 \\ &= 4 - 1 \\ &= 3 \\ b &= \sqrt{3} && \text{Take the principal square root of both sides} \end{aligned}$$

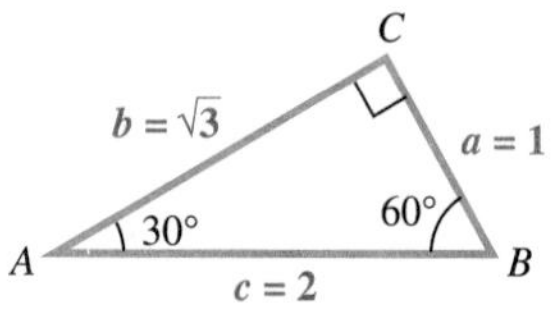

FIGURE 9.7
30°–60° Right Triangle

> **NOTE** In general, if a is the side opposite the 30° angle in a right triangle, $c = 2a$ and $b = \sqrt{3}a$.

EXAMPLE 6 **Solving a 30°–60° Right Triangle**

In right $\triangle ABC$, $\angle C$ is the right angle, $\angle A$ has measure 30°, and $a = 5$. Find c and b.

First sketch the triangle as in Figure 9.8. Since $a = 5$ is one-half the hypotenuse, c must be 10. Also $b = \sqrt{3}a = \sqrt{3}(5) = 5\sqrt{3}$. We reach the same result using the Pythagorean theorem.

$$\begin{aligned} b^2 &= c^2 - a^2 \\ &= 10^2 - 5^2 \\ &= 100 - 25 = 75 \\ b &= \sqrt{75} = \sqrt{25 \cdot 3} = 5\sqrt{3} \quad \blacksquare \end{aligned}$$

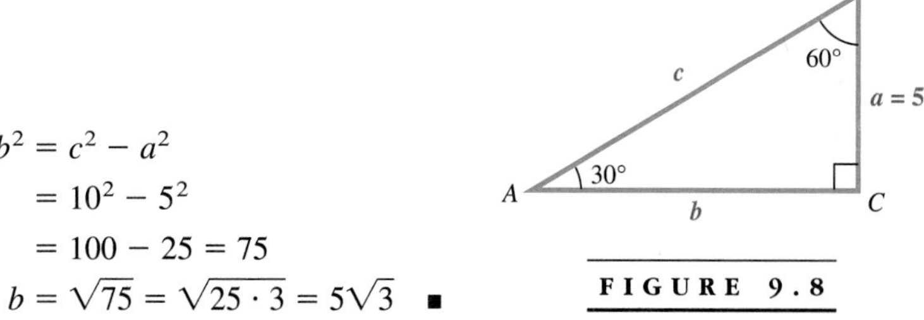

FIGURE 9.8

A right triangle with both acute angles measuring 45° is called a **45°–45° right triangle.** Since a 45°–45° right triangle is isosceles, the legs have equal length, and the Pythagorean theorem can be used to find the length of the hypotenuse. In Figure 9.9, since a and b are both 1, and

$$\begin{aligned} c^2 &= a^2 + b^2 \\ &= 1^2 + 1^2 = 1 + 1 = 2, \end{aligned}$$

we have that $c = \sqrt{2}$.

In general, if the legs are of length a then the hypotenuse is $\sqrt{2}a$.

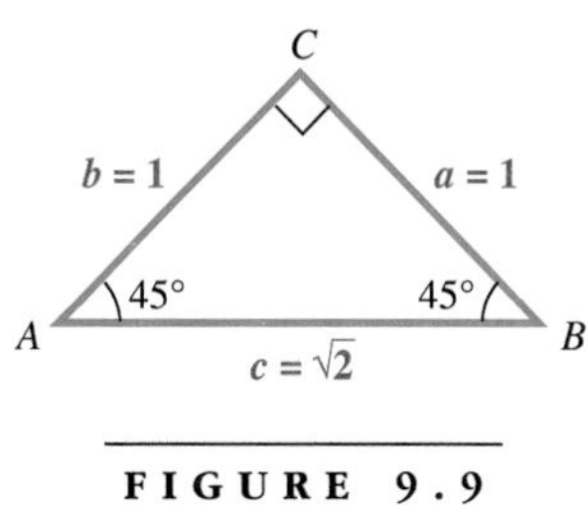

FIGURE 9.9
45°–45° Right Triangle

9.7 EXERCISES

Find the unknown leg or hypotenuse of each right triangle described in Exercises 1–6.

1. $a = 12, b = 5$ **2.** $a = 7, c = 10$ **3.** $b = 5, c = 9$

4. $a = 6, b = 8$ **5.** $a = 1, c = 5$ **6.** $b = 10, c = 20$

GEOMETRY *Solve each problem in Exercises 7–10.*

7. A ladder 8 m long is placed on a building. If the base is 3 m from the building, how high up the side of the building is the top of the ladder?

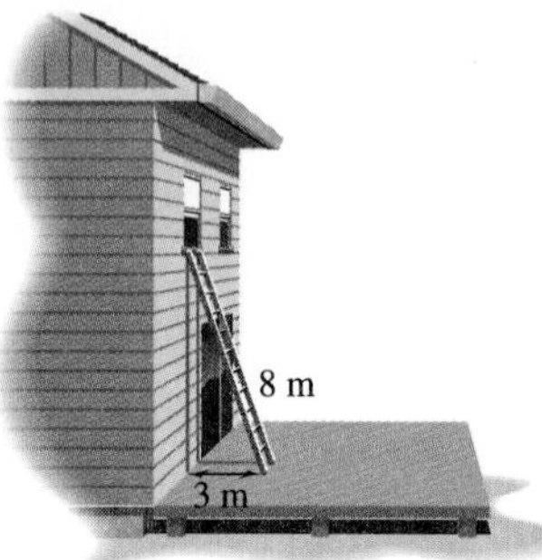

8. The diagonal of a square is 12 centimeters. Find the length of the sides.

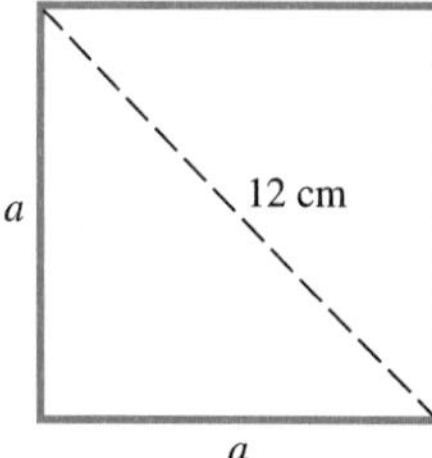

9. Find the length of the diagonal of a rectangle if the sides are 20 inches and 30 inches.

10. How long must a wire be to reach from the top of a 40-foot telephone pole to a point on the ground 30 feet from the base of the pole?

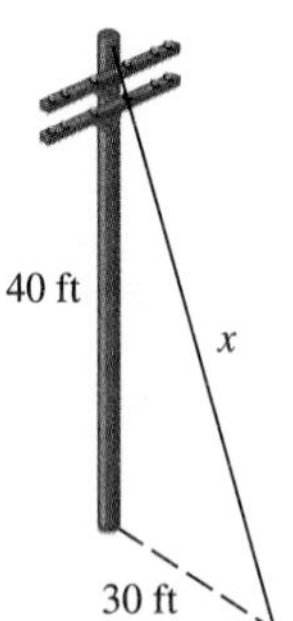

NUMBER *In Exercises 11–14, remember that principal square root means the nonnegative root.*

11. Three times the principal square root of a number is 6. Find the number.

12. Twice the principal square root of a number is 6 less than 12. Find the number.

13. The principal square root of 5 more than a number is twice the principal square root of the number. Find the number.

14. Twice the principal square root of one more than a number is the same as the principal square root of 13 more than the number. Find the number.

BUSINESS *A manufacturer finds that the total cost per day of producing appliances is given by the equation* $c = 100\sqrt{n + 36}$ *where c is the total cost and n is the number produced. Use this information for Exercises 15–18.*

15. What is c when no appliances are produced (overhead cost)?

16. What is the cost when 64 appliances are produced?

17. What is the cost when 39 appliances are produced?

18. How many appliances were made on a day when the cost was \$2000?

PHYSICS *The distance in miles to the horizon from a point h miles above the earth is given by* $d = \sqrt{8000h}$. *Use this information in Exercises 19–22.*

19. Find d when the altitude is 20 miles.

20. Find the distance to the horizon when the altitude is $\frac{1}{2}$ mile.

21. Find the altitude when the distance to the horizon is 120 miles.

22. Find the altitude when the distance to the horizon is 20 miles.

In Exercises 23–26, use the Pythagorean theorem to find the length of the missing legs or hypotenuse in each triangle.

23.

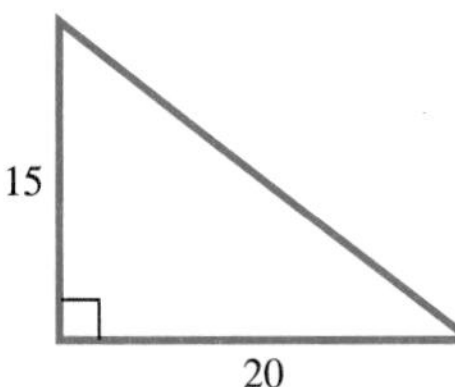

24.

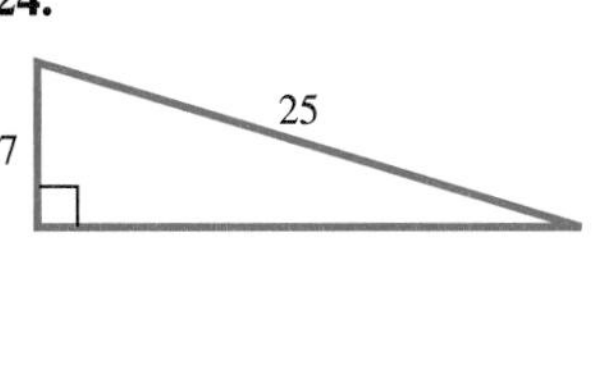

25.

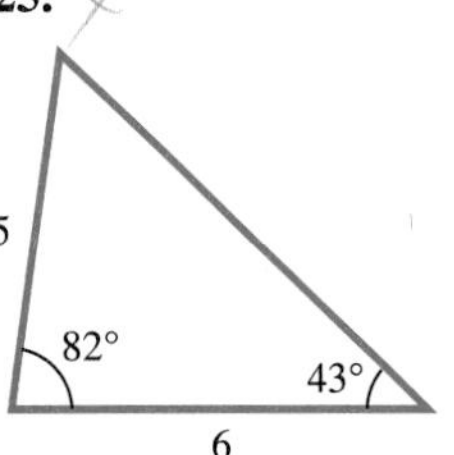

26.

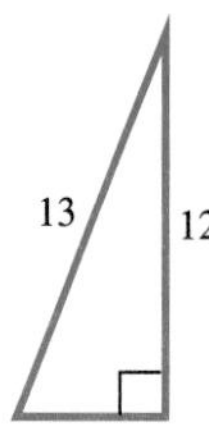

In Exercises 27–30, use the properties of 30°–60° or 45°–45° right triangles to find the missing legs or hypotenuse.

27.

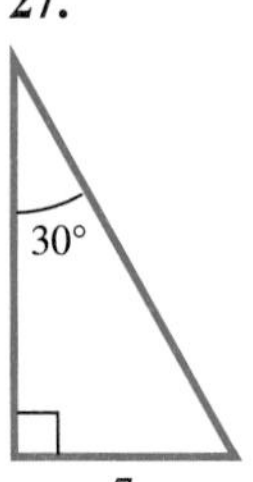

28.

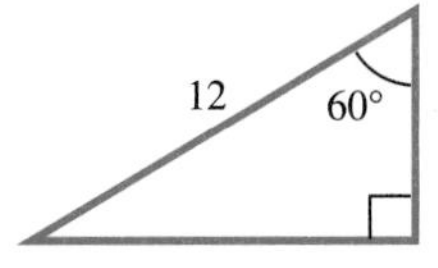

29.

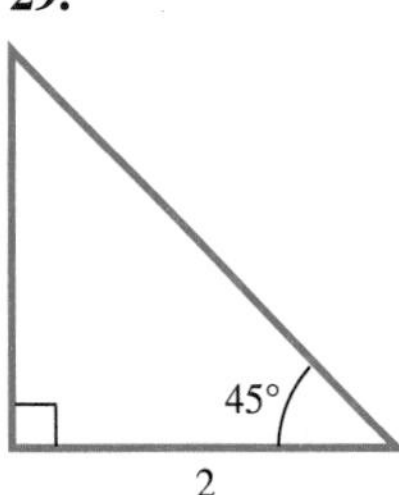

30.

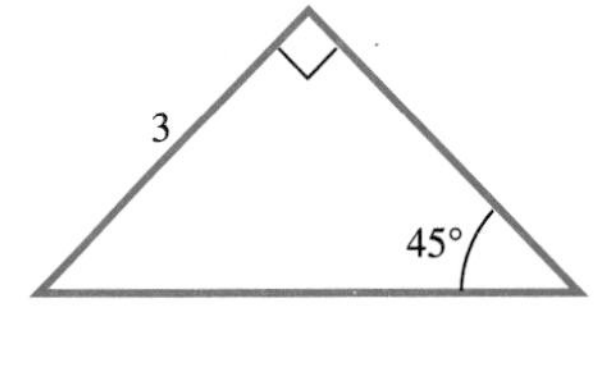

FOR REVIEW

Solve each radical equation in Exercises 31–32.

31. $2\sqrt{y^2 + 1} - 2y - 1 = 0$

32. $2\sqrt{3y + 1} - \sqrt{15y - 11} = 0$

Exercises 33–36 review material from Section 6.1 to prepare for the next section. Answer true *or* false. *If the statement is false, tell why.*

33. $-27x^3 = (-3x)^3$

34. $a^4 = a^3 + a$

35. $(8x^2)(2x^3) = 16x^4x$

36. $\dfrac{16x^6}{2x^2} = 8x^3$

9.7 PARALLEL EXERCISES

Find the unknown leg or hypotenuse of each right triangle described in Exercises 1–6.

1. $a = 4, b = 4$
2. $a = 5, c = 8$
3. $b = 14, c = 20$
4. $a = 9, b = 12$
5. $a = 3, c = 7$
6. $b = 20, c = 30$

GEOMETRY *Solve each problem in Exercises 7–10.*

7. How long would a ladder need to be to reach the top of a 10-m building if the base of the ladder is 4 m from the building?

8. The diagonal of a square is 10 cm. Find the length of the sides.

9. Find the length of the diagonal of a rectangular pasture if the sides are 40 yards and 60 yards.

10. A wire 50 feet long is attached to the top of a tower and to the ground 20 feet from the base of the tower. How tall is the tower?

NUMBER *In Exercises 11–14, remember that principal square root means the nonnegative root.*

11. Four times the principal square root of a number is 20. Find the number.

12. Twice the principal square root of a number is 5 more than 15. Find the number.

13. The principal square root of 8 more than a number is 3 times the principal square root of the number. Find the number.

14. Twice the principal square root of 4 less than a number is the same as the principal square root of 1 less than the number. Find the number.

BUSINESS *A retailer finds that the total cost per day of selling widgets is given by the equation* $c = 50\sqrt{n} + 200$, *where c is the total cost and n is the number sold. Use this information for Exercises 15–18.*

15. Find c when no widgets are sold (overhead cost).

16. Find the cost when 81 widgets are sold.

17. Find the number of widgets sold on a day when the cost was \$950.

18. Find the number of widgets sold on a day when the cost was \$150.

PHYSICS *The distance d in miles to the horizon from a point h miles above the earth is given by* $d = 10\sqrt{80h}$. *Use this information in Exercises 19–22.*

19. Find d when the altitude is $\frac{1}{5}$ mile.

20. Find the distance to the horizon when the altitude is 10 miles.

21. Find the altitude when the distance to the horizon is 320 miles.

22. Find the altitude when the distance to the horizon is 8 miles.

In Exercises 23–26, use the Pythagorean theorem to find the length of the missing legs or hypotenuse in each triangle.

23.

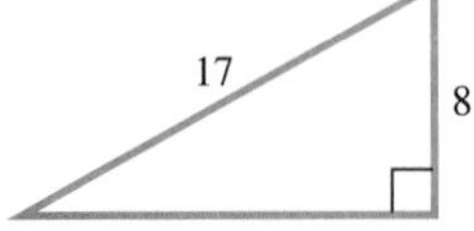

24.

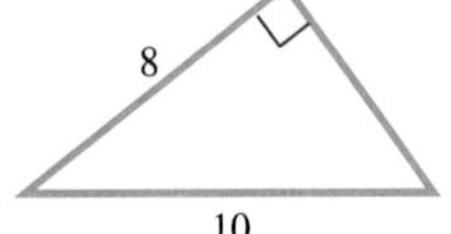

25.

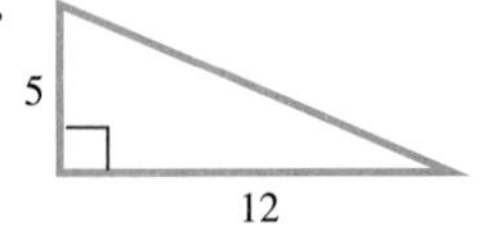

26.

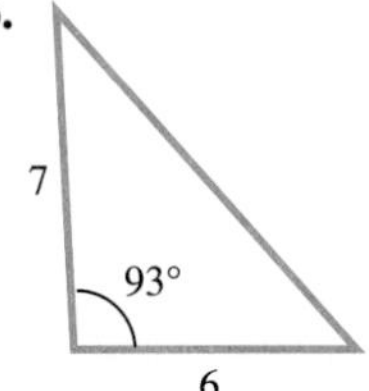

In Exercises 27–30, use the properties of 30°–60° *or* 45°–45° *right triangles to find the missing legs or hypotenuse.*

27.
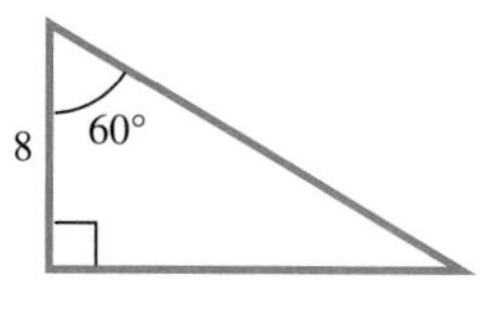

28.
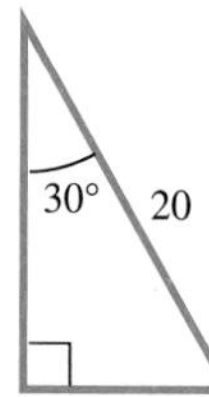

29. **30.**
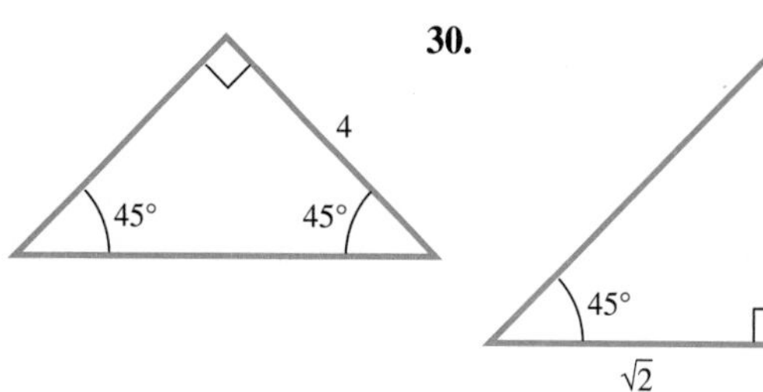

FOR REVIEW

Solve each radical equation in Exercises 31–32.

31. $\sqrt{y^2+2} - y - 1 = 0$

32. $\sqrt{2y+1} + \sqrt{y+1} = 0$

Exercises 33–36 review material from Section 6.1 to prepare for the next section. Answer true *or* false. *If the statement is false, tell why.*

33. $(-2x)^2 = -2x^2$

34. $a^3a^4 = a^{12}$

35. $(2y^2)(3y^3) = 5y^5$

36. $\dfrac{4x^5}{2x^3} = 2x^8$

9.7 ENRICHMENT EXERCISES

1. An airplane flew 120 km north from an airport and then 200 km west. How far was the plane from the airport?

△ **2.** A scientist uses the formula $a = \sqrt{1 + \frac{b}{x}}$. Solve this equation for b and find b when $a = 3$ and $x = \frac{1}{2}$.

3. Look up Pythagoreas in a history of mathematics book and write several paragraphs about him and his accomplishments.

SECTION 9.8 Higher Order Radicals and Rational Exponents

Student guideposts

- ▶ *Higher order roots*
- ▶ *Simplifying radicals*
- ▶ *Rationalizing denominators*
- ▶ *Rational exponents*

▶ *Higher order roots*

We have seen that if a and x are real numbers such that

$$a^2 = x,$$

then a is a square root of x. The principal square root of a nonnegative number x is denoted by $\sqrt{x}$, and the square root of a negative number is not a real number. If b and y are real numbers such that

$$b^3 = y,$$

we call b a **cube root** of y, and write b as $\sqrt[3]{y}$. The number 3 is called the **index** on the radical. For convenience, with square roots, we do not write the index 2. In a similar manner we consider the **fourth root** of a nonnegative real number z and write $\sqrt[4]{z}$, and so on.

> NOTE A number x must be *nonnegative* to have a real *even* root (square root, fourth root, and so on). Symbols such as $\sqrt{x}$, $\sqrt[4]{x}$, and $\sqrt[6]{x}$, represent the nonnegative or principal root of x. On the other hand, *every* real number y (positive, negative, or zero) has a real *odd* root (cube root, fifth root, and so on) denoted by, for example, $\sqrt[3]{y}$, $\sqrt[5]{y}$, and $\sqrt[7]{y}$.

EXAMPLE 1

Finding Roots

Find each root.

(a) $\sqrt[3]{8}$

Since $2^3 = 8$, $\sqrt[3]{8} = 2$. Note that $\sqrt[3]{8}$ cannot be -2 since $(-2)^3 = -8$, not 8.

(b) $\sqrt[3]{-64}$

Since $(-4)^3 = -64$, $\sqrt[3]{-64} = -4$. Notice that $\sqrt[3]{-64}$ cannot be 4 since $4^3 = 64$, not -64.

(c) $\sqrt[4]{16}$

Since $2^4 = 16$, $\sqrt[4]{16} = 2$. Notice that although $(-2)^4 = 16$ also, we have agreed to use the symbol $\sqrt[4]{16}$ to represent the *positive* fourth root of 16. In order to represent the negative fourth root of 16, we use $-\sqrt[4]{16}$. That is, $-\sqrt[4]{16} = -2$.

(d) $\sqrt[4]{-16}$

This is not a real number since the index is even and the radicand is negative. That is, there is no real number that can be raised to the fourth power and have the result be negative, let alone -16. ■

▶ *Simplifying radicals*

As with square roots, higher order roots may involve variables in the radicand. For example,

$$\sqrt[3]{x^3} = x$$

for every real number x, and if $a \geq 0$,

$$\sqrt[4]{a^4} = a.$$

We must restrict a to be nonnegative in the second case to be certain that we obtain a real number for the principal (nonnegative) fourth root. Similar remarks apply to other even-indexed radicals. As a result, similar to what we did for square roots earlier in the chapter, we make the following agreement.

Taking Even-Indexed Roots from This Point Forward

All variables under even-indexed radicals represent nonnegative real numbers. Thus, for $x \geq 0$ and k an integer,

$$\sqrt[k]{x^k} = x.$$

EXAMPLE 2

Simplifying Radicals

Simplify each radical. Assume that variables are nonnegative when the root is even.

(a) $\sqrt[5]{x^5} = x$

(b) $\sqrt[4]{(ab)^4} = ab$

(c) $\sqrt[3]{-27x^3} = \sqrt[3]{(-3x)^3} = -3x$ ■

The product and quotient simplifying rules for square roots

$$\sqrt{ab} = \sqrt{a}\sqrt{b} \quad \text{and} \quad \sqrt{\frac{a}{b}} = \frac{\sqrt{a}}{\sqrt{b}},$$

introduced in Section 7.2, can be extended to higher order radicals

$$\sqrt[k]{ab} = \sqrt[k]{a}\sqrt[k]{b} \quad \text{and} \quad \sqrt[k]{\frac{a}{b}} = \frac{\sqrt[k]{a}}{\sqrt[k]{b}}.$$

When working with cube roots, for example, we identify perfect cubes in the radicand much like we identified perfect squares when simplifying square roots. Higher order roots are treated the same way. That is, factor the radicand and look for powers that are the same as the index on the radical.

EXAMPLE 3

Simplifying Radicals

Simplify each radical.

(a)
$$\begin{aligned} \sqrt[3]{16} &= \sqrt[3]{8 \cdot 2} && \text{8 is a perfect cube since } 2^3 = 8 \\ &= \sqrt[3]{8}\sqrt[3]{2} && \sqrt[3]{ab} = \sqrt[3]{a}\sqrt[3]{b} \\ &= 2\sqrt[3]{2} && \sqrt[3]{8} = 2 \end{aligned}$$

(b)
$$\begin{aligned} \sqrt[3]{\frac{125}{8}} &= \frac{\sqrt[3]{125}}{\sqrt[3]{8}} && \sqrt[3]{\frac{a}{b}} = \frac{\sqrt[3]{a}}{\sqrt[3]{b}} \\ &= \frac{5}{2} && \sqrt[3]{125} = 5 \text{ and } \sqrt[3]{8} = 2 \end{aligned}$$

(c)
$$\begin{aligned} \sqrt[3]{a^4} &= \sqrt[3]{a^3 \cdot a} && a^3 \text{ is a perfect cube} \\ &= \sqrt[3]{a^3}\sqrt[3]{a} && \sqrt[3]{ab} = \sqrt[3]{a}\sqrt[3]{b} \\ &= a\sqrt[3]{a} && \sqrt[3]{a^3} = a \end{aligned}$$ ■

When the simplifying rules are used in the reverse order, we obtain the product and quotient rules

$$\sqrt[k]{a}\sqrt[k]{b} = \sqrt[k]{ab} \quad \text{and} \quad \frac{\sqrt[k]{a}}{\sqrt[k]{b}} = \sqrt[k]{\frac{a}{b}}$$

used to multiply and divide higher order radicals. In all cases, we will assume that variables have been restricted so that all expressions are defined and are real numbers.

EXAMPLE 4

Multiplying and Dividing Radicals

Perform each operation and simplify.

(a) $\sqrt[3]{4}\sqrt[3]{6} = \sqrt[3]{4 \cdot 6}$ $\quad \sqrt[3]{a}\sqrt[3]{b} = \sqrt[3]{ab}$

$= \sqrt[3]{2 \cdot 2 \cdot 2 \cdot 3}$ $\quad$ Factor and look for perfect cubes

$= \sqrt[3]{8 \cdot 3}$ $\quad$ $8 = 2 \cdot 2 \cdot 2$ is a perfect cube

$= \sqrt[3]{8}\sqrt[3]{3}$ $\quad \sqrt[3]{ab} = \sqrt[3]{a}\sqrt[3]{b}$

$= 2\sqrt[3]{3}$

(b) $\sqrt[4]{8x^2}\sqrt[4]{2x^3} = \sqrt[4]{(8x^2)(2x^3)}$ $\quad \sqrt[4]{a}\sqrt[4]{b} = \sqrt[4]{ab}$

$= \sqrt[4]{16x^4x}$ $\quad$ 16 and x^4 are perfect fourth powers

$= \sqrt[4]{16}\sqrt[4]{x^4}\sqrt[4]{x}$ $\quad$ The product rule extends to three factors

$= 2x\sqrt[4]{x}$

(c) $\dfrac{\sqrt[3]{16x^5}}{\sqrt[3]{2x^2}} = \sqrt[3]{\dfrac{16x^5}{2x^2}}$ $\quad \dfrac{\sqrt[3]{a}}{\sqrt[3]{b}} = \sqrt[3]{\dfrac{a}{b}}$

$= \sqrt[3]{8x^3}$ $\quad$ Simplify the fraction

$= \sqrt[3]{8}\sqrt[3]{x^3} = 2x$ ∎

Rationalizing denominators

To simplify an expression with a square root radical in a denominator, we rationalized the denominator. Denominators containing higher order roots are rationalized in a similar way. For example, if a cube root is in a denominator, change the radicand to a perfect cube by multiplying numerator and denominator by an appropriate radical. This is shown in the next example.

EXAMPLE 5

Rationalizing Denominators

Rationalize each denominator.

(a) $\dfrac{\sqrt[3]{2}}{\sqrt[3]{9}} = \dfrac{\sqrt[3]{2}\sqrt[3]{3}}{\sqrt[3]{9}\sqrt[3]{3}}$ $\quad$ Multiplying by $\sqrt[3]{3}$ results in a perfect cube in the denominator radicand

$= \dfrac{\sqrt[3]{2 \cdot 3}}{\sqrt[3]{9 \cdot 3}}$ $\quad \sqrt[3]{a}\sqrt[3]{b} = \sqrt[3]{ab}$

$= \dfrac{\sqrt[3]{6}}{\sqrt[3]{27}}$

$= \dfrac{\sqrt[3]{6}}{3}$ $\quad \sqrt[3]{27} = 3$

(b) $\sqrt[4]{\frac{5}{8}} = \frac{\sqrt[4]{5}}{\sqrt[4]{8}}$ $\qquad \sqrt[4]{\frac{a}{b}} = \frac{\sqrt[4]{a}}{\sqrt[4]{b}}$

$= \frac{\sqrt[4]{5}\sqrt[4]{2}}{\sqrt[4]{8}\sqrt[4]{2}}$ Multiplying by $\sqrt[4]{2}$ results in a perfect fourth power in the denominator radicand

$= \frac{\sqrt[4]{5 \cdot 2}}{\sqrt[4]{8 \cdot 2}}$

$= \frac{\sqrt[4]{10}}{\sqrt[4]{16}}$

$= \frac{\sqrt[4]{10}}{2}$ ■

NOTE In summary, higher order radicals are simplified in exactly the same way as square roots. We make sure that there are no perfect powers in the radicand and that fractional radicands and radicals in denominators are removed.

As with multiplication and division, addition and subtraction of higher order radicals parallel the same operations with square roots. Only **like radicals,** those with the same index and the same radicand, can be combined.

EXAMPLE 6 **Adding and Subtracting Radicals**

Add or subtract and simplify.

(a) $2\sqrt[3]{5} + 7\sqrt[3]{5} = (2 + 7)\sqrt[3]{5} = 9\sqrt[3]{5}$

(b) $\sqrt[3]{2} + \sqrt[4]{2}$ Cannot be simplified since the radicals are not like radicals

(c) $\sqrt[3]{2} + 5\sqrt[3]{16} = \sqrt[3]{2} + 5\sqrt[3]{8 \cdot 2}$ Simplify first

$= \sqrt[3]{2} + 5\sqrt[3]{8}\sqrt[3]{2}$

$= \sqrt[3]{2} + 5 \cdot 2\sqrt[3]{2}$

$= \sqrt[3]{2} + 10\sqrt[3]{2} = (1 + 10)\sqrt[3]{2} = 11\sqrt[3]{2}$ ■

▶*Rational exponents* In Chapter 6 we developed the properties of integer exponents. What happens in cases where the exponents are rational numbers or fractions? For example, how might we define $3^{1/2}$? It would be nice if such expressions were defined so that the rules of exponents studied earlier still hold true. If the power rule $(a^m)^n = a^{mn}$ is to apply, for example,

$$(3^{1/2})^2 = 3^{2/2} = 3^1 = 3.$$

But from our work with square roots in Section 9.1, we know that

$$(\sqrt{3})^2 = 3.$$

Thus, we must have

$$3^{1/2} = \sqrt{3}.$$

Similarly, since

$$(2^{1/3})^3 = 2 \quad \text{and} \quad (\sqrt[3]{2})^3 = 2.$$

it seems appropriate that

$$2^{1/3} = \sqrt[3]{2}.$$

These observations are generalized in the next definition.

Rational Exponents of the Form $1/n$

If a is a real number and n is any positive integer, then

$$a^{1/n} = \sqrt[n]{a},$$

provided that $\sqrt[n]{a}$ is a real number (provided that $a \geq 0$ when n is even).

EXAMPLE 7 **Working with Rational Exponents**

Write each expression as a radical and simplify.

(a) $4^{1/2} = \sqrt{4} = 2$

(b) $8^{1/3} = \sqrt[3]{8} = \sqrt[3]{(2)^3} = 2$

(c) $32^{1/5} = \sqrt[5]{32} = \sqrt[5]{(2)^5} = 2$

(d) $81^{1/3} = \sqrt[3]{81} = \sqrt[3]{27 \cdot 3} = \sqrt[3]{27}\,\sqrt[3]{3} = 3\sqrt[3]{3}$ ■

Next we give meaning to expressions like $8^{2/3}$. Using the power rule,

$$8^{2/3} = (8^{1/3})^2 = (\sqrt[3]{8})^2 = 2^2 = 4.$$

On the other hand we could have written

$$8^{2/3} = (8^2)^{1/3} = (64)^{1/3} = \sqrt[3]{64} = 4.$$

Either approach gives the same result, but taking the root first involves smaller numbers and might, therefore, be preferred. This is generalized in the next definition.

Rational Exponents of the Form m/n

If a is a real number and m and n are positive integers, then

$$a^{m/n} = (\sqrt[n]{a})^m = \sqrt[n]{a^m}$$

provided that the radicals are defined as real numbers.

EXAMPLE 8 **Working with Rational Exponents**

Write each expression as a radical and simplify.

(a) $4^{3/2} = (\sqrt{4})^3 = 2^3 = 8$

(b) $8^{5/3} = (\sqrt[3]{8})^5 = 2^5 = 32$

(c) $(-27)^{2/3} = (\sqrt[3]{-27})^2 = (-3)^2 = 9$ ■

> NOTE When writing an expression with a rational exponent using radicals, for example $a^{m/n}$, remember that the denominator n becomes the index and the numerator m becomes the power.

We can extend the definition of rational exponents to include negative rational numbers in exactly the same way we defined negative integer exponents as follows.

$$a^{-m/n} = \frac{1}{a^{m/n}} \qquad a \neq 0$$

Then all of the rules for integer exponents also apply to rational exponents as illustrated in the next example.

EXAMPLE 9

Simplifying Expressions with Rational Exponents

Simplify each expression. Write each answer with only positive exponents.

(a) $8^{-2/3} = \dfrac{1}{8^{2/3}} = \dfrac{1}{(\sqrt[3]{8})^2} = \dfrac{1}{2^2} = \dfrac{1}{4}$

(b) $(-32)^{-3/5} = \dfrac{1}{(-32)^{3/5}} = \dfrac{1}{(\sqrt[5]{-32})^3} = \dfrac{1}{(-2)^3} = \dfrac{1}{-8} = -\dfrac{1}{8}$

(c) $2^{1/3} \cdot 2^{5/3} = 2^{1/3+5/3} = 2^{6/3} = 2^2 = 4$

(d) $\dfrac{3^{1/4}}{3^{3/4}} = 3^{1/4-3/4} = 3^{-2/4} = 3^{-1/2} = \dfrac{1}{3^{1/2}}$

(e) $(9^{1/6})^3 = 9^{3/6} = 9^{1/2} = \sqrt{9} = 3$

(f) $\left(\dfrac{4}{9}\right)^{3/2} = \dfrac{4^{3/2}}{9^{3/2}} = \dfrac{(\sqrt{4})^3}{(\sqrt{9})^3} = \dfrac{2^3}{3^3} = \dfrac{8}{27}$

(g) $x^{-2/3} = \dfrac{1}{x^{2/3}}$

(h) $y^{-1/2} \cdot y^{3/2} = y^{-1/2+3/2} = y^{2/2} = y^1 = y$

(i) $\dfrac{w^{1/5}}{w^{4/5}} = w^{1/5-4/5} = w^{-3/5} = \dfrac{1}{w^{3/5}}$

(j) $(a^2b^4)^{1/2} = (a^2)^{1/2}(b^4)^{1/2} = a^1b^2 = ab^2$ ■

9.8 EXERCISES

Find each root in Exercises 1–6.

1. $\sqrt[3]{27}$ **2.** $\sqrt[4]{1}$ **3.** $\sqrt[4]{-4}$
4. $\sqrt[5]{32}$ **5.** $-\sqrt[3]{-1}$ **6.** $\sqrt[6]{64}$

Simplify each radical in Exercises 7–12. Assume that variables represent nonnegative real numbers when the index is even.

7. $\sqrt[6]{y^6}$ **8.** $\sqrt[3]{(-2x)^3}$ **9.** $\sqrt[4]{16a^4}$
10. $\sqrt[3]{24}$ **11.** $\sqrt[3]{\frac{54}{8}}$ **12.** $\sqrt[3]{x^5}$

In Exercises 13–18, perform the indicated operation and simplify.

13. $\sqrt[3]{4}\sqrt[3]{10}$ **14.** $\sqrt[4]{8}\sqrt[4]{10}$ **15.** $\sqrt[3]{2a^2}\sqrt[3]{4a}$
16. $\sqrt[3]{4a^2}\sqrt[3]{2a^2}$ **17.** $\frac{\sqrt[3]{16a^4}}{\sqrt[3]{2a}}$ **18.** $\frac{\sqrt[4]{32a^5}}{\sqrt[4]{2a}}$

Rationalize each denominator in Exercises 19–24.

19. $\frac{\sqrt[3]{3}}{\sqrt[3]{4}}$ **20.** $\frac{\sqrt[4]{3}}{\sqrt[4]{8}}$ **21.** $\frac{3}{\sqrt[3]{a^2}}$
22. $\sqrt[3]{\frac{5}{2}}$ **23.** $\sqrt[4]{\frac{11}{8}}$ **24.** $\sqrt[3]{\frac{a}{x^2}}$

In Exercises 25–30, add or subtract and simplify.

25. $\sqrt[3]{2} + 3\sqrt[3]{2}$ **26.** $\sqrt[3]{2} + 2\sqrt[3]{16}$ **27.** $\sqrt[3]{16} + \sqrt[3]{54}$
28. $a\sqrt[3]{a} + \sqrt[3]{a^4}$ **29.** $3y\sqrt[3]{y} - \sqrt[3]{y^4}$ **30.** $3a\sqrt[4]{a} - \sqrt[4]{a^5}$

31. **SPORTS** The head athletic trainer at NAU, Mike Nesbitt, has found that he can estimate the number of boxes of tape t necessary for a season of competition by the formula $t = 50\sqrt[3]{n - 11}$, where n is the number of team members. Find the number of boxes needed when the team has 12 members.

Write each expression in Exercises 32–37 as a radical and simplify.

32. $9^{1/2}$ **33.** $27^{1/3}$ **34.** $9^{3/2}$
35. $(-8)^{2/3}$ **36.** $16^{1/3}$ **37.** $32^{1/4}$

Write each radical in Exercises 38–43 with a rational exponent.

38. $\sqrt{5}$ **39.** $\sqrt[3]{4}$ **40.** $\sqrt[4]{2}$
41. $(\sqrt[3]{2})^2$ **42.** $\sqrt[3]{2^2}$ **43.** $\sqrt[5]{3^2}$

Simplify each expression in Exercises 44–55. Write each answer with only positive exponents and assume that all variables represent positive real numbers.

44. $25^{-1/2}$ **45.** $16^{-3/2}$ **46.** $(-8)^{-1/3}$
47. $3^{1/2} \cdot 3^{5/2}$ **48.** $\frac{4^{3/2}}{4^{1/2}}$ **49.** $(4^{1/8})^4$
50. $w^{-2/3}$ **51.** $y^{-1/3}y^{4/3}$ **52.** $\frac{w^{3/4}}{w^{5/4}}$
53. $(a^2b^6)^{1/2}$ **54.** $\frac{m^{3/4}m^{5/4}}{m^{1/4}}$ **55.** $\left(\frac{a^{1/2}}{b^{1/3}}\right)^6$

FOR REVIEW

56. Find the hypotenuse of a right triangle with $a = 2$ and $b = 7$.

57. In a 30°–60° right triangle, the shortest side is 2. Find the other two sides.

58. In a 45°–45° right triangle, the hypotenuse is 12. Find the other two sides.

59. **AERONAUTICS** The distance in miles to the horizon from a point h miles above the earth is given by $d = 10\sqrt{80h}$. Find the altitude of an airplane when the distance to the horizon is 100 miles.

Exercises 60–62 review material from Chapter 7 to help you prepare for material in Chapter 10. Factor each polynomial.

60. $x^2 + 6x - 16$ **61.** $x^2 + 6x + 9$ **62.** $x^2 - 7x$

9.8 PARALLEL EXERCISES

Find each root in Exercises 1–6.

1. $\sqrt[3]{125}$ **2.** $\sqrt[4]{81}$ **3.** $\sqrt[4]{-81}$

4. $\sqrt[5]{1}$ **5.** $-\sqrt[3]{-8}$ **6.** $\sqrt[6]{1}$

Simplify each radical in Exercises 7–12. Assume that variables represent nonnegative real numbers when the index is even.

7. $\sqrt[7]{z^7}$ **8.** $\sqrt[5]{(-5y)^5}$ **9.** $\sqrt[3]{8w^3}$

10. $\sqrt[3]{40}$ **11.** $\sqrt[3]{\dfrac{16}{27}}$ **12.** $\sqrt[5]{z^8}$

In Exercises 13–18, perform the indicated operation and simplify.

13. $\sqrt[3]{9}\sqrt[3]{6}$ **14.** $\sqrt[4]{27}\sqrt[4]{15}$ **15.** $\sqrt[3]{3x}\sqrt[3]{9x^2}$

16. $\sqrt[3]{9x^2}\sqrt[3]{3x^2}$ **17.** $\dfrac{\sqrt[3]{32y^5}}{\sqrt[3]{4y}}$ **18.** $\dfrac{\sqrt[4]{162y^7}}{\sqrt[4]{2y^3}}$

Rationalize each denominator in Exercises 19–24.

19. $\dfrac{\sqrt[3]{5}}{\sqrt[3]{9}}$ **20.** $\dfrac{\sqrt[4]{2}}{\sqrt[4]{27}}$ **21.** $\dfrac{7}{\sqrt[3]{y}}$

22. $\sqrt[3]{\dfrac{7}{3}}$ **23.** $\sqrt[4]{\dfrac{5}{27}}$ **24.** $\sqrt[3]{\dfrac{w^2}{z}}$

In Exercises 25–30, add or subtract and simplify.

25. $\sqrt[4]{7} - 8\sqrt[4]{7}$ **26.** $\sqrt[4]{2} - 3\sqrt[4]{32}$ **27.** $\sqrt[3]{54} - 2\sqrt[3]{16}$

28. $x\sqrt[3]{x^2} + \sqrt[3]{x^5}$ **29.** $\sqrt[3]{x^5} - x\sqrt[3]{x^2}$ **30.** $\sqrt[4]{w^7} - w\sqrt[4]{w^3}$

31. **BUSINESS** A manufacturer of puzzles has found that his daily expenses for production can be estimated by $E = 100\sqrt[3]{n + 8}$, where E represents total expenses and n is the number of puzzles produced. Find the total expenses when no puzzles are produced.

Write each expression in Exercises 32–37 as a radical and simplify.

32. $25^{1/2}$ **33.** $125^{1/3}$ **34.** $8^{2/3}$
35. $(-27)^{4/3}$ **36.** $256^{1/3}$ **37.** $243^{1/4}$

Write each radical in Exercises 38–43 with a rational exponent.

38. $\sqrt{7}$ **39.** $\sqrt[3]{9}$ **40.** $\sqrt[4]{8}$
41. $(\sqrt[3]{7})^2$ **42.** $\sqrt[3]{7^2}$ **43.** $\sqrt[6]{7^5}$

Simplify each expression in Exercises 44–55. Write each answer with only positive exponents and assume that all variables represent positive real numbers.

44. $16^{-1/2}$ **45.** $4^{-3/2}$ **46.** $(-27)^{-1/3}$
47. $5^{2/3} \cdot 5^{5/3}$ **48.** $\dfrac{9^{5/2}}{9^{3/2}}$ **49.** $(16^{1/6})^3$
50. $m^{-4/5}$ **51.** $x^{5/4}x^{-1/4}$ **52.** $\dfrac{m^{5/6}}{m^{1/3}}$
53. $(x^3y^9)^{1/3}$ **54.** $\dfrac{x^{2/3}x^{5/3}}{x^{4/3}}$ **55.** $\left(\dfrac{u^{2/3}}{v^{3/2}}\right)^6$

FOR REVIEW

56. Find the hypotenuse of a right triangle with $a = 3$ and $b = 8$.
57. In a 30°–60° right triangle, the shortest side is 4. Find the other two sides.
58. In a 45°–45° right triangle, the hypotenuse is 8. Find the other two sides.
59. **AERONAUTICS** The distance in miles to the horizon from a point h miles above the earth is given by $d = 10\sqrt{80h}$. Find the altitude of an airplane when the distance to the horizon is 85 miles.

Exercises 60–62 review material from Chapter 7 to help you prepare for material in Chapter 10. Factor each polynomial.

60. $2x^2 + 9x - 5$ **61.** $9x^2 - 6x + 1$ **62.** $9x^2 - 25$

9.8 ENRICHMENT EXERCISES

Finding higher order roots uses the y^x *key on a calculator. For example, to find* $\sqrt[3]{2}$ *write this in exponential form,* $2^{1/3}$ *and follow the sequence of steps below.*

2 [y^x] [(] 1 [÷] 3 [)] [=] → 1.25992105

In this sequence, 2 is entered as **y** *and 1/3 is entered as* **x**. *Follow this example and evaluate the following roots, correct to the nearest tenth.*

1. $\sqrt[4]{2}$ **2.** $\sqrt[5]{3}$ **3.** $\sqrt[6]{17}$
4. $\sqrt[3]{25.1}$ **5.** $\sqrt[4]{38.2}$ **6.** $\sqrt[7]{105}$

7. The radius of a sphere with volume V is given by $r = \sqrt[3]{\dfrac{3V}{4\pi}}$. Find the radius, to the nearest tenth of an inch, of a sphere with volume 84 in^3. Use 3.14 for π.

CHAPTER 9 REVIEW

KEY WORDS

9.1 A **perfect square** is the square of an integer or rational number.
If $a^2 = x$, then a is a **square root** of x.
The **principal square root** is the nonnegative square root of a positive real number.
In $\sqrt{x}$ the symbol $\sqrt{}$ is called a **radical** and x is the **radicand.**

9.2 The process of removing radicals from the denominator is called **rationalizing the denominator.**

9.4 **Like radicals** have the same radicand.
Unlike radicals have different radicands.

9.5 The expressions $\sqrt{a} + \sqrt{b}$ and $\sqrt{a} - \sqrt{b}$ are **conjugates** of each other.

9.6 An **extraneous root** is a "solution" obtained which is not a solution to the original problem.

9.7 A **right triangle** is a triangle with a 90° angle.
The **hypotenuse** is the side opposite the right angle and the **legs** are the other sides of a right triangle.

9.8 **1.** If $b^3 = y$, b is a **cube root** of y, and we write $b = \sqrt[3]{y}$. The number 3 is the **index** on the radical.
2. **Like radicals** are radicals that have the same index and the same radicand.

KEY CONCEPTS

9.1 The radical alone indicates the principal (nonnegative) square root of a number. Thus $\sqrt{9} = 3$, not -3.

9.2 **1.** If $a \geq 0$ and $b \geq 0$, then

$$\sqrt{ab} = \sqrt{a}\sqrt{b}. \qquad \text{Multiplication rule}$$

2. If $a \geq 0$ and $b > 0$, then

$$\sqrt{\frac{a}{b}} = \frac{\sqrt{a}}{\sqrt{b}}. \qquad \text{Division rule}$$

3. When removing a perfect square from under a radical, multiply all factors; do not add. For example,

$$3\sqrt{4a} = 3\sqrt{4}\sqrt{a} = 3 \cdot 2\sqrt{a} = 6\sqrt{a}, \textit{ not } (3 + 2)\sqrt{a}, \text{ which is } 5\sqrt{a}.$$

9.4 $\sqrt{a + b} \neq \sqrt{a} + \sqrt{b}$ and $\sqrt{a - b} \neq \sqrt{a} - \sqrt{b}$.

9.5 To rationalize a binomial denominator, multiply both numerator and denominator of the fraction by the conjugate of the denominator and simplify.

9.6
1. To solve a radical equation, isolate a radical on one side of the equation and square both sides.
2. Check all solutions to a radical equation in the *original* equation.

9.7
1. Pythagorean theorem: In a right triangle with legs a and b and hypotenuse c, $a^2 + b^2 = c^2$.
2. In the 30°–60° triangle below, $c = 2a$ and $b = \sqrt{3}a$.

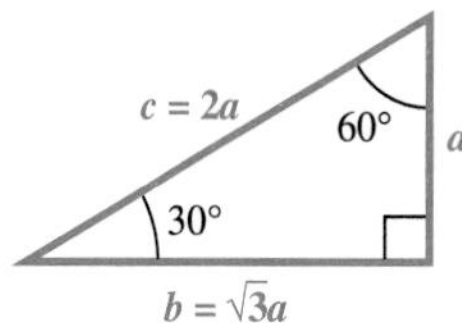

3. In the 45°–45° triangle below, $c = \sqrt{2}a$ and $b = a$.

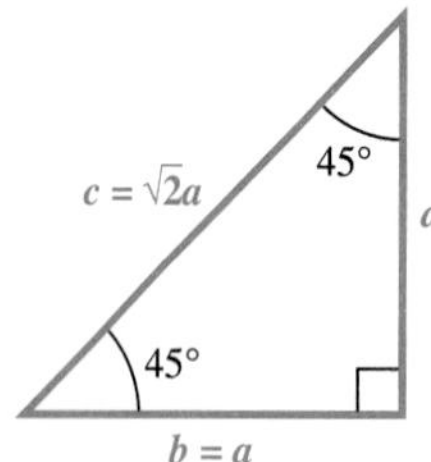

9.8
1. If a and b are real numbers and k is a positive integer, then $\sqrt[k]{a^k} = a$, $\sqrt[k]{a}\sqrt[k]{b} = \sqrt[k]{ab}$, and $\dfrac{\sqrt[k]{a}}{\sqrt[k]{b}} = \sqrt[k]{\dfrac{a}{b}}$, provided the radicals are defined to be real numbers.
2. If a is a real number and n is a positive integer, then $a^{1/n} = \sqrt[n]{a}$ and $a^{m/n} = (\sqrt[n]{a})^m = \sqrt[n]{a^m}$, provided the radicals are defined as real numbers.
3. All of the rules for integer exponents also apply to exponents that are rational numbers.
4. Higher order radicals are simplified using the same techniques as those for square roots.

CHAPTER 9 REVIEW EXERCISES

PART I

9.1 *Give the number of square roots of each number in Exercises 1–3.*

1. 81
2. -81
3. 0

Evaluate each square root in Exercises 4–9. Assume all variables and expressions are nonnegative.

4. $\sqrt{(-9)^2}$
5. $\pm\sqrt{144}$
6. $\sqrt{\dfrac{25}{16}}$
7. $\sqrt{-16}$
8. $\sqrt{4a^2}$
9. $\sqrt{x^2 + 2x + 1}$

9.2 *Simplify each radical in Exercises 10–18.*

10. $5\sqrt{8}$ **11.** $\sqrt{3^4}$ **12.** $\sqrt{8y^2}$

13. $\sqrt{50x^2y^3}$ **14.** $\sqrt{\frac{32}{81}}$ **15.** $\sqrt{\frac{16y^2}{x^2}}$

16. $\sqrt{\frac{x^2y^3}{81}}$ **17.** $\frac{6}{\sqrt{7}}$ **18.** $\sqrt{\frac{50x^2}{y}}$

9.3 *Multiply and simplify in Exercises 19–24.*

19. $\sqrt{8}\sqrt{18}$ **20.** $\sqrt{7}\sqrt{7}$ **21.** $3\sqrt{5}\sqrt{7}$

22. $\sqrt{12y}\sqrt{3y}$ **23.** $\sqrt{3xy}\sqrt{2xy^2}$ **24.** $\sqrt{5x}\sqrt{5y}\sqrt{5xy}$

Divide and simplify in Exercises 25–30.

25. $\frac{\sqrt{99}}{\sqrt{11}}$ **26.** $\frac{\sqrt{50}}{\sqrt{8}}$ **27.** $\frac{3\sqrt{35}}{\sqrt{20}}$

28. $\frac{\sqrt{25x^2}}{\sqrt{2x^2}}$ **29.** $\frac{\sqrt{18x^2y}}{\sqrt{8y}}$ **30.** $\frac{\sqrt{25x^2}}{\sqrt{3y}}$

9.4 *Add or subtract in Exercises 31–39.*

31. $5\sqrt{7} + 12\sqrt{7}$ **32.** $2\sqrt{5} - 7\sqrt{5}$ **33.** $3\sqrt{8} + 7\sqrt{8}$

34. $3\sqrt{16x} + 4\sqrt{36x}$ **35.** $2\sqrt{28} - 5\sqrt{112} + 3\sqrt{63}$ **36.** $3\sqrt{12x} + 2\sqrt{27x} - \sqrt{48x}$

37. $5\sqrt{48x^2} - \sqrt{27x^2} - \sqrt{3x^2}$ **38.** $\sqrt{5} + \frac{1}{\sqrt{5}}$ **39.** $\sqrt{\frac{3}{2}} - \sqrt{6}$

9.5 *In Exercises 40–45, perform the indicated operations and simplify.*

40. $\sqrt{5}\sqrt{125} + \sqrt{3}\sqrt{27}$ **41.** $\sqrt{5}(\sqrt{3} - \sqrt{5})$ **42.** $\sqrt{7}\left(\sqrt{7} - \frac{1}{\sqrt{7}}\right)$

43. $(\sqrt{7} + 1)(\sqrt{7} - 1)$ **44.** $(\sqrt{2} + \sqrt{3})(2\sqrt{2} - \sqrt{3})$ **45.** $(\sqrt{5} + 3)(\sqrt{5} - 1)$

Rationalize the denominator in Exercises 46–49.

46. $\frac{2}{\sqrt{3} + 1}$ **47.** $\frac{-4}{\sqrt{7} - \sqrt{5}}$ **48.** $\frac{\sqrt{3}}{\sqrt{3} - \sqrt{2}}$ **49.** $\frac{\sqrt{7}}{\sqrt{7} - 1}$

9.6 *Solve each radical equation in Exercises* 50–52.

50. $2\sqrt{x} = \sqrt{x + 2}$ **51.** $\sqrt{x^2 - 13} - x + 1 = 0$ **52.** $\sqrt{y + 5} + y - 1 = 0$

9.7 *Find the unknown leg or hypotenuse of each right triangle described in Exercises 53–54.*

53. $a = 6$, $b = 12$ **54.** $a = 5$, $c = 13$

55. **GEOMETRY** Find the length of a diagonal of a rectangular table with sides 8 feet and 12 feet.

56. **NUMBER** Twice the principal square root of 4 less than a number is equal to the principal square root of 8 more than the number. Find the number.

BUSINESS *A manufacturer finds that the total cost per day of producing wabbles is given by the equation* $c = 500\sqrt{n + 144}$, *where c is the total cost and n is the number produced. Use this information in Exercises 57–58.*

57. Find the cost when 25 wabbles are produced.

58. How many wabbles were produced on a day when the cost was $10,000?

AERONAUTICS *The distance d in miles to the horizon from a point h miles above the earth is given by* $d = 10\sqrt{80h}$. *Use this information in Exercises 59–60.*

59. Find the distance to the horizon when the altitude is 0.05 miles.

60. Find the altitude when the distance to the horizon is 80 miles.

61. In a 30°–60° right triangle, a is the shorter leg and $a = 10$. Find b and c.

62. In a 45°–45° right triangle, $a = 7$. Find b and c.

9.8 *Simplify each radical in Exercises 63–66.*

63. $\sqrt[3]{125}$ **64.** $\sqrt[4]{80}$ **65.** $\sqrt[4]{w^7}$ **66.** $\sqrt[4]{\dfrac{81}{625}}$

Perform the indicated operation and simplify in Exercises 67–69.

67. $\sqrt[3]{4}\sqrt[3]{10}$ **68.** $\sqrt[4]{\dfrac{32x^7}{2x^3}}$ **69.** $\sqrt[3]{9a^2}\sqrt[3]{9a}$

Rationalize each denominator in Exercises 70–72.

70. $\dfrac{3}{\sqrt[3]{a^2}}$ **71.** $\dfrac{\sqrt[4]{3}}{\sqrt[4]{8}}$ **72.** $\sqrt[3]{\dfrac{3}{25}}$

In Exercises 73–74, add or subtract and simplify.

73. $\sqrt[3]{3} + 2\sqrt[3]{81}$ **74.** $3y\sqrt[4]{y} - 2\sqrt[4]{y^5}$

Write each expression in Exercises 75–78 as a radical and simplify.

75. $9^{1/2}$ **76.** $32^{4/5}$ **77.** $(-27)^{4/3}$ **78.** $8^{-5/3}$

PART II

In Exercises 79–93, perform the indicated operations and simplify when appropriate, and write each answer with positive exponents. Rationalize all denominators.

79. $(\sqrt{6} - \sqrt{2})(\sqrt{6} + \sqrt{2})$ **80.** $\sqrt{x} + \dfrac{x}{\sqrt{x}}$ **81.** $\sqrt{5xy}\sqrt{10x^2y}$

82. $\sqrt{\dfrac{14x^2y^3}{7xy}}$ **83.** $\dfrac{3}{\sqrt{5}}$ **84.** $\dfrac{5}{\sqrt{7} - \sqrt{2}}$

85. $6x\sqrt{8y^2} - 4xy\sqrt{2}$ **86.** $(\sqrt{2} - \sqrt{5})(3\sqrt{2} + \sqrt{5})$ **87.** $\dfrac{\sqrt{32x^2y^5}}{\sqrt{2xy^3}}$

88. $2^{1/3} \cdot 2^{8/3}$ **89.** $\dfrac{5^{1/5}}{5^{4/5}}$ **90.** $(27^{1/6})^2$

91. $x^{-3/4}$ **92.** $(a^3b^6)^{1/3}$ **93.** $(a^3b^6)^{-1/3}$

PHYSICS *The pressure p in pounds per square foot of a wind blowing against a flat surface is related to the velocity of the wind by the formula*

$$v = \sqrt{\frac{p}{0.003}}$$

where v is in miles per hour. Use this information in Exercises 94–97.

94. A pressure gauge on a building registers a wind pressure of 10.8 lb/ft². What is the velocity of the wind?

95. During a storm, the wind pressure against the side of a mobile home measured 14.7 lb/ft^2. What was the velocity of the wind?

96. What is the pressure of the wind blowing 50 mph against the side of a bridge?

97. If the wind is blowing 15 mph, what pressure does it exert against the side of an apartment building?

Solve each radical equation in Exercises 98–99.

98. $\sqrt{3x+1} - 5 = 2$

99. $\sqrt{y-1} - y + 3 = 0$

100. If a is the shorter of the two legs of a 30°–60° right triangle and $a = 12$ cm, find b and c.

101. If the hypotenuse of a 45°–45° right triangle is $7\sqrt{2}$ ft, find the length of each leg.

In Exercises 102–110, answer true *or* false. *If the answer is false, explain why.*

102. The radical $\sqrt{4}$ only represents the principal square root of 4, which is 2.

103. If x is a positive real number, then $\sqrt{x^2} = x$.

104. $\sqrt{16} + \sqrt{9} = \sqrt{16+9}$.

105. $3\sqrt{x} + 2\sqrt{x} = 5\sqrt{2x}$.

106. When solving a radical equation, always check possible solutions in the original equation.

107. The equation $\sqrt{x+1} + 7 = 0$ has no solution.

108. In a 30°–60° right triangle, the side opposite the 60° angle is half the hypotenuse.

109. Another way to write $x^{1/3}$ is $\sqrt[3]{x}$.

110. Another way to write $y^{3/4}$ is $\sqrt[3]{y^4}$.

CHAPTER 9 TEST

1. How many square roots does 36 have?

Evaluate each square root. Assume all variables and expressions are nonnegative.

2. $\sqrt{(-5)^2}$

3. $\pm\sqrt{121}$

4. $\sqrt{\dfrac{81}{16}}$

5. $\sqrt{16x^2}$

6. $3\sqrt{48}$

7. $\sqrt{\dfrac{8x}{y^2}}$

8. $\sqrt{\dfrac{98x^2}{y}}$

Multiply or divide and simplify.

9. $2\sqrt{6}\sqrt{24}$

10. $\sqrt[4]{8x^3}\sqrt[4]{4x^5}$

11. $\dfrac{\sqrt{27x^3}}{\sqrt{3x}}$

Perform the indicated operations and simplify.

12. $\sqrt{20} + \sqrt{80}$

13. $3\sqrt{18} - 5\sqrt{50}$

14. $6\sqrt{12x} + 3\sqrt{3x} - \sqrt{75x}$

15. $5\sqrt[3]{5} - \sqrt[3]{625}$

16. $\sqrt{11} + \dfrac{1}{\sqrt{11}}$

17. $\sqrt{2}\sqrt{8} + \sqrt{3}\sqrt{12}$

18. $(\sqrt{5} + \sqrt{3})(\sqrt{5} - \sqrt{3})$

19. $(\sqrt{2} + \sqrt{7})(2\sqrt{2} - \sqrt{7})$

Rationalize the denominator.

20. $\dfrac{\sqrt{5}}{\sqrt{5} - 1}$

Solve.

21. $\sqrt{x + 6} = \sqrt{3x - 1}$

22. $\sqrt{x^2 + 7} + x - 1 = 0$

23. Find the length of the diagonal of a rectangle with sides 6 cm and 8 cm.

24. Given $d = 10\sqrt{80h}$.

(a) Find d when h is $\frac{1}{16}$.

(b) Find h when d is 400.

25. In a right triangle, $\angle A = 30°$ and $a = 20$. Find b and c.

26. In a right triangle, $\angle B = 45°$ and the hypotenuse is 8. Find the length of each leg.

27. Write $(-27)^{5/3}$ as a radical and simplify.

28. Write $(x^{-4}y^6)^{-1/2}$ using only positive exponents.

CHAPTER 10

Quadratic Equations

CHAPTER 7 GAVE A brief introduction to quadratic equations and ways to solve certain special types by factoring. This chapter expands the development and derives a formula that can be used for all types of quadratic equations. Factoring, finding square roots, and simplifying radical expressions are techniques that play an essential role in understanding the concepts we will study.

The following example is one of many applied problems that translate into quadratic equations. We solve it in Example 9 of Section 10.1.

ARCHEOLOGY A pyramid in Mexico has a square base with height 40 m and volume 38,880 m^3. If the volume of a pyramid is given by $V = \frac{1}{3}Bh$, where B is the area of the base, find the length of each side of the base.

We begin this chapter with a review of the factoring method, and then solve quadratic equations by taking roots and completing the square. Next we develop the quadratic formula, solve several types of equations that can be written as quadratic equations, and examine a variety of applications. We conclude the chapter with an introduction to graphing quadratic equations and solving equations with complex-number solutions.

SECTION 10.1 Factoring and Taking Roots

Student guideposts

- ▶ *Quadratic equations*
- ▶ *Solving by factoring*
- ▶ *Solving by taking roots*

▶ *Quadratic equations*

Most of the equations we have solved have had the variable raised only to the first power. However, in Section 5.5 we briefly introduced the idea of a *quadratic equation.* An equation that can be expressed in the form

$$ax^2 + bx + c = 0,$$

where a, b, and c are constant real numbers and $a \neq 0$, is called a **quadratic equation.** (If a were 0, the term in which the variable is squared would be missing and the equation would not be quadratic.) We call $ax^2 + bx + c = 0$ the **general form** of a quadratic equation.

EXAMPLE 1 Identifying Constants in General Form

Write each equation in general form and identify each constant a, b, and c.

(a) $3x^2 + 2x - 6 = 0 \qquad (3x^2 + 2x + (-6) = 0)$

This equation is already in general form with $a = 3$, $b = 2$ and $c = -6$. Note that $c = -6$ and not 6. In the general form of an equation, all signs are + so any negative sign goes with the constant a, b, or c.

(b) $2y^2 = 3y + 1$

Collect all terms on one side of the equation to obtain

$$2y^2 - 3y - 1 = 0$$

so that $a = 2$, $b = -3$, and $c = -1$.

(c) $y^2 = 3y + 1$

Collect all terms on the left side.

$$y^2 - 3y - 1 = 0$$

Then $a = 1$, $b = -3$, and $c = -1$. If we collect all terms on the right side we obtain

$$0 = -y^2 + 3y + 1$$

so that $a = -1$, $b = 3$, and $c = 1$. Both of these are correct since the equations are equivalent. However, it is common practice to write the equation so that the coefficient of the squared term is positive.

(d) $2x + 1 = 3 - 4x + 2$

Since there is no term in which the variable is squared, this is not a quadratic equation.

(e) $2y - 5y^2 = 3y^2 + 2y + 1$

Collect all like terms to obtain

$$8y^2 + 1 = 0 \quad \text{or} \quad 8y^2 + 0 \cdot y + 1 = 0$$

so that $a = 8$, $b = 0$, and $c = 1$.

(f) $4 = 6x + 12x^2$

Collect all terms on one side.

$$12x^2 + 6x - 4 = 0$$

This is a general form of the equation. However, we should simplify by factoring out 2 and multiplying both sides by $\frac{1}{2}$. That is,

$$2(6x^2 + 3x - 2) = 0 \quad \text{or} \quad 6x^2 + 3x - 2 = 0.$$

After removing common factors, we have $a = 6$, $b = 3$, and $c = -2$. ■

▶ *Solving by factoring*

Recall that an equation of the type

$$(x - 2)(x + 1) = 0$$

is solved by using the zero-product rule, which states that if the product of two numbers is zero then one or both of the numbers must be zero. Using this rule we set each factor equal to zero and solve.

$$x - 2 = 0 \quad \text{or} \quad x + 1 = 0$$
$$x = 2 \qquad\qquad x = -1$$

Since $(x - 2)(x + 1) = x^2 - x - 2$, in effect we have solved the quadratic equation

$$x^2 - x - 2 = 0.$$

To Solve a Quadratic Equation by Factoring

1. Write the equation in general form by dividing out any constant factors and making the coefficient of the squared term positive.
2. Factor the expression.
3. Using the zero-product rule, set each factor equal to 0 and solve the resulting equations.
4. Check your answers in the original equation.

EXAMPLE 2 **Solving a Quadratic Equation by Factoring**

Solve $2x^2 - x - 1 = 0$.

$$(2x + 1)(x - 1) = 0 \qquad \text{Factor}$$

$$2x + 1 = 0 \quad \text{or} \quad x - 1 = 0 \qquad \text{Zero-product rule}$$

$$2x = -1 \qquad x = 1$$

$$x = -\frac{1}{2}$$

Check: $2\left(-\frac{1}{2}\right)^2 - \left(-\frac{1}{2}\right) - 1 \stackrel{?}{=} 0 \qquad 2(1)^2 - (1) - 1 \stackrel{?}{=} 0$

$$2\left(\frac{1}{4}\right) + \frac{1}{2} - 1 \stackrel{?}{=} 0 \qquad 2 - 1 - 1 \stackrel{?}{=} 0$$

$$\frac{2}{4} + \frac{1}{2} - 1 \stackrel{?}{=} 0 \qquad 2 - 2 = 0$$

$$1 - 1 = 0$$

The solutions are 1 and $-\frac{1}{2}$. ■

EXAMPLE 3 **Removing Common Factor First**

Solve $2x^2 - 2x = 12$.

$$2x^2 - 2x - 12 = 0 \qquad \text{Write in general form}$$

$$2(x^2 - x - 6) = 0 \qquad \text{2 is a common factor}$$

$$x^2 - x - 6 = 0 \qquad \text{Divide both sides by 2}$$

$$(x - 3)(x + 2) = 0 \qquad \text{Factor}$$

$$x - 3 = 0 \quad \text{or} \quad x + 2 = 0 \qquad \text{Zero-product rule}$$

$$x = 3 \qquad x = -2$$

The solutions are 3 and -2. Check. ■

NOTE Although a numerical factor of an equation can be divided out, never divide out a factor that contains the variable. For example, if a quadratic equation in general form has $c = 0$, $ax^2 + bx = 0$, one factor is always x.

$$x(ax + b) = 0$$

As a result, using the zero product rule, one equation will be $x = 0$ so that 0 is always one solution to this type of equation. If you incorrectly divide both sides by x, this solution will be lost.

EXAMPLE 4 **Working with One Solution Zero**

Solve $5x^2 = 3x$.

$$\begin{aligned} 5x^2 - 3x &= 0 && \text{Write in general form} \\ x(5x - 3) &= 0 && \text{Factor} \\ x = 0 \quad \text{or} \quad 5x - 3 &= 0 && \text{Zero-product rule} \\ 5x &= 3 \\ x &= \frac{3}{5} \end{aligned}$$

The solutions are 0 and $\frac{3}{5}$. Check. ■

CAUTION Never divide both sides of an equation by an expression involving the variable. In Example 4 if we had divided by x we would have lost the solution 0.

EXAMPLE 5 **Working with A More Complex Equation**

Solve $5z(z - 6) - 8z = 2z$.

$$\begin{aligned} 5z^2 - 30z - 8z &= 2z && \text{Clear parentheses} \\ 5z^2 - 38z &= 2z \\ 5z^2 - 40z &= 0 && \text{Write in general form} \\ 5(z^2 - 8z) &= 0 && \text{Factor out the constant factor 5} \\ z^2 - 8z &= 0 && \text{Divide out the common factor of 5} \\ z(z - 8) &= 0 && \text{Factor} \\ z = 0 \quad \text{or} \quad z - 8 &= 0 \\ z &= 8 \end{aligned}$$

The solutions are 0 and 8. Check. ■

Solving by taking roots

A quadratic equation with $b = 0$, that is, $ax^2 + c = 0$, can be solved using a different technique. Consider the equation

$$x^2 - 4 = 0$$

or

$$x^2 = 4.$$

What number squared is 4? Clearly $2^2 = 4$ and $(-2)^2 = 4$ so that x is either 2 or -2. By taking the square root of both sides of the equation and using the symbol $\pm$ to indicate both the positive (principal) square root and the negative square root, we have

$$x = \pm\sqrt{4}$$

$$x = \pm 2.$$

Remember that $x = \pm 2$ is simply a shorthand way of writing $x = +2$ *or* $x = -2$.

To Solve a Quadratic Equation by Taking Roots

If the general form of a quadratic equation has $b = 0$, that is, $ax^2 + c = 0$:

1. Solve the equation for x^2, getting an equation of the form $x^2 = A$.
2. Take the square root of both sides to obtain the solutions

$$x = \pm\sqrt{A}.$$

NOTE The method of taking roots gives real-number solutions only when $A \geq 0$. We will consider the case when $A < 0$ in Section 10.7.

EXAMPLE 6 **Solving a Quadratic Equation by Taking Roots**

Solve $3x^2 - 75 = 0$.

$$\begin{aligned} 3x^2 &= 75 && \text{Add 75 to both sides} \\ x^2 &= \frac{75}{3} && \text{Divide both sides by 3} \\ x^2 &= 25 \\ x &= \pm\sqrt{25} && \text{Take square root of both sides} \\ &= \pm 5 \end{aligned}$$

Check:

$$\begin{aligned} 3(+5)^2 - 75 &\stackrel{?}{=} 0 \qquad & 3(-5)^2 - 75 &\stackrel{?}{=} 0 \\ 3(25) - 75 &\stackrel{?}{=} 0 & 3(25) - 75 &\stackrel{?}{=} 0 \\ 75 - 75 &= 0 & 75 - 75 &= 0 \end{aligned}$$

The solutions are 5 and -5. ■

Some equations of the form $ax^2 + c = 0$ that we solve by taking roots can also be solved by factoring. For instance, consider the equation in Example 6.

$$\begin{aligned} 3x^2 - 75 &= 0 \\ 3(x^2 - 25) &= 0 && \text{Factor out 3} \\ x^2 - 25 &= 0 && \text{Divide both sides by 3} \\ (x - 5)(x + 5) &= 0 && \text{Factor} \\ x - 5 = 0 \quad &\text{or} \quad x + 5 = 0 \\ x = 5 \quad & \qquad\quad x = -5 \end{aligned}$$

We obtain the same solutions as before. However, some equations of this type cannot be factored using integer coefficients, and the method of taking roots must be used. This is illustrated in the next example.

EXAMPLE 7

Solving An Equation with Irrational Solutions

Solve $5x^2 - 40 = 0$.

$$5x^2 = 40 \qquad \text{Add 40}$$

$$x^2 = \frac{40}{5} \qquad \text{Divide by 5}$$

$$x = \pm\sqrt{8} \qquad \text{Take square root of both sides}$$

$$x = \pm\sqrt{4 \cdot 2} = \pm 2\sqrt{2}$$

The solutions are $2\sqrt{2}$ and $-2\sqrt{2}$. Check. ■

Some equations, written in a special form, can be solved by extending the method of taking roots. This is shown in the next example.

EXAMPLE 8

Taking Roots

Solve $(y + 3)^2 = 16$.

Although not in the form $ax^2 + c = 0$, we can use the same basic technique of taking the square root of both sides to solve.

$$y + 3 = \pm\sqrt{16}$$

$$y + 3 = \pm 4$$

$$y = -3 \pm 4 \qquad \text{Subtract 3 from both sides}$$

$$y = \begin{cases} -3 + 4 = 1 & \text{Use + to obtain solution 1} \\ -3 - 4 = -7 & \text{Use − to obtain solution −7} \end{cases}$$

It is easy to substitute 1 and -7 into the original equation to see that they check and are the solutions. ■

There are many applications of quadratic equations including the one given in the chapter introduction which is solved in the next example. For purposes of review we show all the steps of the ATTACK method of problem solving.

EXAMPLE 9

Solving an Application to Archeology

A pyramid in Mexico has a square base with height 40 m and volume 38,880 m³ (see Figure 10.1). If the volume of a pyramid is given by $V = \frac{1}{3}Bh$, where B is the area of the base, find the length of each side of the base.

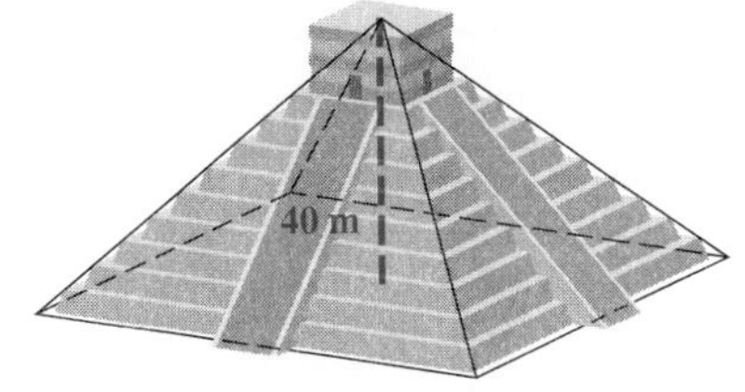

FIGURE 10.1

Analysis: We must find the side of a square that serves as the base of a pyramid. Since the height and the volume of the pyramid are given, we will use this information in the formula for the volume.
Tabulation:

Let x = the length of a side of the square base.

Since the area of a square is the square of the length of a side, we have:

$x^2 = B$, the area of the base of the pyramid.

Translation: Substitute 38,880 for V, x^2 for B, and 40 for h in the formula for the volume of a pyramid to obtain an equation in x.

$$V = \frac{1}{3}Bh$$

$$38{,}880 = \frac{1}{3}(x^2)(40)$$

$$116{,}640 = 40x^2 \qquad \text{Multiply both sides by 3}$$

$$2916 = x^2 \qquad \text{Divide both sides by 40}$$

$$\pm\sqrt{2916} = x \qquad \text{Take square root of both sides}$$

$$\pm 54 = x \qquad \text{Use a calculator}$$

Approximation: The length of a side of a square cannot be negative, so we discard the solution -54. Since 54 m is a reasonable length for the side of a square, we proceed to the check.
Check: A square with sides 54 m has area $54^2\ m^2 = 2916\ m^2$, so $B = 2916\ \text{m}^2$. Then $V = \frac{1}{3}Bh = \frac{1}{3}(2916)(40) = 38{,}880\ \text{m}^3$, so 54 m does indeed check.
Thus, the base of the pyramid is 54 m. ■

NOTE When a quadratic equation that has two solutions serves as a model for an applied problem, only one of the solutions might actually make sense. This happened in Example 9 where one solution was discarded because a length cannot be negative. As a result, the *Approximation* step in problem solving is very important in these types of applications.

10.1 EXERCISES

Write each equation in Exercises 1–6 in general quadratic form and identify the constants a, b, and c.

1. $2x^2 + x = 5$

2. $x^2 = 3x$

3. $x^2 + 1 = 0$

4. $\frac{1}{2}y^2 - y = 3 - y$

5. $2(x^2 + x) + x^3 = x^3 - 5$

6. $3x = 3(x + 1)$

7. Given the quadratic equation $-x^2 + 2x - 3 = 0$, we might conclude that $a = -1$, $b = 2$, and $c = -3$. Would $a = 1$, $b = -2$, and $c = 3$ be incorrect? Explain.

Solve each equation in Exercises 8–31.

8. $x^2 - 3x - 28 = 0$
9. $x^2 = 2x + 35$
10. $2z^2 - 5z = 3$
11. $6x^2 - 2x - 8 = 0$
12. $4z^2 = 7z$
13. $y^2 - 10y = -25$
14. $3(y^2 + 8) = 24 - 15y$
15. $z(8 - 2z) = 6$
16. $x(3x + 20) = 7$
17. $(3z - 1)(2z + 1) = 3(2z + 1)$
18. $(2y - 3)(y + 1) = 4(2y - 3)$
19. $4x^2 - 9 = 3$
20. $z^2 - 81 = 0$
21. $2y^2 - 128 = 0$
22. $y^2 - \dfrac{9}{4} = 0$
23. $-3z^2 = -27$
24. $2x^2 - 150 = 0$
25. $2x^2 - 50 = 0$
26. $-3y^2 = -6$
27. $3 - y^2 = y^2 - 3$
28. $z^2 + 2z = 2z + 4$
29. $(x - 2)^2 = 9$
30. $(y + 1)^2 = 49$
31. $(z - 1)^2 = 5$

---

32. **NUMBER** The square of a number, decreased by 2, is equal to the negative of the number. Find the number.

33. **NUMBER** The square of 2 more than a number is 64. Find the number.

34. **GEOMETRY** The area of a circle with radius r is given by $A = \pi r^2$. If the area of a circular flower bed is 56.25π yd^2, find the radius of the bed.

35. **GEOMETRY** The volume of a right circular cylinder is given by $V = \pi r^2 h$, where h is the height and r is the radius of the base of the cylinder. If a grain silo is cylindrical in shape with volume 1080π ft^3 and height 30 ft, find the radius of the silo.

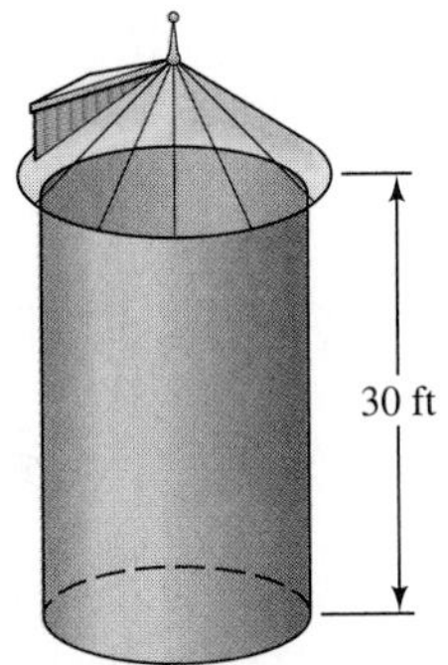

36. **GEOMETRY** The volume of a pyramid is given by $V = \frac{1}{3}Bh$, where B is the area of the base and h is the height. If the base of a pyramid is a rectangle with length twice the width, height 20 ft, and volume 1080 ft^3, find the dimensions of the base.

37. **GEOMETRY** The volume of a rectangular solid with a square base is 147 in^3. If the height of the solid is 12 in, find the length of a side of the base.

BANKING *The amount of money A that will result if a principal P is invested at r percent interest compounded annually for 2 years is given by $A = P(1 + r)^2$. Use this formula to find the interest rate for the given values of A and P in Exercises 38–39. Give the answer to the nearest tenth of a percent if appropriate.*

38. $A = \$2645, P = \$2000$

39. $A = \$1765, P = \$1500$

Tell what is wrong with each of Burford's "solutions" in Exercises 40–41.

40.
$$x^2 - x = 3(x - 1)$$
$$x(x - 1) = 3(x - 1)$$
$$x = 3$$
(the factors $(x-1)$ are crossed out)

41.
$$x^2 - x = 2$$
$$x(x - 1) = 2$$
$$x = 2 \text{ or } x - 1 = 2$$
$$x = 3$$

FOR REVIEW

The following exercises review material from Sections 6.6, 7.4, and 9.1. They will help you prepare for the next section. Find the products in Exercises 42–44.

42. $(x + 6)^2$

43. $(x - 10)^2$

44. $\left(x + \frac{1}{9}\right)^2$

Factor the trinomials in Exercises 45–47.

45. $x^2 - 4x + 4$

46. $x^2 + 10x + 25$

47. $x^2 + x + \frac{1}{4}$

Simplify the square roots in Exercises 48–50.

48. $\sqrt{8}$

49. $\sqrt{\frac{49}{4}}$

50. $\sqrt{\frac{7}{4}}$

10.1 PARALLEL EXERCISES

Write each equation in Exercises 1–6 in general form and identify the constants a, b, and c.

1. $3x^2 + x = 7$

2. $z^2 = 9z$

3. $w^2 + 5 = 0$

4. $\frac{1}{3}x^2 - x = 5 - x$

5. $3(y^2 + y) - y^3 = 6 - y^3$

6. $5x^3 = x^2 + 7$

7. Given the quadratic equation $-y^2 + y - 7 = 0$, we might conclude that $a = -1$, $b = 1$, and $c = -7$. Would $a = 1$, $b = -1$, and $c = 7$ be incorrect? Explain.

Solve each equation in Exercises 8–31.

8. $x^2 + x - 6 = 0$

9. $x^2 = 2x + 24$

10. $2z^2 + 3 = 7z$

11. $3x^2 - 2x - 5 = 0$

12. $2z^2 = 3z$

13. $z^2 - 20 = z$

14. $3(y^2 + 4y) = -6y$

15. $z(z - 3) = -2$

16. $x(2x + 9) = 5$

17. $(z - 2)(z + 1) = 3(z + 1)$

18. $5x^2 - 10 = 5$

19. $y(2y - 1) = 7(1 - 2y)$

20. $z^2 - 36 = 0$

21. $2y^2 - 98 = 0$

22. $y^2 - \frac{25}{4} = 0$

23. $-8z^2 = -32$

24. $2x^2 - 100 = 0$

25. $3x^2 - 75 = 0$

26. $-6y^2 = -18$

27. $7 - x^2 = x^2 - 7$

28. $z^2 + 5z = 5z + 1$

29. $(x - 5)^2 = 4$

30. $(y + 2)^2 = 1$

31. $(z - 3)^2 = 3$

32. NUMBER The square of a number, less 10 is equal to three times the number. Find the number.

33. NUMBER The square of 5 more than a number is 9. Find the number.

34. GEOMETRY The area of a circle with radius r is given by $A = \pi r^2$. If the area of a circular park is $22{,}500\pi$ yd^2, find the radius of the park.

35. GEOMETRY The volume of a right circular cylinder is given by $V = \pi r^2 h$, where h is the height and r is the radius of the base of the cylinder. If a storage container is cylindrical in shape with volume 324π ft^3 and height 16 ft, find the radius of the container.

36. **GEOMETRY** The volume of a pyramid is given by $V = \frac{1}{3}Bh$, where B is the area of the base and h is the height. If the base of a pyramid is a rectangle with width half the length, height 9 m, and volume 216 m^3, find the dimensions of the base.

37. **GEOMETRY** The volume of a rectangular solid with a square base is 845 in^3. If the height of the solid is 20 in, find the length of a side of the base.

BANKING *The amount of money A that will result if a principal P is invested at r percent interest compounded annually for 2 years is given by $A = P(1 + r)^2$. Use this formula to find the interest rate for the given values of A and P in Exercises 38–39. Give the answer to the nearest tenth of a percent if appropriate.*

38. $A = \$1210, P = \$1000$

39. $A = \$2785, P = \$2400$

Tell what is wrong with each of Burford's "solutions" in Exercises 40–41.

40. $x^2 - 2x = 0$

$x(x - 2) = 0$

$\frac{\not{x}(x - 2)}{\not{x}} = \frac{0}{x}$

$x - 2 = 0$

$x = 2$

41. $x(x - 5) = 6$

$x = 6 \text{ or } x - 5 = 6$

$x = 11$

FOR REVIEW

The following exercises review material from Sections 6.6, 7.4, and 9.1. They will help you prepare for the next section. Find the products in Exercises 42–44.

42. $(x + 3)^2$

43. $(x - 7)^2$

44. $\left(x - \frac{1}{6}\right)^2$

Factor the trinomials in Exercises 45–47.

45. $x^2 + 22x + 121$

46. $x^2 - 20x + 100$

47. $x^2 + \frac{2}{3}x + \frac{1}{9}$

Simplify the square roots in Exercises 48–50.

48. $\sqrt{32}$

49. $\sqrt{\frac{144}{25}}$

50. $\sqrt{\frac{11}{9}}$

10.1 ENRICHMENT EXERCISES

Solve.

1. $6x^2 + 47x - 8 = 0$

2. $(2x - 1)(x + 5) = (4x + 3)(x + 5)$

3. $(x^2 - 5)^2 = 8$

4. **COMMUNICATIONS** Ace Communications plans to stabilize a radio tower that is 150 ft tall using three guy wires. Each wire is to be attached from the top of the tower to the ground 85 ft from the base of the tower. Each point of attachment will require an extra 2 ft of wire. How many feet of wire will be needed for the project?

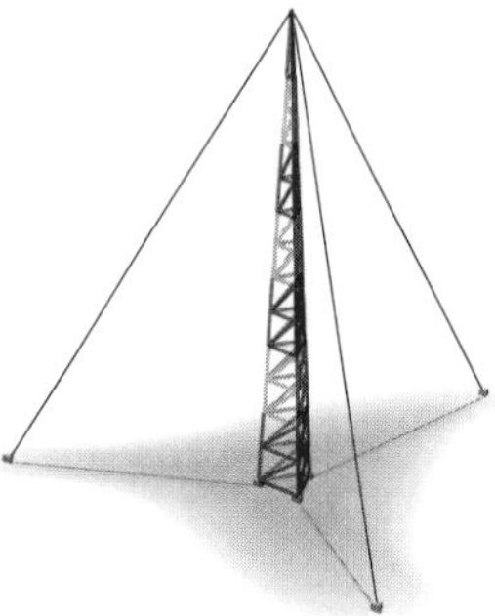

In Exercises 5–6, solve each literal equation for x. Assume that $a > 0$.

5. $x^2 - a = 0$
6. $(x - 5)^2 = a$
7. $(x - 5)^2 = a^2$.
8. Explain why the equation $2x^2 + 8 = 0$ has no real-number solutions.
9. In your own words, outline the factoring method for solving a quadratic equation and discuss when to use this method.
10. In your own words, outline the method of taking roots for solving a quadratic equation and discuss when to use this method.
11. When solving an equation such as $x^2 = 4$ by taking roots, we only use $\pm$ on one side of the equation. Actually, when we take the square root of both sides, we should write $\pm x = \pm 2$. Notice that this represents four equations, $+x = +2$, $+x = -2$, $-x = +2$, and $-x = -2$. With this in mind, write a paragraph explaining why we are able to use only $x = \pm 2$.

SECTION 10.2 Solving By Completing the Square

Student guideposts

- *Completing the square*
- *Solving by completing the square*

Completing the square

A trinomial $x^2 + bx + c$ is a perfect square trinomial if it factors into the square of a binomial. Notice that the trinomials in the left column below are perfect square trinomials. Also notice in the right column that for each perfect square trinomial, the constant term, c, is the square of one half the coefficient of the x term, b.

$$x^2 + 6x + 9 = (x + 3)^2 \qquad 9 = \left(\frac{1}{2} \cdot 6\right)^2$$

$$x^2 - 10x + 25 = (x - 5)^2 \qquad 25 = \left(\frac{1}{2} \cdot (-10)\right)^2$$

$$x^2 - x + \frac{1}{4} = \left(x - \frac{1}{2}\right)^2 \qquad \frac{1}{4} = \left(\frac{1}{2} \cdot (-1)\right)^2$$

In general, whenever we are given the first two terms of a trinomial, $x^2 + bx$, we can add $\left(\frac{1}{2} \cdot b\right)^2$ to it to get a perfect square trinomial. This process, called **completing the square,** can be used only when the coefficient in the squared term is 1.

EXAMPLE 1

Completing the Square

What must be added to complete the square?

(a) $x^2 + 12x +$ ____

Add $\left(\frac{1}{2} \cdot 12\right)^2 = 6^2 = 36.$

(b) $x^2 - 20x +$ ____

Add $\left(\frac{1}{2} \cdot (-20)\right)^2 = (-10)^2 = 100.$

(c) $x^2 + \frac{2}{3}x +$ ____

Add $\left(\frac{1}{2} \cdot \frac{2}{3}\right)^2 = \left(\frac{1}{3}\right)^2 = \frac{1}{9}.$ ■

▶ *Solving by completing the square*

We can solve quadratic equations by completing the square (a method that will have applications in the next algebra course). For example, the equation

$$x^2 + 3x - 10 = 0$$

which can be solved by factoring,

$$(x + 5)(x - 2) = 0$$
$$x = -5, 2$$

can also be solved by completing the square. To do so, first isolate the constant term on the right side. (Leave space as indicated.)

$$x^2 + 3x \qquad = 10$$

To complete the square on the left side, add the square of half the coefficient of x. The coefficient of x is 3.

$$\left(\frac{1}{2} \cdot 3\right)^2 = \left(\frac{3}{2}\right)^2 = \frac{9}{4}$$

But if $\frac{9}{4}$ is added on the left, to keep equality we must add $\frac{9}{4}$ on the right.

$$x^2 + 3x + \frac{9}{4} = 10 + \frac{9}{4}$$

$$\left(x + \frac{3}{2}\right)^2 = \frac{49}{4} \qquad \text{Factor left side, simplify right side}$$

Take the square root of each side, remembering to write both the positive and negative root.

$$x + \frac{3}{2} = \pm\sqrt{\frac{49}{4}} = \pm\frac{7}{2}$$

$$x = -\frac{3}{2} \pm \frac{7}{2} \qquad \text{Subtract } \tfrac{3}{2} \text{ from both sides}$$

$$x = -\frac{3}{2} + \frac{7}{2} \quad \text{or} \quad x = -\frac{3}{2} - \frac{7}{2}$$

$$x = \frac{4}{2} = 2 \qquad\qquad x = \frac{-10}{2} = -5$$

The solutions are the same as before, 2 and -5.

To Solve a Quadratic Equation by Completing the Square

1. Isolate the constant term on the right side of the equation.
2. If the coefficient of the squared item is 1, proceed to step 4.
3. If the coefficient of the squared term is not 1, divide each term by that coefficient.
4. Complete the square on the left side and add the same number to the right side.
5. Factor (check by multiplying the factors) and take the square root of both sides (positive and negative roots).
6. Use both the positive root and the negative root to obtain the solutions to the original equation.

EXAMPLE 2

Solving by Completing the Square

Solve $y^2 - 6y + 8 = 0$ by completing the square.

$$y^2 - 6y = -8 \qquad \text{Isolate the constant, } b = -6$$

$$y^2 - 6y + 9 = -8 + 9 \qquad \text{Add 9 to both sides; } \left(\frac{-6}{2}\right)^2 = (-3)^2 = 9$$

$$(y - 3)^2 = 1$$

$$y - 3 = \pm\sqrt{1} \qquad \text{Take the square root of both sides}$$

$$y - 3 = \pm 1 \qquad \sqrt{1} = 1$$

$$y = 3 \pm 1$$

$$y = 3 + 1 \quad \text{or} \quad y = 3 - 1$$

$$y = 4 \qquad\qquad y = 2$$

The solutions are 2 and 4. ■

As mentioned earlier, we can use the technique above to complete the square when the coefficient of the squared item is 1. If this is not the case, we need to divide each term of the equation by the coefficient of the squared term before we can use the method.

EXAMPLE 3 **Making the Coefficient of x^2 One**

Solve $2x^2 + 2x - 3 = 0$ by completing the square.

$$2x^2 + 2x = 3 \qquad \text{Isolate the constant}$$

$$x^2 + x = \frac{3}{2} \qquad \text{Divide both sides of the equation by 2; } b = 1$$

$$x^2 + x + \frac{1}{4} = \frac{3}{2} + \frac{1}{4} \qquad \text{Complete the square by adding } \tfrac{1}{4} \text{ to both sides}$$

$$\left(x + \frac{1}{2}\right)^2 = \frac{7}{4} \qquad \frac{3}{2} + \frac{1}{4} = \frac{6}{4} + \frac{1}{4} = \frac{7}{4}$$

$$x + \frac{1}{2} = \pm\sqrt{\frac{7}{4}} = \pm\frac{\sqrt{7}}{\sqrt{4}} = \pm\frac{\sqrt{7}}{2}$$

$$x + \frac{1}{2} = \frac{\sqrt{7}}{2} \quad \text{or} \quad x + \frac{1}{2} = -\frac{\sqrt{7}}{2}$$

$$x = -\frac{1}{2} + \frac{\sqrt{7}}{2} \qquad x = -\frac{1}{2} - \frac{\sqrt{7}}{2}$$

$$x = \frac{-1 + \sqrt{7}}{2} \qquad x = \frac{-1 - \sqrt{7}}{2}$$

The solutions are $\dfrac{-1 \pm \sqrt{7}}{2}$. ∎

> **NOTE** When you are given an equation to solve, if either factoring or taking roots is applicable, you should use one of these methods rather than completing the square. This is probably clear since completing the square requires much more work. Actually, as we will see in the next section, there is a better way to solve equations that cannot be solved by factoring or taking roots. However, since the technique of completing the square is used in other ways in mathematics, it is important for us to be familiar with it.

10.2 EXERCISES

What must be added to each expression in Exercises 1–6 to complete the square?

1. $x^2 - 8x +$ ____ **2.** $z^2 + 7z +$ ____ **3.** $x^2 - x +$ ____

4. $z^2 + \frac{1}{3}z +$ ____ **5.** $x^2 - \frac{1}{2}x +$ ____ **6.** $y^2 - \frac{4}{3}y +$ ____

Solve by completing the square in Exercises 7–12.

7. $x^2 + 8x + 15 = 0$ **8.** $x^2 - 2x - 1 = 0$ **9.** $2x^2 + x - 1 = 0$

10. $2y^2 - 5y = -2$ **11.** $z^2 + 16z + 50 = 0$ **12.** $x^2 - 10x + 22 = 0$

Solve by any method in Exercises 13–15.

13. $2x^2 - 5x - 3 = 0$ **14.** $2y^2 - 3y = 1$ **15.** $z^2 + z = z + 10$

16. **PHYSICS** A free-falling object, starting from rest, will fall d feet in t seconds according to the formula $d = 16t^2$.

(a) How far will the object fall in 1 second?

(b) How far will the object fall in 5 seconds?

(c) How many seconds does it take for the object to fall 64 feet?

FOR REVIEW

The following exercises review material from Chapter 2 and Sections 8.4, 9.2, 9.4, and 9.7. They will help prepare for the next section. Evaluate each expression in Exercises 17–22 if $a = 2$, $b = -4$, and $c = 1$.

17. $-b$ **18.** b^2 **19.** $4ac$

20. $b^2 - 4ac$ **21.** $\sqrt{b^2 - 4ac}$ **22.** $-b + \sqrt{b^2 - 4ac}$

Solve each equation in Exercises 23–24.

23. $\frac{1}{x-1} + \frac{2}{x+1} = \frac{5}{x^2-1}$ **24.** $\sqrt{x^2 - 3} - x = 1$

GEOMETRY *The Pythagorean theorem states that $a^2 + b^2 = c^2$ where a and b are legs of a right triangle and c is the hypotenuse. In Exercises 25–26, find the missing leg or hypotenuse.*

25. $a = 6$ and $b = 4$ **26.** $b = \frac{1}{2}$ and $c = \frac{3}{2}$

10.2 PARALLEL EXERCISES

What must be added to each expression in Exercises 1–6 to complete the square?

1. $x^2 + 24x +$ ____ **2.** $z^2 + 3z +$ ____ **3.** $z^2 + \frac{1}{2}z +$ ____

4. $x^2 - \frac{1}{3}x +$ ____ **5.** $y^2 + \frac{2}{3}y +$ ____ **6.** $z^2 - z +$ ____

Solve by completing the square in Exercises 7–12.

7. $z^2 - 3z - 10 = 0$ **8.** $x^2 - 4x - 1 = 0$ **9.** $2x^2 - 3x + 1 = 0$

10. $2y^2 - 5y = 3$ **11.** $z^2 - z = 3$ **12.** $2x^2 + 6x + 1 = 0$

Solve by any method in Exercises 13–15.

13. $2x^2 - 3x - 2 = 0$ **14.** $3y^2 - 6 = 2y$ **15.** $z^2 - z = 8 - z$

16. **PHYSICS** A free falling object, starting at rest, will fall d feet in t seconds according to the formula $d = 16t^2$.

(a) How far will the object fall in 2 seconds?

(b) How far will the object fall in 10 seconds?

(c) How many seconds does it take for the object to fall 144 feet?

FOR REVIEW

The following exercises review material from Chapter 2 and Sections 8.4, 9.2, 9.4, and 9.7. They will help prepare for the next section. Evaluate each expression in Exercises 17–22 if $a = 3$, $b = -6$ and $c = 2$.

17. $-b$ **18.** b^2 **19.** $4ac$

20. $b^2 - 4ac$ **21.** $\sqrt{b^2 - 4ac}$ **22.** $-b + \sqrt{b^2 - 4ac}$

Solve each equation in Exercises 23–24.

23. $\frac{3}{x-2} + \frac{4}{x+2} = \frac{-1}{x^2-4}$ **24.** $\sqrt{x^2+5} - x = 1$

GEOMETRY *The Pythagorean theorem states that $a^2 + b^2 = c^2$ where a and b are legs of a right triangle and c is the hypotenuse. In Exercises 25–26, find the missing leg or hypotenuse.*

25. $a = 9$ and $b = 2$ **26.** $a = \frac{1}{3}$ and $c = \frac{4}{3}$

10.2 ENRICHMENT EXERCISES

Solve each equation for x in Exercises 1–4.

1. $5x^2 - 2x - 10 = 0$ △ **2.** $x^2 + 2x + c = 0$

3. $x^2 + bx - 2 = 0$ △ **4.** $x^2 + bx + c = 0$

5. Complete the square on x in $x^2 - 4x - y + 7 = 0$ and write the equation in the form $y - k = (x - h)^2$. Changing the form of an equation like this is an important application of the technique of completing the square. [*Hint:* Start by writing all the terms with x on the one side and all other terms on the other.]

6. When Burford tried to solve $2x^2 + 6x - 5 = 0$ by completing the square, he added 5 to both sides and then took half of 6 and squared the result obtaining 9. When he added 9 to both sides, he had trouble factoring. Explain to Burford what he is doing wrong, and write out a detailed description of how to solve this equation for him.

SECTION 10.3 The Quadratic Formula and the Discriminant

Student guideposts

- *Quadratic formula*
- *Using the quadratic formula*
- *The discriminant*
- *Applications requiring the quadratic formula*

▶ *Quadratic formula*

The methods of factoring and taking roots are generally faster and easier to use than completing the square. But since not all equations can be solved by factoring or taking roots, we were forced to use completing the square in these cases. The process of completing the square is a tedious one, and with each different equation, we repeated the same process over and over. When this happens in mathematics, we often perform the process once in general and try to develop a formula that will save us time. This is how the *quadratic formula* is developed. Starting with a general quadratic equation

$$ax^2 + bx + c = 0 \quad (a > 0)$$

we complete the square.

$$ax^2 + bx = -c$$ Isolate the constant term

$$\frac{\not{a}x^2}{\not{a}} + \frac{b}{a}x = -\frac{c}{a}$$ Divide by the coefficient of x^2, a

$$x^2 + \frac{b}{a}x + \left(\frac{b}{2a}\right)^2 = -\frac{c}{a} + \left(\frac{b}{2a}\right)^2$$ Add $\left(\frac{1}{2}\cdot\frac{b}{a}\right)^2 = \left(\frac{b}{2a}\right)^2$ to complete the square

$$\left(x + \frac{b}{2a}\right)^2 = -\frac{c}{a} + \frac{b^2}{4a^2}$$ Factor the left side

$$\left(x + \frac{b}{2a}\right)^2 = -\frac{4ac}{4a^2} + \frac{b^2}{4a^2}$$ Find the common denominator on the right side

$$= \frac{b^2 - 4ac}{4a^2}$$ Subtract the fractions

$$x + \frac{b}{2a} = \pm\sqrt{\frac{b^2 - 4ac}{4a^2}}$$ Take square roots

$$= \frac{\pm\sqrt{b^2 - 4ac}}{2a}$$ $\sqrt{\frac{u}{v}} = \frac{\sqrt{u}}{\sqrt{v}}$, and $\sqrt{4a^2} = 2a$ since $a > 0$

$$x = -\frac{b}{2a} \pm \frac{\sqrt{b^2 - 4ac}}{2a}$$ Subtract $\frac{b}{2a}$ from both sides

$$x = \frac{-b \pm \sqrt{b^2 - 4ac}}{2a}$$ Note that $2a$ is the denominator of the entire expression

▶ *Using the quadratic formula*

This last formula is called the **quadratic formula** and it must be memorized since it is used in this and all courses that follow. To use it to solve a quadratic equation, we identify the constants, a, b, and c and substitute into the quadratic formula.

To Solve a Quadratic Equation Using the Quadratic Formula

1. Write the equation in general form ($ax^2 + bx + c = 0$).
2. Identify the constants a, b, and c.
3. Substitute the values of a, b, and c into the quadratic formula,
$$x = \frac{-b \pm \sqrt{b^2 - 4ac}}{2a}.$$
4. Simplify the numerical expression to obtain the solutions.

EXAMPLE 1 **Using the Quadratic Formula**

Solve $x^2 - 5x + 6 = 0$ using the quadratic formula.

We have $a = 1$, $b = -5$ (not 5), and $c = 6$.

$$x = \frac{-b \pm \sqrt{b^2 - 4ac}}{2a} = \frac{-(-5) \pm \sqrt{(-5)^2 - 4(1)(6)}}{2(1)} \qquad \text{Substitute}$$

$$= \frac{5 \pm \sqrt{25 - 24}}{2} \qquad \text{Watch all signs}$$

$$= \frac{5 \pm \sqrt{1}}{2} = \frac{5 \pm 1}{2} = \begin{cases} \frac{5+1}{2} = \frac{6}{2} = 3 \\ \frac{5-1}{2} = \frac{4}{2} = 2 \end{cases}$$

The solutions are 2 and 3. ∎

EXAMPLE 2 **Working with Irrational Solutions**

Solve $3x^2 - 5 = -4x$ using the quadratic formula.

First we write the equation in general form, $3x^2 + 4x - 5 = 0$, and identify $a = 3$, $b = 4$, and $c = -5$ (not 5), then substitute.

$$x = \frac{-b \pm \sqrt{b^2 - 4ac}}{2a} = \frac{-(4) \pm \sqrt{(4)^2 - 4(3)(-5)}}{2(3)}$$

$$= \frac{-4 \pm \sqrt{16 + 60}}{6} \qquad \text{Watch the signs}$$

$$= \frac{-4 \pm \sqrt{76}}{6} = \frac{-4 \pm \sqrt{4 \cdot 19}}{6}$$

$$= \frac{-4 \pm 2\sqrt{19}}{6} = \frac{\cancel{2}(-2 \pm \sqrt{19})}{\cancel{2} \cdot 3}$$

$$= \frac{-2 \pm \sqrt{19}}{3}$$

The solutions are $\frac{-2 + \sqrt{19}}{3}$ and $\frac{-2 - \sqrt{19}}{3}$. ∎

Students often will ask, ''What method should I use?'' The best answer to this question is presented in the following:

To Solve a Quadratic Equation

1. First try factoring or taking roots.
2. If the first two methods do not work, go directly to the quadratic formula. Never use completing the square unless specifically told to do so.

> NOTE The quadratic equation in Example 1 could be solved much more quickly by factoring than by using the quadratic formula. If we were not using the equation to illustrate the formula, we would have solved it as follows.
>
> $$x^2 - 5x + 6 = 0$$
> $$(x - 2)(x - 3) = 0$$
> $$x - 2 = 0 \quad \text{or} \quad x - 3 = 0$$
> $$x = 2 \quad \text{or} \quad x = 3$$

The discriminant

For a quadratic equation $ax^2 + bx + c = 0$, the number $b^2 - 4ac$, called the **discriminant,** can be used to find out whether the equation has solutions that are real numbers. Notice that the discriminant is simply the number under the radical sign in the quadratic formula

$$x = \frac{-b \pm \sqrt{b^2 - 4ac}}{2a}.$$

Since the square root of a negative number is not a real number, a quadratic equation has no real-number solutions when the discriminant is a negative number. Consider

$$x^2 + x + 1 = 0.$$

Here $a = 1$, $b = 1$, and $c = 1$, so $b^2 - 4ac = (1) - 4(1)(1) = 1 - 4 = -3$. Since -3 is a negative number, $\sqrt{-3}$ is not a real number and $x^2 + x + 1 = 0$ has no real-number solutions.

Another helpful technique for solving quadratic equations with fractional coefficients is to clear all fractions first. For example, to solve

$$\frac{1}{3}x^2 - x + \frac{1}{3} = 0,$$

it would be difficult to use $a = \frac{1}{3}$, $b = -1$, and $c = \frac{1}{3}$ in the quadratic formula. However, if we multiply through by the LCD 3, we obtain the equivalent equation

$$x^2 - 3x + 1 = 0,$$

in which $a = 1$, $b = -3$, and $c = 1$. Avoiding fractions makes the arithmetic simpler.

Applications requiring the quadratic formula

In many applications of quadratic equations, solutions containing radicals must be estimated by using an approximate value for the radical.

EXAMPLE 3

Using the Quadratic Formula in an Agriculture Problem

A large wheat field is in the shape of a right triangle with hypotenuse 5 km long and one leg 4 km longer than the other. Find the measure of each leg (side) of the field.

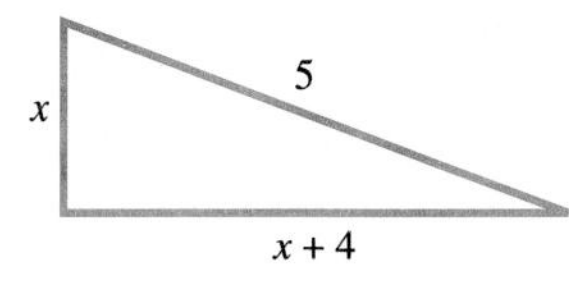

FIGURE 10.2

The triangular field is shown in Figure 10.2. Remember the Pythagorean theorem: the sum of the squares of the legs of a right triangle is equal to the square of the hypotenuse.

Let x = the measure of one leg,
$x + 4$ = the measure of the other leg.
Use the Pythagorean theorem.

$$x^2 + (x + 4)^2 = 5^2$$

$$x^2 + x^2 + 8x + 16 = 25 \qquad \text{Don't forget the } 8x\text{, } (x+4)^2 \text{ is not } x^2 + 16$$

$$2x^2 + 8x - 9 = 0$$

Since we cannot factor, use the quadratic formula. Note that $a = 2$, $b = 8$, and $c = -9$.

$$x = \frac{-b \pm \sqrt{b^2 - 4ac}}{2a} \qquad \text{Quadratic formula}$$

$$= \frac{-8 \pm \sqrt{(8)^2 - 4(2)(-9)}}{2(2)} \qquad \text{Substitute 2 for } a\text{, 8 for } b\text{, and } -9 \text{ for } c$$

$$= \frac{-8 \pm \sqrt{64 + 72}}{4}$$

$$= \frac{-8 \pm \sqrt{136}}{4}$$

$$= \frac{-8 \pm \sqrt{4 \cdot 34}}{4}$$

$$= \frac{-8 \pm 2\sqrt{34}}{4} \qquad \sqrt{4 \cdot 34} = \sqrt{4}\sqrt{34} = 2\sqrt{34}$$

$$= \frac{\not{2}[-4 \pm \sqrt{34}]}{\not{2} \cdot 2} \qquad \text{Factor and divide out 2}$$

$$= \frac{-4 \pm \sqrt{34}}{2}$$

Since $\frac{-4 - \sqrt{34}}{2}$ is a negative number, we can discard it (a length must be positive or zero). Thus, the length of one leg is exactly $\frac{-4 + \sqrt{34}}{2}$ km. Using a calculator to get a decimal approximation, we find $\sqrt{34} \approx 5.8$. Thus,

$$\frac{-4 + \sqrt{34}}{2} \approx \frac{-4 + 5.8}{2} = \frac{1.8}{2} = 0.9,$$

and the lengths of the sides of the field are approximately 0.9 km and 4.9 km ($x = 0.9$, $x + 4 = 4.9$). As a check,

$$(0.9)^2 + (4.9)^2 = 0.81 + 24.01 = 24.82 \approx 25 = 5^2. \quad \blacksquare$$

NOTE Unless you are working an applied problem in which an approximate value would make more sense, or unless instructed otherwise, you should always leave answers in radical form.

10.3 EXERCISES

Solve using the quadratic formula in Exercises 1–12.

1. $x^2 + x - 20 = 0$
2. $x^2 - 9 = 0$
3. $0 = 7y - 2 + 15y^2$
4. $5z - 2 = 3z^2$
5. $5x^2 - x = 1$
6. $2y^2 - 4y + 1 = 0$
7. $4z^2 + 9z + 3 = 0$
8. $x^2 + 2x = 5$
9. $y^2 - 6y = 1$
10. $x^2 - 3x - 9 = 0$
11. $y(y + 1) + 2y = 4$
12. $(z + 1)^2 = 5 + 3z$

Solve using any method in Exercises 13–21.

13. $x^2 - 2x + 5 = 0$
14. $4y^2 - 1 = 0$
15. $(2z - 1)(z - 2) - 11 = 2(z + 4) - 8$
16. $2x^2 - 7x + 3 = 0$
17. $3z^2 + 10z - 1 = 0$
18. $3y^2 - 12 = 0$
19. $3x^2 - 2 = -5x$
20. $x^2 + x - 1 = 0$
21. $-x^2 - x + 1 = 0$

22. How do the solutions in Exercises 20 and 21 compare? Explain?

Solve each equation in Exercises 23–25.

23. $\frac{2}{3}x^2 - \frac{1}{3}x - 1 = 0$
24. $\frac{1}{2}x^2 + x - 1 = 0$
25. $\frac{1}{4}x^2 + \frac{1}{2}x - \frac{3}{4} = 0$

26. Write the solutions to Exercise 5 using a decimal approximation.

27. Write the solutions to Exercise 6 using a decimal approximation.

28. **GEOMETRY** The hypotenuse of a right triangle is 3 cm long, and one leg is 1 cm more than the other. Find the approximate measure of each leg.

29. **GEOMETRY** Winnie has a square garden measuring 4 yards on each side. She wishes to place a picket fence diagonally across the garden. What is the approximate length of the fence?

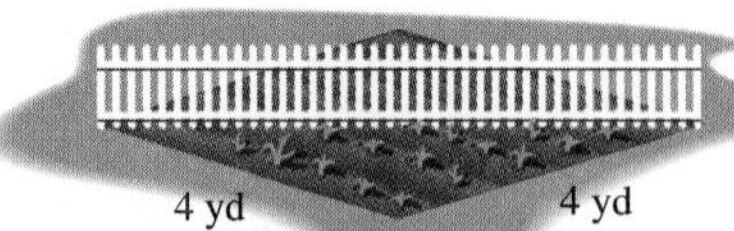

30. **PHYSICS** If an object is thrown upward with initial velocity of 128 feet per second, its height, h, above the ground in t seconds is given by $h = 128t - 16t^2$. How long will it take for the object to reach a height of 240 feet?

31. Show that the sum of the solutions to the equation $y^2 - 6y - 1 = 0$ is equal to $-\frac{b}{a}$. Note that $a = 1$ and $b = -6$.

FOR REVIEW

32. Solve $x^2 + x = 13 + x$ by taking roots.

33. Solve $2y^2 + 2y = 3$ by completing the square.

Exercises 34–35 review material from Sections 8.5 and 9.6 to prepare for the next section. Solve each equation.

34. $\frac{1}{x} + \frac{2}{x-3} = \frac{4}{x^2 - 3x}$

35. $\sqrt{x^2 - 11} - x + 1 = 0$

10.3 PARALLEL EXERCISES

Solve using the quadratic formula in Exercises 1–12.

1. $x^2 - 4x - 21 = 0$
2. $x^2 - 49 = 0$
3. $0 = 20y^2 - y - 1$
4. $7z - 3 = 4z^2$
5. $2x^2 - x = 2$
6. $y^2 + 5y + 5 = 0$
7. $3z^2 + 3 = 7z$
8. $x^2 - 4x = 1$
9. $3y^2 + 2y = 7$
10. $x^2 - 5x + 3 = 0$
11. $y(y + 3) + 2y = 6$
12. $3(z - 1)^2 = 3z$

Solve using any method in Exercises 13–21.

13. $x^2 - 3x + 7 = 0$
14. $6y^2 + 7y = 3$
15. $(z + 1)^2 = 5(1 + z)$
16. $2x^2 - x - 1 = 0$
17. $7y^2 - 49 = 0$
18. $z^2 - 5z - 2 = 0$
19. $2x^2 = \frac{1}{2}(27x + 7)$
20. $x^2 + 6x - 1 = 0$
21. $-x^2 - 6x + 1 = 0$

22. How do the solutions in Exercises 20 and 21 compare? Explain?

Solve each equation in Exercises 23–25.

23. $x^2 - \frac{1}{2}x - 5 = 0$
24. $\frac{1}{3}x^2 + x + \frac{1}{6} = 0$
25. $\frac{1}{11}x^2 + \frac{9}{11}x - 2 = 0$

26. Write the solution to Exercise 5 using a decimal approximation.

27. Write the solution to Exercise 6 using a decimal approximation.

28. **GEOMETRY** The hypotenuse of a right triangle is 7 cm long, and one leg is 3 cm more than the other. Find the approximate measure of each leg.

29. **SPORTS** A baseball diamond is a square 90 ft on each side. How far is it from home plate directly across to second base?

30. **PHYSICS** If an object is thrown upward with initial velocity of 64 feet per second its height h, above the ground in t seconds is given by $h = 64t - 16t^2$. How long will it take for the object to reach a height of 48 feet?

31. Show that the product of the solutions to the equation $y^2 - 6y - 1 = 0$ is equal to $\frac{c}{a}$. Note that $a = 1$ and $c = -1$.

FOR REVIEW

32. Solve $2y^2 - 50 = 0$ by taking roots.

33. Solve $2x^2 - 6x + 3 = 0$ by the method of completing the square.

Exercises 34–35 review material from Sections 8.5 and 9.6 to prepare for the next section. Solve each equation.

34. $\frac{3}{x+5} - \frac{2}{x} = \frac{5}{x^2 + 5x}$

35. $\sqrt{x^2 + 7} - x = 1$

10.3 ENRICHMENT EXERCISES

Solve for x using the quadratic formula in Exercises 1–2.

1. $0.3x^2 - 0.1x - 1.6 = 0$ [*Hint:* Multiply by 10.]

2. $x^2 + 3xy + y^2 = 0$

Use the quadratic formula and your calculator to solve each quadratic equation in Exercises 3–4. Give answers to two decimal places.

3. $\sqrt{2}x^2 - 3x - 7.1 = 0$

4. $3x^2 + \sqrt{5}x - \frac{1}{2} = 0$

Burford's solutions to two quadratic equations are given in Exercises 5–6. Find the error in Burford's work. What is the correct answer to each?

5. $x^2 - 2x - 5 = 0$

$$x = \frac{-2 \pm \sqrt{4 + 20}}{2} = \frac{-2 \pm 2\sqrt{6}}{2} = -1 \pm \sqrt{6}$$

6. $x^2 + 2x - 5 = 0$

$$x = \frac{-2 \pm \sqrt{4 + 20}}{2} = \frac{-2 \pm \sqrt{24}}{2} = \frac{-\cancel{2} \pm 2\sqrt{6}}{\cancel{2}} = -1 \pm 2\sqrt{6}$$

7. Without solving, can you explain why the equation $x^2 - 2x + 5 = 0$ has no real-number solutions?

8. Write a few sentences explaining which method to use when solving a quadratic equation.

SECTION 10.4 Solving Fractional and Radical Equations

Student guideposts

- *Fractional equations*
- *Radical equations*

Fractional equations

In Chapter 8 we learned that to solve fractional equations we multiply both sides by the LCD. The fractional equations we look at in this section will result in quadratic equations when both sides are multiplied by the LCD. Remember that we always need to check when solving fractional equations and discard any answer that makes a denominator 0.

EXAMPLE 1 Solving a Fractional Equation

Solve $\frac{6}{x} - x = 5$.

The LCD is x.

$$x\left[\frac{6}{x} - x\right] = x \cdot 5 \quad \text{Multiply both sides by the LCD}$$

$$\not{x} \cdot \frac{6}{\not{x}} - x \cdot x = 5x \quad \text{Use distributive law on left side}$$

$$6 - x^2 = 5x$$

$$x^2 + 5x - 6 = 0$$

$$(x + 6)(x - 1) = 0$$

$$x + 6 = 0 \quad \text{or} \quad x - 1 = 0$$

$$x = -6 \qquad\qquad x = 1$$

Check: $\frac{6}{(-6)} - (-6) \stackrel{?}{=} 5 \qquad \frac{6}{(1)} - (1) \stackrel{?}{=} 5$

$$-1 + 6 = 5 \qquad\qquad 6 - 1 = 5$$

The solutions are -6 and 1. ■

EXAMPLE 2 **Solving a Fractional Equation**

Solve $\frac{12}{x^2 - 4} - \frac{3}{x - 2} = -1$.

The LCD = $(x - 2)(x + 2)$.

$$(x - 2)(x + 2)\left[\frac{12}{x^2 - 4} - \frac{3}{x - 2}\right] = (x - 2)(x + 2)(-1) \quad \text{Multiply both sides by LCD}$$

$$\cancel{(x - 2)}\cancel{(x + 2)} \cdot \frac{12}{\cancel{(x - 2)}\cancel{(x + 2)}} - \cancel{(x - 2)}(x + 2) \cdot \frac{3}{\cancel{(x - 2)}} \quad \text{Distribute}$$

$$= (x - 2)(x + 2)(-1)$$

$$12 - 3(x + 2) = (x^2 - 4)(-1) \quad \text{Watch parentheses}$$

$$12 - 3x - 6 = -x^2 + 4 \quad \text{Watch signs}$$

$$x^2 - 3x + 2 = 0 \quad \text{Collect terms}$$

$$(x - 1)(x - 2) = 0 \quad \text{Factor}$$

$$x - 1 = 0 \quad \text{or} \quad x - 2 = 0$$

$$x = 1 \qquad\qquad x = 2$$

Check: $\frac{12}{(1)^2 - 4} - \frac{3}{(1) - 2} \stackrel{?}{=} -1 \qquad \frac{12}{(2)^2 - 4} - \frac{3}{(2) - 2} \stackrel{?}{=} -1$

$$\frac{12}{-3} - \frac{3}{-1} \stackrel{?}{=} -1 \qquad \frac{2}{4 - 4} - \frac{3}{2 - 2} \stackrel{?}{=} -1$$

$$-4 + 3 = -1 \qquad \frac{12}{0} - \frac{3}{0} \neq -1$$

Cannot divide by 0

The only solution is 1. Notice that 2 makes a denominator zero in the original equation. In general, any number for which a fraction is undefined must be discarded as a solution. ■

EXAMPLE 3 **Solving a Fractional Equation**

Solve $\frac{y+1}{y} = \frac{-2}{y-2}$.

The LCD = $y(y-2)$.

$$y(y-2)\left[\frac{y+1}{y}\right] = y(y-2)\left[\frac{-2}{y-2}\right] \quad \text{Multiply by LCD}$$

$$(y-2)(y+1) = -2y$$

$$y^2 - y - 2 = -2y$$

$$y^2 + y - 2 = 0$$

$$(y+2)(y-1) = 0$$

$$y + 2 = 0 \quad \text{or} \quad y - 1 = 0$$

$$y = -2 \qquad\qquad y = 1$$

Check:

$$\frac{(-2)+1}{(-2)} \stackrel{?}{=} \frac{-2}{(-2)-2} \qquad \frac{(1)+1}{(1)} \stackrel{?}{=} \frac{-2}{(1)-2}$$

$$\frac{-1}{-2} \stackrel{?}{=} \frac{-2}{-4} \qquad \frac{2}{1} \stackrel{?}{=} \frac{-2}{-1}$$

$$\frac{1}{2} = \frac{1}{2} \qquad 2 = 2$$

The solutions are -2 and 1. ■

▶ *Radical equations* With radical equations in Chapter 9, we squared both sides of the equation to eliminate a radical. Now we consider other radical equations that become quadratic equations when both sides are squared. We always need to check our answers when solving radical equations, since answers that do not satisfy the *original* equation may be introduced by the process of squaring.

EXAMPLE 4 **Solving a Radical Equation**

Solve $\sqrt{12 - x} = x$.

$$(\sqrt{12-x})^2 = x^2 \quad \text{Indicate the square of both sides}$$

$$12 - x = x^2 \quad \text{Square both sides}$$

$$x^2 + x - 12 = 0 \quad \text{Collect terms}$$

$$(x-3)(x+4) = 0 \quad \text{Factor}$$

$$x - 3 = 0 \quad \text{or} \quad x + 4 = 0$$

$$x = 3 \qquad\qquad x = -4 \quad \text{Remember to check these in the original equation}$$

Check: $\sqrt{12-(3)} \stackrel{?}{=} 3$ $\qquad \sqrt{12-(-4)} \stackrel{?}{=} (-4)$

$\sqrt{9} \stackrel{?}{=} 3 \qquad \sqrt{16} \neq -4 \qquad (\sqrt{16} = 4, \textit{not } -4.)$

$3 = 3$

The only solution is 3. ■

EXAMPLE 5 **Solving a Radical Equation**

Solve $x + 2 = \sqrt{x+8}$.

$$
\begin{aligned}
(x+2)^2 &= (\sqrt{x+8})^2 && \text{Indicate the square of both sides} \\
x^2 + 4x + 4 &= x + 8 && \text{Square both sides, } (x+2)^2 \neq (x^2+4) \\
x^2 + 3x - 4 &= 0 && \text{Collect terms} \\
(x+4)(x-1) &= 0 && \text{Factor} \\
x + 4 = 0 \quad &\text{or} \quad x - 1 = 0 \\
x = -4 \quad & \qquad\quad x = 1
\end{aligned}
$$

Check: $(-4) + 2 \stackrel{?}{=} \sqrt{(-4)+8} \qquad (1) + 2 \stackrel{?}{=} \sqrt{(1)+8}$

$-2 \neq \sqrt{4} \qquad 3 \stackrel{?}{=} \sqrt{9}$

$3 = 3$

The only solution is 1. ■

EXAMPLE 6 **Solving a Radical Equation**

Solve $x = 4\sqrt{x+1} - 4$.

$$
\begin{aligned}
x + 4 &= 4\sqrt{x+1} && \text{Add 4 to both sides to isolate the radical} \\
(x+4)^2 &= (4\sqrt{x+1})^2 && \text{Indicate the square of both sides} \\
x^2 + 8x + 16 &= 16(x+1) && \text{Do not forget the middle term on left and to square 4 on right} \\
x^2 + 8x + 16 &= 16x + 16 && \text{Distribute the 16} \\
x^2 - 8x &= 0 && \text{Collect terms} \\
x(x-8) &= 0 && \text{Factor out } x \\
x = 0 \quad &\text{or} \quad x - 8 = 0 \\
& \qquad\quad x = 8
\end{aligned}
$$

Check: $(0) \stackrel{?}{=} 4\sqrt{(0)+1} - 4 \qquad (8) \stackrel{?}{=} 4\sqrt{(8)+1} - 4$

$0 \stackrel{?}{=} 4\sqrt{1} - 4 \qquad 8 \stackrel{?}{=} 4\sqrt{9} - 4$

$0 \stackrel{?}{=} 4 - 4 \qquad 8 \stackrel{?}{=} 4 \cdot 3 - 4$

$0 = 0 \qquad 8 \stackrel{?}{=} 12 - 4$

$8 = 8$

The solutions are 0 and 8. ■

10.4 EXERCISES

Solve each equation in Exercises 1–18.

1. $\dfrac{3}{x-4} = 1 + \dfrac{5}{x+4}$
2. $\dfrac{y-3}{y} = \dfrac{-4}{y+1}$
3. $\dfrac{3}{1+z} + \dfrac{2}{1-z} = -1$
4. $\dfrac{1}{x+2} + \dfrac{x}{x-2} = \dfrac{1}{2}$
5. $\dfrac{60}{y+3} = \dfrac{60}{y} - 1$
6. $\dfrac{5}{z+3} - \dfrac{1}{z+3} = \dfrac{z+3}{z+2}$
7. $\dfrac{16}{a+2} = 1 + \dfrac{2}{a-4}$
8. $\dfrac{x^2}{2x+1} - \dfrac{5}{2x+1} = 0$
9. $\dfrac{x+2}{2} = \dfrac{x+5}{x+2}$
10. $x = \sqrt{3x+10}$
11. $\sqrt{5y+6} - y = 0$
12. $1 + 2\sqrt{x-1} = x$
13. $y = 1 + 6\sqrt{y-9}$
14. $\sqrt{1-2a} = a - 1$
15. $\sqrt{2x+7} - 4 = x$
16. $\sqrt{z^2+2} = z + 1$
17. $3\sqrt{y+1} - y - 1 = 0$
18. $\sqrt{2x^2-5} = x$
19. **NUMBER** A number increased by its reciprocal is the same as $\frac{5}{2}$. Find the number.
20. **NUMBER** The principal square root of 2 more than a number is equal to the number itself. Find the number.

FOR REVIEW

Solve each equation in Exercises 21–22.

21. $z^2 - 8z + 8 = 0$
22. $x^2 - \dfrac{2}{3}x - 1 = 0$
23. **GEOMETRY** It can be shown that a polygon (many-sided geometric figure) with x sides has a total of n diagonals where $n = \frac{1}{2}x^2 - \frac{3}{2}x$. A hexagon has 6 sides; how many diagonals does it have? Draw a hexagon and verify your answer by actual count.
24. **GEOMETRY** Use the formula in Exercise 23 to find the number of sides that a polygon has if it is known to have 20 diagonals. Draw a polygon with the number of sides that you determine and count its diagonals.

10.4 PARALLEL EXERCISES

Solve each equation in Exercises 1–18.

1. $\dfrac{3}{x-1} = 1 + \dfrac{2}{x+1}$
2. $\dfrac{y}{1+y} = \dfrac{3-y}{4}$
3. $\dfrac{1}{x+2} + \dfrac{1}{x-2} = \dfrac{3}{8}$
4. $\dfrac{6}{x+3} + \dfrac{x}{x-3} = 1$
5. $\dfrac{32}{y+5} = \dfrac{6}{y} + 2$
6. $\dfrac{4}{z+1} - \dfrac{1}{z+1} = \dfrac{z-1}{z+3}$
7. $x + \dfrac{2}{x-2} = \dfrac{1}{x-2}$
8. $\dfrac{x^2}{1+3x} - \dfrac{11}{1+3x} = 0$
9. $\dfrac{x+3}{x+1} = \dfrac{x+1}{3}$
10. $x = \sqrt{2x+24}$
11. $\sqrt{4y+5} - y = 0$
12. $\sqrt{2x-1} = x - 2$
13. $z = \sqrt{z+7} - 1$
14. $\sqrt{7-3a} = 1 + a$
15. $2\sqrt{3-x} - 5 = x$
16. $\sqrt{y^2+8} = y - 2$
17. $2\sqrt{y+15} + y - 9 = 0$
18. $\sqrt{5x^2-11} = 2x$
19. **NUMBER** A number decreased by its reciprocal is the same as $\frac{15}{4}$. Find the number.
20. **NUMBER** The principal square root of 8 more than a number is equal to three times the number. Find the number.

FOR REVIEW

Solve each equation in Exercises 21–22.

21. $x^2 - 6x + 6 = 0$

22. $y^2 - \frac{1}{3}y - 1 = 0$

23. **GEOMETRY** It can be shown that a polygon with x sides has a total of n diagonals where $n = \frac{1}{2}x^2 - \frac{3}{2}x$. An octagon has 8 sides; how many diagonals does it have? Draw an octagon and verify your answer by actual count.

24. **GEOMETRY** Use the formula in Exercise 23 to find the number of sides that a polygon has if it is known to have 5 diagonals. Draw a polygon with the number of sides that you determine and count its diagonals.

10.4 ENRICHMENT EXERCISES

Solve each equation in Exercises 1–2.

△ **1.** $\dfrac{3}{x^2 - 5x + 6} - \dfrac{2}{x^2 + 3x - 10} = \dfrac{x + 2}{x^2 + 2x - 15}$

2. $\sqrt{2x - 2} - \sqrt{x + 6} = -1$

Solve each literal equation for x in Exercises 3–5. Assume all constants represent positive real numbers.

3. $T = \sqrt{\dfrac{x^2}{w}}$

△ **4.** $T = \sqrt{\dfrac{w}{x^2}}$

5. $\sqrt{x^2 + t} = P$

6. Discuss why it is important to check any possible solutions to a fractional equation or a radical equation in the original equation.

SECTION 10.5 Problem Solving Using Quadratic Equations

Student guideposts

- ▶ *Basic applications*
- ▶ *Geometry applications*
- ▶ *Work problems*
- ▶ *Motion applications*

▶ *Basic applications*

Many applied problems can be solved using a quadratic equation as a model. We illustrated this in the preceding sections using several types of problems, and now we consider a variety of additional applications. We use the first example to review the ATTACK method showing all of the steps.

EXAMPLE 1 Solving an Age Problem

In three years, Sandy's kitten will be four times the square of its present age. How old is Sandy's kitten?

Analysis: We are looking for the present age of a kitten with its age described in the problem.

Tabulation: Let x = the present age of Sandy's kitten,
$x + 3$ = the age of the kitten in 3 years,
x^2 = the square of the present age,
$4x^2$ = four times the square of the present age.

Translation: Since the age in 3 years and four times the square of the present age are the same, we have the equation:

$$4x^2 = x + 3$$

$$4x^2 - x - 3 = 0 \quad \text{Write in general form}$$

$$(4x + 3)(x - 1) = 0 \quad \text{Factor}$$

$$4x + 3 = 0 \quad \text{or} \quad x - 1 = 0 \quad \text{Zero-product rule}$$

$$4x = -3 \qquad x = 1$$

$$x = -\frac{3}{4}$$

Approximation: Since $-\frac{3}{4}$ is not a reasonable answer for the age of a kitten, we discard it as a possible solution. The other answer, 1, is reasonable.

Check: If the age of the kitten is 1 year, in 3 years it will be 4 yr old. Also, four times the square of 1 is $4(1)^2 = 4$ yr, and since these are equal, 1 yr does indeed check.

Thus, Sandy's kitten is presently 1 year old. ■

NOTE Remember that the approximation step is essential in word problems involving quadratic equations. Often the equation will have two solutions, and only one of them will actually fit the words of the problem.

In some problems, an approximate value will provide the most meaningful answer. This is illustrated in the following example from business.

EXAMPLE 2

Solving a Business Problem

The Hacker Company makes and sells specialized tennis rackets. The daily cost of manufacturing x rackets is given by $C = 10x^2 + 650$, and the daily revenue produced on the sale of x rackets by $R = 170x$. Because of the specialized nature of the rackets, to maintain quality control, the company can make no more than 8 rackets per day. What is the break-even point for the company, that is, the number of rackets for which the cost and revenue are the same?

Let x = the number of rackets to be made and sold daily.

To find the break-even point, we must solve:

$$C = R$$

$$10x^2 + 650 = 170x \quad \text{Substitute}$$

$$10x^2 - 170x + 650 = 0 \quad \text{Write in general form}$$

$$10(x^2 - 17x + 65) = 0 \quad \text{Factor out 10}$$

$$x^2 - 17x + 65 = 0 \quad \text{Divide both sides by 10}$$

Since this will not factor, we use the quadratic formula with $a = 1$, $b = -17$, and $c = 65$.

$$\begin{aligned} x &= \frac{-b \pm \sqrt{b^2 - 4ac}}{2a} \\ &= \frac{-(-17) \pm \sqrt{(-17)^2 - 4(1)(65)}}{2(1)} \\ &= \frac{17 \pm \sqrt{289 - 260}}{2} \\ &= \frac{17 \pm \sqrt{29}}{2} \end{aligned}$$

There are two possible solutions, and we use a calculator to approximate $\sqrt{29}$.

$$x = \frac{17 + \sqrt{29}}{2} = 11.1925824 \quad \text{and} \quad x = \frac{17 - \sqrt{29}}{2} = 5.807417596.$$

Since the maximum number of rackets the company can make and sell each day is 8, we can clearly discard the first solution. Of course, it is impossible to make and sell 5.807417596 rackets, so the best we can do in this case is give an approximate value of 6 for the break-even point. Thus, when the company makes and sells about 6 rackets a day, it will break even. ■

> **NOTE** If the condition of ''no more than 8 rackets per day'' were deleted from the problem in Example 2, we would obtain two answers: about 6 or about 11 rackets daily.

▶ *Geometry applications*

When working a geometry problem remember to sketch a figure as shown in the next two examples.

EXAMPLE 3

Working a Rectangle Problem

Find the length and width of a rectangular pasture if the length is 3 mi more than the width and the area is 180 mi^2.

Make a sketch as in Figure 10.3.

Let w = width of the pasture,

$w + 3$ = length of the pasture.

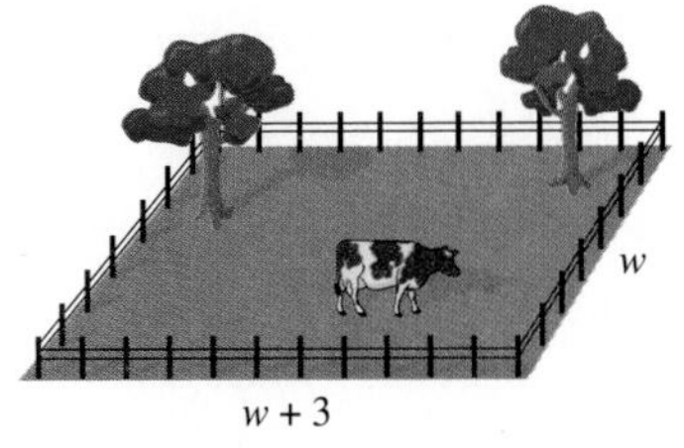

FIGURE 10.3

Use the formula for the area of a rectangle, $A = lw$, to get the following equation.

$$
\begin{aligned}
(w + 3)w &= 180 \\
w^2 + 3w &= 180 \\
w^2 + 3w - 180 &= 0 \\
(w + 15)(w - 12) &= 0
\end{aligned}
$$

$$
\begin{array}{lcl}
w + 15 = 0 & \text{or} & w - 12 = 0 \\
w = \cancel{-15} & & w = 12 \\
 & & w + 3 = 15
\end{array}
$$

Since -15 could not be the width of a rectangle, 12 is the only possible solution.

Check: $12(12 + 3) \stackrel{?}{=} 180$

$12 \cdot 15 \stackrel{?}{=} 180$

$180 = 180$

The width of the pasture is 12 mi and the length is 15 mi. ■

EXAMPLE 4

Working with Area and Perimeter

The number of square inches in the area of a square is 12 more than the number of inches in its perimeter. Find the length of a side.

A sketch of the square is shown in Figure 10.4.

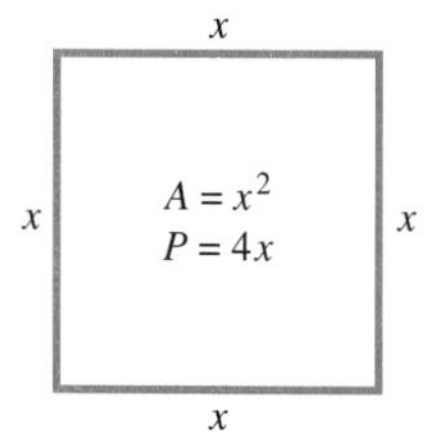

FIGURE 10.4

Let x = length of a side (all sides are the same length, x),

x^2 = area of the square ($A = lw = x \cdot x$),

$4x$ = perimeter of the square ($P = 2l + 2w = 2x + 2x = 4x$).

Since the area is 12 more than the perimeter, adding 12 to the perimeter, $4x$, will give us the area, x^2.

$$
\begin{aligned}
x^2 &= 4x + 12 \\
x^2 - 4x - 12 &= 0 \\
(x + 2)(x - 6) &= 6
\end{aligned}
$$

$$
\begin{array}{lcl}
x + 2 = 0 & \text{or} & x - 6 = 0 \\
x = \cancel{-2} & & x = 6
\end{array}
$$

Since the length of a side cannot be negative, 6 is the only possible solution. Each side is 6 in. ■

▶ *Work problems*

Another variation of the work problems introduced in Section 8.5 results in a quadratic equation.

EXAMPLE 5

Solving a Work Problem

When each works alone, Ralph can do a job in 3 hours less time than Bert. When they work together, it takes 2 hours. How long does it take each to do the job by himself?

Since 2 = number of hrs to do the job together,

then $\frac{1}{2}$ = amount done together in 1 hr.

Let x = number of hrs for Bert to do the job,
$\frac{1}{x}$ = amount done by Bert in 1 hr.

Then $x - 3$ = number of hrs for Ralph to do the job,
$\frac{1}{(x-3)}$ = amount done by Ralph in 1 hr.

$\left(\text{Note: } \frac{1}{(x-3)} \neq \frac{1}{x} - \frac{1}{3}\text{. To see this, substitute } x = 2.\right)$

We need to solve the following equation.

$$\frac{1}{x} + \frac{1}{(x-3)} = \frac{1}{2}$$ (amount by Bert) + (amount by Ralph) = (amount together)

$$2x(x-3)\left(\frac{1}{x} + \frac{1}{(x-3)}\right) = 2x(x-3)\cdot\frac{1}{2}$$ The LCD is $2x(x-3)$

$$2\cancel{x}(x-3)\frac{1}{\cancel{x}} + 2x\cancel{(x-3)}\frac{1}{\cancel{(x-3)}} = x(x-3)$$

$$2(x-3) + 2x = x^2 - 3x$$

$$2x - 6 + 2x = x^2 - 3x$$

$$0 = x^2 - 7x + 6$$

$$0 = (x-6)(x-1)$$

$$x - 6 = 0 \quad \text{or} \quad x - 1 = 0$$

$$x = 6 \qquad\qquad x = 1$$

If Bert did the job in 1 hr, Ralph would do it in $1 - 3 = -2$ hr, which makes no sense. Thus, Bert would take 6 hr and Ralph 3 hr. ■

▶ *Motion applications*

The last example in this section can be classified as a motion or rate problem.

EXAMPLE 6

Solving a Motion Problem

A backpacker can hike 10 miles up a mountain and then return in a total time of 7 hours. Her hiking rate uphill is 3 mph slower than her rate downhill. At what rate does she hike up the mountain?

Let x = the rate hiking up the mountain.
Then $x + 3$ = the rate hiking down the mountain.

We use the distance formula $d = rt$, solved for $t = \frac{d}{r}$, to express the two times. Since the distance hiked uphill and the return distance downhill are both 10, we have

$$\frac{10}{x} = \text{the time spent hiking up the mountain,}$$

$$\frac{10}{x+3} = \text{the time spent hiking down the mountain.}$$

Since the total time of the hike is 7 hours, we need to solve the following equation.

$$\frac{10}{x} + \frac{10}{x+3} = 7 \qquad \text{LCD} = x(x+3)$$

$$x(x+3)\left[\frac{10}{x} + \frac{10}{x+3}\right] = 7x(x+3) \qquad \text{Multiply both sides by the LCD}$$

$$\cancel{x}(x+3)\frac{10}{\cancel{x}} + x\cancel{(x+3)}\frac{10}{\cancel{x+3}} = 7x(x+3) \qquad \text{Use the distributive law}$$

$$10(x+3) + 10x = 7x^2 + 21x$$

$$10x + 30 + 10x = 7x^2 + 21x$$

$$20x + 30 = 7x^2 + 21x$$

$$0 = 7x^2 + x - 30 \qquad \text{Collect like terms in the quadratic equation}$$

$$0 = (7x + 15)(x - 2) \qquad \text{Factor}$$

$$7x + 15 = 0 \quad \text{or} \quad x - 2 = 0$$

$$x = \frac{-15}{7} \quad \text{or} \quad x = 0$$

Since $\frac{-15}{7}$ cannot represent a rate in this problem, we can discard it. Thus, her rate up the mountain is 2 mph and down the mountain is 5 mph. ■

> **CAUTION** It is important when working any word problem to be neat and complete. Do not try to take shortcuts, especially when writing down the pertinent information. Writing complete descriptions of the variables can eliminate time-consuming errors.

10.5 EXERCISES

Solve each applied problem in Exercises 1–24.

1. **NUMBER** If five is added to the square of a number the result is 41. Find the number.
2. **AGE** If the square of Mary's age is decreased by 44, the result is 100. How old is Mary?
3. **NUMBER** If the square of a number is decreased by 10 the result is three times the number. Find the number.
4. **AGE** Twice the square of Ernie's age, less 9, is the same as seventeen times his age. How old is Ernie?
5. **NUMBER** The product of 1 more than a number and 1 less than the number is 99. Find the number.
6. **AGE** Sam's present age times his age in five years is 84. How old is Sam?

7. **BUSINESS** The CC Graphics Company makes and sells software package for personal computers. The daily cost of making x packages is given by $C = 2x^2 + 192$, and the daily revenue produced by selling x packages is given by $R = 40x$. Find the break-even point(s) for the company.

8. **BUSINESS** Water Arts makes and sells fountains for backyard decoration. The daily cost of making x fountains is given by $C = 2x^2 + 285$, and the revenue produced by selling x fountains by $R = 54x$. If the company can make and sell at most 10 fountains each day, how many fountains should be made and sold daily to break even?

9. **AGE** Adding 4 to the square of Marvin's age is the same as subtracting 3 from eight times his age. How old is Marvin?

10. **GEOMETRY** Find the length and width of a rectangle if the length is 4 cm longer than the width and the area is 140 cm^2.

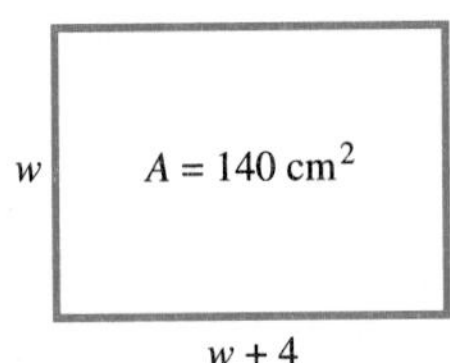

11. **GEOMETRY** The number of square inches in the area of a square is 21 more than the number of inches in its perimeter. Find the length of a side.

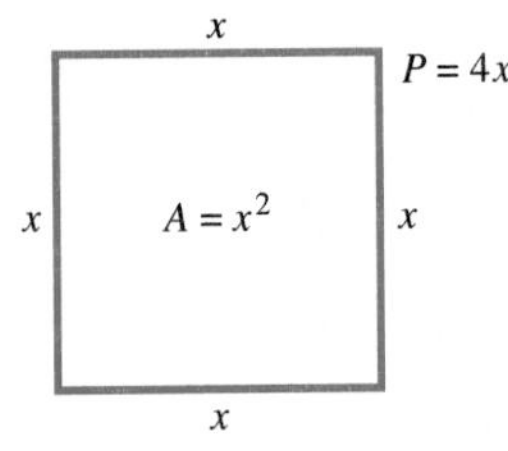

12. **GEOMETRY** If the hypotenuse of a right triangle is 13 feet long and one leg is 7 feet longer than the other, find the measure of each leg.

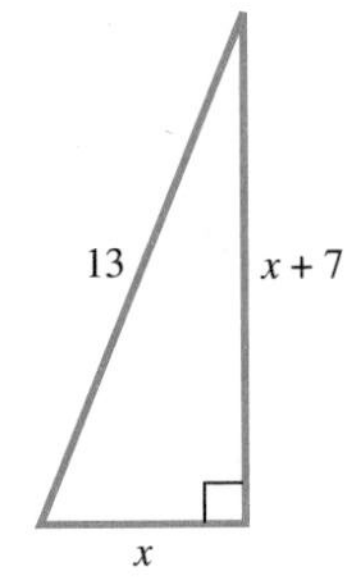

13. **GEOMETRY** If the sides of a square are lengthened by 2 cm, its area becomes 169 cm^2. Find the length of a side.

14. **GEOMETRY** The area of a triangle is 24 ft^2 and the base is $\frac{1}{3}$ as long as the height. Find the base and height.

15. **GEOMETRY** A box is 6 inches high. The length is 8 inches longer than the width and the volume is 1080 in^3. Find the width and length.

16. **GEOMETRY** The area of a circle is 1256 cm^2. Find the radius. (Use $\pi \approx 3.14$.)

17. **GEOMETRY** The area of a parallelogram is 55 ft^2. If the base is 1 ft greater than twice the height, find the base and height.

18. **GEOMETRY** The perimeter of a rectangle is 62 inches and the length is 3 inches more than the width. Find the dimensions.

19. **WORK** It takes one pipe 6 hours longer to fill a tank than it takes a second pipe. Working together they fill the tank in 4 hours. How long would it take each working alone to fill the tank?

20. **WORK** It takes Joe 9 hours longer to grade a set of tests than Dan. If they work together they can grade them in 20 hours. How long would it take each to grade the tests if they worked alone?

21. **GEOMETRY** A picture frame is 24 in by 18 in as in the sketch below. If the area of the picture itself is 216 in^2, what is the width of the frame?

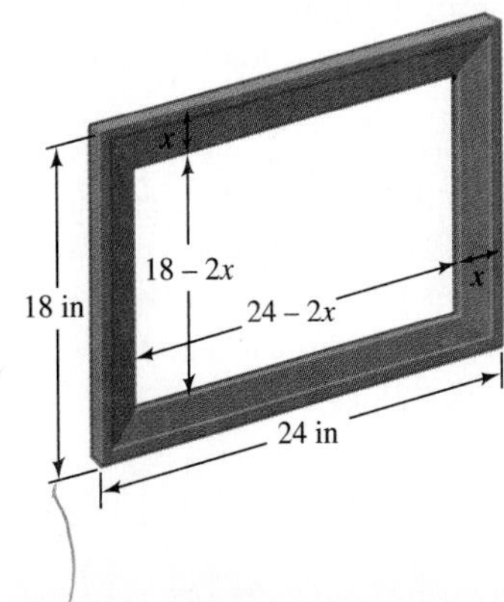

22. **PHYSICS** The pressure p, in lb per sq ft, of a wind blowing v mph can be approximated by the equation $p = 0.003v^2$. What is the approximate velocity of the wind when it creates a pressure of 1.875 lb per sq ft against the side of a house?

23. **MOTION** A boat travels 48 miles upstream and then returns in a total time of 10 hours. If the speed of the stream is 2 mph, what is the speed of the boat in still water?

24. **RECREATION** Mary Conners can walk 8 miles up a mountain and then return in a total time of 6 hours. Her speed downhill is 2 mph faster than her speed uphill. What is her speed uphill?

FOR REVIEW

Solve each equation or problem in Exercises 25–28.

25. $\dfrac{x^2}{x-3} = \dfrac{9}{x-3} + 10$

26. $x = \sqrt{7x + 18} - 4$

27. $\sqrt{x^2 + 3} + 2 = 0$

28. **AGE** The principal square root of Neil's age in 6 years is the same as one-fifth of his present age. How old is Neil?

Exercises 29–30 review material from Chapter 4 to help you prepare for the next section. Graph each equation.

29. $y + 2x - 4 = 0$

30. $y = 3x + 6$

10.5 PARALLEL EXERCISES

Solve each applied problem in Exercises 1–24.

1. **NUMBER** If 4 is added to the square of a number, the result is 85. Find the number.

2. **AGE** If the square of Rosemary's age is decreased by 24, the result is 300. How old is Rosemary?

3. **NUMBER** If the square of a number is decreased by 32, the result is four times the number. Find the number.

4. **AGE** Twice the square of Arlo's age, less 22, is the same as twenty times his age. How old is Arlo?

5. **NUMBER** The product of 1 more than a number and 1 less than the number is 224. Find the number.

6. **AGE** Troy's present age times his age in seven years is 260. How old is Troy?

7. **BUSINESS** Trail-EZ makes and sells trailer hitches. The daily cost of producing x hitches is given by $C = 2x^2 + 360$, and the daily revenue produced by selling x hitches by $R = 56x$. Find the daily break-even point(s).

8. **BUSINESS** Outdoor Manufacturing makes and sells picnic tables. The daily cost of making x tables is given by $C = 5x^2 + 1000$, and the revenue produced on the sale of x tables each day by $R = 145x$. If the company can make at most 15 tables daily, find the break-even point.

9. **AGE** Subtracting 100 from the square of Raul's age is the same as adding 60 to twelve times his age. How old is Raul?

10. **GEOMETRY** Find the length and width of a rectangle if the length is 7 meters more than the width and the area is 198 m^2.

11. **GEOMETRY** The number of square inches in the area of a square is 5 more than the number of inches in its perimeter. Find the length of a side.

12. **GEOMETRY** If the hypotenuse of a right triangle is 26 cm long and one leg is 14 cm longer than the other, find the measure of each leg.

13. **GEOMETRY** If the sides of a square are lengthened by 2 feet, its area becomes 100 ft^2. Find the length of a side.

14. **GEOMETRY** The area of a triangle is 18 m^2 and the base is $\frac{1}{4}$ as long as the height. Find the base and height.

15. **GEOMETRY** A box is 8 yards high. The length is 4 yards longer than the width and the volume is 360 yd^3. Find the width and length.

16. **GEOMETRY** The area of a circle is 200.96 cm^2. Find the radius. (Use $\pi \approx 3.14$.)

17. **GEOMETRY** The area of a parallelogram is 175 ft^2. If the base is 4 feet more than three times the height, find the base and height.

18. **GEOMETRY** The perimeter of a rectangular garden is 28 meters and the length is 4 meters more than the width. Find the dimensions of the garden.

19. **WORK** It takes Jeff 16 hours longer to repair his car than it takes his father, who is a mechanic, to do the same job. If they could do the job together in 6 hours, how long would it take each if they worked alone?

20. **WORK** Graydon, the registered cheese cutter at Perko's Delicatessen, is training a new assistant, Burford. It takes Burford 24 hours longer to process the Tillamook cheese shipment than it takes Graydon. If together they could process the cheese in 5 hours, how long would it take each, working alone, to cut and display the cheese?

21. **GEOMETRY** A rectangular backyard is to have a sidewalk placed entirely around its perimeter in such a way that 875 ft^2 of lawn area are enclosed inside the walk. If the dimensions of the yard are 40 ft by 30 ft, what is the width of the sidewalk?

22. **PHYSICS** The pressure p, in lb per sq ft, of a wind blowing v miles per hour can be approximated by the equation $p = 0.003v^2$. What is the approximate wind velocity when a pressure of 2.7 lb per sq ft is exerted against the side of a camper?

23. **MOTION** Pat Marx swims 4 miles downstream and then returns in a total time of 3 hours. If the speed of the stream is 1 mph, what is Pat's speed in still water?

24. **RECREATION** Chuck Little rode a bicycle with the wind for 18 miles. He then returned against the wind and the total time of his trip was 5 hours. If his speed with the wind was 3 mph faster than against the wind, what was his speed against the wind?

FOR REVIEW

Solve each equation or problem in Exercises 25–28.

25. $\frac{z^2}{z-2} = \frac{4}{z-2} + 5$

26. $\sqrt{8y-7} = y$

27. $\sqrt{x^2+5} + 3 = 0$

28. **NUMBER** The principal square root of 6 more than a number is the same as 6 less than the number. Find the number.

Exercises 29–30 review material from Chapter 4 to help you prepare for the next section. Graph each equation.

29. $2y - x - 6 = 0$

30. $y = -3x - 3$

10.5 ENRICHMENT EXERCISES

Solve each applied problem in Exercises 1–7.

1. **GEOMETRY** Two boats leave an island with one heading south and the other west. After 4 hours they are 100 miles apart. What is the speed of each boat if one travels 5 mph faster than the other?

2. **MOTION** A boat requires one hour longer to go 80 miles upstream than to make the return trip downstream. What is the speed of the boat in still water if the speed of the stream is 2 mph?

3. **PHYSICS** If a car is traveling at a rate of v mph, the shortest distance in feet d needed to bring the car to a complete stop under ideal conditions, including the reaction time of the driver, can be approximated by $d = 0.05v^2 + 1.05v$. If a dog runs into the street 70 feet in front of your car, what is the maximum speed you can be driving to avoid hitting the dog?

PHYSICS *The length l of the tire skid marks at the scene of an accident can be used by the attending police officer to determine the speed s of the accident vehicle. The officer might drive the accident car (if possible) at a fixed speed S, skid it to a stop in the same area, and measure the length L of these marks. A formula in physics that relates these variables is*

$$\frac{l}{s^2} = \frac{L}{S^2}$$

Use this information and your calculator in Exercises 4–5.

4. Estimate the speed of an accident vehicle which left skid marks measuring 110 ft when the test run produced skid marks of 40 ft when driven 30 mph.

5. Repeat Exercise 4 for an accident vehicle that left skid marks measuring 230 ft.

6. **NUMBER** The sum of the squares of two consecutive even positive integers is 164. Find the integers.

7. **NUMBER** Twice the product of two positive consecutive odd integers is 126. Find the integers.

SECTION 10.6 Graphing Quadratic Equations

Student guideposts

- ▶ *Parabolas*
- ▶ *Graphing quadratic equations*
- ▶ *Vertex of a parabola*
- ▶ *Graphs for $a > 0$ and $a < 0$*

▶ *Parabolas* In Chapter 4 we learned how to graph a linear equation

$$ax + by = c \quad \text{Standard form}$$

$$\text{or} \quad y = mx + b \quad \text{Slope-intercept form}$$

by plotting the intercepts (or the intercept and one additional point if the intercepts are both (0, 0)) and drawing the straight line through them. The graph of every **quadratic equation in two variables** of the form

$$y = ax^2 + bx + c \quad (a \neq 0)$$

is a **parabola,** a U-shaped curve similar to the one shown in Figure 10.5. Applications of parabolas or surfaces in the shape of a parabola are numerous in science, engineering, business, and architecture.

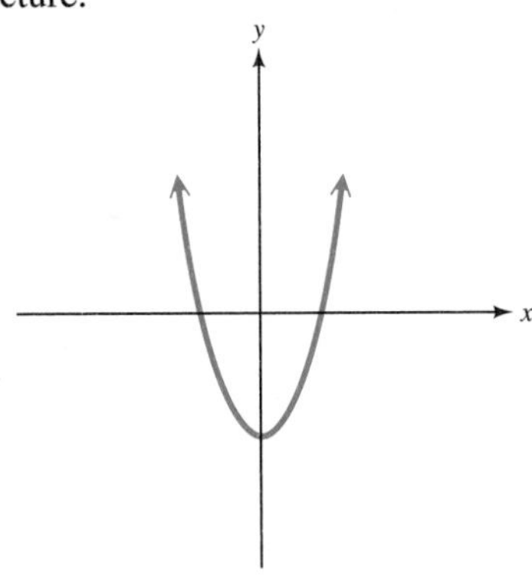

FIGURE 10.5

Graphing quadratic equations

To graph a quadratic equation, we choose several values for x, calculate the corresponding y-values, and plot the resulting points. A table of values helps us keep a record of the points.

EXAMPLE 1

Graphing a Parabola

Graph $y = x^2$.

Find y-values for the following values of x.

If $x = 0$, $y = x^2 = 0^2 = 0$. If $x = -1$, $y = x^2 = (-1)^2 = 1$.

If $x = 1$, $y = x^2 = 1^2 = 1$. If $x = -2$, $y = x^2 = (-2)^2 = 4$.

If $x = 2$, $y = x^2 = 2^2 = 4$.

The completed table is shown below. Plotting the ordered pairs, we obtain the parabola in Figure 10.6. ∎

x	y
0	0
1	1
2	4
−1	1
−2	4

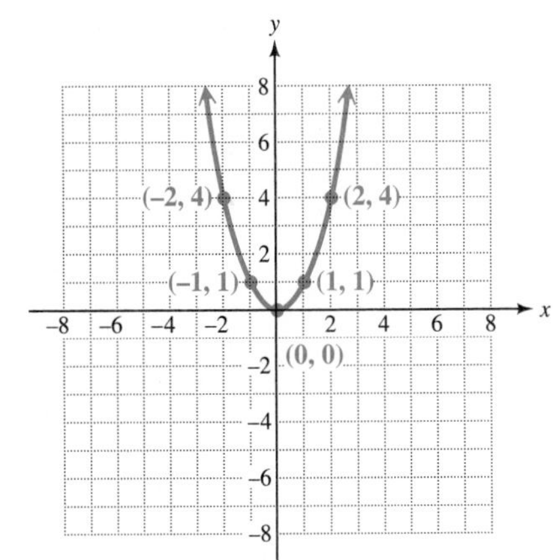

FIGURE 10.6

▶ *Vertex of a parabola*

Notice that the parabola in Figure 10.6 has a low or minimum point at (0, 0). Every parabola that *opens up* like this has a minimum point, and every parabola that *opens down* has a maximum point called the **vertex** of the parabola. If we can find the coordinates of the vertex of a parabola, this will be helpful when we obtain the graph. It can be shown that the vertex of the parabola with equation

$$y = ax^2 + bx + c$$

has $-\frac{b}{2a}$ as the x-coordinate. To find the y-coordinate, all we need to do is substitute $-\frac{b}{2a}$ for x in the equation and find the corresponding value of y. Notice in Example 1, $y = x^2$, so $a = 1$, $b = 0$, and $c = 0$. Thus,

$$-\frac{b}{2a} = -\frac{0}{2(1)} = \frac{0}{2} = 0$$

so the x-coordinate of the vertex is 0. When $x = 0$, $y = x^2 = 0^2 = 0$, so the vertex is at the point with coordinates (0, 0), as shown in Figure 10.6.

EXAMPLE 2

Graphing a Parabola

Graph $y = -x^2$.

Notice that $a = -1$, $b = 0$, and $c = 0$. Begin by finding the x-coordinate of the vertex.

$$-\frac{b}{2a} = -\frac{0}{2(-1)} = \frac{0}{2} = 0$$

When $x = 0$, $y = -(0)^2 = 0$, so the vertex is (0, 0). Choose two other values for x to the right of 0 and two values to the left of 0 to obtain four additional points on the parabola. Be careful when finding values for y in this case. For example, when $x = 1$, $y = -x^2 = -(1)^2 = -1$. The completed table of values appears beside the graph given in Figure 10.7. ■

x	y
0	0
1	-1
2	-4
-1	-1
-2	-4

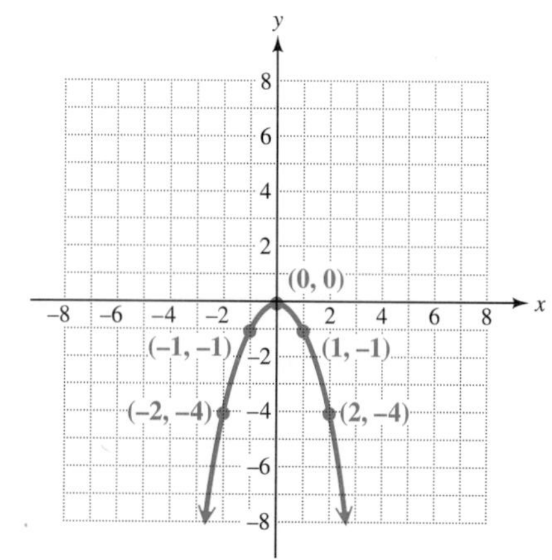

FIGURE 10.7

Graphs for $a > 0$ and $a < 0$

Notice that the parabola in Example 1 opens up while the one in Example 2 opens down. In general, the direction in which a parabola opens depends on the sign of the coefficient of the x^2-term, a. If $a > 0$ (as in Example 1) the parabola opens up, and if $a < 0$ (as in Example 2), the parabola opens down.

Direction a Parabola Opens

The graph of $y = ax^2 + bx + c$ $(a \neq 0)$ is a parabola which

1. opens up when the coefficient of x^2 is positive,
2. opens down when the coefficient of x^2 is negative.

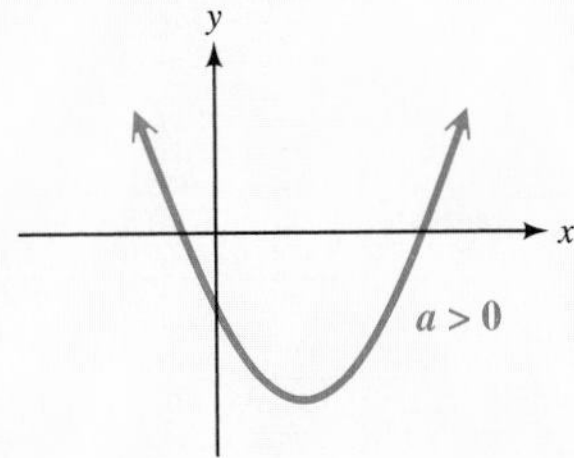

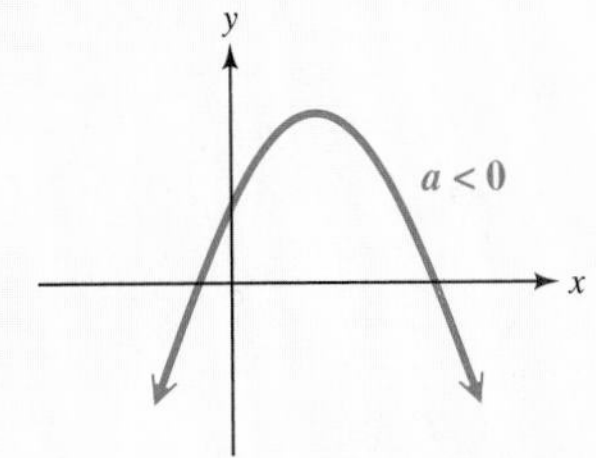

EXAMPLE 3

Working with a Graph Opening Up

Graph $y = x^2 - 2x - 3$.

Since $a = 1 > 0$, we know that the parabola opens up. Also, $b = -2$ so the x-coordinate of the vertex is $-\frac{b}{2a} = -\frac{-2}{2(1)} = \frac{2}{2} = 1$, and when $x = 1$, $y = x^2 - 2x - 3 = (1)^2 - 2(1) - 3 = 1 - 2 - 3 = -4$. Thus, the vertex is at the point $(1, -4)$. Choose two values for x to the right of 1, say, 2 and 3, and two values for x to the left of 1, say, 0 and -1. The values computed in the table are plotted and joined to form the graph given in Figure 10.8. ■

x	y
0	−3
1	−4
2	−3
3	0
−1	0

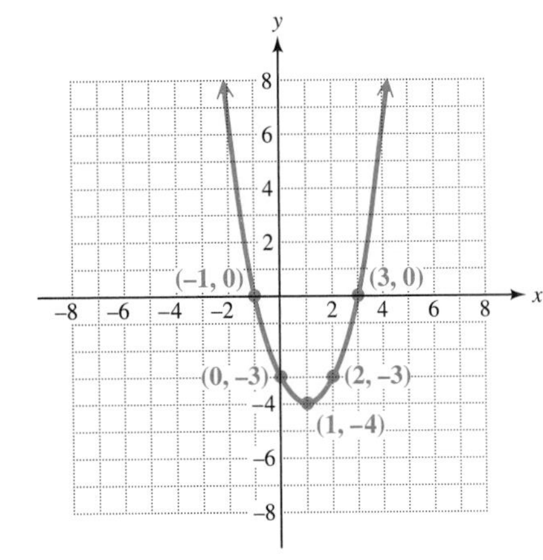

FIGURE 10.8

EXAMPLE 4 **Working with a Graph Opening Down**

Graph $y = -x^2 + 2x$.

Since $a = -1 < 0$, the parabola opens down. Also, $b = 2$, so the x-coordinate of the vertex is $-\frac{b}{2a} = -\frac{2}{2(-1)} = \frac{2}{2} = 1$, and when $x = 1$, $y = -x^2 + 2x = -(1)^2 + 2(1) = -1 + 2 = 1$. Thus, the vertex is at the point (1, 1). Choose two values for x to the right of 1, say, 2 and 3, and two values of x to the left of 1, say, 0 and -1. The completed table is shown below beside the graph of the parabola in Figure 10.9. ■

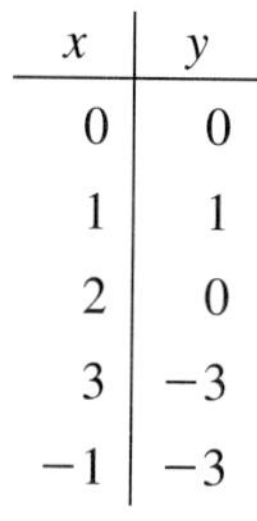

x	y
0	0
1	1
2	0
3	-3
-1	-3

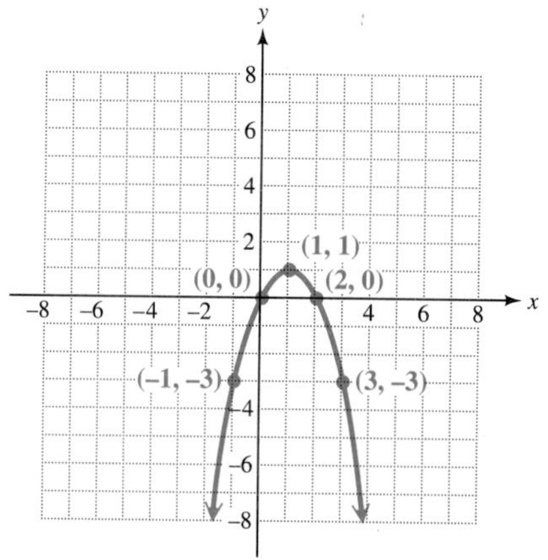

FIGURE 10.9

When the equation of a parabola is given in a special form, it is possible to find the vertex more directly. Consider the following equation.

$$\begin{aligned} y &= (x - 1)^2 - 4 \\ &= x^2 - 2x + 1 - 4 \\ &= x^2 - 2x - 3 \end{aligned}$$

Thus, $y = (x - 1)^2 - 4$ and $y = x^2 - 2x - 3$ have the same graph, given in Figure 10.7. Notice that $(1, -4)$ is the vertex of the parabola. If the equation of a parabola is written in the form

$$y = (x - h)^2 + k,$$

then (h, k) is the vertex and the graph is a parabola opening up.

A similar rule holds for parabolas opening down. Consider

$$\begin{aligned} y &= -(x - 1)^2 + 1 \\ &= -(x^2 - 2x + 1) + 1 \\ &= -x^2 + 2x - 1 + 1 \\ &= -x^2 + 2x. \end{aligned}$$

Thus, $y = -(x - 1)^2 + 1$ and $y = -x^2 + 2x$ have the same graph, given in Figure 10.8, with vertex (1, 1). If the equation of a parabola is written in the form

$$y = -(x - h)^2 + k,$$

then (h, k) is the vertex, and the graph is a parabola opening down.

EXAMPLE 5 **Finding the Vertex**

Find the vertex of each parabola.

(a) $y = (x + 3)^2 - 5$
We must have the form $y = (x - h)^2 + k$.

$$\begin{aligned} y &= (x + 3)^2 - 5 \\ &= [x - (-3)]^2 + (-5) \end{aligned}$$

Thus, $h = -3$ and $k = -5$. The vertex is $(-3, -5)$.

(b) $y = -(x + 1)^2 + 7$
Write in the form $y = -(x - h)^2 + k$.

$$\begin{aligned} y &= -(x + 1)^2 + 7 \\ &= -[x - (-1)]^2 + 7 \end{aligned}$$

Thus, $h = -1$ and $k = 7$. The vertex is $(-1, 7)$.

(c) $y = (x + 5)^2$
Write in the form $y = (x - h)^2 + k$.

$$\begin{aligned} y &= (x + 5)^2 \\ &= [x - (-5)]^2 + 0 \end{aligned}$$

Thus, $h = -5$ and $k = 0$. The vertex is $(-5, 0)$. ■

CAUTION Remember that the graph of any quadratic equation $y = ax^2 + bx + c$ is always a parabola, *not* a straight line. Students who are graphing these equations for the first time often plot too few points and try to connect them in a straight line. Another common error is to make the curve V-shaped, not "rounded smoothly" at the vertex.

10.6 EXERCISES

In Exercises 1–6, tell whether the parabola opens up or down, give the vertex, and graph the equation.

1. $y = x^2 + 1$
2. $y = -x^2 + 1$
3. $y = x^2 - 2$
4. $y = -x^2 - 2x - 1$
5. $y = x^2 + 2x$
6. $y = -x^2 + 3x - 2$

Give the vertex of each parabola in Exercises 7–9.

7. $y = (x - 4)^2 + 2$
8. $y = -(x + 10)^2 - 9$
9. $y = x^2 - 3$

FOR REVIEW

Solve each problem in Exercises 10–13.

10. **NUMBER** The product of 2 less than a number and 3 more than the number is 176. Find the number.

11. **GEOMETRY** The hypotenuse of a right triangle is 5 cm and one leg is 1 cm longer than the other. Find the measure of each leg.

12. **GEOMETRY** The area of a triangle is 24 ft^2, and the base is 3 times as long as the height. Find the base and height.

13. **WORK** Laura takes 2 days to type a manuscript and Holly takes 8 days. How long would it take if they worked together?

Exercises 14–16 review material from Chapter 9 to help you prepare for the next section. Simplify each radical expression.

14. $\sqrt{20}$ **15.** $\sqrt{\frac{1}{3}}$ **16.** $(2\sqrt{3})(4\sqrt{6})$

10.6 PARALLEL EXERCISES

In Exercises 1–6, tell whether the parabola opens up or down, give the vertex, and graph the equation.

1. $y = x^2 + 2$ **2.** $y = -x^2 - 1$ **3.** $y = x^2 - 1$

4. $y = -x^2 + 2x - 1$ **5.** $y = x^2 + 4x$ **6.** $y = -x^2 - 3x - 2$

Give the vertex of the parabola in Exercises 7–9.

7. $y = -(x - 4)^2 + 8$ **8.** $y = (x + 12)^2 - 8$ **9.** $y = (x + 1)^2$

FOR REVIEW

Solve each problem in Exercises 10–13.

10. **NUMBER** Of two positive numbers, one is 4 larger than the other and the sum of the squares of the two is 136. Find the numbers.

11. **GEOMETRY** The height of a triangle is 8 inches more than the base. If the area is 90 in^2, find the height and base.

12. **GEOMETRY** The length of a rectangle is 4 cm more than the width and the area is 96 cm^2. Find the dimensions.

13. **INVESTMENT** The amount of money A that will result if a principal P is invested at r percent interest compounded annually for 2 years is given by $A = P(1 + r)^2$. If \$5000 grows to \$6498 in 2 years using this formula, what is the interest rate?

Exercises 14–16 review material from Chapter 9 to help you prepare for the next section. Simplify each radical expression.

14. $\sqrt{54}$ **15.** $\sqrt{\frac{1}{5}}$ **16.** $(3\sqrt{2})(5\sqrt{14})$

10.6 ENRICHMENT EXERCISES

In Exercises 1–2, find the vertex of each parabola by completing the square to obtain the special form.

1. $y = x^2 + 10x + 20$
2. $y = -x^2 + 6x - 4$
3. If $y = -2x^2 + 5$, what is the largest value y can be? What is the smallest value y can be?
4. If $y = 3x^2 - 4$, what is the largest value y can be? What is the smallest value y can be?
5. Does the graph of $y = (x - 3)^2 + 2$ open up or down?
6. Does the graph of $y = -(x - 3)^2 + 2$ open up or down?
7. Discuss how to graph an equation of the form $y = ax^2 + bx + c$. Be sure to include remarks about the direction the parabola opens and the vertex of the parabola.
8. The ***x*-intercepts** of the graph of an equation of the form $y = ax^2 + bx + c$ are the points where the parabola crosses the x-axis. Describe a method for finding the intercepts, and include a discussion of cases where there are no x-intercepts.

SECTION 10.7 Quadratic Equations with Complex Solutions (Optional)

Student guideposts

- *Imaginary numbers*
- *Complex numbers*

Imaginary numbers

Suppose we attempt to solve the following quadratic equation by taking roots.

$$x^2 + 9 = 0$$
$$x^2 = -9$$
$$x = \pm\sqrt{-9}$$

In Section 10.1 we said that there were no real solutions to this type of equation. This is true since no real number squared is -9. However, in some fields of study it is important to have solutions to equations like this. Thus, we introduce a new kind of number. The square root of a negative number is called an **imaginary number.** We use i as the numeral for $\sqrt{-1}$.

$$\sqrt{-1} = i \quad \text{and} \quad i^2 = -1$$

Heron of Alexandria (circa 150 B.C. to 250 A.D.) was the first to notice that the square root of a negative number posed an interesting problem. René Descartes (1596–1650) was first to use the terms *real* and *imaginary numbers.* Don't let the term *imaginary* mislead you, however, since imaginary numbers are no more ''imaginary'' than real numbers. Every imaginary number can be written as a product of a real number and the number i. For example,

$$\sqrt{-9} = \sqrt{9(-1)} = \sqrt{9}\sqrt{-1} = 3i.$$

Thus the two solutions to the equation

$$x^2 + 9 = 0$$

are

$$x = 3i \quad \text{and} \quad x = -3i.$$

Suppose we now use our knowledge of imaginary numbers and the quadratic formula to solve

$$\begin{aligned} x^2 - 2x + 2 &= 0. \qquad a = 1,\ b = -2,\ c = 2 \\ x &= \frac{-b \pm \sqrt{b^2 - 4ac}}{2a} \\ &= \frac{-(-2) \pm \sqrt{(-2)^2 - 4(1)(2)}}{2(1)} \\ &= \frac{2 \pm \sqrt{4 - 8}}{2} \\ &= \frac{2 \pm \sqrt{-4}}{2} \\ &= \frac{2 \pm \sqrt{(4)(-1)}}{2} = \frac{2 \pm \sqrt{4}\sqrt{-1}}{2} \\ &= \frac{2 \pm 2i}{2} = \frac{\cancel{2}(1 \pm i)}{\cancel{2}} = 1 \pm i \end{aligned}$$

▶ *Complex numbers*

The number $1 + i$ is a real number added to the imaginary number i. If a and b are real numbers, any number of the form

$$a + bi$$

is called a **complex number.** Thus the solutions to the equation $x^2 - 2x + 2 = 0$ are the two complex numbers $1 + i$ and $1 - i$.

Since we can now use imaginary and complex numbers, we are able to solve any quadratic equation. The following examples give us practice in obtaining complex solutions.

EXAMPLE 1 **Working with Imaginary Solutions**

Solve $x^2 + 25 = 0$.

We use the method of taking roots from Section 8.1.

$$\begin{aligned} x^2 + 25 &= 0 \\ x^2 &= -25 \\ x &= \pm\sqrt{-25} \\ &= \pm\sqrt{25(-1)} \\ &= \pm\sqrt{25}\sqrt{-1} = \pm 5i \end{aligned}$$

The solutions are the imaginary numbers $5i$ and $-5i$. Since $5i = 0 + 5i$, we note that $5i$ is also a complex number. Every imaginary number is also a complex number. ■

CAUTION We have been using the rule $\sqrt{ab} = \sqrt{a}\sqrt{b}$ for $a > 0$ and $b = -1$. Do not try to use this rule when $a < 0$ and $b < 0$. For example $\sqrt{-4}\sqrt{-9} \neq \sqrt{(-4)(-9)}$ since $\sqrt{-4}\sqrt{-9} = (2i)(3i) = 6i^2 = -6$ while $\sqrt{(-4)(-9)} = \sqrt{36} = 6$.

EXAMPLE 2 **Working with Complex Solutions**

(a) Solve $2x^2 + 2x + 5 = 0$.
We will use the quadratic formula with $a = 2$, $b = 2$, and $c = 5$.

$$
\begin{aligned}
x &= \frac{-b \pm \sqrt{b^2 - 4ac}}{2a} \\
&= \frac{-2 \pm \sqrt{(2)^2 - 4(2)(5)}}{2(2)} \\
&= \frac{-2 \pm \sqrt{4 - 40}}{4} \\
&= \frac{-2 \pm \sqrt{-36}}{4} \\
&= \frac{-2 \pm \sqrt{36(-1)}}{4} \\
&= \frac{-2 \pm \sqrt{36}\sqrt{-1}}{4} \\
&= \frac{-2 \pm 6i}{4} = \frac{\not{2}(-1 \pm 3i)}{\not{2} \cdot 2} \\
&= \frac{-1 \pm 3i}{2} = -\frac{1}{2} \pm \frac{3}{2}i
\end{aligned}
$$

(b) Solve $3x^2 - 5x + 7 = 0$.
Here $a = 3$, $b = -5$, and $c = 7$.

$$
\begin{aligned}
x &= \frac{-b \pm \sqrt{b^2 - 4ac}}{2a} \\
&= \frac{-(-5) \pm \sqrt{(-5)^2 - 4(3)(7)}}{2(3)} \\
&= \frac{5 \pm \sqrt{25 - 84}}{6} \\
&= \frac{5 \pm \sqrt{-59}}{6} = \frac{5 \pm \sqrt{-1}\sqrt{59}}{6} \\
&= \frac{5 \pm i\sqrt{59}}{6} = \frac{5}{6} \pm \frac{\sqrt{59}}{6}i
\end{aligned}
$$

Note that $i\sqrt{59}$ is the same as $\sqrt{59}i$. ■

10.7 EXERCISES

Solve each quadratic equation in Exercises 1–12.

1. $x^2 + 1 = 0$
2. $x^2 + 16 = 0$
3. $x^2 - 1 = 0$
4. $u^2 + 12 = 0$
5. $u^2 + 50 = 0$
6. $u^2 - 12 = 0$
7. $y^2 + 2y + 5 = 0$
8. $y^2 - 2y + 5 = 0$
9. $x^2 - x + 1 = 0$
10. $2y^2 - 3y + 8 = 0$
11. $5x^2 = 4x - 5$
12. $4x = -5x^2 - 5$

FOR REVIEW

In Exercises 13–14, state whether the parabola opens up or down and give its vertex. Then graph the equation.

13. $y = x^2 - 4x$
14. $y = -(x - 2)^2 + 4$

10.7 PARALLEL EXERCISES

Solve each quadratic equation in Exercises 1–12.

1. $x^2 + 4 = 0$
2. $x^2 + 81 = 0$
3. $x^2 - 4 = 0$
4. $u^2 + 20 = 0$
5. $u^2 + 72 = 0$
6. $u^2 - 20 = 0$
7. $y^2 - 4y + 5 = 0$
8. $y^2 + 4y + 5 = 0$
9. $x^2 + 3x + 4 = 0$
10. $y^2 - 9y + 1 = 0$
11. $4x^2 = -x - 7$
12. $4x^2 = x - 7$

FOR REVIEW

In Exercises 13–14, state whether the parabola opens up or down and give its vertex. Then graph the equation.

13. $y = x^2 - 6x$
14. $y = -(x + 1)^2 - 5$

10.7 ENRICHMENT EXERCISES

Without solving each equation, use the discriminant ($b^2 - 4ac$) to determine whether each quadratic equation in Exercises 1–6 has 2 real solutions, 1 real solution, or 2 complex solutions.

1. $x^2 - 4x - 5 = 0$
2. $x^2 - 4x + 5 = 0$
3. $x^2 - 6x + 9 = 0$
4. $x^2 + 37 = 0$
5. $x^2 - 37 = 0$
6. $3x^2 + x + 5 = 0$

7. Show that $-(3i)^2 = 9$, and explain how to use the result to factor $x^2 + 9$ into the product $(x + 3i)(x - 3i)$.

8. We learned to solve equations of the form $x^2 + c = 0$ using the method of taking roots. In view of Exercise 7, what can you say about such equations relative to the method of factoring?

9. Give one good reason for developing imaginary and complex numbers.

CHAPTER 10 REVIEW

KEY WORDS

10.1 A **quadratic equation** is an equation that can be written in the form $ax^2 + bx + c = 0$, $a \neq 0$.

10.2 To **complete the square** on $x^2 + bx$ add $\left(\frac{1}{2}b\right)^2$ to make the expression a perfect square.

10.3 The **discriminant** of $ax^2 + bx + c = 0$ is $b^2 - 4ac$.

10.6 A **quadratic equation in two variables** is an equation of the form $y = ax^2 + bx + c$, $a \neq 0$.
A **parabola** is the graph of a quadratic equation in two variables.
The **vertex** is the low point of a parabola opening up and the high point of a parabola opening down.

10.7 **1.** The square root of a negative number is an **imaginary number.** We use $i = \sqrt{-1}$, and if b is a positive real number, then $\sqrt{-b} = i\sqrt{b}$.
2. If a and b are real numbers, $a + bi$ is a **complex number.**

KEY CONCEPTS

10.1, 10.2 The best ways to solve a quadratic equation are by factoring and taking roots. If these methods do not work, use the quadratic formula instead of completing the square.

10.3 The quadratic formula for solving $ax^2 + bx + c = 0$ is

$$x = \frac{-b \pm \sqrt{b^2 - 4ac}}{2a}.$$

Make sure that an equation is put into the above general form before trying to identify the constants a, b, and c. Also, the entire numerator $-b \pm \sqrt{b^2 - 4ac}$, is divided by $2a$, *not* just the radical term.

10.4 **1.** To solve a fractional equation, multiply both sides by the LCD of all fractions. Be sure to check all possible solutions in the original equation and exclude those that make any denominator zero.
2. To solve a radical equation, isolate a radical and square both sides of the equation. If a binomial occurs on one side, don't forget the middle term when squaring. For example,

$$x + 4 = 3\sqrt{x + 1} \quad \text{becomes}$$
$$x^2 + 8x + 16 = 9(x + 1).$$

Be sure to square 3 also. Finally, check all possible answers in the *original* equation and remember that the radical only represents the positive (principal) square root.

10.5 Use the ATTACK method to solve applied problems that result in a quadratic equation. Be precise and write out complete descriptions of the variable, and always make a sketch for a geometry problem.

10.6 **1.** The graph of a quadratic equation $y = ax^2 + bx + c$ $(a \neq 0)$ is a parabola that opens up if $a > 0$ and down if $a < 0$.

2. The x-coordinate of the vertex of the parabola with equation $y = ax^2 + bx + c$ is $-\frac{b}{2a}$. To find the y-coordinate, substitute $-\frac{b}{2a}$ for x and find the value of y.
3. The vertex of the parabola with equation $y = (x - h)^2 + k$ or $y = -(x - h)^2 + k$ is at the point with coordinates (h, k).

10.7 Once we have imaginary numbers and complex numbers, every quadratic equation has a solution.

CHAPTER 10 REVIEW EXERCISES

PART I

10.1 *Solve each quadratic equation in Exercises 1–3.*

1. $x^2 + 6x - 72 = 0$
2. $(z - 5)^2 = 25$
3. $21x^2 - 4x - 32 = 0$

10.2 *What must be added to complete the square for each expression in Exercises 4–5?*

4. $x^2 + x +$ ____
5. $y^2 + \frac{1}{4}y +$ ____
6. Solve $x^2 - 3x + 1 = 0$ by completing the square.

10.3 *Solve each quadratic equation in Exercises 7–9.*

7. $2y^2 + y = 5$
8. $2z^2 + 11z = -(10 + z)$
9. $x^2 + 2x - 5 = 0$

10.4 *Solve each fractional or radical equation in Exercises 10–12.*

10. $\dfrac{z + 2}{-z} = \dfrac{1}{z + 2}$
11. $\dfrac{3}{1 + x} = -1 - \dfrac{2}{1 - x}$
12. $4 = 4\sqrt{x + 1} - x$

10.5 13. **NUMBER** One number is 5 more than another. The square of the larger exceeds the square of the smaller by 95. Find the number.

14. **AGE** Mike's present age times his age in 7 years is 30. Find his present age.
15. **GEOMETRY** The number of square inches in a square is 3 less than the number of inches in its perimeter. Find the length of its sides.
16. **NUMBER** Find the number whose square is 18 more than three times the number.
17. **PHYSICS** The pressure p, in lb per sq ft, of a wind blowing v mph can be approximated by the equation $p = 0.003v^2$. What is the approximate wind velocity when a pressure of 3.675 lb per sq ft is exerted against the side of a skyscraper?
18. **INVESTMENT** Use $A = P(1 + r)^2$ to find the interest rate if \$3000 grows to \$3630 in 2 years.
19. **BUSINESS** Video Accents makes and sells storage units for video cassettes. The daily cost of making x storage units is given by $C = 3x^2 + 720$, and the daily revenue produced by selling x units by $R = 96x$. Find the daily break-even point(s) for the company.
20. **MOTION** A boat sails 96 miles upstream and then returns to the starting point in a total of 10 hours. If the speed of the boat in still water is 20 mph, what is the speed of the stream?

10.6 **21.** Tell whether the parabola with the given equation opens up or down.

(a) $y = 3x^2 + x - 1$

(b) $y = -2x^2 + 5$

Graph each quadratic equation in Exercises 22–23.

22. $y = x^2 - 3$

23. $y = x^2 - 6x + 8$

Give the vertex of each parabola in Exercises 24–25.

24. $y = -(x + 4)^2 - 3$

25. $y = x^2 + 6$

10.7 *Solve each quadratic equation in Exercises 26–28.*

26. $x^2 + 100 = 0$

27. $2x^2 - 2x + 7 = 0$

28. $2x^2 - 4x + 11 = 0$

PART II

29. **INVESTMENT** The amount of money A that will result if a principal P is invested at r percent interest compounded annually for 2 years is given by $A = P(1 + r)^2$. If \$2000 grows to \$2645 in 2 years using this formula, what is the interest rate?

30. **RECREATION** Beth hikes 10 miles up a mountain and returns in a total time of 6 hours. If her speed hiking up the mountain is 2.5 mph less than her speed down, what is her speed hiking down?

31. **NUMBER** The square of a number, less 7, is equal to 9. Find the number.

32. **NUMBER** Twice the principal square root of 2 more than a number is the same as 1 less than the number. Find the number.

33. **GEOMETRY** Lennie has a garden in the shape of a square 12 yards on a side. He wishes to lay a water pipe from one corner diagonally across to the other. What is the approximate length of this pipe?

34. **WORK** If it takes Bill 12 hours longer to paint a room than Peter and together they can complete the job in 8 hours, how long would it take each to do it alone?

Solve each equation in Exercises 35–40.

35. $\dfrac{5}{x-2} + 1 = \dfrac{2}{x-3}$

36. $x^2 - 6x + 2 = 0$

37. $1 - x^2 = 7x - 5$

38. $x^2 + 121 = 0$

39. $x^2 + 121x = 0$

40. $x^2 - 4x = -6$

In Exercises 41–42, give the vertex of each parabola and tell whether it opens up or down.

41. $y = -x^2 - 8$

42. $y = -(x - 2)^2 + 5$

What must be added to complete the square for each expression in Exercises 43–44?

43. $x^2 - 14x +$ ____

44. $y^2 + \dfrac{1}{3}y +$ ____

Answer true *or* false *in Exercises 45–60. If the answer is false, explain why.*

45. Every quadratic equation can be solved using the quadratic formula.

46. Every quadratic equation has two different solutions.

47. If the discriminant of a quadratic equation is negative, the equation has complex solutions.

48. The quadratic equation $x^2 + 7 = 0$ has imaginary solutions.

49. To solve $x^2 + 6x = 8$ by completing the square, add 16 to both sides.

50. If a quadratic equation cannot be solved by factoring or taking roots, the next best method to use is the quadratic formula.
51. The quadratic formula is developed by completing the square on a general quadratic equation.
52. One way to write the quadratic formula is $x = -b \pm \frac{\sqrt{b^2 - 4ac}}{2a}$.
53. If Max can do an entire job in x hours, in one hour he can do $\frac{1}{x}$ of the job.
54. If the speed of a boat in still water is x mph, when the boat sails upstream, its speed is $x + 3$ mph if the stream speed is 3 mph.
55. The number $2 + 5i$ is a complex number.
56. Another way to write $\sqrt{-25}$ is $25i$.
57. If we have complex and imaginary numbers, every quadratic equation can be solved.
58. The graph of $y = -x^2 + 3x - 14$ is a parabola that opens up.
59. The vertex of the parabola with equation $y = 3x^2 + 6x - 2$ is $(-1, -5)$.
60. The vertex of the parabola with equation $y = (x - 5)^2 + 8$ is $(-5, 8)$.

CHAPTER 10 TEST

Solve the following quadratic equations.

1. $x^2 + 13x + 36 = 0$
2. $3z^2 - z = 27 - z$
3. $y(y - 2) = 3y$
4. $x^2 + 24 = 0$
5. $x^2 - 4x + 1 = 0$
6. $y^2 - 2y = -3$
7. What must be added to complete the square? $y^2 + \frac{1}{2}y +$ ____

Solve.

8. $\frac{2}{x - 1} + 2 = \frac{3}{x - 2}$
9. $4 = x + \sqrt{2 + x}$

Solve.

10. The amount of money A that will result if a principal P is invested at r percent interest compounded annually for 2 years is given by $A = P(1 + r)^2$. If \$1000 grows to \$1210 in 2 years using this formula, what is the interest rate?
11. It takes 8 hours less time to fill a pond using a large pipe than it takes using a smaller pipe. If when used together they fill the pond in 3 hours, how long would it take each to fill it alone?
12. A boat travels 70 miles upstream and then returns in a total time of 12 hours. If the speed of the stream is 2 mph, what is the speed of the boat in still water?
13. The daily cost of making x items is given by $C = 3x^2 + 405$, and the daily revenue produced on the sale of x items by $R = 72x$. Find the break-even point(s).
14. Consider the equation $y = x^2 + 2$.
    (a) What is the graph of this equation called?
    (b) Does the graph open up or down?
    (c) What is the vertex of the graph?
    (d) Graph the equation.

Answer true *or* false. *If the answer is false, explain why.*

15. The equation $x^2 + 10 = 0$ has imaginary solutions.
16. The vertex of the graph of $y = (x - 6)^2 + 5$ is $(-6, 5)$.
17. $\sqrt{-16}$ is a real number.

Appendix A
A Review of Geometry

Student guideposts

- ***Lines and angles***
- ***Triangles***
- ***Perimeter and area***
- ***Volume and surface area***

▶ *Lines and angles*

The material in this Geometry Appendix is included for students who need a review of some of the concepts of geometry.

A point is a precise location in space often symbolized by a dot and labeled with a capital letter, such as the point A shown below.

$\cdot A$

Figure A.1 displays three geometric figures. An arrowhead indicates that the curve continues in that direction without end.

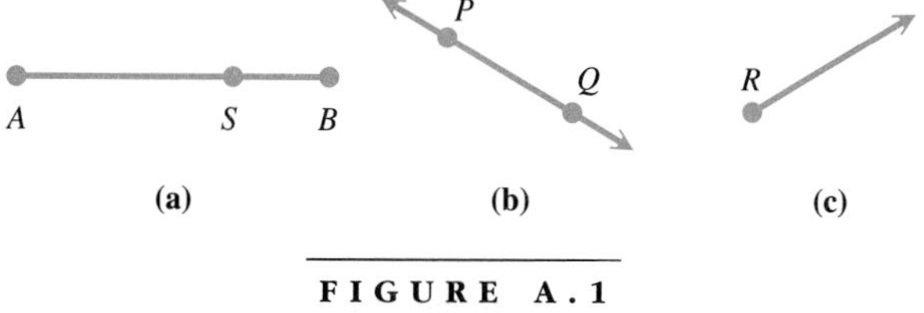

FIGURE A.1

A **segment** is a geometric figure made up of two **endpoints** and all points between them. The segment with endpoints A and B in Figure A.1(a) can be denoted by either $\overline{AB}$ or $\overline{BA}$. The point S is said to be **on the segment** $\overline{AB}$. Figure A.1(b) represents a straight **line,** which consists of the points on the segment $\overline{PQ}$ together with all points beyond P and Q. We denote this line by $\overleftrightarrow{PQ}$ or $\overleftrightarrow{QP}$.

Any two distinct points determine one and only one line. The two distinct points E and F determine the unique line $\overleftrightarrow{EF}$ shown in Figure A.2. For convenience, we often use a small letter such as l to represent a line.

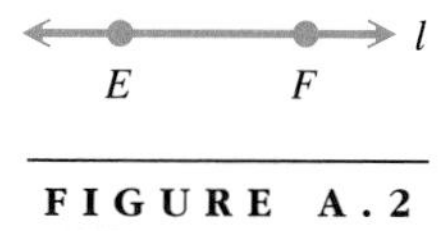

FIGURE A.2

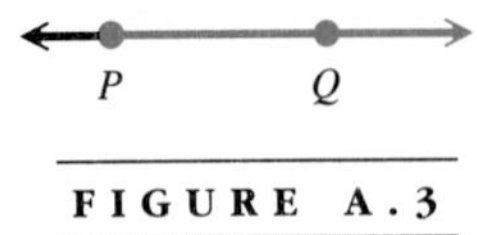

FIGURE A.3

A **ray** is that part of a line lying on one side of a point P on the line, and includes the point P. A ray is shown in color in Figure A.3. By selecting another point Q on the ray, we have a way to denote the ray by $\overrightarrow{PQ}$. Unlike the notations used for segments and lines, the rays $\overrightarrow{PQ}$ and $\overrightarrow{QP}$ are different. A ray has only one endpoint and it is always written first. Taken together, the rays $\overrightarrow{PQ}$ and $\overrightarrow{QP}$ make up the line $\overleftrightarrow{PQ}$. Another example of a ray is shown in Figure A.1(c).

A **plane** is a surface with the property that any two points in it can be joined by a line, all points of which are also contained in the surface. Intuitively, a plane can be thought of as any flat surface such as a blackboard or a desktop. If two lines in a plane represent the same line, they are **coinciding lines.** When two lines share exactly one common point, they are **intersecting lines.** When two distinct lines in a plane do not intersect, the lines are called **parallel lines.** These three situations are illustrated in Figure A.4.

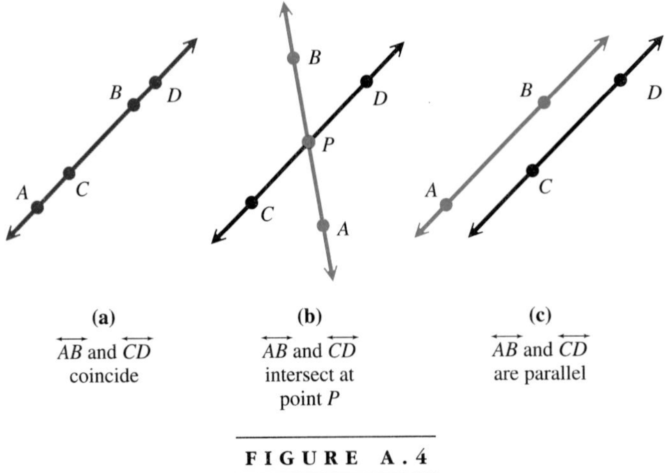

FIGURE A.4

Two segments, two rays, or a segment and a ray can also be called **parallel** if they are on parallel lines. Thus, in Figure A.4(c) $\overline{AB}$ is parallel to $\overline{CD}$, $\overrightarrow{AB}$ is parallel to $\overrightarrow{DC}$, and $\overline{AB}$ is parallel to $\overrightarrow{CD}$.

An **angle** is a geometric figure consisting of two rays which share a common endpoint, called the **vertex** of the angle. In Figure A.5, the two rays $\overrightarrow{AC}$ and $\overrightarrow{AB}$ form the angle denoted by $\angle BAC$, $\angle CAB$, or simply $\angle A$. The rays $\overrightarrow{AC}$ and $\overrightarrow{AB}$ are the **sides** of $\angle A$.

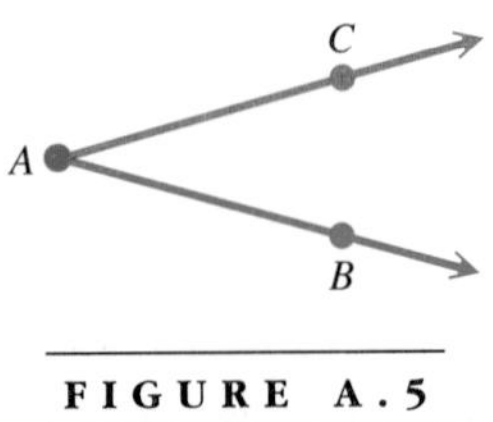

FIGURE A.5

We are familiar with measuring the length of segments by some suitable unit of measure such as inch, centimeter, foot, or meter. In order to measure an angle, we need a measuring unit. The most common unit is the degree (°). An angle with measure 0° is formed by two coinciding rays such as $\overrightarrow{AB}$ and $\overrightarrow{AC}$ in Figure A.6. As the ray $\overrightarrow{AB}$ rotates in a counterclockwise direction from ray $\overrightarrow{AC}$, the two rays form larger and larger angles as shown in Figure A.7.

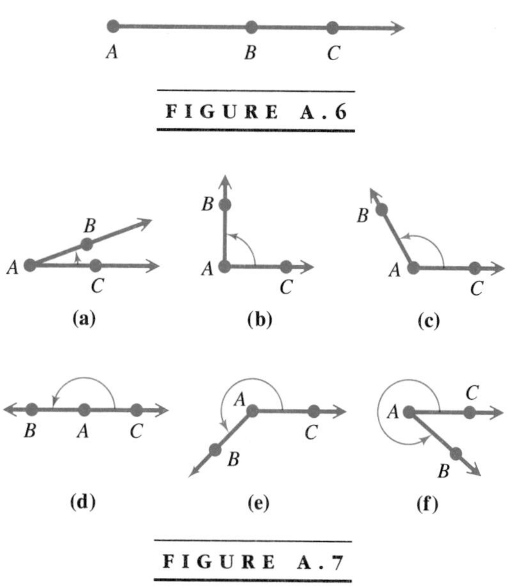

FIGURE A.6

FIGURE A.7

If $\overrightarrow{AB}$ is allowed to rotate completely around until it coincides with ray $\overrightarrow{AC}$ again, the resulting angle is said to measure 360°. Thus, an angle of measure 1° is formed by making $\frac{1}{360}$ of a complete rotation, as in Figure A.8.

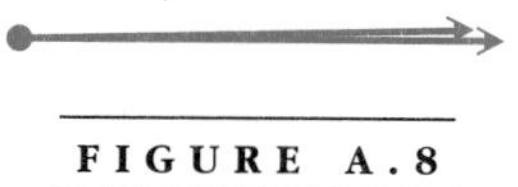

FIGURE A.8

When two rays forming an angle are in opposite directions, such as in Figure A.7(d), the resulting angle is a **straight angle** and has measure 180°. When a ray $\overrightarrow{AB}$ is rotated through one-fourth of a complete revolution from $\overrightarrow{AC}$, as in Figure A.7(b), the resulting angle is a **right angle** and has measure 90°. Right angles are often marked with a square corner at the vertex, such as ∟. Angles measuring between 0° and 90°, such as the angle in Figure A.7(a), are **acute angles.** Angles measuring between 90° and 180°, such as the angle in Figure A.7(c), are **obtuse angles.**

Two angles with the same measure are **equal** or **congruent.** Two angles whose measures total 90° are **complementary,** and two angles whose measures total 180° are **supplementary.**

When two lines intersect, four angles are formed. The intersecting lines $\overleftrightarrow{AB}$ and $\overleftrightarrow{CD}$ in Figure A.9 form the four angles $\angle APD$, $\angle DPB$, $\angle BPC$, and $\angle CPA$. $\angle APC$ and $\angle DPB$ are **vertical angles** to each other. The same is true for $\angle APD$ and $\angle BPC$.

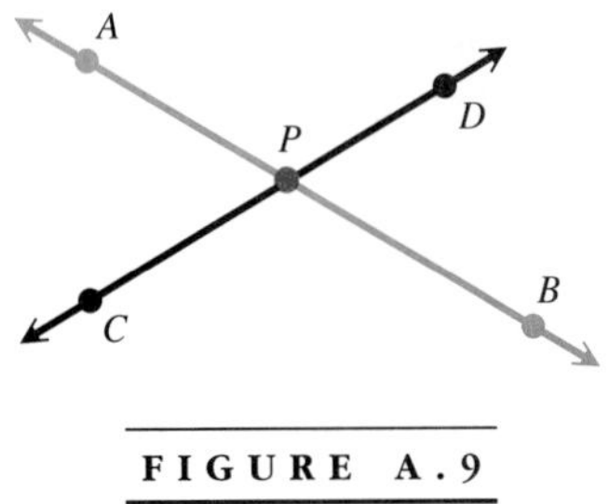

FIGURE A.9

Vertical angles have the same measure. Thus, in Figure A.9, $\angle APC$ and $\angle DPB$ are equal, as are $\angle APD$ and $\angle BPC$. When the four angles formed by two intersecting lines all have measure 90°, that is, when they are all right angles, the lines are **perpendicular.**

A line that intersects each of two parallel lines is called a **transversal.** The two lines are said to be "cut" by the transversal and several angles are formed. In Figure A.10, transversal $\overleftrightarrow{AD}$ cuts parallel lines $\overleftrightarrow{GF}$ and $\overleftrightarrow{HE}$ forming four **interior angles,** $\angle GBC$, $\angle FBC$, $\angle BCH$, and $\angle BCE$, and four **exterior angles,** $\angle ABG$, $\angle ABF$, $\angle HCD$, and $\angle ECD$. Since $\angle GBC$ and $\angle BCE$ are on alternate sides of the transversal, they are called **alternate interior angles.** Similarly, $\angle FBC$ and $\angle BCH$ are alternate interior angles. In Figure A.10, $\angle ABF$ and $\angle BCE$ are **corresponding angles.** Three other pairs of corresponding angles are $\angle ABG$ and $\angle BCH$, $\angle GBC$ and $\angle HCD$, and $\angle FBC$ and $\angle ECD$.

Alternate interior angles always have the same measure. Thus, referring to Figure A.10 again, $\angle FBC$ and $\angle BCH$ have the same measure, as do $\angle GBC$ and $\angle BCE$. Also, corresponding angles always have the same measure so that, for example, $\angle ABF$ has the same measure as $\angle BCF$ in Figure A.10.

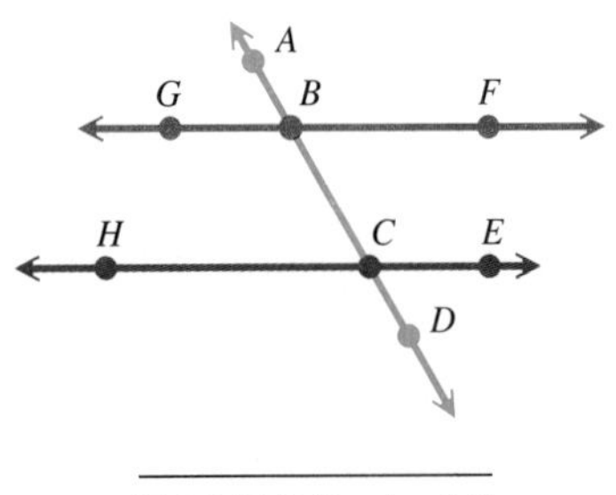

FIGURE A.10

▶ *Triangles* We now present an introduction to the study of triangles and their properties. Consider three noncollinear points A, B, and C and the corresponding segments $\overline{AB}$, $\overline{BC}$, and $\overline{CA}$, as shown in Figure A.11. The resulting geometric figure is a **triangle** with sides $\overline{AB}$, $\overline{BC}$, and $\overline{CA}$, **vertices** (plural of **vertex**) A, B, and C, and is denoted by $\triangle ABC$ ($\triangle$ represents the word "triangle").

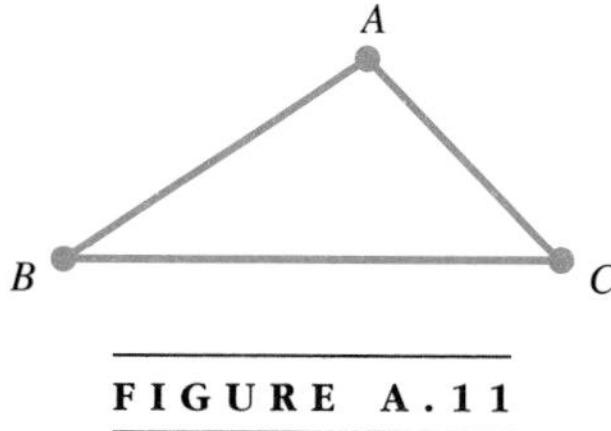

FIGURE A.11

Triangles are often classified by their angles, as shown in Figure A.12. They can also be classified by their sides, as in Figure A.13. We can also describe triangles with a combination of these terms, as in Figure A.14.

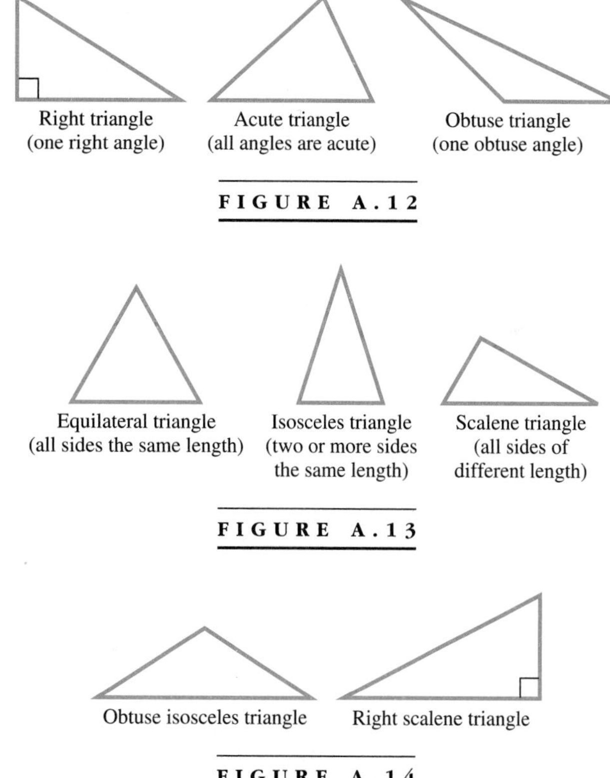

FIGURE A.12

FIGURE A.13

FIGURE A.14

In Chapter 9, after the study of radicals, we discuss some of the properties of isosceles right triangles and right triangles with acute angles of 30° and 60°. Here we restrict ourselves to some general properties of triangles.

Sum of Angles

The sum of the measures of the angles in any triangle is 180°.

For example, if we know that two angles of a triangle are 70° and 35°, then the third angle is

$$180° - (70° + 35°) = 180° - 105° = 75°.$$

Two triangles are **congruent** if they can be made to coincide by placing one on top of the other, either directly or by flipping one of them over. In Figure A.15, $\triangle ABC$ and $\triangle DEF$ are congruent, since $\triangle ABC$ could be placed on top of $\triangle DEF$. $\triangle ABC$ and $\triangle GHI$ are also congruent, since if $\triangle GHI$ were flipped over it could be made to coincide with $\triangle ABC$. On the other hand, $\triangle ABC$ and $\triangle JKL$ are not congruent, since they cannot be made to coincide.

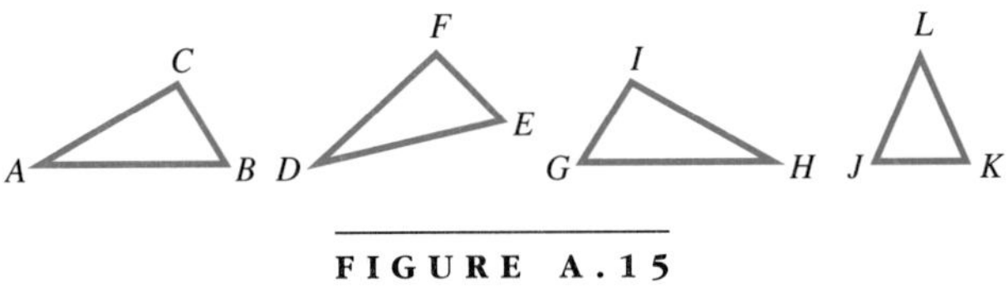

FIGURE A.15

More precisely, two triangles are congruent if the three sides of one triangle are equal in length to the three sides of the other, and the measures of the three angles of one are equal to the measures of the three angles of the other. Fortunately, in practical situations we do not need to establish equality of all six parts to show that two triangles are congruent. Three ways to show congruence are summarized as follows.

Congruent Triangles

Two triangles are congruent when one of the following can be shown.

1. Each of the three sides of one triangle is equal in length to a side of the other triangle (congruence by side-side-side or SSS).
2. Two sides of one triangle are equal in length to two sides of the other triangle, and the angle formed by these sides in one triangle is equal in measure to the angle formed by the corresponding sides in the other triangle (congruence by side-angle-side or SAS).
3. Two angles of one triangle are equal in measure to two angles of the other triangle, and the side between these two angles in one triangle is equal in length to the corresponding side in the other triangle (congruence by angle-side-angle or ASA).

Congruent triangles have the same size and shape. Triangles that have the same shape but may differ in size are called **similar.** Congruent triangles are always similar, but similar triangles need not be congruent. For example, the triangles in Figure A.16 are similar but clearly not congruent.

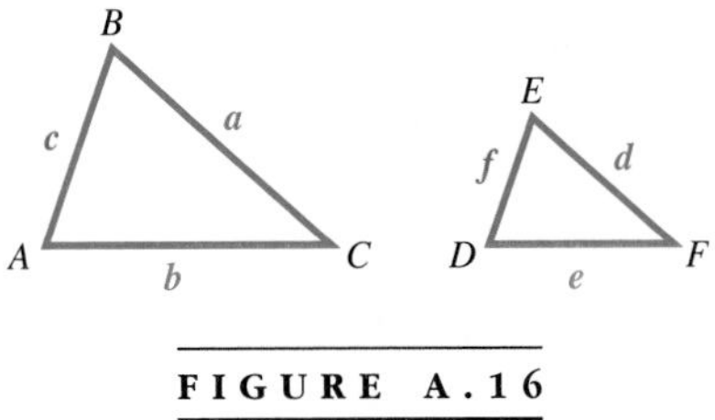

FIGURE A.16

To determine if two triangles are similar, we need compare only the angles.

Similar Triangles

Two triangles are similar when the angles of one are equal in measure to the angles of the other.

Since the sum of the angles of any triangle equals 180°, whenever two angles of one triangle are equal to two angles of a second, the remaining angles are also equal, making the triangles similar.

Similar triangles have the property that corresponding sides are proportional. In the case of the similar triangles in Figure A.16, the corresponding sides are a and d, b and e, and c and f. This means that

$$\frac{a}{d} = \frac{b}{e} = \frac{c}{f}.$$

▶ *Perimeter and area*

We now review formulas for finding the perimeter and area of six geometric figures. These formulas provide problem-solving tools for numerous applications in algebra. We begin with the **rectangle,** a four-sided figure having four right angles and parallel opposite sides of equal length. Figure A.17 shows a rectangle with **length** l and **width** w.

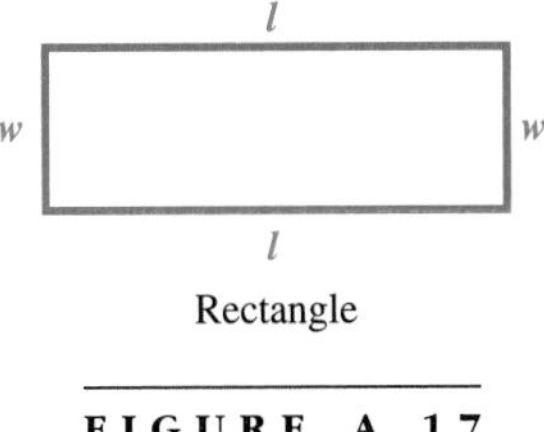

FIGURE A.17

The **perimeter** of a geometric figure is the distance around the figure. Thus, the perimeter of a rectangle is

$$\begin{aligned} l + w + l + w &= l + l + w + w \\ &= 2l + 2w. \end{aligned}$$

Perimeter of a Rectangle

The perimeter P of a rectangle is twice the length plus twice the width.

$$P = 2l + 2w$$

A special type of rectangle, called a **square,** is shown in Figure A.18. All its sides have the same length. If s is the length of a side, then the perimeter of a square is

$$\begin{aligned} P &= 2l + 2w \\ &= 2s + 2s \\ &= 4s. \end{aligned}$$

FIGURE A.18

Perimeter of a Square

The perimeter of a square is four times the length of a side.

$$P = 4s$$

In Figure A.19, the area of a square which has side 1 cm is one **square centimeter** and is written 1 cm^2. Likewise, if the side is 1 in, the area is one **square inch,** 1 in^2. Similarly, if some other unit of length is used, the area is 1 square unit, or 1 $unit^2$.

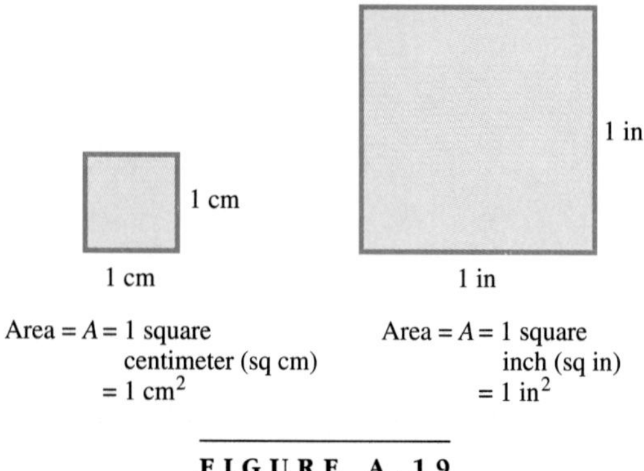

FIGURE A.19

Areas of rectangles are given in square units. The rectangle in Figure A.20 has area 10 cm^2 since 10 of the 1-cm^2 squares are contained in it. In general, this is what is meant by *area.* Notice that 10 cm^2 can be found by multiplying 5 cm by 2 cm.

$$10 \text{ cm}^2 = 5 \text{ cm} \cdot 2 \text{ cm}$$

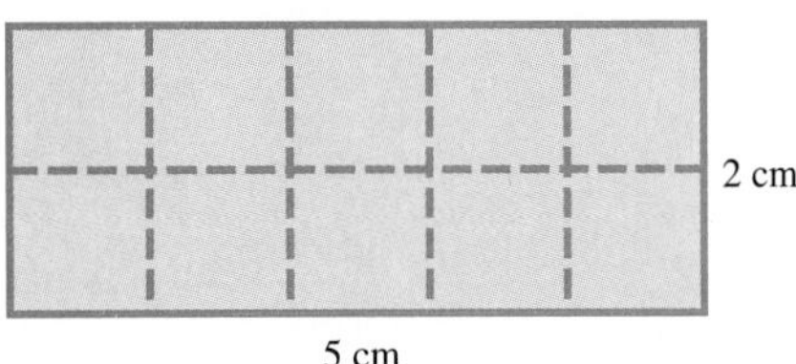

FIGURE A.20

Area of a Rectangle

The area A of a rectangle is the length times the width.

$$A = lw$$

Since all sides of a square have the same measure s, the area of a square is

$$lw = ss = s^2.$$

Area of a Square

The area of a square is the square of a side.

$$A = s^2$$

A four-sided figure whose opposite sides are parallel is a **parallelogram.** A rectangle is a special case of this type of figure. Several parallelograms are shown in Figure A.21.

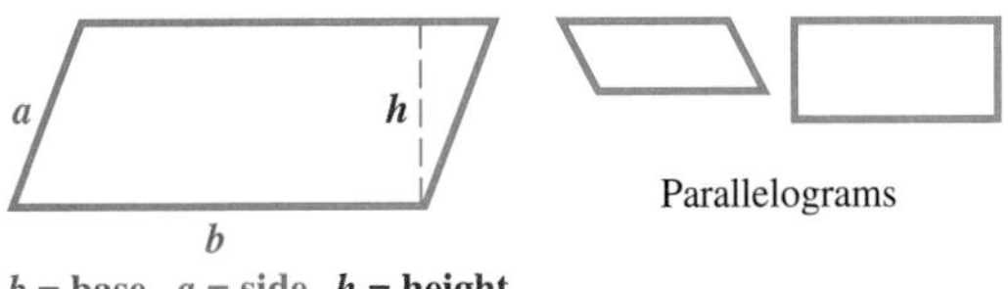

FIGURE A.21

Perimeter of a Parallelogram

The perimeter of a parallelogram with side a and base b is given by

$$P = 2a + 2b.$$

To discover how to find the area of a parallelogram, cut off one end and put it on the other end. This forms a rectangle (Figure A.22) with length $l = b$ and width $w = h$. Thus, the area of the parallelogram (which is the area of the rectangle) is the base times the height.

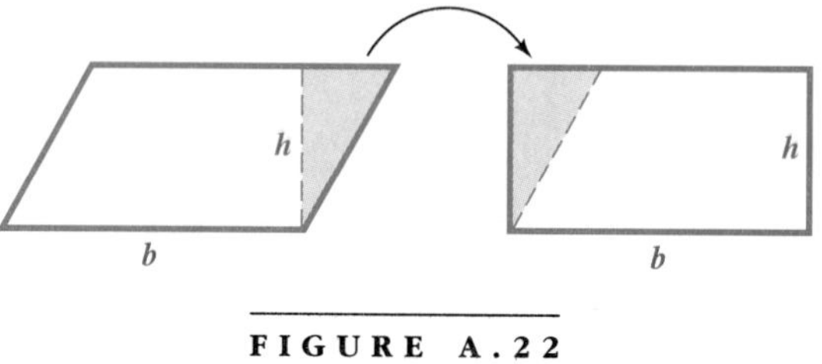

FIGURE A.22

Area of a Parallelogram

The area of a parallelogram with base b and height h is

$$A = bh.$$

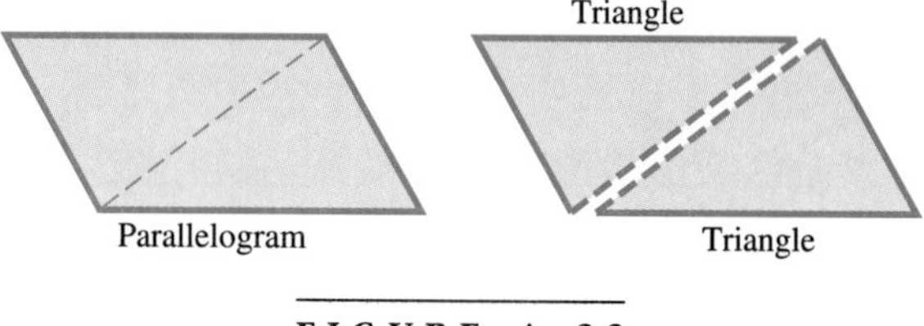

FIGURE A.23

If the parallelogram in Figure A.23 is cut along the dotted line, the area of each of the two triangles formed is one-half the area of the parallelogram. Thus, a triangle can be made into a parallelogram by adding to it a triangle of the same size. This is shown in Figure A.24, where triangle B is the same size and shape as the original triangle A. Since the heights of the triangle and the parallelogram are the same, the area of the triangle must be one-half the area of the parallelogram.

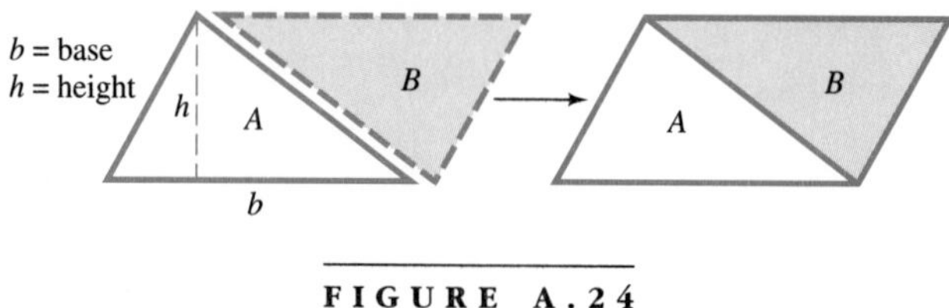

FIGURE A.24

Area of a Triangle

The area of a triangle with base b and height h is

$$A = \frac{1}{2}bh.$$

A **circle** is a figure consisting of all points located the same distance r from a fixed point O called its **center.** In Figure A.25 the segment $\overline{OA}$ or r is a **radius** of the circle. The segment $\overline{DE}$, with length d, is a **diameter** of the circle. The distance around the circle is the **circumference** C of the circle. Since the diameter is twice the radius, we can write

$$d = 2r \quad \text{and} \quad r = \frac{d}{2}.$$

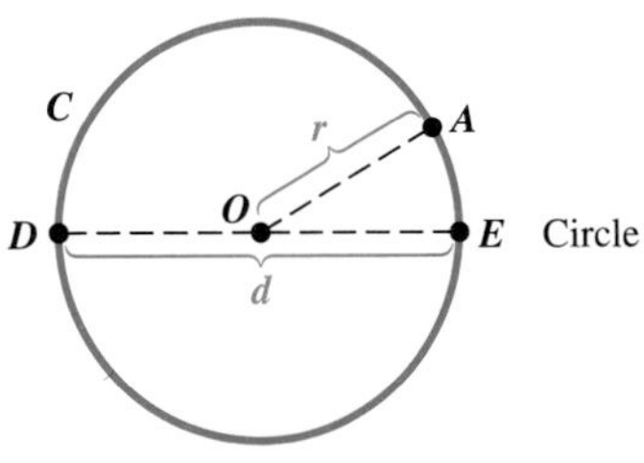

FIGURE A.25

Circumference and Area of a Circle

The circumference of a circle with diameter d and radius r is

$$C = \pi d = 2\pi r.$$

The area A of a circle is given by

$$A = \pi r^2.$$

Volume and surface area

To measure length we use units like 1 cm and 1 inch. When we talk about area we use square units like 1 cm^2 and 1 in^2. To find volume we will use cubic units like 1 cm^3 and 1 in^3.

The **volume** of a cube that is 1 cm by 1 cm by 1 cm is one **cubic centimeter** and is written 1 cm^3. Similarly, a cube that is 1 in by 1 in by 1 in is one **cubic inch,** 1 in^3. See Figure A.26. If some other unit were used for measuring, the volume of the cube would be 1 cubic unit, or 1 unit^3.

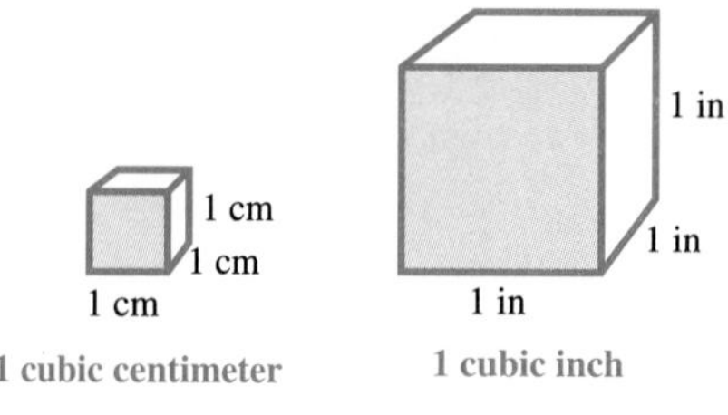

FIGURE A.26

The cubic unit of measure is used for the volume of solids. The **rectangular solid** in Figure A.27(a) has volume 20 cm^3 since there are 10 cm^3 on the bottom layer and 10 cm^3 on the top layer. In Figure A.27(b) there is one more layer (10 cm^3) than in Figure A.27(a), so the volume is 30 cm^3. To find these volumes without a diagram, multiply the area of the base by the height.

$$20 \text{ cm}^3 = \underbrace{5 \text{ cm} \cdot 2 \text{ cm}}_{\text{Area of base}} \cdot \underbrace{2 \text{ cm}}_{\text{Height}}$$

$$30 \text{ cm}^3 = \underbrace{5 \text{ cm} \cdot 2 \text{ cm}}_{\text{Area of base}} \cdot \underbrace{3 \text{ cm}}_{\text{Height}}$$

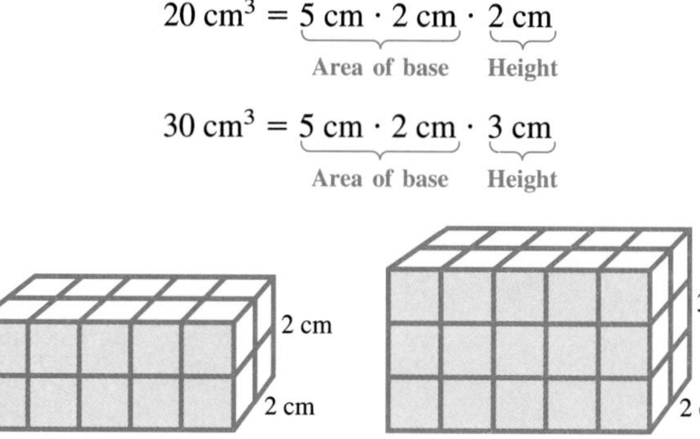

FIGURE A.27

Volume of a Rectangular Solid

The volume V of a rectangular solid is the area of the base lw times the height h.

$$V = lwh$$

A **cube** is a rectangular solid for which $l = w = h$. We talk about *edges* of the cube, and call the length of each edge e.

Volume of a Cube

The volume V of a cube is the cube of the edge.

$$V = e^3 \quad (e^3 \text{ is } e \text{ times } e \text{ times } e)$$

Another problem involving a rectangular solid is finding the area of the surface. If we can do this, we can find the amount of material needed to make a rectangular tank or the amount of paint needed to paint a building. The **surface area** of an object is the area of all its surfaces. Consider the solid in Figure A.28, which was used earlier to count cubic centimeters. Now, we count square centimeters on its surface. There are

$$(5 \text{ cm})(3 \text{ cm}) = 15 \text{ cm}^2$$

on the front face. But the back is just like the front, so there are

$$2(15 \text{ cm}^2) = 30 \text{ cm}^2 \qquad 2lh$$

on the front and back together. On the two ends there are

$$2(2 \text{ cm})(3 \text{ cm}) = 12 \text{ cm}^2. \qquad 2wh$$

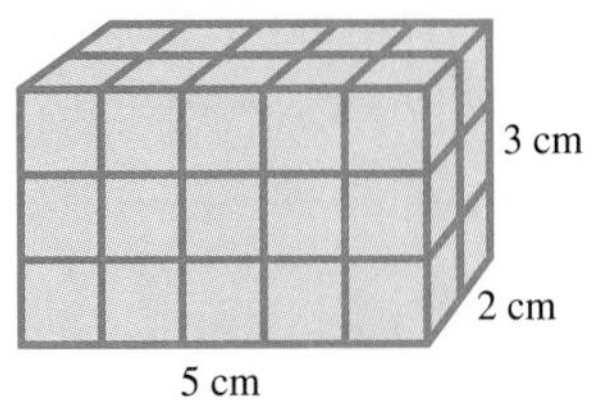

FIGURE A.28

On the bottom there are

$$(5 \text{ cm})(2 \text{ cm}) = 10 \text{ cm}^2,$$

and the same number on the top. The total of the top and bottom is

$$2(10 \text{ cm}^2) = 20 \text{ cm}^2. \qquad 2lw$$

The total surface area is the sum of all surfaces.

Area of front and back:	30 cm^2	$2lh$
Area of two ends:	12 cm^2	$2wh$
Area of bottom and top:	20 cm^2	$2lw$
Total surface area:	62 cm^2	

Surface Area of a Rectangular Solid

The total surface area A of a rectangular solid is

$$A = 2lh + 2wh + 2lw.$$

The surface area of a cube with edge e is

$$A = 6e^2.$$

A **cylinder** (see Figure A.29) is a solid with circular ends of the same radius. For example, a can of beans is in the shape of a cylinder.

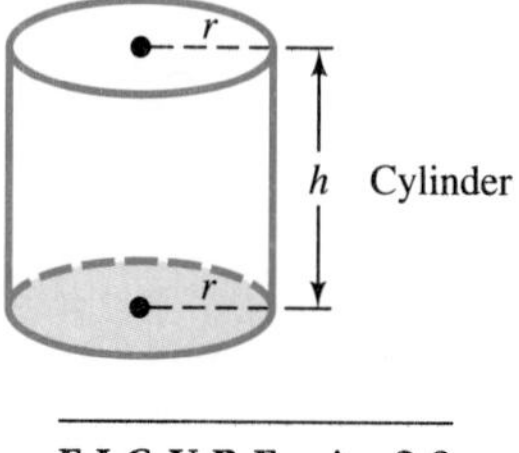

FIGURE A.29

Remember that the volume of a rectangular solid is the area of the base times the height. The same is true for a cylinder. Since the base is a circle with area πr^2, we have the following formula.

Volume of a Cylinder

The volume V of a cylinder is the area of the base, πr^2, times the height, h.

$$V = \pi r^2 h$$

To see how to find the surface area of a cylinder, consider a can without top or bottom. See Figure A.30(a). If it is cut along the seam and pressed flat, as in Figure A.30(b), a rectangle is formed. The length of the rectangle is the circumference of the circle and the width is the height. Thus, the surface area of the side of the can is $2\pi rh$. Since the area of the top of the can is πr^2, and the area of the bottom is also πr^2, we have the following.

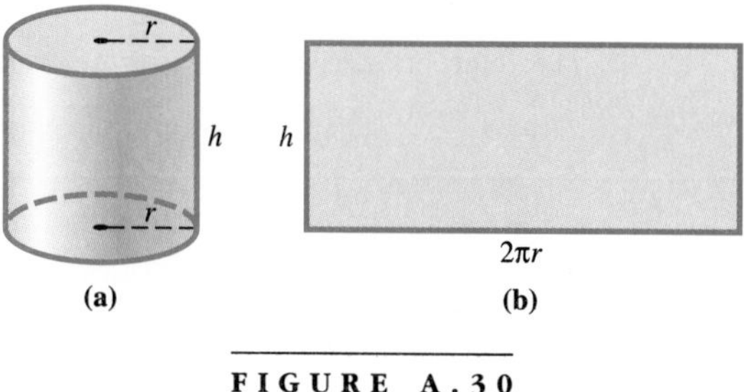

FIGURE A.30

Surface Area of a Cylinder

The surface area A of a cylinder is

$$A = 2\pi rh + 2\pi r^2.$$

A **sphere** (Figure A.31) is a solid in the shape of a ball. The radius of a sphere is the distance from its center to the surface. The diameter is twice the radius. If a sphere is cut through the center, the cut surface is a circle.

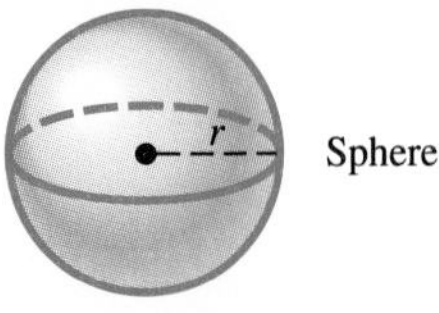

FIGURE A.31

Volume and Surface Area of a Sphere

The volume V of a sphere is

$$V = \frac{4}{3}\pi r^3.$$

The surface area A of a sphere is

$$A = 4\pi r^2.$$

APPENDIX A EXERCISES

Use the figure to answer true *or* false *in Exercises 1–10. If the statement is false, tell why.*

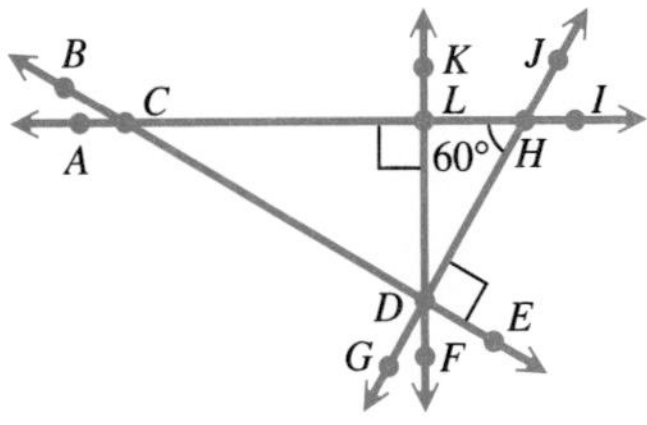

1. $\angle CDH$ is a straight angle.
2. $\angle LDB$ has measure 60°.
3. $\overleftrightarrow{FK}$ is perpendicular to $\overleftrightarrow{AC}$.
4. The measure of $\angle CDE$ is 180°.
5. $\angle LCD$ and $\angle LHD$ are supplementary.
6. $\angle BCA$ has measure 30°.
7. $\overrightarrow{CD}$ is parallel to $\overline{HI}$.
8. $\angle LHD$ is similar to $\triangle CLD$.
9. $\triangle CDH$ is congruent to $\triangle CLD$.
10. $\triangle CDH$ is a right triangle.

Find the perimeter and area of the rectangle or square in Exercises 11–13.

11. 9 cm by 20 cm
12. $6\frac{1}{2}$ ft by 4.2 ft
13. 3.2 mi by 3.2 mi

Find the area of each figure in Exercises 14–15.

14.

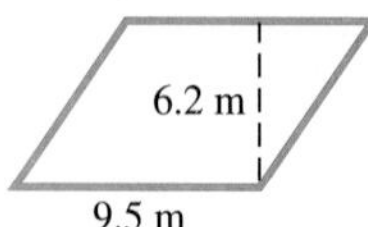

15.

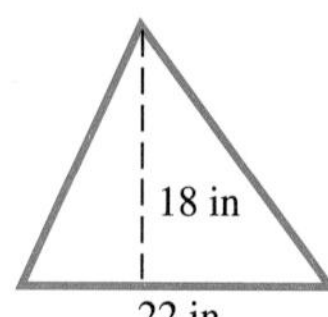

Find the perimeter of each figure in Exercises 16–17.

16.

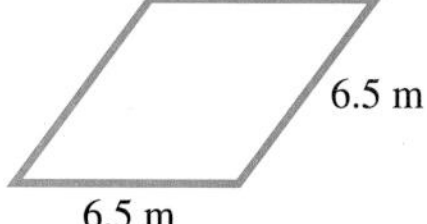

17.

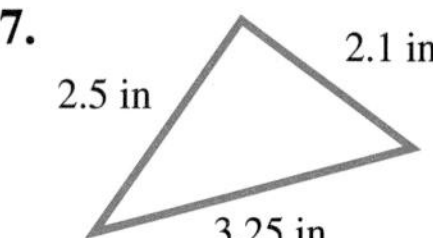

18. **CONSUMER** What will it cost to carpet the area shown if carpet costs \$22.50 per square yard?

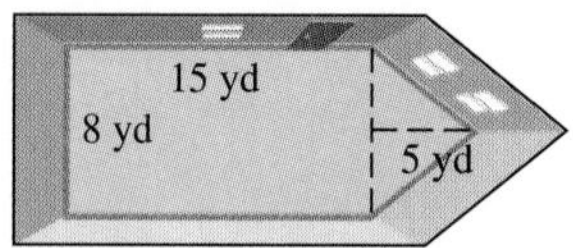

In Exercises 19–21, find the circumference and area of each circle. Use 3.14 *for* π *and round answers to the nearest tenth.*

19. $r = 6.8$ km

20. $d = 22$ in

21. $r = 8\frac{1}{2}$ ft

Find the volume of each rectangular solid in Exercises 22–23.

22. 2.2 ft by 1.5 ft by 6.4 ft

23. 52 cm by 22 cm by 8 cm

In Exercises 24–25, find the volume of each cube with the given edge.

24. 16 m

25. 8.2 in

Find the surface area of each rectangular solid in Exercises 26–27.

26. 2.2 ft by 1.5 ft by 6.4 ft

27. 53 cm by 22 cm by 8 cm

In Exercises 28–29, find the surface area of each cube with the given edge.

28. 16 m

29. 8.2 in

In Exercises 30–31, find the volume of each cylinder. Use 3.14 *for* π.

30. $r = 8$ cm, $h = 12$ cm

31. $d = 2.2$ in, $h = 1.5$ in

Find the surface area of each cylinder in Exercises 32–33.

32. $r = 8$ cm, $h = 12$ cm

33. $d = 2.2$ in, $h = 1.5$ in

Find the volume of each sphere in Exercises 34–35.

34. $r = 10$ ft

35. $d = 8.8$ m

Find the surface area of each sphere in Exercises 36–37.

36. $r = 10$ ft

37. $d = 8.8$ m

38. **CONSUMER** How many grams of water will a tank 10 cm by 8 cm by 2.5 cm hold?

39. **CONSUMER** How many square centimeters of glass did it take to make the sides and bottom of the tank in Exercise 38?

40. **CONSUMER** The area shown is to be carpeted. How much will it cost if carpet is $19.50 per square yard?

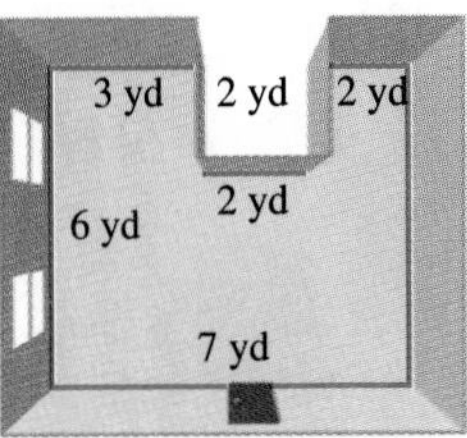

41. **BUSINESS** A 12-inch diameter pizza costs $5.00 and a 16-inch diameter pizza costs $8.00. Which pizza costs less per square inch?

42. Are the given triangles congruent? Explain.

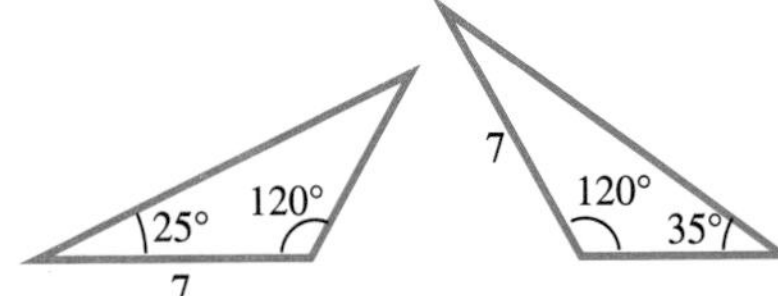

43. **BUSINESS** A spherical tank with radius 12 is to be insulated. If insulation costs $0.50 per square foot, how much will it cost to insulate the tank?

Appendix B
Introduction to Functions

Student guideposts

- ▶ *Definition of function*
- ▶ *Functional notation*
- ▶ *Evaluating functions*
- ▶ *Types of functions*
- ▶ *Vertical line test*

▶*Definition of function*

Functions are important in mathematics and are used widely in our society. In this elementary course we will discuss only the basic concepts of this subject. Even topics such as the difference between functions and more general relations will be saved for discussion in intermediate algebra.

As an example of a function, suppose walnuts sell for \$2 per pound and are packaged in 2-lb, 5-lb, and 10-lb bags. The cost y of a bag is related to the weight x of the bag by the equation

$$y = 2x.$$

For each weight x there corresponds one cost y.

$$\begin{aligned} &\text{For } x = 2, \quad y = 2(2) = 4. \\ &\text{For } x = 5, \quad y = 2(5) = 10. \\ &\text{For } x = 10, \quad y = 2(10) = 20. \end{aligned}$$

Thus the 2-lb bag sells for \$4, the 5-lb bag for \$10, and the 10-lb bag for \$20. This is an example of a *function.* The set of values of x, $\{2, 5, 10\}$, is called the *domain* of the function and the set of values of y, $\{4, 10, 20\}$, is called the *range* of the function.

A **function** is a correspondence between a first set of objects, the **domain,** and a second set of objects, the **range,** with the property that to each element in the domain there corresponds exactly one element in the range.

The functions that we will discuss can be described by an equation. For example,

$$y = 5, \quad y = x, \quad y = 2x + 3, \quad y = x^2 + 1, \quad \text{and } y = \sqrt{x}$$

all describe functions. For a given real number x, there is one and only one corresponding value for y that makes the equation true. (Remember that $\sqrt{x}$ represents the principal root only, *not* both the positive and negative roots of x.) Equations such as

$$y^2 = x \text{ and } |y| = x$$

do not describe functions since for each x in the domain there is more than one y in the range. For example, if $y^2 = x$ and $x = 9$, then there are two values of y that make the equation $y^2 = 9$ true. Those values are 3 and -3.

To completely describe a function, we must give the domain as well as the equation. In the example of the price of walnuts above we gave the equation, $y = 2x$, but by specifying 2 lb, 5 lb, and 10 lb bags we gave the domain as $\{2, 5, 10\}$. If only the equation is given, we will assume that the domain is the set of all real numbers x for which y is defined as a real number. For example, the domains of

$$y = 5, \quad y = x, \quad y = 2x + 3, \quad \text{and } y = x^2 + 1$$

are the entire set of real numbers. However, the domain of

$$y = \sqrt{x}$$

is the set of all nonnegative real numbers, since the square root of a negative number is not defined as a real number. The domain of a function is restricted in two situations:

1. Negative numbers under a radical are not permitted.
2. Numbers that make a denominator zero are not permitted.

EXAMPLE 1

Finding the Domain of a Function

Specify the domain of each function defined by the given equation.

(a) $y = \dfrac{1}{x}$ is defined for all real numbers except when $x = 0$. Thus, the domain is the set of all real numbers except 0.

(b) $y = \dfrac{1}{x+1}$ is defined for all real numbers except when $x + 1 = 0$. Thus, the domain is the set of all real numbers except -1.

(c) $y = \sqrt{x+1}$ is defined for all real numbers satisfying $x + 1 \geq 0$. Thus, the domain is the set of all real numbers $x \geq -1$.

(d) $y = \dfrac{5}{\sqrt{x^2+1}}$ is defined for all real numbers since $x^2 + 1$ is always positive, never zero. Thus, the domain is the set of all real numbers.

(e) $y = 3x^2 + x + 1$ is defined for all real numbers. Thus, the domain is the set of all real numbers. ∎

▶ *Functional notation* Sometimes we use a letter to name a function (f and g are common choices). Suppose that a function f is described by the equation

$$y = x^2 + 1.$$

We are usually interested in finding the number y that corresponds to a given number x. For example, we may ask the question:

What number y corresponds to $x = 2$ under the function f?

This question can be shortened if we use functional notation. We let

$$f(x),$$

read "f of x," denote

the number that corresponds to the number x under the function f

or

the value of the function f at x.

With this notation the question above becomes:

What is $f(2)$?

In general, $y = f(x)$. Hence in our example,

$$f(x) = x^2 + 1. \qquad (y = x^2 + 1)$$

▶ *Evaluating functions* To **evaluate** a function at a particular value of x, we substitute the value into the formula

$$f(x) = x^2 + 1.$$

It is sometimes helpful to use parentheses in the formula, as in

$$f(\quad) = (\quad)^2 + 1.$$

To compute $f(2)$, for example, we place a 2 inside both sets of parentheses and perform the necessary simplification.

$$f(2) = (2)^2 + 1 = 4 + 1 = 5$$
$$f(-3) = (-3)^2 + 1 = 9 + 1 = 10$$
$$f(0) = (0)^2 + 1 = 0 + 1 = 1$$

EXAMPLE 2

Finding Values of a Function

Consider the function g defined by

$$g(x) = 2x + 3 \qquad [g(\quad) = 2(\quad) + 3].$$

(a) $g(0) = 2(0) + 3 = 0 + 3 = 3$ — 3 corresponds to 0

(b) $g(4) = 2(4) + 3 = 8 + 3 = 11$ — 11 corresponds to 4

(c) $g(-2) = 2(-2) + 3 = -4 + 3 = -1$ $\qquad$ -1 corresponds to -2

(d) $g(a) = 2(a) + 3 = 2a + 3$ $\qquad$ $2a + 3$ corresponds to a

(e) $g(b + 1) = 2(b + 1) + 3 = 2b + 2 + 3 = 2b + 5$ ■

▶ *Types of functions*

Several functions, many of which we have already discussed, are worth special mention. Any function that can be described by an equation such as $y = c$ (c a constant), or

$$f(x) = c \qquad (y = f(x))$$

is called a **constant function.** No matter what value (in the domain) x assumes, the corresponding y value, $f(x)$, is the same constant c. Since the graph of every equation of the form $y = c$ is a horizontal line, every constant function has as its graph a straight line parallel to the x-axis.

EXAMPLE 3

Evaluating and Graphing a Constant Function

The constant function f defined by

$$f(x) = 3 \qquad [f(\ \ ) = 3]$$

has the following values and is graphed in Figure B.1.

$f(0) = 3$

$f(1) = 3$

$f(2) = 3$

$f(-1) = 3$

$f(a + 1) = 3$

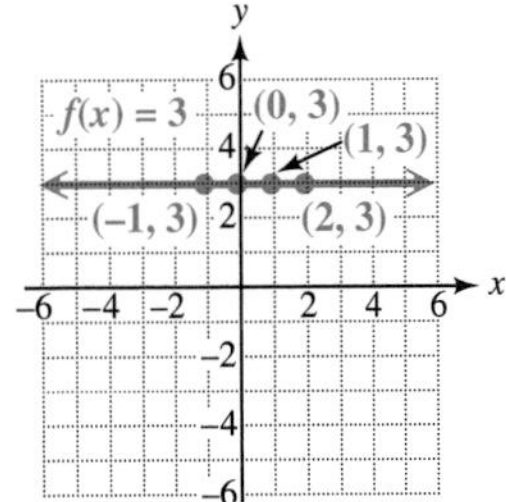

FIGURE B.1

The notation $f(0) = 3$ means that when $x = 0$ then $y = 3$ or that the point $(0, 3)$ is on the graph of $f(x) = 3$. Likewise the points $(1, 3)$, $(2, 3)$, and $(-1, 3)$ are on the graph, and the graph is the horizontal line in Figure B.1. ■

Any function that can be described by an equation of the form

$$f(x) = mx + b \qquad m \text{ and } b \text{ constants}$$

is a **linear function.** Recall that every equation of the form $y = mx + b$ has as its graph a straight line (hence the term *linear* function). Also, if $m = 0$, the linear function $f(x) = mx + b$ becomes $f(x) = b$, a constant function that still has as its graph a straight line. Thus, a constant function is actually a special type of linear function.

EXAMPLE 4

Evaluating and Graphing a Linear Function

The linear function f defined by

$$f(x) = 2x + 1 \qquad [f(\ \ ) = 2(\ \ ) + 1]$$

has the following values.

$$f(0) = 2(0) + 1 = 1$$
$$f(1) = 2(1) + 1 = 3$$
$$f(2) = 2(2) + 1 = 5$$
$$f(-1) = 2(-1) + 1 = -1$$
$$f(a + 1) = 2(a + 1) + 1 = 2a + 2 + 1$$
$$= 2a + 3$$

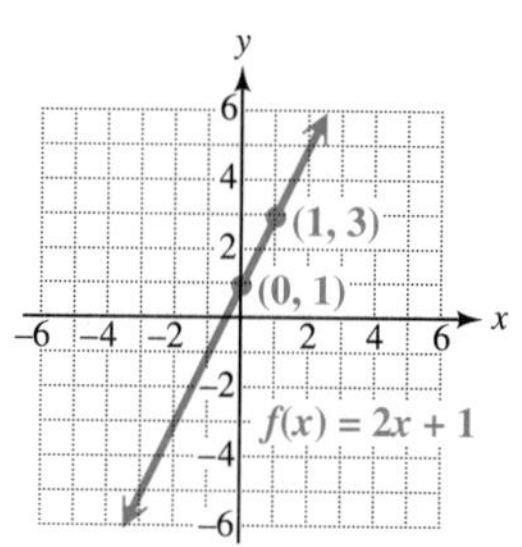

FIGURE B.2

When $x = 0, f(x) = 1$, and when $x = 1, f(x) = 3$, giving us the two points (0, 1) and (1, 3) on the graph of $f(x) = 2x + 1$. See Figure B.2. ■

A special linear function is the **identity function**

$$f(x) = x.$$

This function identifies a number with itself. For example, $f(4) = 4, f(100) = 100$, and $f(-1) = -1$. The identity function is graphed in Figure B.3.

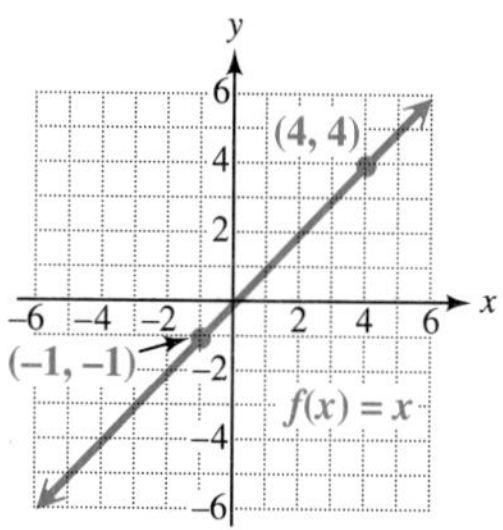

FIGURE B.3

Any function that can be described by an equation of the form

$$f(x) = ax^2 + bx + c \qquad (a, b, c \text{ constants}, a \neq 0)$$

is a **quadratic function.** If a were zero, we would lose the squared term and have a linear function.

EXAMPLE 5 **Evaluating and Graphing a Quadratic Function**

The quadratic function f defined by

$$f(x) = 2x^2 - 4x - 3 \quad [f(\ \ ) = 2(\ \ )^2 - 4(\ \ ) - 3]$$

has the following values.

$$
\begin{aligned}
f(0) &= 2(0)^2 - 4(0) - 3 = 2(0) - 0 - 3 = 0 - 0 - 3 = -3\\
f(1) &= 2(1)^2 - 4(1) - 3 = 2(1) - 4 - 3 = 2 - 4 - 3 = -5\\
f(-1) &= 2(-1)^2 - 4(-1) - 3 = 2(1) + 4 - 3 = 2 + 4 - 3 = 3\\
f(2) &= 2(2)^2 - 4(2) - 3 = 2(4) - 8 - 3 = 8 - 8 - 3 = -3\\
f(3) &= 2(3)^2 - 4(3) - 3 = 2(9) - 12 - 3 = 18 - 12 - 3 = 3\\
f(-3) &= 2(-3)^2 - 4(-3) - 3 = 2(9) + 12 - 3 = 18 + 12 - 3 = 27\\
f(a) &= 2(a)^2 - 4(a) - 3 = 2a^2 - 4a - 3\\
f(a + 1) &= 2(a + 1)^2 - 4(a + 1) - 3 = 2(a^2 + 2a + 1) - 4a - 4 - 3\\
&= 2a^2 + 4a + 2 - 4a - 4 - 3 = 2a^2 - 5
\end{aligned}
$$

To graph this function, we refer to Section 10.6 to find the x-coordinate of the vertex as

$$x = -\frac{b}{2a} = -\frac{-4}{2(2)} = 1.$$

Then the y-coordinate of the vertex is $f(1) = -5$ which we calculated above. Also from our calculations, we have as points on the graph $(-1, 3)$, $(0, -3)$, $(2, -3)$, and $(3, 3)$. The graph is given in Figure B.4. ■

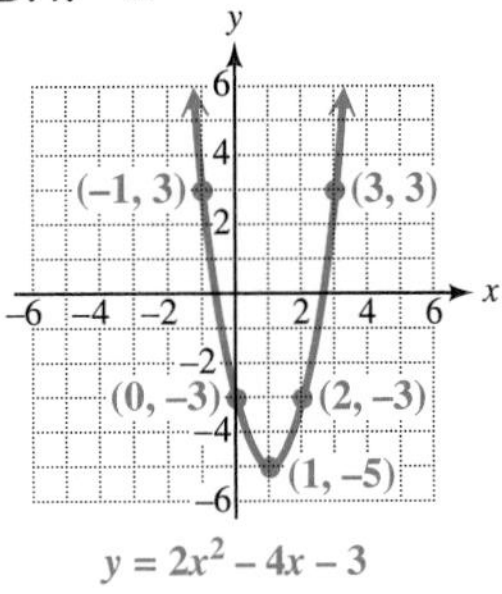

FIGURE B.4

EXAMPLE 6 **Working with an Application of Functions**

The height h of an object dropped from a height of 256 feet is given as a function of time t by $h(t) = -16t^2 + 256$. Find the height of the object after 2 seconds and after 4 seconds.

To find the height 2 seconds after the object is dropped we must find $h(2)$.

$$
\begin{aligned}
h(t) &= -16t^2 + 256\\
h(2) &= -16(2)^2 + 256\\
&= -16(4) + 256\\
&= -64 + 256 = 192
\end{aligned}
$$

The object is 192 feet above ground level after 2 seconds.

Find $h(4)$ to determine the height after 4 seconds.

$$\begin{aligned} h(4) &= -16(4)^2 + 256 \\ &= -16(16) + 256 \\ &= -256 + 256 = 0 \end{aligned}$$

The object reaches the ground in 4 seconds. ■

▶ *Vertical line test* From the definition of function we can conclude that the graph of a function will have the property that for any x value there will be exactly one y value on the graph. This is best described in terms of the following test.

Vertical Line Test

If each vertical line that can be drawn through a graph intersects it in no more than one point, then it is the graph of a function.

Notice that if any vertical line is drawn in Figures B.1–4, it will intersect the graph in at most one point. Thus, the graphs of these functions satisfy the conditions of the vertical line test. On the other hand, the graph in Figure B.5 is the graph of $y^2 = x$, which is not a function, and the vertical line that is drawn intersects it in more than one point.

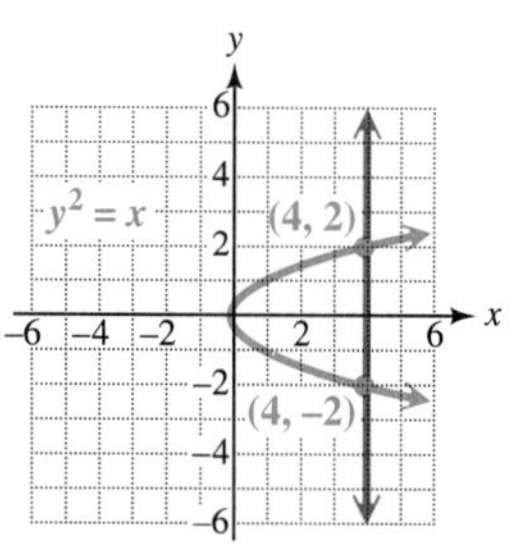

FIGURE B.5

APPENDIX B EXERCISES

Specify the domain of each function defined by the equation in Exercises 1–6.

1. $y = 3x + 1$ **2.** $y = \sqrt{x - 2}$ **3.** $y = \dfrac{5}{x + 5}$

4. $y = \sqrt{4 - x}$ **5.** $y = \dfrac{x}{x - 1}$ **6.** $y = \dfrac{1}{\sqrt{x^2 + 5}}$

For each function in Exercises 7–9, evaluate: **(a)** $f(0)$ **(b)** $f(1)$ **(c)** $f(2)$ **(d)** $f(-3)$ **(e)** $f(b)$ **(f)** $f(-a)$.

7. $f(x) = 2x + 5$ **8.** $f(x) = 2x^3 - 1$ **9.** $f(x) = -7$

For each function in Exercises 10–12, evaluate: **(a)** $g(0)$ **(b)** $g(-1)$ **(c)** $g(-2)$ **(d)** $g(3)$ **(e)** $g(a)$ **(f)** $g(b-1)$

10. $g(x) = -3x + 1$ **11.** $g(x) = 4x^2 - 3x + 1$ **12.** $g(x) = -x$

State whether each function in Exercises 13–15 is a constant, linear, or quadratic function.

13. $f(x) = 1 - x$ **14.** $f(x) = -2$ **15.** $f(x) = 3x^2 - 2x + 1$

16. **SALES** Write an equation for the cost function f described by selling x books at \$11.95 per book. How much do 15 books cost?

17. **TRAVEL** The distance that a car travels at 55 mph can be found by multiplying the total number of hours driven x by the hourly rate. Express this function relationship using the letter g, and use it to find the distance traveled in 8 hours.

Use the vertical line test in Exercises 18–20 to determine if the graph is the graph of a function.

18.

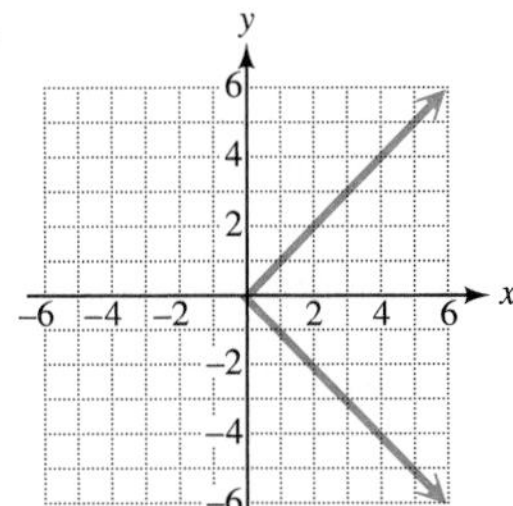

19.

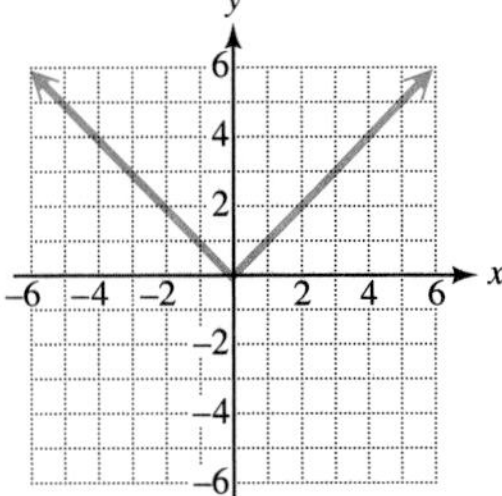

20.

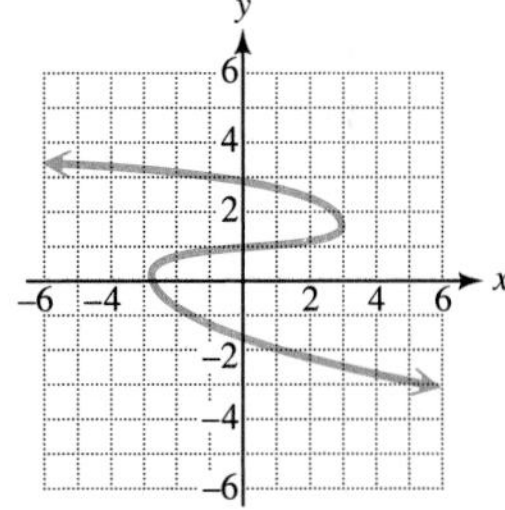

Use $f(x) = 5x + 2$ *and* $g(x) = -3x + 1$ *to find the function values in Exercises 21–26. For these exercises use the following definitions:* $(f + g)(x) = f(x) + g(x)$, $(f - g)(x) = f(x) - g(x)$, $fg(x) = f(x)g(x)$, $\frac{f}{g}(x) = \frac{f(x)}{g(x)}$, *and* $f(g(x))$ *is* f *evaluated at* $g(x)$.

21. $(f + g)(4)$ **22.** $(f - g)(-4)$ **23.** $fg(3)$

24. $\frac{f}{g}(-1)$ **25.** $f(g(2))$ **26.** $g(f(2))$

FINAL REVIEW EXERCISES

CHAPTER 1

1. Reduce $\frac{242}{220}$ to lowest terms.
2. Bill received 28 of the 42 votes cast. What fractional part of the votes did he receive? Reduce the fraction to lowest terms.

Perform the indicated operations in Exercises 3–10.

3. $\frac{5}{11} \cdot \frac{33}{35}$
4. $\frac{20}{39} \div \frac{6}{13}$
5. $\frac{2}{15} + \frac{8}{3}$
6. $\frac{11}{14} - \frac{3}{4}$
7. $29.705 + 3.01$
8. $17.6 - 9.72$
9. $(0.0049)(52.8)$
10. $2.86 \div 0.052$
11. Change $\frac{43}{18}$ to a mixed number.
12. Change $8\frac{3}{13}$ to an improper fraction.
13. **RETAIL** There are 475 light bulbs in a shipment. If $\frac{1}{25}$ of them are defective, how many are defective?
14. **CONSUMER** Harry bought $2\frac{3}{8}$ pounds of one candy and $3\frac{11}{16}$ pounds of another. What total weight of candy did he buy?
15. Convert $\frac{3}{8}$ to a percent.
16. Convert 2.72 to a fraction.
17. **TAXES** The tax rate in Upstate, NY, is 6%. What is the tax on a $38.50 purchase?
18. **CHEMISTRY** There is 0.05% water in 200 ml of solution. How many milliliters of water are in the solution?

CHAPTER 2

19. Evaluate $x^2 + 4(x - y)$ for $x = 5$ and $y = 3$.
20. **INVESTMENT** If $A = P(1 + r)^t$, find A when P is $2000, the interest is 8% compounded annually, and t is 2 years.
21. Find the reciprocal of $-\frac{3}{4}$.
22. Find $|-8|$.

Place the correct symbol, =, <, or >, between the pairs of numbers in Exercises 23–24.

23. $-8 \quad -10$
24. $\frac{8}{31} \quad \frac{4}{17}$

Perform the indicated operations in Exercises 25–28.

25. $-4 - (-16)$
26. $14 + (-24)$
27. $\left(-\frac{5}{9}\right) \cdot \left(-\frac{3}{20}\right)$
28. $(7.5) \div (-2.5)$

Evaluate each expression in Exercises 29–30.

29. $2 \cdot 4 + (8 - 12) - 2(3 - 1)$
30. $-8 - [-(-8)]$

Factor each expression in Exercises 31–32.

31. $2y + 12$
32. $-14x - 21$

Collect like terms in Exercises 33–34.

33. $-8a + 3b - 4a - 5 - b$

34. $7y - (2y - 5) + 3$

35. Evaluate $2u^2 - v^2$ when $u = -2$ and $v = 4$.

36. Write $-5x^4$ without exponents.

37. Evaluate. $-\sqrt{144}$

38. Evaluate. $\sqrt{\frac{12}{75}}$

CHAPTER 3

Solve each equation or applied problem in Exercises 39–52.

39. $x + 10 = 19$

40. $16x = 4$

41. $x - \frac{5}{3} = \frac{7}{3}$

42. $-5.5x = 33$

43. $\frac{2}{3}x = 26$

44. $\frac{x}{\frac{3}{4}} = 12$

45. $4x + 8 = 7x - 4$

46. $-3x - 2 = -5x + 9$

47. $5(x + 2) - 2(x - 10) = 0$

48. $3b - 2a = 6c + a$ for a

49. **SALARY** Randee Wire got a 12% raise and now makes \$34,720. What was her salary before the raise?

50. **RETAIL** A suit is put on sale at a 20% discount. If the original price was \$160, what is the sale price?

51. **GEOMETRY** The area of a triangle is 85 in^2 and the base is 10 inches. What is the height?

52. **TRAVEL** Two trains leave Portland, one traveling north and the other south. If one is traveling 30 mph faster than the other, how fast is each traveling if they are 360 miles apart after 3 hours?

In Exercises 53–54, graph on the number line.

53. $3x + 8 = 5$

54. $4(x - 2) \geq 4 - (x - 3)$

Solve each inequality in Exercises 55–56.

55. $2x - (3x - 2) < 9x - 8$

56. $-2 \leq 3x + 4 < 10$

CHAPTER 4

57. The point with coordinates $(-3, -5)$ is located in which quadrant?

58. Complete the ordered pair (5,) so that it is a solution to $2x + 3y = 10$.

59. **PRODUCTION** Cost, c, is related to number of items produced, n, by $c = 100n + 50$. Find c when n is 18.

60. True or false: $5 + 3y = 2x$ is a linear equation.

61. Find the slope of the line through the points $(7, -1)$ and $(2, -5)$. Determine the standard form of the equation of the line.

62. Write $3x - 4y = 12$ in slope-intercept form and give the slope and the y-intercept.

63. Find the standard form of the equation of the line with slope $-\frac{4}{5}$ and y-intercept $(0, 7)$.

64. If l_1 passes through $(1, 2)$ and $(-1, 6)$ and l_2 passes through $(0, -3)$ and $(6, 0)$, are the lines parallel, perpendicular, or neither?

In Exercises 65–66, graph in a rectangular coordinate system.

65. $y = -3x + 6$

66. $2x - 3y + 6 \le 0$

CHAPTER 5

67. Without graphing, tell whether the graphs are intersecting, parallel, or coinciding.
$3x + 4y = 7$
$9x + 12y = 5$

68. If the lines in a system of equations are intersecting, the system has ______ solution(s).

Solve each system or applied problem in Exercises 69–76.

69. $3x - y = -2$
$-5x + 2y = 5$

70. $2x + 3y = 8$
$4x + 7y = 16$

71. $2x - 3y = 12$
$3x + 9 = 0$

72. $4x - 1 = 0$
$3y + 2 = 0$

73. **RECREATION** A boat travels 40 miles upstream in 4 hours and returns to the starting point in 2 hours. What is the speed of the stream?

74. **INVESTMENT** Pam Johnson earned \$1180 in one year on an investment of \$12,000. Part of the money was invested at 9% and part at 11% simple interest. How much was invested at 11%?

75. **NUMBER** Twice one number plus a second is 13. The first minus the second is 5. Find the numbers.

76. **RETAIL** A candy shop has one candy that sells for 95¢ per lb and a second that sells for 65¢ per lb. How much of each should be used to make 60 lb of candy selling for 75¢ per lb?

CHAPTER 6

In Exercises 77–80, simplify and write without negative exponents.

77. $3x^2x^3$

78. $\frac{y^6}{y^2}$

79. $(-3a^3)^2$

80. a^{-2}

81. Write 36,200,000 in scientific notation.

82. Write 7.2×10^{-4} using standard notation.

Evaluate using scientific notation in Exercises 83–84.

83. $(0.0000021)(3{,}000{,}000)$

84. $\frac{0.000055}{11{,}000{,}000}$

85. Is $-8x^3y$ a monomial, binomial, or trinomial?

86. Give the degree of $3x^4 - 6x^5 + 5x - 2$.

87. Write in descending order. $3x - 4x^3 - 6x^5 + 4x^2 + x^7$

88. **RETAIL** Profit in dollars when x coats are sold is given by $2x^2 - 5$. What is the profit when 6 coats are sold?

Add the polynomials in Exercises 89–90.

89. $(-5a + 2) + (6a - 1)$

90. $(2x^2y^2 - 3xy + 2) + (-6x^2y^2 - xy - 5)$

Subtract the polynomials in Exercises 91–94.

91. $(9y - 3) - (-2y + 5)$

92. $(3x^2 - 2x + 5) - (4x^2 + 9x - 6)$

93. $(7a - 6) - (-a + 1) - (3a - 5)$

94. $(6x^2y - 4xy) - (4xy^2 + 2xy) - (2x^2y + xy^2)$

Multiply the polynomials in Exercises 95–100.

95. $-3a^2(4a - 2)$
96. $(3x + 4y)(9x - 2y)$
97. $(a - 2)(3a^2 + 2a - 5)$
98. $(5x + 7)^2$
99. $(2x + 5y)(2x - 5y)$
100. $(x^2 - 2)^2$

Divide the polynomials in Exercises 101–102.

101. $\dfrac{6y^9 - 2y^6 + 10y^3}{2y^2}$
102. $(2x^3 - 27x + 20) \div (x + 4)$

CHAPTER 7

In Exercises 103–104, factor by removing the greatest common factor.

103. $24x - 16$
104. $6x^3y^2 - 3x^2y^3 + 9x^2y^2$

In Exercises 105–106, factor by grouping.

105. $3x^3 + 2x^2 + 6x + 4$
106. $a^2b^2 - a^2 + 3b^2 - 3$

Factor in Exercises 107–112.

107. $x^2 + 13x + 40$
108. $y^2 - 18y + 81$
109. $6x^2 - 24y^2$
110. $x^2 + xy - 20y^2$
111. $2x^2 - 9x - 5$
112. $9x^2 + 12xy + 4y^2$

Solve each equation or applied problem in Exercises 113–116.

113. $(2x - 1)(x + 8) = 0$
114. $x^2 - 8x - 20 = 0$

115. **GEOMETRY** The length of a rectangle is four times the width. If the area is 144 cm^2, find the dimensions.

116. **RETAIL** Profit is given by $P = n^2 - 2n + 3$, where n is the number of items sold. How many items were sold when the profit was \$38?

CHAPTER 8

117. What values of the variable must be excluded in $\dfrac{x}{(x + 1)(x - 8)}$?

118. Reduce $\dfrac{a^2 - b^2}{(a - b)^2}$ to lowest terms.

Perform the indicated operations in Exercises 119–122.

119. $\dfrac{x^2 - x - 2}{x^2 - 2x - 3} \cdot \dfrac{x^2 - 3x}{x + 2}$
120. $\dfrac{y^2 - 1}{y^2 + 2y} \div \dfrac{y - 1}{y + 2}$

121. $\dfrac{5}{y^2 - 4y + 3} + \dfrac{7}{y^2 + y - 2}$
122. $\dfrac{x + 6}{x^2 - 4} - \dfrac{x}{x - 2}$

123. Simplify. $\dfrac{x - \dfrac{1}{x}}{1 - \dfrac{1}{x}}$
124. Solve. $\dfrac{1}{y + 2} + \dfrac{1}{y - 2} = \dfrac{1}{y^2 - 4}$

125. **TRAVEL** A car goes 205 miles on 15 gallons of gasoline. How many miles can the car go on 75 gallons of gasoline?

126. **NUMBER** The denominator of a fraction is 5 more than the numerator. If 2 is added to both the numerator and the denominator, the result is $\frac{1}{2}$. Find the fraction.

127. **RETAIL** The cost c of nuts varies directly as the weight w of the nuts. If 12 lb of nuts cost \$30, how much would 80 lb cost?

128. **PHYSICS** The volume V of a gas varies inversely as the pressure P. If V is 16 in^3 when the pressure is 3 pounds per square inch (psi), what is the volume when $P = 12$ psi?

CHAPTER 9

In Exercises 129–134, evaluate. Assume all variables and expressions are nonnegative.

129. $\sqrt{(-16)^2}$ **130.** $\pm\sqrt{169}$ **131.** $\sqrt{81x^2}$

132. $5\sqrt{8x^2y^2}$ **133.** $\sqrt{\dfrac{27x^2}{4y^2}}$ **134.** $\sqrt{\dfrac{49y^2}{x}}$

Perform the indicated operations and simplify in Exercises 135–142.

135. $5\sqrt{15}\sqrt{45}$ **136.** $\dfrac{\sqrt{24x^3y}}{\sqrt{3xy}}$ **137.** $\sqrt{98} + \sqrt{50}$

138. $3\sqrt{45} - 2\sqrt{80} + \sqrt{125}$ **139.** $\sqrt{28x} + 3\sqrt{7x} - 2\sqrt{63x}$ **140.** $\sqrt{3} - \dfrac{2}{\sqrt{3}}$

141. $(\sqrt{7} - 2\sqrt{2})(\sqrt{7} + \sqrt{2})$ **142.** $\dfrac{\sqrt{6}}{\sqrt{3} - \sqrt{2}}$

Solve each equation or applied problem in Exercises 143–148.

143. $\sqrt{2x-1} - \sqrt{3x-7} = 0$ **144.** $\sqrt{x^2+3} + 1 - x = 0$

145. **GEOMETRY** One side of a rectangle is 12 m long and the diagonal is 13 m. Find the length of the other side.

146. **NUMBER** Three times the principal square root of 5 more than a number is equal to 15. Find the number.

147. In a $30° - 60°$ right triangle, a is the side opposite the 30° angle. If $a = 22$, find b and c.

148. In a $45° - 45°$ right triangle, $b = 45$ cm. Find a and c.

In Exercises 149–154, perform the indicated operations and simplify. Rationalize denominators.

149. $\sqrt[3]{625}$ **150.** $\sqrt[4]{9x^3}\sqrt[4]{27x^2}$ **151.** $\sqrt[3]{\dfrac{8}{x^2}}$

152. $4a\sqrt[4]{a} - 3\sqrt[4]{a^5}$ **153.** $32^{2/5}$ **154.** $(-8)^{-2/3}$

CHAPTER 10

Solve each quadratic equation in Exercises 155–162.

155. $x^2 - 12x + 35 = 0$ **156.** $x^2 + 14x + 49 = 0$ **157.** $2x^2 - 11x + 5 = 0$

158. $x^2 - 3x - 1 = 0$ **159.** $3y^2 - 5 = y(y + 3)$ **160.** $(z - 2)(z + 2) = 5z$

161. $\sqrt{7 - 2x} = x - 2$ **162.** $\dfrac{x+2}{x} = \dfrac{2}{x-1}$

163. **GEOMETRY** The number of square inches in a square is 3 less than the perimeter of the square. Find the length of a side.

164. **WORK** Al can do a job in 3 hours less time than Joe. Together they can do the job in 2 hours. How long would it take each to do the job?

165. Graph $y = -x^2 + 1$.

Solve each quadratic equation in Exercises 166–168.

166. $x^2 + 64 = 0$

167. $x^2 - 2x + 2 = 0$

168. $x^2 + 4x + 5 = 0$

Answers to Selected Exercises

FOR THE STUDENT To help you study and understand the course material, a *Student's Solutions Manual* is available from your college bookstore. This book provides complete, step-by-step solutions to all the Exercises in the text and to all Chapter Review and Chapter Test exercises.

CHAPTER 1 PREALGEBRA

1.1 Exercises (PAGE 6)

1. true **2.** true **3.** true **4.** true **5.** true **6.** false (dividing) **7.** **(a)** $\frac{1}{5}$, $\frac{3}{8}$, and $\frac{13}{15}$ **(b)** $\frac{9}{9}$, $\frac{10}{2}$, $\frac{6}{6}$, and $\frac{8}{1}$ *Answers to 8–10 will vary; some possibilities are given.* **8.** $\frac{4}{10}$, $\frac{6}{15}$, $\frac{8}{20}$ **9.** $\frac{4}{1}$, $\frac{8}{2}$, $\frac{12}{3}$ **10.** $\frac{210}{4}$, $\frac{315}{6}$, $\frac{420}{8}$ **11.** 2, 3, 5, 7, 11, 13, 17, 19 **12.** $2 \cdot 5 \cdot 7$ **13.** 47 (prime) **14.** $2 \cdot 3 \cdot 5 \cdot 7 \cdot 7$ **15.** $\frac{1}{4}$ **16.** $\frac{5}{6}$ **17.** $\frac{12}{35}$ (already reduced to lowest terms) **18.** $\frac{9}{2}$ **19.** 1 **20.** $\frac{20}{27}$ **21.** $\frac{28}{32}$ **22.** $\frac{36}{30}$ **23.** 9 **24.** 20 **25.** 80 **26.** 14 **27.** 55 **28.** 6 **29.** **(a)** $\frac{12}{21}$, or $\frac{4}{7}$ when reduced to lowest terms **(b)** $\frac{9}{21}$, or $\frac{3}{7}$ **30.** **(a)** $\frac{55}{150}$, or $\frac{11}{30}$ when reduced **(b)** $\frac{95}{150}$, or $\frac{19}{30}$ when reduced

1.2 Exercises (PAGE 17)

1. 0 **2.** undefined **3.** undefined **4.** $\frac{2}{5}$ **5.** $\frac{6}{5}$ **6.** $\frac{1}{2}$ **7.** $\frac{4}{3}$ **8.** $\frac{10}{3}$ **9.** $\frac{25}{12}$ **10.** 231 **11.** 2 **12.** 450 **13.** $\frac{23}{5}$ **14.** $\frac{58}{15}$ **15.** $\frac{19}{12}$ **16.** $2\frac{7}{8}$ **17.** $33\frac{3}{4}$ **18.** $12\frac{10}{11}$ **19.** $\frac{22}{5}$ **20.** $\frac{200}{3}$ **21.** $\frac{106}{11}$ **22.** $\frac{13}{2}$ **23.** $2\frac{7}{12}$ **24.** $6\frac{2}{15}$ **25.** $\frac{19}{40}$ **26.** $\frac{1}{5}$ **27.** $\frac{10}{21}$ **28.** 30 **29.** $16\frac{2}{3}$ gallons **30.** $6\frac{8}{15}$ mi **31.** $1\frac{13}{24}$ gallons **32.** 200 lb **33.** 59° **34.** **(a)** $\frac{21}{24}$ **(b)** $\frac{63}{72}$ **35.** $\frac{3}{25}$

1.3 Exercises (PAGE 24)

1. $3 + \frac{4}{10} + \frac{7}{100}$ **2.** $100 + 7 + \frac{2}{10} + \frac{8}{100}$ **3.** $200 + 3 + \frac{5}{1000}$ **4.** 427.3 **5.** 503.208 **6.** 4030.025 **7.** 32.47 **8.** 424.18 **9.** 24.3041 **10.** 2.9003 **11.** 291.966 **12.** 47.1997 **13.** 7.182 **14.** 47.44584 **15.** 0.000008 **16.** 5531 **17.** 0.875 **18.** 0.111 . . . **19.** 24,135.7 **20.** 16.47 minutes **21.** \$15.85 **22.** 4.6° **23.** \$258.72 **24.** 36 months **25.** $\frac{23}{36}$ **26.** $\frac{7}{36}$ **27.** $\frac{4}{9}$ **28.** $\frac{1}{9}$ **29.** $8\frac{7}{16}$ mi **30.** $8\frac{8}{9}$ meters

1.4 Exercises (PAGE 32)

1. 0.125 **2.** $0.\overline{5}$ **3.** $2.\overline{142857}$ **4.** $\frac{12}{25}$ **5.** $\frac{3207}{1000}$ **6.** $\frac{25{,}001}{1000}$ **7.** 0.005 **8.** 2 **9.** 0.0825 **10.** 1 **11.** $\frac{11}{300}$ **12.** 10 **13.** 0.5% **14.** $62.\overline{3}$% or $62\frac{1}{3}$% **15.** 110% **16.** 50% **17.** 120% **18.** $1666\frac{2}{3}$% **19.** $\frac{3}{4}$, 75% **20.** $\frac{1}{8}$, 12.5% **21.** 2750 votes **22.** 180 in **23.** $30 + 2 + \frac{5}{10} + \frac{1}{100}$ **24.** 404.246 **25.** 3.2095 **26.** 0.001484 **27.** 21.5 **28.** \$52.82

Chapter 1 Review Exercises (PAGE 35)

1. $2 \cdot 5 \cdot 7 \cdot 7$ **2.** $\frac{2}{7}$ **3.** $\frac{12}{44}$ **4.** 27 **5.** $\frac{1}{2}$ **6.** $\frac{3}{2}$ **7.** $\frac{41}{36}$ **8.** $\frac{5}{18}$ **9.** $54\frac{3}{4}$ **10.** $\frac{37}{7}$ **11.** $1\frac{3}{4}$ mi **12.** $7\frac{7}{8}$ yd
13. $20 + 9 + \frac{3}{10} + \frac{4}{100}$ **14.** 2004.402 **15.** 339.667 **16.** 295.191 **17.** 0.0262 **18.** 7230 **19.** 0.375 **20.** $\frac{5447}{200}$
21. 0.352 **22.** $133\frac{1}{3}\%$ **23.** 1089 **24.** $\frac{3}{4}$ **25.** \$350.66 **26.** 0 **27.** 4.699 **28.** $1\frac{23}{30}$ **29.** 1.124864 **30.** $0.\overline{27}$
31. 2500% **32.** $3\frac{4}{9}$ **33.** $\frac{37}{20}$ **34.** $\frac{158}{27}$ **35.** 157 **36.** $\frac{5}{12}$

Chapter 1 Test (PAGE 37)

1. $\frac{23}{25}$ **2.** $\frac{24}{75}$ **3.** 24 **4.** $\frac{11}{15}$ **5.** $\frac{3}{11}$ **6.** $\frac{9}{4}$ **7.** $\frac{29}{18}$ **8.** $\frac{1}{24}$ **9.** $5\frac{3}{5}$ **10.** $\frac{44}{15}$ **11.** 432 **12.** $4\frac{7}{10}$ liters
13. 17.117 **14.** 18.859 **15.** 2.1252 **16.** 44 **17.** 20% **18.** $\frac{63}{20}$ **19.** 235% **20.** \$1.08 **21.** $\frac{2}{45}$; $4.\overline{4}\%$
22. Because $11\frac{1}{7}$ feet is probably easier to understand than $\frac{78}{7}$ feet.

Chapter 1 Answers to Selected Enrichment Exercises

[1.1] **3.** $\frac{12}{77}$ **5.** Equivalent fractions are not formed by adding the same number to both the numerator and denominator. He should have multiplied both by 3 to obtain the correct answer $\frac{6}{9}$. **[1.2]** **1.** $31\frac{7}{40}$ **5.** Burford made more work for himself than is necessary. When multiplying fractions it is not necessary to change them to fractions with the same LCD. The answer is indeed $\frac{1}{3}$.
[1.3] **2.** 1.0056 **[1.4]** **1.** 2.5% loss **7.** $\frac{41}{333}$ **11.** 244%

CHAPTER 2 INTRODUCTION TO ALGEBRA

2.1 Exercises (PAGE 46)

1. variable **2.** $n + 7$ **3.** $10 - n$ **4.** $3n$ **5.** $\frac{n}{13}$ **6.** $t - 6$ **7.** $s + 200$ **8.** $2V$ **9.** $3000 - c$ **10.** $n + \frac{1}{n}$
11. $s - 20$ **12.** $2v + 300$ **13.** $2(v + 300)$ **14.** $0.04p$ **15.** $c + 0.08c$ **16.** (a) x (b) 7 **17.** 1 **18.** $(2x)^2$
19. $2x^2$ **20.** $6^3y^2z^4$ **21.** $3yyy$ **22.** $(3y)(3y)(3y)$ or $27yyy$ **23.** 1 **24.** 12 **25.** 36 **26.** 27 **27.** 117 **28.** 0
29. 216 **30.** 21 **31.** 0 **32.** undefined **33.** 14 **34.** 0 **35.** 0 **36.** 27 **37.** 117 **38.** 1 **39.** 49 **40.** 15
41. 30 **42.** 18 **43.** 36 **44.** 4 **45.** 16 **46.** 125 **47.** 35 **48.** 26 **49.** 218 **50.** 9 **51.** 28 **52.** 66 ft
53. 605 mi **54.** \$649.80 **55.** 12.25 cm^2 **56.** 60 m^2 **57.** $93.\overline{3}°$ **58.** 37.5 in^2 **59.** 150.72 cm^2 **60.** $45.\overline{45}\%$
61. 0.0775 **62.** 3.9 g

2.2 Exercises (PAGE 55)

1. true **2.** false ($x < y$) **3.** true **4.** false (4500) **5.** true **6.** $<$ **7.** $<$ **8.** $<$ **9.** $=$ **10.** true **11.** false ($0 > -3$) **12.** false ($-2 > -7$) **13.** true **14.**

$-\frac{10}{3}$ $-\frac{7}{4}$ $-\frac{7}{8}$ $\frac{2}{3}$ $\frac{5}{4}$ $\frac{5}{2}$
−4 −3 −2 −1 0 1 2 3 4

15. $>$ **16.** $<$
17. $=$ **18.** $<$ **19.** 1 **20.** 0 **21.** $\frac{3}{4}$ **22.** 3.1 **23.** $200 + 3s$ **24.** $p - 0.20p$ **25.** 75 **26.** 225 **27.** 5
28. 120.7 cm^2

2.3 Exercises (PAGE 63)

1. 7 **2.** -7 **3.** 1 **4.** -1 **5.** 4 **6.** -4 **7.** 0 **8.** -14 **9.** -13 **10.** 8 **11.** -6 **12.** -1 **13.** 7 **14.** -7 **15.** 0 **16.** 10 **17.** -10 **18.** -30 **19.** -1.2 **20.** 1.2 **21.** 1.2 **22.** $-\frac{9}{10}$ **23.** $\frac{9}{10}$ **24.** $-\frac{9}{10}$ **25.** -7 **26.** 12 **27.** -9 **28.** 6 **29.** $2 - 1 = 1 \neq -1 = 1 - 2$; if $a = b$ then $a - b = 0 = b - a$ **30.** 57 **31.** -274 **32.** -101 **33.** $-48°$ **34.** $-\$54$ **35.** 850 ft **36.** $-26°$ **37.** $<$ **38.** $<$ **39.** $=$ **40.** $<$ **41.** 81 **42.** $\frac{5}{4}$ **43.** 17 **44.** 7.25

2.4 Exercises (PAGE 74)

1. 12 **2.** 12 **3.** -12 **4.** -12 **5.** 0 **6.** 27 **7.** -80 **8.** -300 **9.** 3 **10.** -3 **11.** 0 **12.** undefined **13.** -9 **14.** 9 **15.** -1 **16.** 3 **17.** -2.76 **18.** $-\frac{3}{2}$ **19.** $\frac{3}{2}$ **20.** 8 **21.** -8 **22.** -1 **23.** 1 **24.** -1 **25.** -1 **26.** 6 **27.** 24 **28.** -720 **29.** $(4 \div 2) \div 2 = 2 \div 2 = 1 \neq 4 = 4 \div 1 = 4 \div (2 \div 2)$; if $a = b = c = 1$, then $(1 \div 1) \div 1 = 1 \div 1 = 1 = 1 \div 1 = 1 \div (1 \div 1)$ **30.** $-\$48$ **31.** 363 points **32.** -2 **33.** 12 **34.** $\frac{5}{2}$ **35.** -4 **36.** x **37.** 3 **38.** -4 **39.** 0 **40.** 12 **41.** -1 **42.** 10 **43.** 0 **44.** 1 **45.** -3 **46.** -3 **47.** 23 **48.** 7 **49.** -135 **50.** -45 **51.** -262 **52.** $-\$2450$

2.5 Exercises (PAGE 81)

1. (a) 10 **(b)** 10 **(c)** distributive law **2. (a)** -18 **(b)** -18 **(c)** distributive law **3.** like **4.** 3 **5.** 4 **6.** 1 **7–12.** answers given in exercises 13–18 **13–18.** answers given in exercises 7–12 **19.** $a + b$ **20.** $-2y + 2$ **21.** $x - 3 + b$ **22.** $-x + y + 4$ **23.** $-1 - x + a - b$ **24.** $u - v - w + 3$ **25.** $-5x$ **26.** $1 - x$ **27.** $-3x$ **28.** $2a - 2b$ **29.** $-3a + 3 + 2b$ **30.** $-u - 2 + 3v$ **31.** $-2x - y$ **32.** $\frac{1}{4} - \frac{1}{4}b$ **33.** $-3 - 3.7u$ **34.** $5a - 1$ **35.** $3x + 2$ **36.** $10u + 6$ **37.** $4x + 6$ **38.** $-4a + 1$ **39.** 0 **40.** $7x - 12y - 6$ **41.** $15a - 5b$ **42.** $-4u + 14v$ **43.** 7 **44.** -18 **45.** 36 **46.** 6 **47.** 4 **48.** -2 **49.** 17 **50.** -8 **51.** -26 **52.** 0 **53.** 4 **54.** 2 **55.** -33 **56.** 33 **57.** -2 **58.** 2 **59.** $\frac{1}{4}$ **60.** 7

2.6 Exercises (PAGE 87)

1. 15 **2.** -14 **3.** 0 **4.** -1 **5.** $\frac{3}{5}$ **6.** $-\frac{2}{5}$ **7.** $\frac{2}{13}$ **8.** $\frac{1}{3}$ **9.** $\frac{2}{3}$ **10.** $-\frac{1}{5}$ **11.** $\frac{1}{2}$ **12.** $\frac{5}{11}$ **13. (a)** 256 **(b)** 16 **14. (a)** 289 **(b)** 17 **15. (a)** 324 **(b)** 18 **16. (a)** 361 **(b)** 19 **17.** x **18.** $-x$ **19. (a)** 81 **(b)** 3 **20. (a)** $\frac{1}{16}$ **(b)** $\frac{1}{2}$ **21.** 3 and 4 **22.** 12 and 13 **23.** none **24.** 0 **25.** $-1, 0, -3$ **26.** $-\frac{7}{2}, -1, 0, -3, 2.66$ **27.** $-\sqrt{11}, 2\pi, \frac{\sqrt{2}}{2}$ **28.** all the numbers **29.** integers **30.** whole numbers **31.** rational numbers **32.** real numbers **33.** $2a$ **34.** $-4y + 4$ **35.** 0

Chapter 2 Review Exercises (PAGE 90)

1. $n - 5$ **2.** $4A$ **3.** $c + 0.25c$ **4.** $3 + \frac{1}{n}$ **5.** a^5 **6.** $(3z)^3$ **7.** $(a + w)^2$ **8.** $bbbbbbb$ **9.** $2xxx$ **10.** $(2x)(2x)(2x)$ or $8xxx$ **11.** 8 **12.** 30 **13.** 12 **14.** 36 **15.** 22 **16.** 12 **17.** 7 **18.** 2.51 **19.** true **20.** false **21.** true **22.** $=$ **23.** $>$ **24.** $<$ **25.** $-41°$ **26.** -7 **27.** -3 **28.** 7 **29.** 2 **30.** -3.8 **31.** $\frac{1}{10}$ **32.** -21 **33.** 39-yard line **34.** -8 **35.** 2 **36.** $-\frac{5}{8}$ **37.** -24 **38.** -42 pounds **39.** 0 **40.** 4 **41.** 0 **42.** 9 **43.** -8 **44.** x **45.** $-4(x - 3)$ **46.** $-2(1 + 3x + 5y)$ **47.** $-5(x + 5y)$ **48.** $-5a + 2$ **49.** $3x - 2y + 2$ **50.** $y + 1$ **51.** $-8a + 15$ **52.** -28 **53.** 196 **54.** 0 **55.** -13 **56.** $\frac{4}{5}$ **57.** -3 **58. (a)** 625 **(b)** 5 **59.** natural numbers **60.** integers **61.** rational numbers **62.** real numbers **63.** rational numbers **64.** whole numbers **65.** $-\frac{2}{5}$ **66.** 48 **67.** $-\frac{1}{14}$ **68.** -28 **69.** 2 **70.** -7 **71.** -8 **72.** $\frac{4}{5}$ **73.** $-\frac{13}{12}$ **74.** 125 **75.** 27 **76.** -4 **77.** -4 **78.** $-y - 17$ **79.** \$6612.50 **80.** $10 + 2c$ **81.** $t - 20$ **82.** false **83.** false **84.** true **85.** true **86.** true **87.** true **88.** false **89.** false **90.** false **91.** false **92.** false

Chapter 2 Test (PAGE 93)

1. a^3 **2.** 1 **3.** 75 **4.** 225 **5.** -9 **6.** -1 **7.** -19 **8.** 3 **9.** \$594.05 **10.** 13 **11.** $<$ **12.** 141° **13.** $100 + 2w$ **14.** -22 **15.** 8 **16.** $-\frac{1}{8}$ **17.** 3 **18.** 5 **19.** -18 **20.** -6 **21.** $-3(y - 5)$ **22.** $5 - b - 2y$ **23.** 3 **24.** 15 **25.** $-12y + 6$ **26.** 11 **27.** $-\frac{5}{4}$ **28.** true **29.** false **30.** false **31.** $a \leq 0$ **32.** The absolute value of a number a is the distance from 0 to a on a number line.

Chapter 2 Answers to Selected Enrichment Exercises

[2.1] **3.** 1600 **7.** 3 times the sum of a and b **[2.3]** **3.** $-34\frac{25}{48}$ **[2.4]** **3.** -102 **[2.5]** **2.** $-36a - 28b$ **4.** $90a + 145b$ **6.** He made an error in the last step when he tried to collect terms that are not like terms. The correct answer is $6y + 2x$. **[2.6]** **4.** $-\frac{11}{12}$ **8.** 13.82

CHAPTER 3 LINEAR EQUATIONS AND INEQUALITIES

3.1 Exercises (PAGE 98)

1–3. Answers will vary. **4.** 2 **5.** 4 **6.** 0 **7.** any number is a solution. **8.** no solution **9.** 0 **10.** y **11.** $y - 1$ **12.** no **13.** 4 **14.** 13 **15.** -16 **16.** 3 **17.** 3 **18.** -5 **19.** 5.5 **20.** -5.9 **21.** 1.3 **22.** $2\frac{1}{2}$ **23.** $7\frac{2}{3}$ **24.** $-1\frac{1}{8}$ **25.** true **26.** true **27.** true **28.** false (contradiction) **29.** $10x$ **30.** z **31.** y **32.** x

3.2 Exercises (PAGE 103)

1. 5 **2.** 7 **3.** -7 **4.** 72 **5.** -1 **6.** -6 **7.** -12 **8.** -20 **9.** -21 **10.** -2 **11.** -4 **12.** 6 **13.** -6.2 **14.** 6 **15.** 8 **16.** 4 **17.** -6 **18.** 15 **19.** -4 **20.** -1 **21.** -10.6 **22.** yes **23.** yes

3.3 Exercises (PAGE 109)

1. 2 **2.** $-\frac{1}{2}$ **3.** 1 **4.** 10 **5.** 2 **6.** $\frac{7}{2}$ **7.** -12 **8.** 2 **9.** $\frac{1}{2}$ **10.** -29 **11.** 0 **12.** 3 **13.** -1 **14.** every real number (identity) **15.** -4 **16.** $-\frac{3}{5}$ **17.** 3 **18.** 22 **19.** -13 **20.** 18 **21.** -9 **22.** 3 **23.** $\frac{1}{7}$ **24.** contradiction; no solution **25.** $\frac{3}{2}$ **26.** $\frac{11}{2}$ **27.** $-\frac{15}{4}$ **28.** $-\frac{5}{3}$ **29.** $-\frac{5}{2}$ **30.** $-\frac{1}{2}$ **31.** contradiction; no solution **32.** $\frac{2}{3}$ **33.** -1 **34.** 1 **35.** -5 **36.** -4 **37.** 10 **38.** -14 **39.** 8 **40.** $\frac{7}{9}$ **41.** -3.6

3.4 Exercises (PAGE 114)

1. $x = g - h$ **2.** $x = t - k$ **3.** $x = \frac{e - d}{b}$ **4.** $x = \frac{g - m}{a}$ **5.** $t = \frac{d}{r}$ **6.** $I = \frac{E}{R}$ **7.** $r = \frac{I}{Pt}$ **8.** $d = C - 20c$ **9.** $b = \frac{2A}{h}$ **10.** $d = rt$ **11.** $m = \frac{E}{c^2}$ **12.** $C = \frac{5}{9}(F - 32)$ **13.** $c = 2A - d$ **14.** $a = \frac{2A - hb}{h}$ **15.** $r = \frac{A - P}{Pt}$ **16.** $y = 3x + 5$ **17.** $y = -\frac{3}{2}x + 6$ **18.** $y = -\frac{1}{2}x + 4$ **19.** $y = -\frac{b}{a}x + b$ **20.** $x = \frac{-by - c}{a}$ **21.** $x = \frac{y - b}{m}$ **22.** $w = \frac{A}{l}$; 1.6 cm **23.** $P = \frac{I}{rt}$; \$1500 **24.** $R = \frac{P}{I^2}$; 13.9 ohms **25.** $-\frac{5}{3}$ **26.** 6

3.5 Exercises (PAGE 125)

1. $7x = 25$ **2.** $x + 8 = 12$ **3.** $x - 15 = 35$ **4.** $6x = 42$ **5.** $2x + 3 = 27$ **6.** $3x - 8 = 24$ **7.** $x - 5 = 12$ **8.** $8 = 3x - 4$ **9.** $x - 3 = 9$ **10.** $7x - 2 = 31$ **11.** $3x - 5 = 34$ **12.** $10 + 3x = 2x + 12$ **13.** $0.03x = 12$ **14.** $x + 3x = 24$ **15.** $7(x - 2) = 31$ **16.** $2(x + 5) = 3x$ **17.** $7 + x = 13$ **18.** $4(x + 3) = 48$ **19.** $\frac{4}{x} = \frac{1}{2}$ **20.** $\frac{1}{2}n - 2\frac{1}{n} = \frac{3}{2}$ **21.** 6 **22.** 150, 30 **23.** 186 **24.** 186 lb **25.** 7542 **26.** 7542 mi^2 **27.** 3, 6 **28.** 3 ft, 6 ft **29.** 5 ft and 12 ft **30.** Angela is 3, Tony is 12, Theresa is 24. **31.** 300 **32.** 41 **33.** 126 **34.** $6\frac{1}{4}$% **35.** 5% **36.** 625 **37.** 30% **38.** 80% **39.** \$950 **40.** \$525 **41.** 150 **42.** \$73.50 **43.** \$35.80 **44.** 35¢ **45.** 78¢ **46.** \$1200 **47.** 30% **48.** \$1250 **49.** 50¢ **50.** \$1450 **51.** 903,750 mi^2 **52.** 160 lb **53.** 14.4 ft^2 **54.** $\frac{5}{3}$ in^2 **55.** 28.9 yd **56.** 51.2 cm^2

3.6 Exercises (PAGE 135)

Some answers are rounded. **1.** 17 in, 13 in **2.** 15°, 75°, 90° **3.** 13 in **4.** 14 cm **5.** 87.9 ft **6.** 10 ft, 15 ft, 20 ft **7.** 7 in **8.** 45°, 45°, 90° **9.** 48 m, 48 m, 12 m **10.** 145 in, 170 in **11.** 13 m **12.** 24 cm **13.** 7234.6 yd^2 **14.** 21 m **15.** 15.9 m **16.** 12 ft **17.** 0.5 ft **18.** 33.5 m^3 **19.** 0.4 m **20.** $18,480.00 **21.** 35 km **22.** 150 minutes **23.** 22 mi **24.** 75 mph, 55 mph **25.** 40 nautical miles **26.** 50 mph, 60 mph **27.** 7 in, 14 in, 21 in **28.** 50¢, 58¢ **29.** 85% **30.** $10,500 **31.** $<$ **32.** $<$ **33.** $>$ **34.** $>$ **35.** **(a)** yes **(b)** no

3.7 Exercises (PAGE 148)

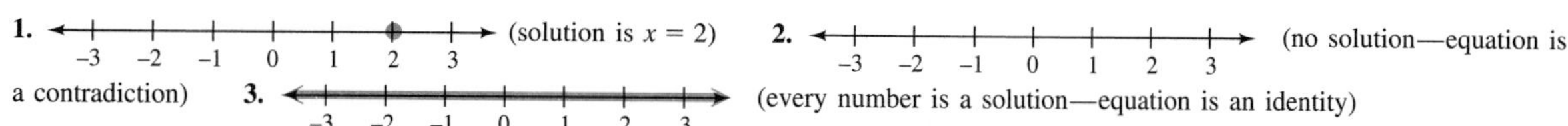

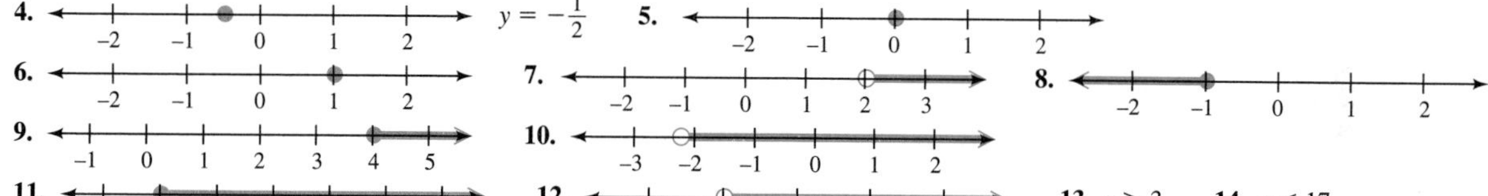

13. $x > 3$ **14.** $x < 17$

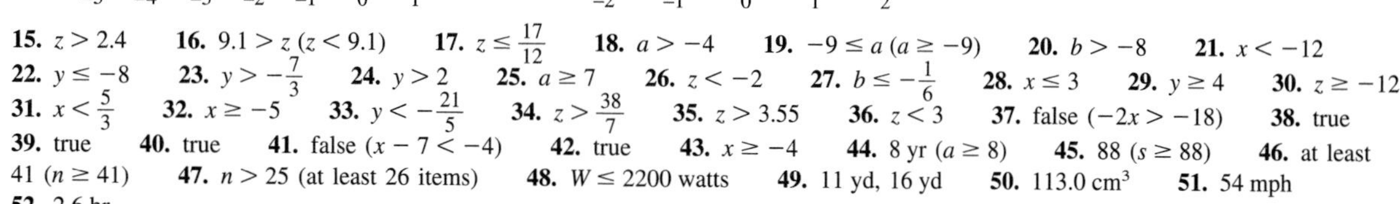

15. $z > 2.4$ **16.** $9.1 > z$ $(z < 9.1)$ **17.** $z \le \frac{17}{12}$ **18.** $a > -4$ **19.** $-9 \le a$ $(a \ge -9)$ **20.** $b > -8$ **21.** $x < -12$ **22.** $y \le -8$ **23.** $y > -\frac{7}{3}$ **24.** $y > 2$ **25.** $a \ge 7$ **26.** $z < -2$ **27.** $b \le -\frac{1}{6}$ **28.** $x \le 3$ **29.** $y \ge 4$ **30.** $z \ge -12$ **31.** $x < \frac{5}{3}$ **32.** $x \ge -5$ **33.** $y < -\frac{21}{5}$ **34.** $z > \frac{38}{7}$ **35.** $z > 3.55$ **36.** $z < 3$ **37.** false $(-2x > -18)$ **38.** true **39.** true **40.** true **41.** false $(x - 7 < -4)$ **42.** true **43.** $x \ge -4$ **44.** 8 yr $(a \ge 8)$ **45.** 88 $(s \ge 88)$ **46.** at least 41 $(n \ge 41)$ **47.** $n > 25$ (at least 26 items) **48.** $W \le 2200$ watts **49.** 11 yd, 16 yd **50.** 113.0 cm^3 **51.** 54 mph **52.** 2.6 hr

3.8 Exercises (PAGE 156)

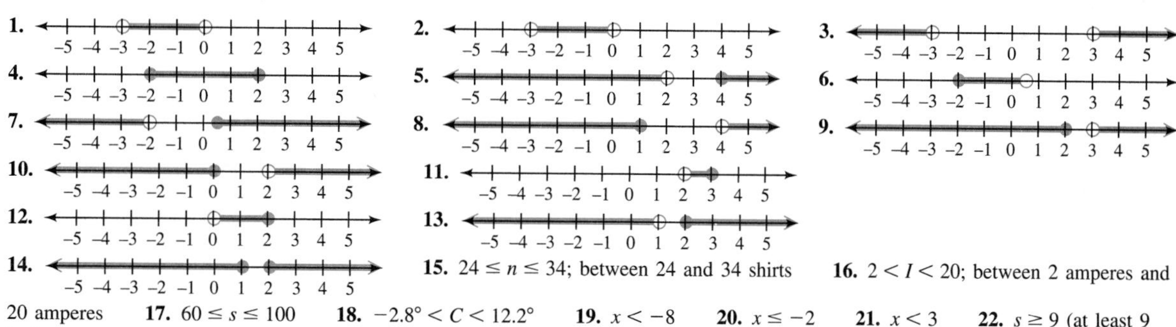

15. $24 \le n \le 34$; between 24 and 34 shirts **16.** $2 < I < 20$; between 2 amperes and 20 amperes **17.** $60 \le s \le 100$ **18.** $-2.8° < C < 12.2°$ **19.** $x < -8$ **20.** $x \le -2$ **21.** $x < 3$ **22.** $s \ge 9$ (at least 9 inches)

Chapter 3 Review Exercises (PAGE 160)

1. (a) x **(b)** $2(x + 1)$ **(c)** $2x + 2$ **(d)** every real number **(e)** yes **(f)** no **2.** 4 **3.** $\frac{2}{9}$ **4.** -2 **5.** 5 **6.** 0 **7.** 6 **8.** $-\frac{2}{7}$ **9.** $\frac{5}{3}$ **10.** $b = \frac{w - 2a}{2}$ **11.** $y = \frac{M + 3d}{3}$ **12.** $y = -\frac{2}{5}x + 4$ **13.** $y = -\frac{2}{3}x + 2$ **14.** $c = \frac{T}{n}$; $3.00 **15.** $x + 5 = 7$ **16.** $4x = 23$ **17.** $2x + 7 = -12$ **18.** $6x + 5 = x - 3$ **19.** Fred is 31; Bertha is 19. **20.** 12% **21.** $16.80 **22.** 660 **23.** 7 **24.** 65% **25.** $36 **26.** $640 **27.** 3.78 cm **28.** 4.2 ft **29.** 15 ft, 25 ft **30.** 72 mph, 67 mph

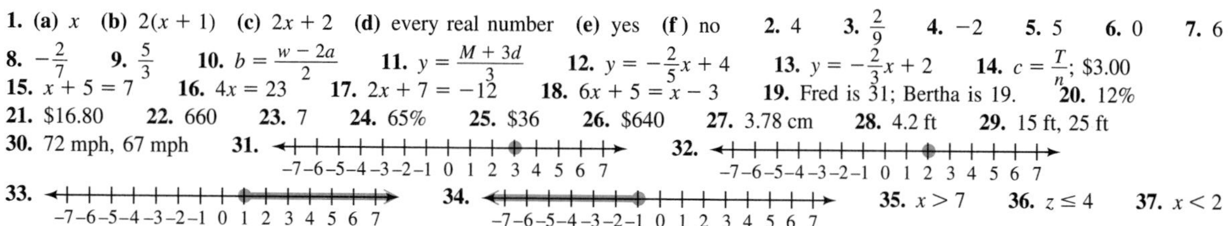

35. $x > 7$ **36.** $z \le 4$ **37.** $x < 2$

38. $x > -6$ **39.** $x \geq 5$ **40.** $x > \frac{25}{8}$ **41.** when both sides are multiplied or divided by a negative number **42.** $n > 24$ (at least 25 chimes) **43.** $l \geq 150$; the length must be at least 150 yd. **44.** −7 −6 −5 −4 −3 −2 −1 0 1 2 3 4 5 6 7

45. −7 −6 −5 −4 −3 −2 −1 0 1 2 3 4 5 6 7 **46.** −7 −6 −5 −4 −3 −2 −1 0 1 2 3 4 5 6 7

47. −7 −6 −5 −4 −3 −2 −1 0 1 2 3 4 5 6 7 **48.** −7 −6 −5 −4 −3 −2 −1 0 1 2 3 4 5 6 7

49. −7 −6 −5 −4 −3 −2 −1 0 1 2 3 4 5 6 7 **50.** $68° \leq F \leq 86°$ **51.** \$8.25 **52.** approximately 2.9 cm **53.** 4.7 **54.** $-\frac{1}{2}$

55. $\frac{5}{2}$ **56.** $x < -\frac{7}{4}$ **57.** $x \leq -\frac{2}{5}$ **58.** $x \geq -1$ **59.** $v = t - u - b$ **60.** $y = \frac{2}{3}x - \frac{5}{3}$

61. −7 −6 −5 −4 −3 −2 −1 0 1 2 3 4 5 6 7 **62.** −7 −6 −5 −4 −3 −2 −1 0 1 2 3 4 5 6 7

63. −7 −6 −5 −4 −3 −2 −1 0 1 2 3 4 5 6 7 **64.** −7 −6 −5 −4 −3 −2 −1 0 1 2 3 4 5 6 7 **65.** $F = \frac{9}{5}C + 32$; 113° **66.** false (equation) **67.** true **68.** false (contradiction) **69.** true **70.** true **71.** true **72.** true **73.** false ($x < 3$) **74.** false ($x \leq 3$) **75.** true **76.** false ($x > 35$) **77.** false ($-3x < -6$) **78.** false ($10 \leq x \leq 20$) **79.** true **80.** false (*or* statements can never be written as a chain)

Chapter 3 Test (PAGE 163)

1. 15 **2.** 8 **3.** $-\frac{}{2}$ **4.** −2 **5.** 36 **6.** 4 **7.** −3 **8.** 13 **9.** 3 **10.** \$180,000 **11.** \$62.10 **12.** 40 cm **13.** 48 mph, 57 mph **14.** 4 hr; 24 mi **15.** $g = \frac{U - W}{Wm}$ **16.** $w = \frac{P - 2l}{2}$; 1.7 cm **17.** $x \geq -3$ **18.** $x < \frac{1}{2}$

19. −7 −6 −5 −4 −3 −2 −1 0 1 2 3 4 5 6 7 **20.** −7 −6 −5 −4 −3 −2 −1 0 1 2 3 4 5 6 7

21. −7 −6 −5 −4 −3 −2 −1 0 1 2 3 4 5 6 7 **22.** −7 −6 −5 −4 −3 −2 −1 0 1 2 3 4 5 6 7 **23.** A conditional equation is an equation such as $x + 7 = -9$ which is true for some replacements of the variable and false for others. An identity is an equation such as $x + 5 = 5 + x$, which has the entire set of real numbers for its solution set. A contradiction is an equation such as $x - 1 = x + 2$, which has no solution. **24.** A compound statement using *and* can be written as $x > -1$ and $x < 2$ or as a chain, $-1 < x < 2$. Compound statements with *or* can only be written as $x < -1$ or $x > 2$ and can never be written as a chain.

Chapter 3 Answers to Selected Enrichment Exercises

[3.1] **3.** −30.675 **4.** $a = 2$ **8.** $n + 5 = 2$ **[3.2]** **3.** $-0.0\overline{3}$ **4.** $a = 3$ **7.** $2n = 36$ **[3.3]** **2.** $\frac{241}{49}$ **4.** $-\frac{11}{8}$ **7.** $a = 2$ **[3.4]** **4.** $x = -5a$ **8.** $x = -\frac{1}{a + 1}$ **[3.5]** **2.** \$90.00 **[3.6]** **10.** 264 mi **[3.7]** **2.** $x < 0$ **3.** $n \geq 500$ (at least 500 items) **[3.8]** **2.** Between \$212.50 and \$362.50, inclusive

CHAPTER 4 GRAPHING

4.1 Exercises (PAGE 170)

1.

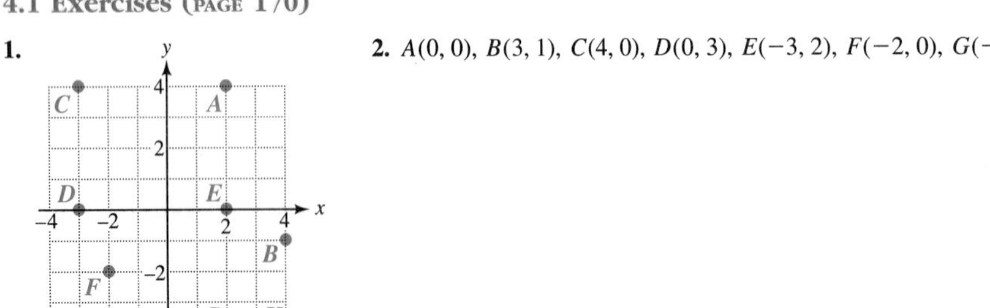

2. $A(0, 0)$, $B(3, 1)$, $C(4, 0)$, $D(0, 3)$, $E(-3, 2)$, $F(-2, 0)$, $G(-4, -3)$, $H(1, -2)$.

3.

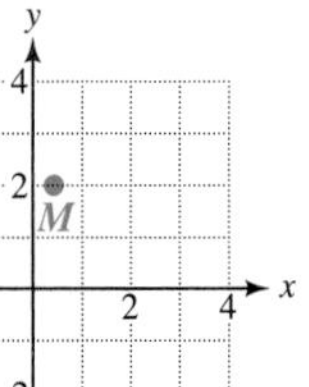

4. M:I, N:II, P:III, Q:IV **5.** III **6.** IV **7.** I **8.** II **9.** quadrants **10.** -2

11. -8 **12.** $(0, 0)$ **13.** x-axis **14.** IV **15.** II **16. (a)** $(0, -2)$ **(b)** $(2, 0)$ **(c)** $(4, 2)$ **(d)** $(-1, -3)$ **17. (a)** x cannot be 0 **(b)** $(5, 0)$ **(c)** $(5$, any number$)$ **(d)** $(5, -10)$ **18. (a)** $(0, 5)$ **(b)** $(5, 0)$ **(c)** $(3, 2)$ **(d)** $(9, -4)$ **19. (a)** $(0, -4)$ **(b)** $(2, 0)$ **(c)** $(-2, -8)$ **(d)** $(5, 6)$ **20. (a)** $(0, 2)$ **(b)** $(10, 0)$ **(c)** $(-10, 4)$ **(d)** $(-5, 3)$ **21. (a)** $(0, -5)$ **(b)** $(2, 0)$ **(c)** $\left(7, \frac{25}{2}\right)$ **(d)** $\left(\frac{2}{5}, -4\right)$ **22.** $(1, 55)$, $(5, 275)$, $(10, 550)$ **(a)** 55 miles **(b)** 275 miles **(c)** 550 miles **23.** $2300

24.

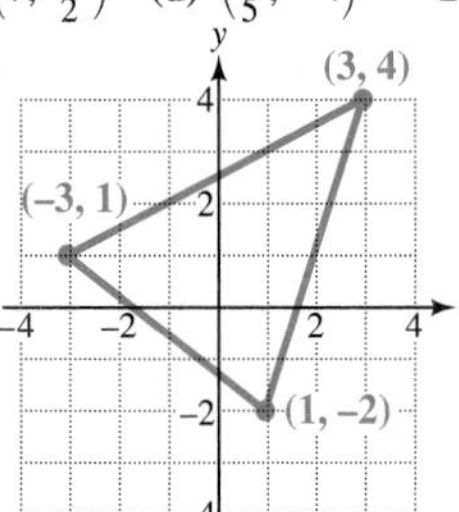

25.

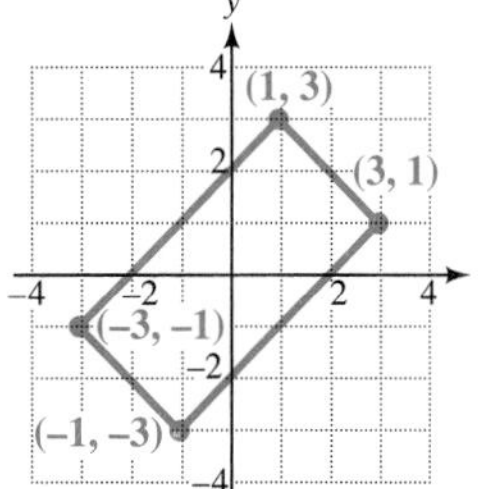

26. 0 **27.** 0 **28.** Answers will vary. Two such points are $(1, 1)$ and $(-1, 3)$. The points all appear to be on the straight line through the above two points.

29.

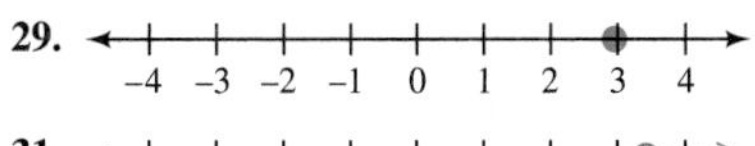

30.

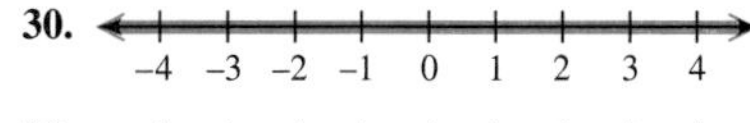

31.

32.

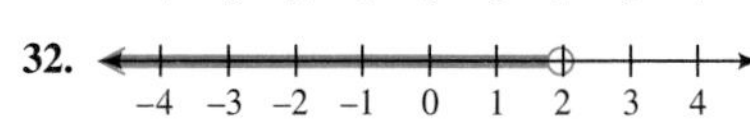

33. $y = -\frac{4}{3}x + 4$ **34.** $5x - y = 6$

4.2 Exercises (PAGE 181)

1.

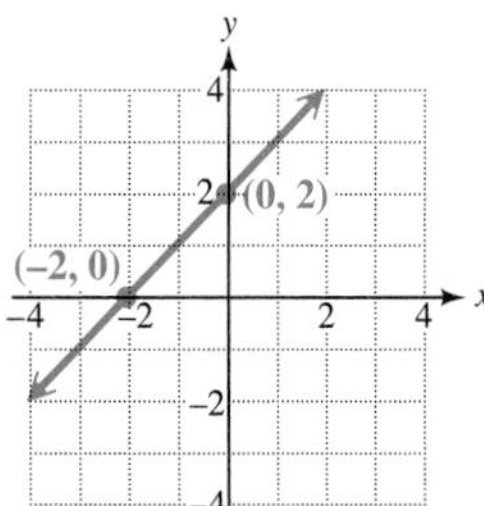

2.

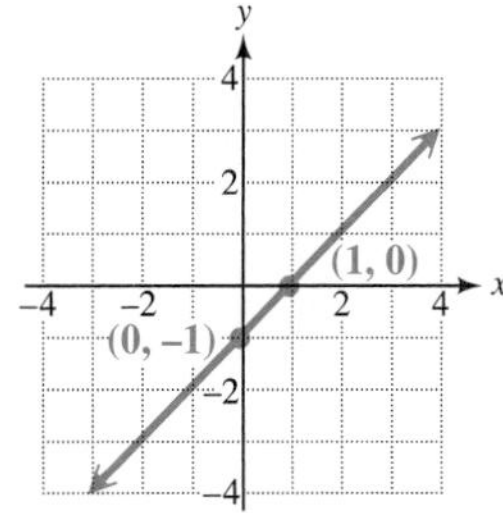

3.

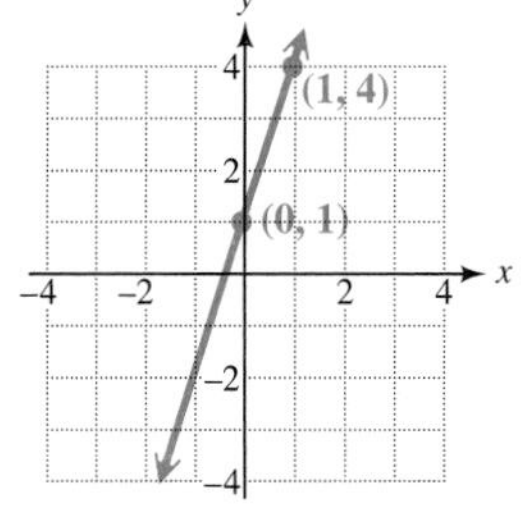

4.

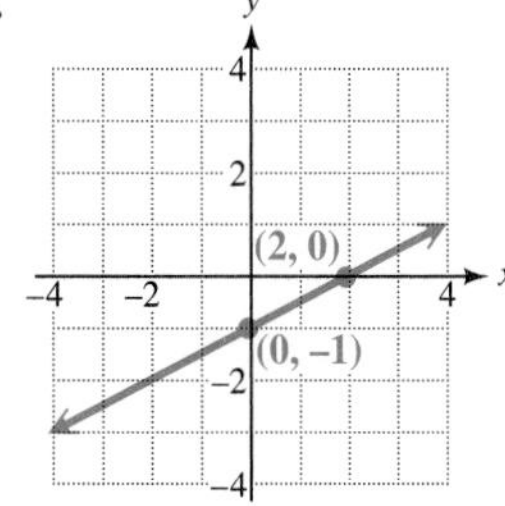

5.

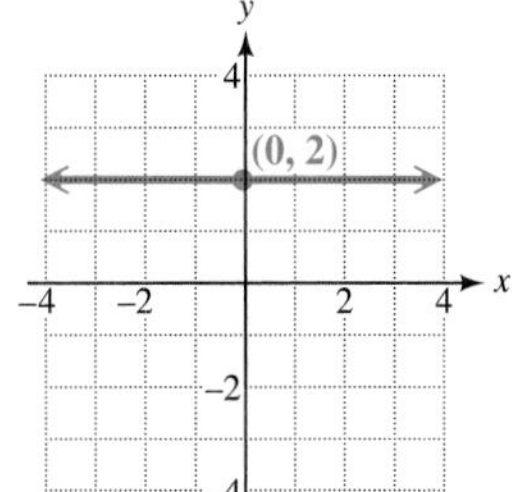

6.

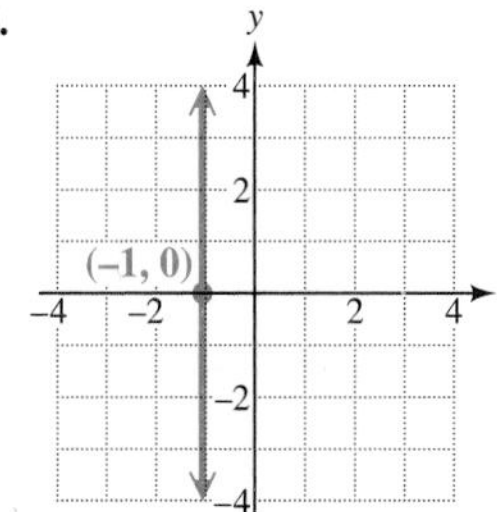

7. (a) and (f) are the only linear equations **8.** the variables appear only to the first power **9.** the standard form of a linear equation **10.** y-axis

11. x-axis **12.** an x-intercept **13.** a y-intercept **14.** intercepts

15. x-intercept (2, 0); y-intercept (0, 4)

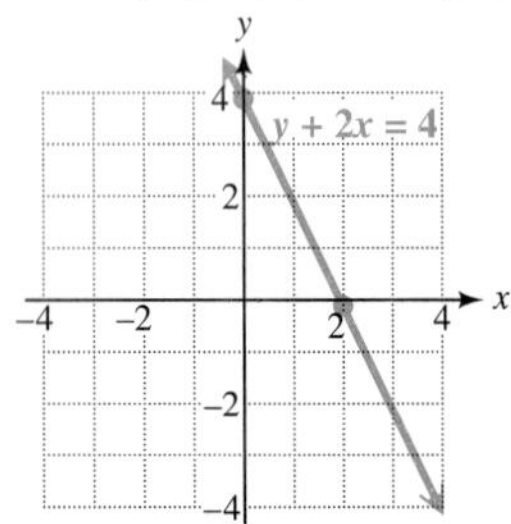

16. x-intercept (−6, 0); y-intercept (0, 4)

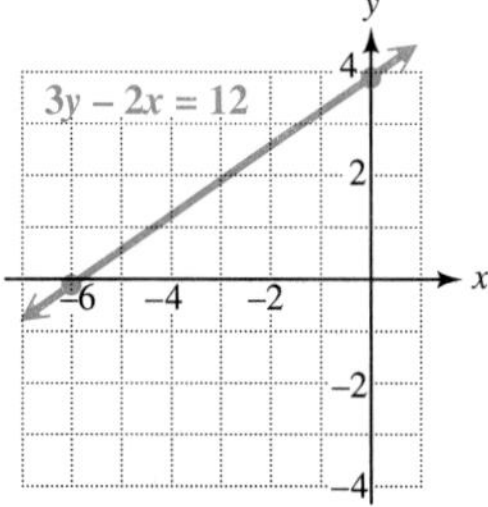

17. x-intercept (0, 0); y-intercept (0, 0); another point is (1, −1)

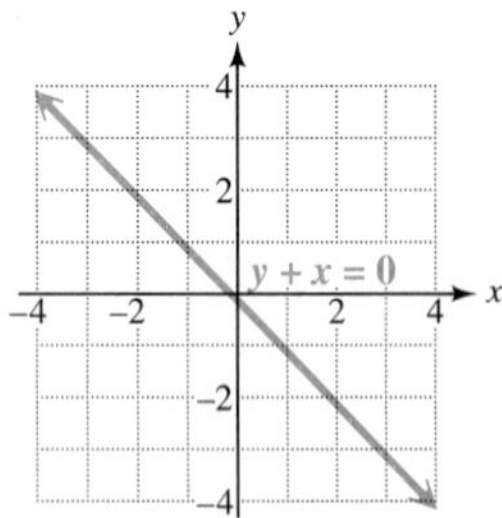

18. no x-intercept; y-intercept (0, 3)

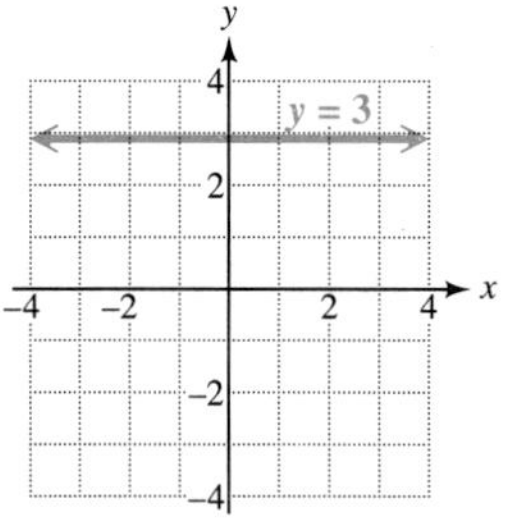

19. x-intercept $\left(\frac{1}{2}, 0\right)$; no y-intercept

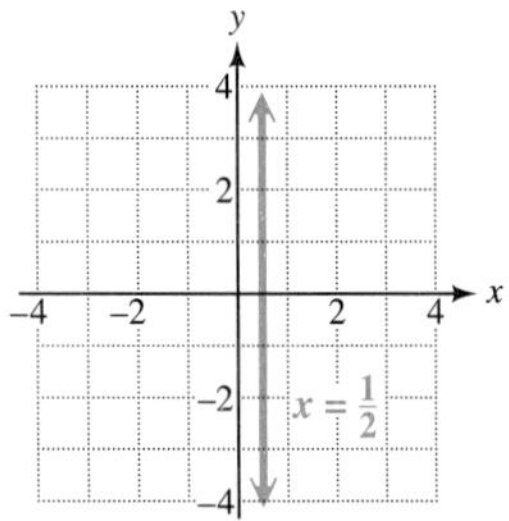

20. x-intercept (0, 0); y-intercept (0, 0); another point is (1, −2)

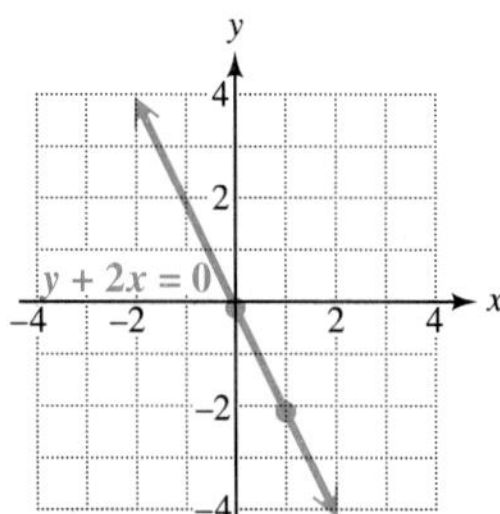

21. x-intercept (3, 0); y-intercept (0, 2)

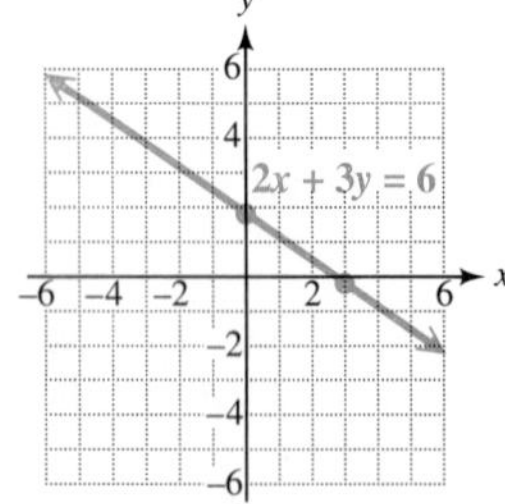

22. x-intercept (5, 0); y-intercept (0, −2)

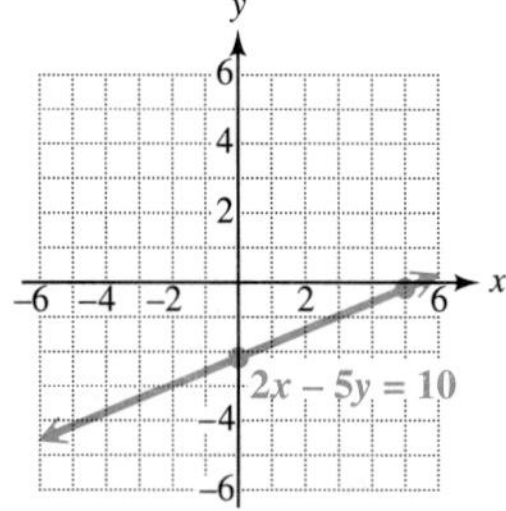

23. x-intercept $(-4, 0)$; y-intercept $(0, 3)$

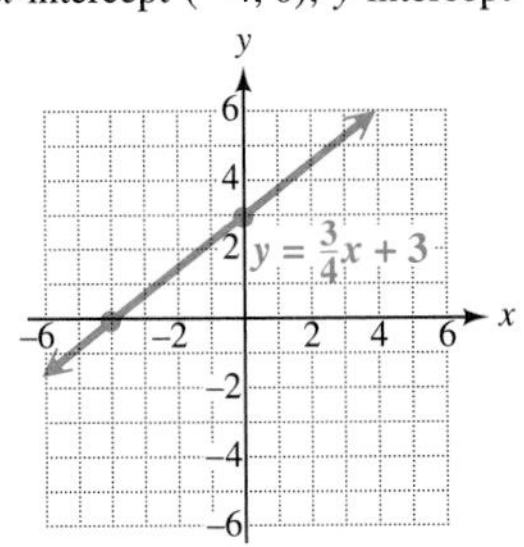

24. x-intercept $(0, 0)$; y-intercept; every point on the y-axis; the graph is the y-axis **26.** **(a)** $(0, -5)$ **(b)** $(3, 0)$ **(c)** $\left(\frac{12}{5}, -1\right)$ **(d)** $\left(-1, \frac{-20}{3}\right)$ **27.** **(a)** $(1, 3)$ **(b)** $(-1, 3)$ **(c)** $(5, 3)$ **(d)** $(-3, 3)$ **28.** (10,000, 11,000), (20,000, 12,000), (50,000, 15,000) **(a)** \$11,000 **(b)** \$12,000 **(c)** \$15,000 **29.** 56 square units **30.** $(2, 4)$ **31.** $(4, 0)$ **32.** $(-1, 5)$ **33.** $(-3, -1)$

4.3 Exercises (Page 190)

1. 1 **2.** 0 **3.** $-\frac{2}{5}$ **4.** undefined slope **5.** positive slope **6.** zero slope **7.** zero slope **8.** parallel: $m_1 = m_2$ **9.** perpendicular: $m_1m_2 = -1$ **10.** neither: $m_1 \neq m_2$ and $m_1m_2 \neq -1$ **11.** Yes. The slope of the line through $(2, 3)$ and $(0, 2)$ is $\frac{1}{2}$, the same as the slope of the line through $(0, 2)$ and $(-2, 1)$. **12.** 4 **13.** undefined slope **14.** $-\frac{3}{5}$ **15.** They are parallel since both have slope 2. **16.** They are perpendicular since $m_1 = \frac{1}{3}$, $m_2 = -3$, and $m_1m_2 = -1$. **17.** They are parallel since both are vertical lines. **18.** They are perpendicular since $m_1 = 1$, $m_2 = -1$, and $m_1m_2 = -1$. **19.** They are perpendicular since l_1 is horizontal and l_2 is vertical. **20.** They are parallel since both have slope $-\frac{3}{2}$. **21.** Divide $m_1m_2 = -1$ by m_1. **22.** 1.5 **23.** 0.61 **24.** x-intercept $(2, 0)$; y-intercept $\left(0, -\frac{1}{3}\right)$

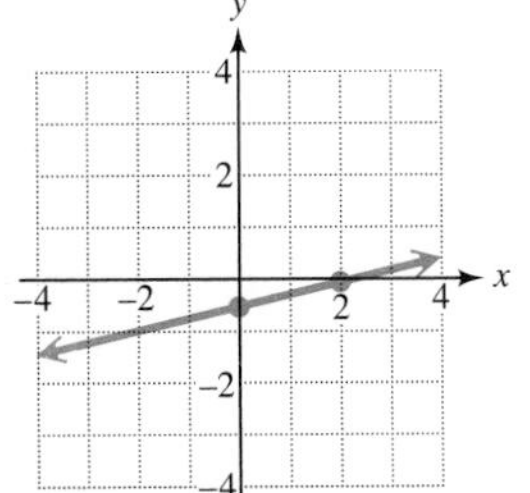

25. x-intercept $(0, 0)$; y-intercept $(0, 0)$; another point is $(1, -5)$

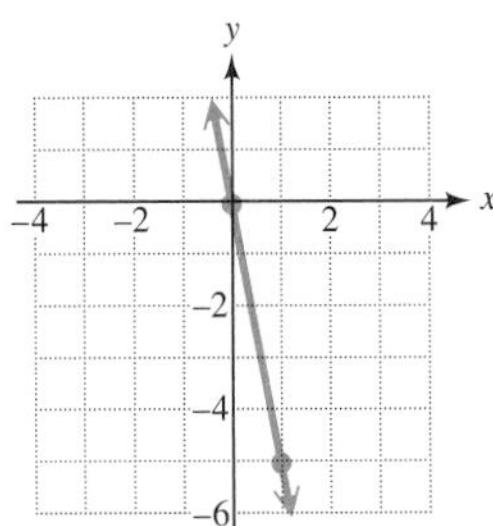

26. x-intercept $(-5, 0)$; no y-intercept

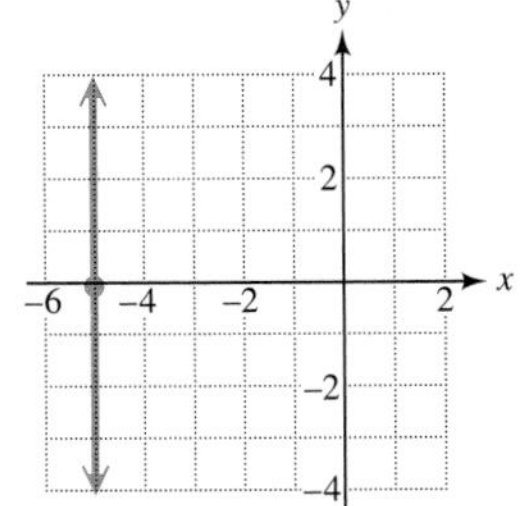

27. no x-intercept; y-intercept $(0, 6)$

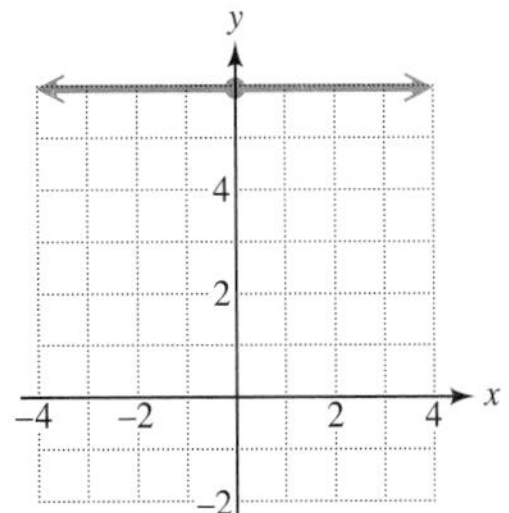

28. No. It cannot be written in the form $ax + by = c$.

4.4 Exercises (PAGE 196)

1. $y = -5x + 12$; slope is -5, y-intercept is $(0, 12)$ **2.** $y = \frac{2}{5}x + 2$; slope is $\frac{2}{5}$, y-intercept is $(0, 2)$ **3.** $y = -\frac{7}{4} = 0\,x - \frac{7}{4}$; slope is 0, y-intercept is $\left(0, -\frac{7}{4}\right)$ **4.** The equation cannot be solved for y, hence it has no slope-intercept form. Also, it has undefined slope and no y-intercept. **5.** $y = -x + 5$; slope is -1, y-intercept is $(0, 5)$ **6.** $y = \frac{2}{3}x + \frac{1}{3}$; slope is $\frac{2}{3}$, y-intercept is $\left(0, \frac{1}{3}\right)$

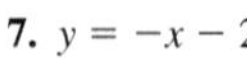

7. $y = -x - 2$ **8.** $y = \frac{2}{5}x + 2$ **9.** $y = -\frac{4}{3}x + 5$

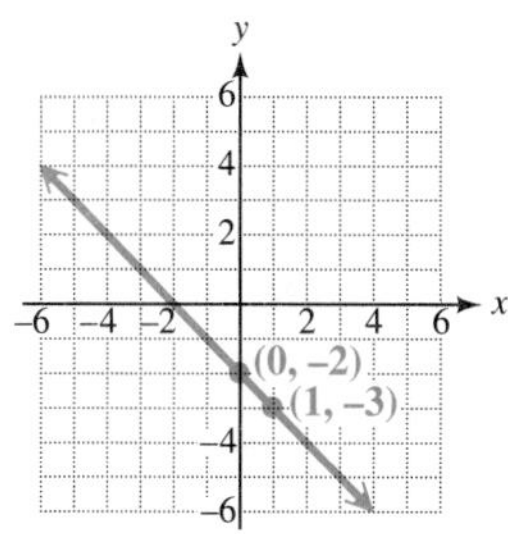

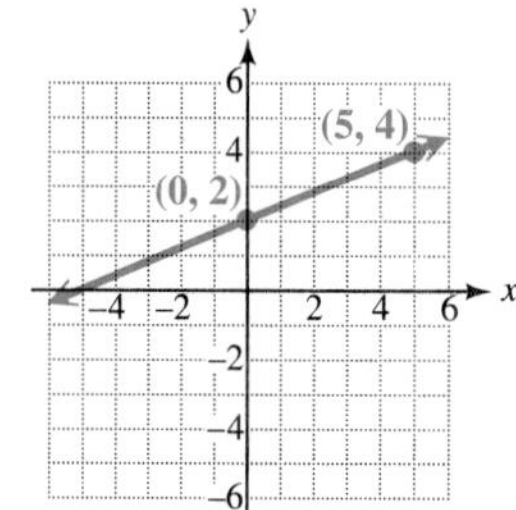

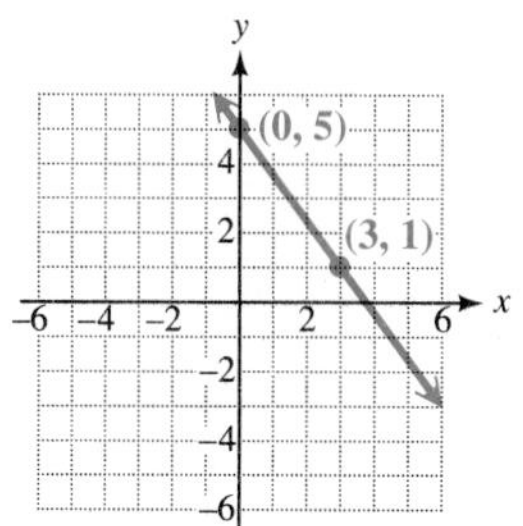

10. $2x - y = -4$ **11.** $4x - y = 3$ **12.** $x + 2y = 12$ **13.** $3x - y = 10$ **14.** $2x + y = 7$ **15.** $x + 2y = -1$ **16.** $x - y = -3$ **17.** $x - 3y = -10$ **18.** $x + 4y = -5$ **19.** $y = 10x + 25$ **20.** $y = 10.50x + 300$ **21.** $x = 2$ **22.** $y = -3$ **23.** $x - 3y = 7$ **24.** $3x + 2y = 7$ **25.** $2x + 5y = -24$ **26.** $x < 2$ **27.** $x \le -3$ **28.** $x \ge \frac{5}{2}$

4.5 Exercises (PAGE 204)

1. solid **2.** dashed **3.**

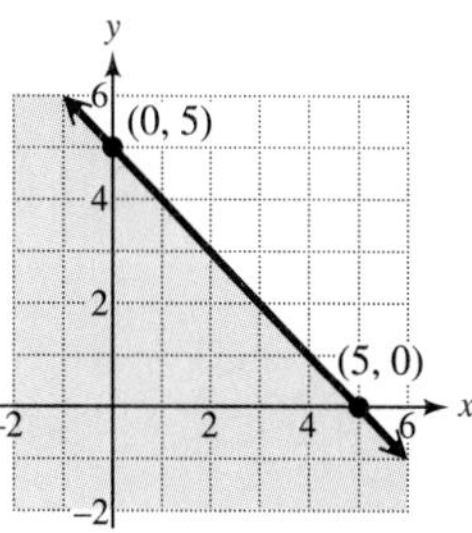

4.

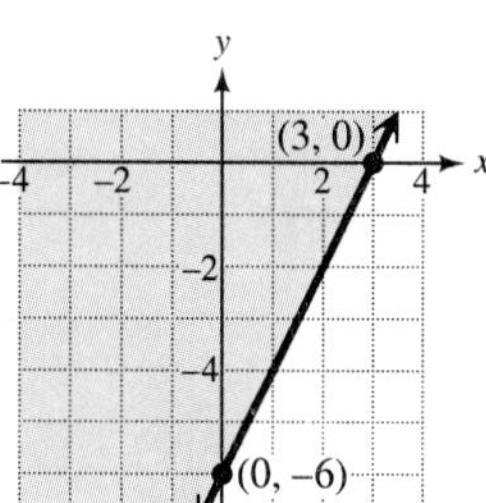

5.

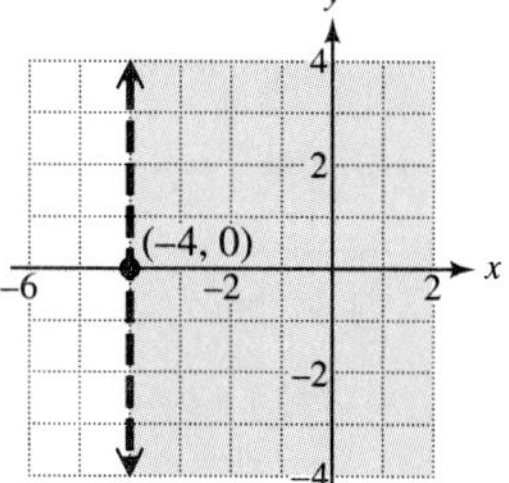

6.

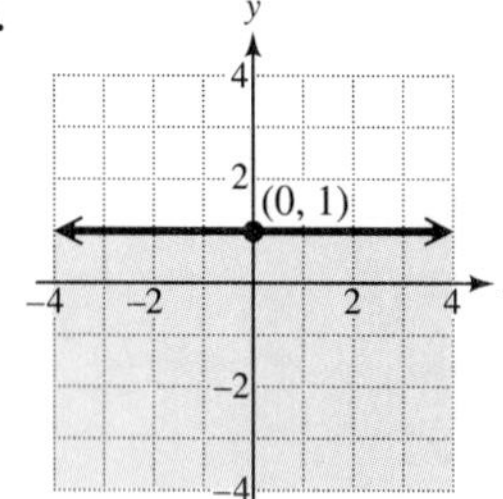

7.

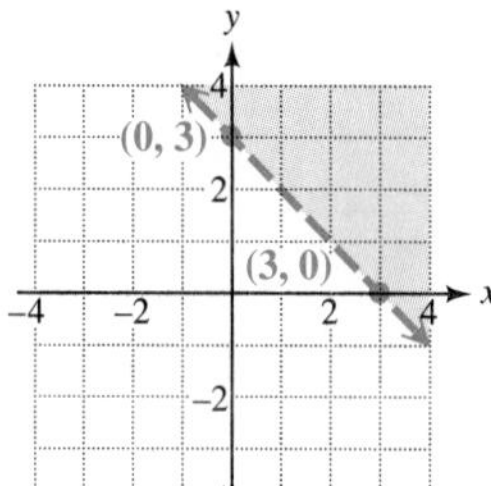

8.

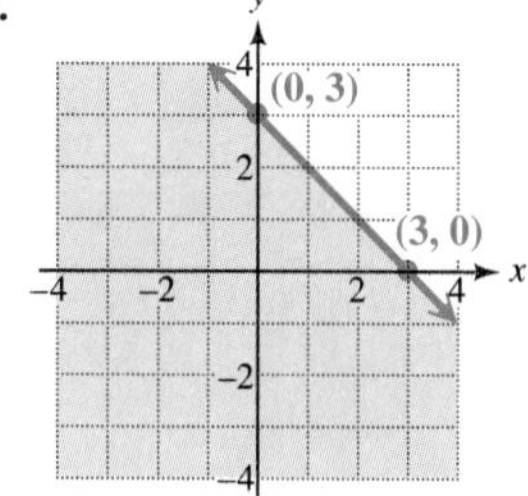

9.
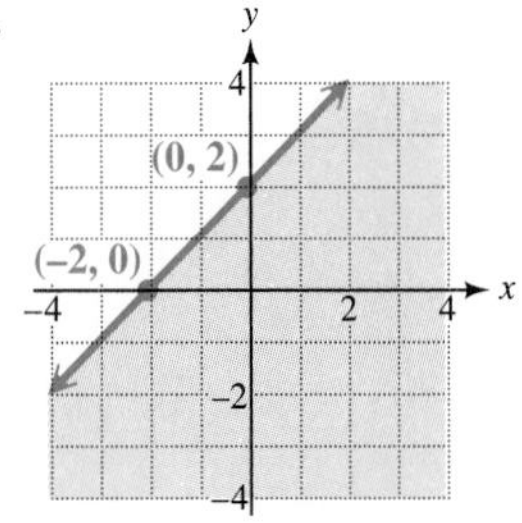

10.
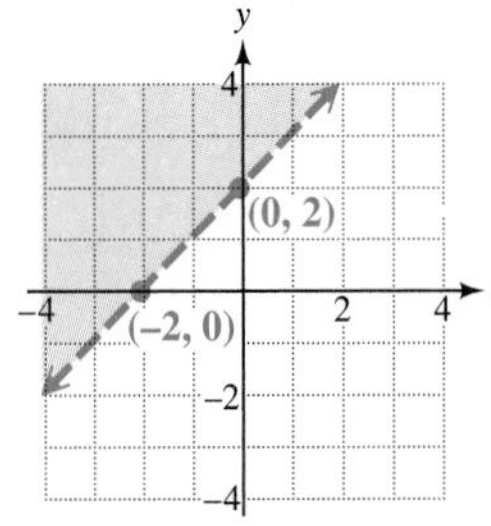

11.
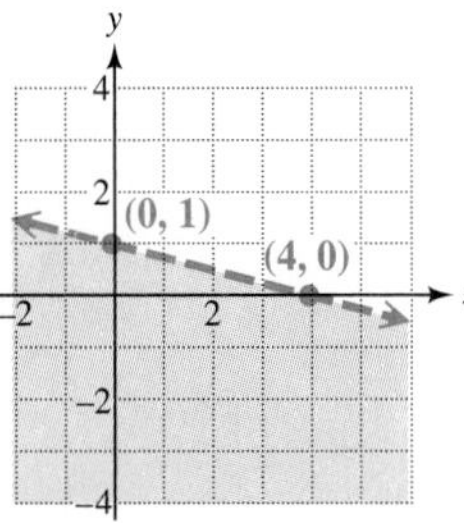

12.
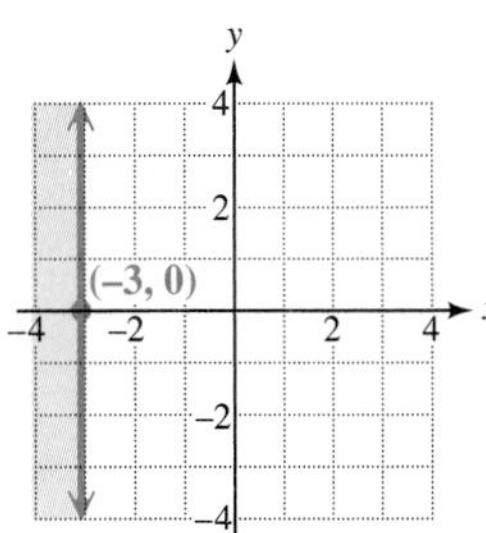

13.
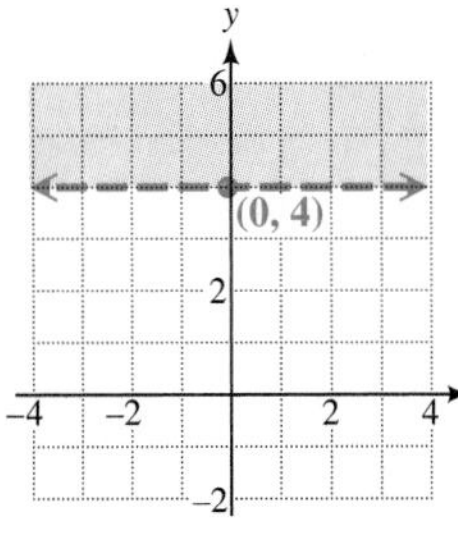

14.
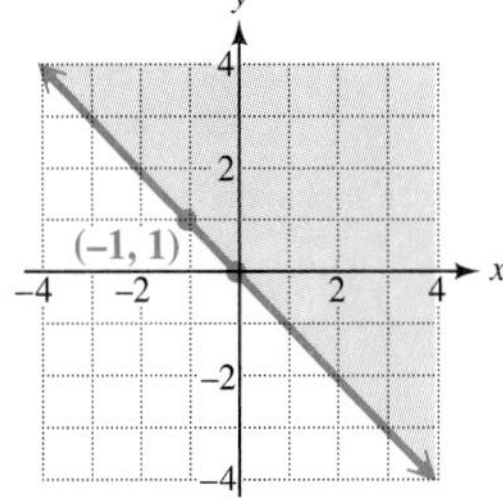

15. $-\frac{8}{13}$ **16.** undefined slope **17.** 0 (zero slope) **18.** $y = \frac{4}{3}x + 4$; slope is $\frac{4}{3}$, y-intercept is (0, 4) **19.** $y = 3 = 0x + 3$; slope is 0, y-intercept is (0, 3) **20.** $x - 5y = -21$ **21.** $3x - 2y = -6$ **22.** The lines are parallel since both have slope $\frac{1}{3}$.

Chapter 4 Review Exercises (PAGE 208)

1.
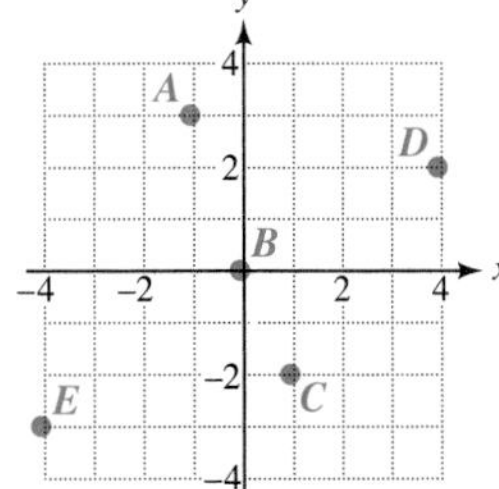

A is in II: *B* is origin; *C* is in IV; *D* is in I; *E* is in III

2. (0, 2), (3, 0), $\left(-2, \frac{10}{3}\right)$ **3.** (3, 17,000); 17,000 **4.** (a), (e), and (f) are linear

5. x-intercept (4, 0); y-intercept (0, −3)

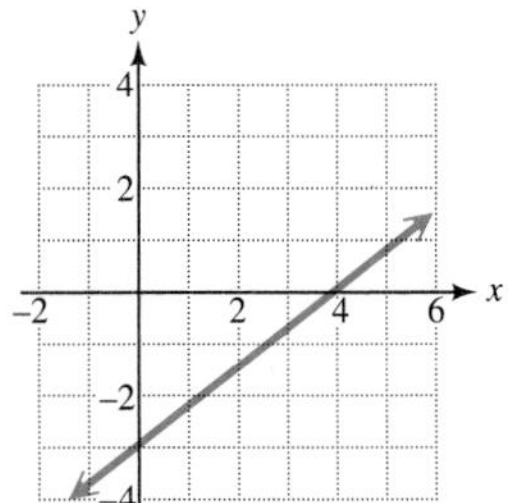

6. x-intercept $\left(-\frac{3}{2}, 0\right)$; no y-intercept

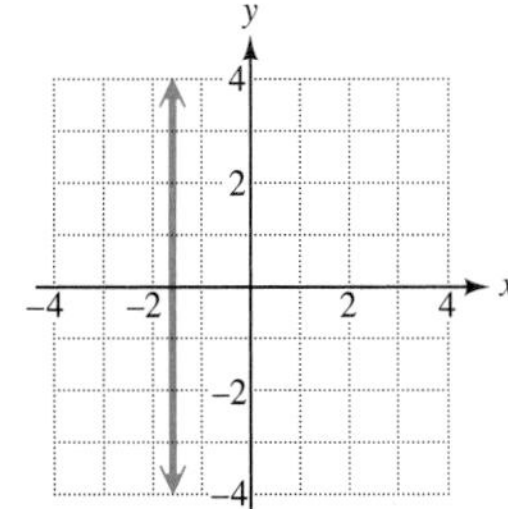

7. x-intercept (0, 0); y-intercept (0, 0); another point is (2, 1)

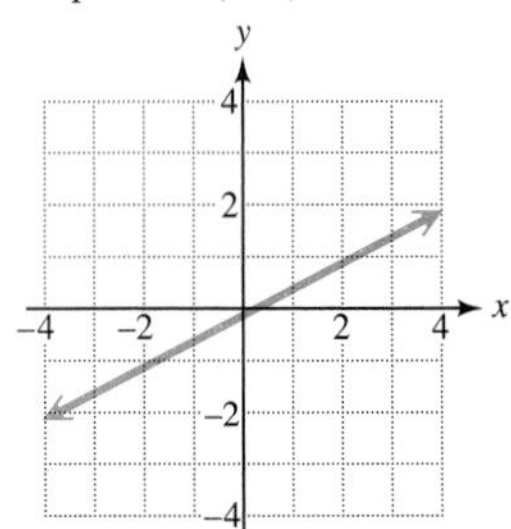

8. no x-intercept; y-intercept (0, 3)

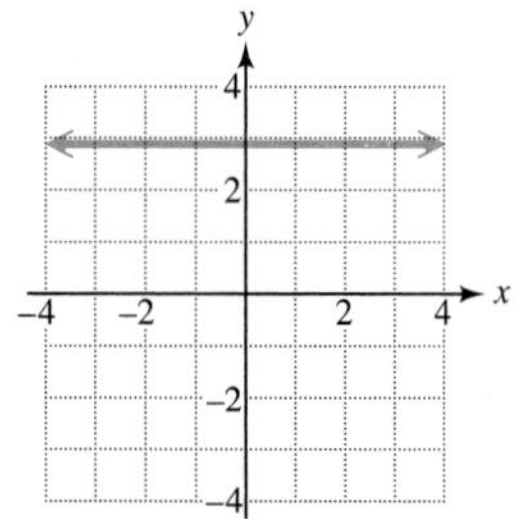

9. $\frac{2}{3}$ **10.** $\frac{2}{3}$ **11.** undefined slope **12.** They are parallel. **13.** They are perpendicular. **14.** $y = -8x + 3$; slope is -8; y-intercept is (0, 3) **15.** $y = 0x - \frac{4}{3}$; slope is 0; y-intercept is $\left(0, -\frac{4}{3}\right)$ **16.** $2x + 3y = 12$ **17.** $5x - 6y = 7$

18.

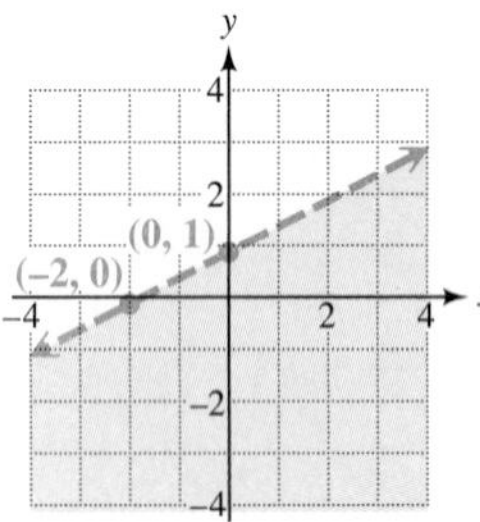

19.

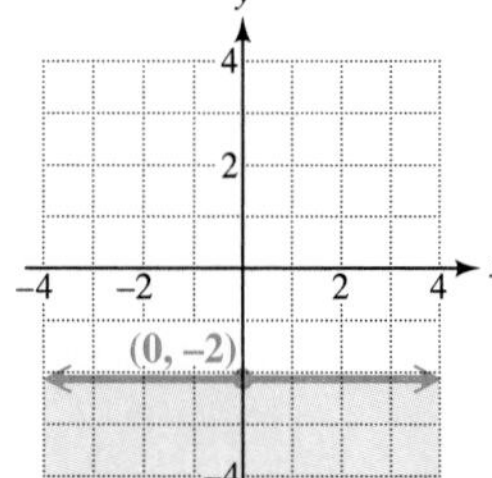

20.

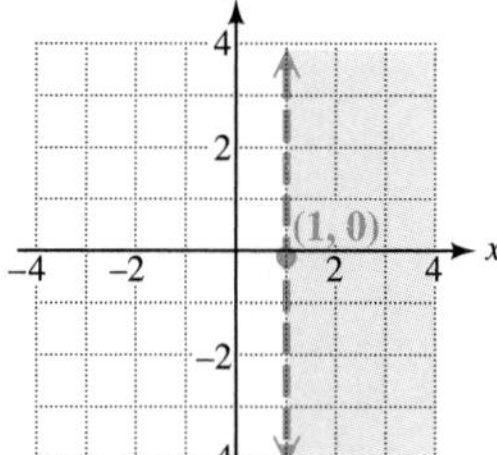

21.

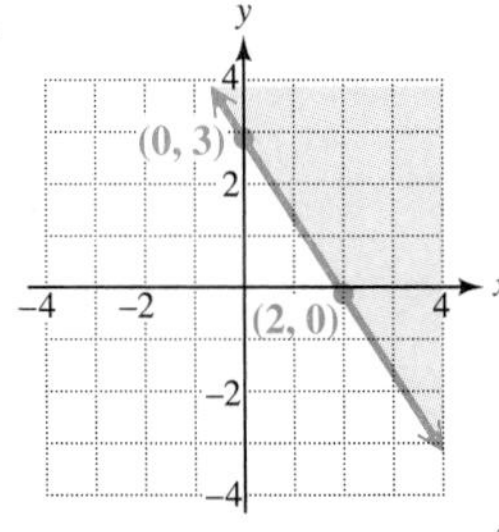

22. They coincide. **23.** $y = \frac{3}{2}x - 4$; slope is $\frac{3}{2}$; y-intercept is $(0, -4)$ **24.** $y = \frac{1}{5}x - \frac{4}{5}$; slope is $\frac{1}{5}$; y-intercept is $\left(0, -\frac{4}{5}\right)$ **25.** $3x + y = 17$ **26.** $x + 3y = 19$ **27.** true **28.** true **29.** false (y-intercept $(0, -3)$) **30.** false (only one intercept (0, 0)) **31.** true **32.** true **33.** false (slope 0) **34.** false $\left(\text{slope } \frac{1}{2}\right)$ **35.** true **36.** true

Chapter 4 Test (PAGE 209)

1. IV **2.** $\left(-3, \frac{2}{5}\right)$ **3.** 400 items **4.** false **5.** $\frac{1}{3}$ **6.** $y = -\frac{2}{5}x + 4$; $-\frac{2}{5}$; (0, 4) **7.** $6x + y = 19$ **8.** perpendicular

9.

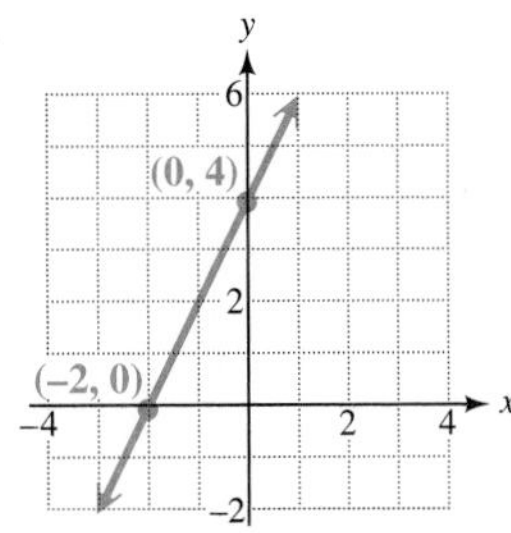

10.

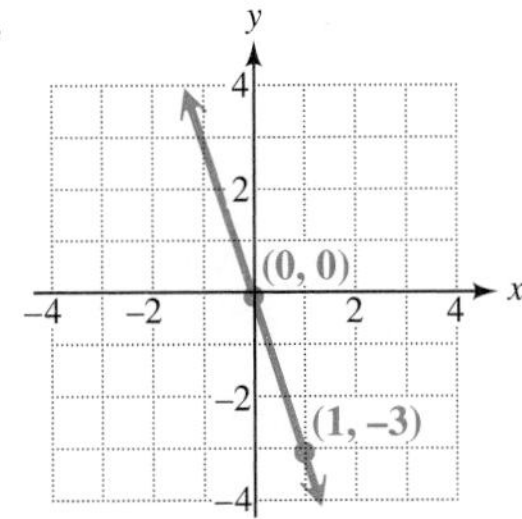

11.

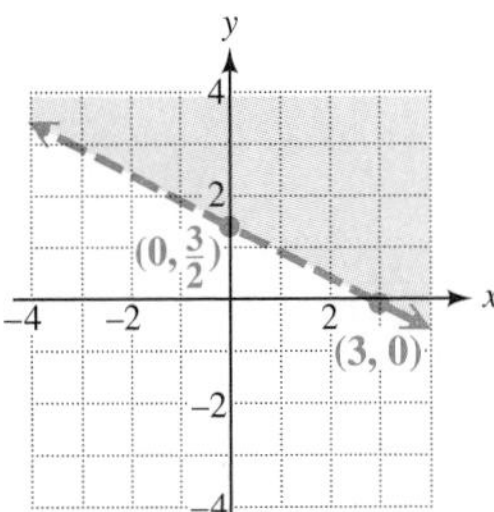

12.

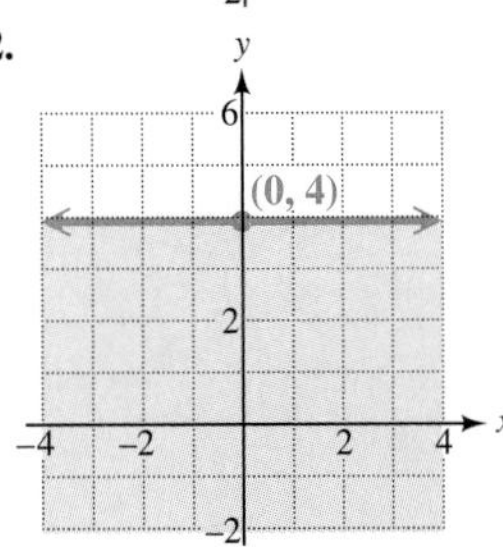

13. false ($a = 0$) **14.** true **15.** true **16.** The formula for slope is the change in y divided by the change in x. For a vertical line this gives a zero in the denominator, which is not defined.

Chapter 4 Answers to Selected Enrichment Exercises

[4.1] **1. (a)** $(0, -1.2)$ **(c)** $(234.75, 0.6)$ **[4.4]** **5.** $2x - y = -5$ **[4.5]** **1. (c)** yes **(d)** no

CHAPTER 5 SYSTEMS OF LINEAR EQUATIONS

5.1 Exercises (PAGE 215)

1. intersecting **2.** coinciding **3. (a)** coinciding **(b)** parallel **4.** intersecting **5.** intersecting **6.** coinciding **7.** parallel **8.** intersecting **9.** intersecting **10.** intersecting **11.** coinciding **12.** intersecting **13.** coinciding **14.** no **15.** yes **16.** yes **17.** yes **18.** no **19.** no **20.** x-intercept: $(2, 0)$; y-intercept: $(0, -4)$ **21.** x-intercept: $\left(\frac{5}{6}, 0\right)$; y-intercept: $\left(0, \frac{5}{2}\right)$ **22.** x-intercept: $\left(-\frac{2}{3}, 0\right)$; y-intercept: $\left(0, \frac{2}{5}\right)$

5.2 Exercises (PAGE 220)

1. none **2.** one (exactly one) **3.** infinitely many **4.** one solution: $(1, 1)$ **5.** infinitely many solutions **6.** no solution **7.** one solution: $(2, 1)$ **8.** one solution: $(1, 2)$ **9.** one solution: $\left(\frac{2}{3}, \frac{3}{2}\right)$ **10.** infinitely many solutions **11.** no solution **12.** yes **13.** no **14.** yes **15.** -7 **16.** 14

5.3 Exercises (PAGE 224)

1. There are infinitely many solutions; any solution to one equation is a solution to the other and therefore a solution to the system. **2.** There are no solutions. **3.** $(3, 11)$; first equation is already solved for y **4.** $(16, 6)$; second equation is already solved for x **5.** $(-2, 10)$ **6.** $(2, -4)$ **7.** no solution **8.** infinitely many solutions **9.** $(6, 5)$ **10.** $(1, 1)$; neither variable is better to solve for than the other **11.** $(5, 3)$ **12.** Neither variable is better to solve for than the other. **13.** y in the first equation **14.** x in the second equation **15.** no solution **16.** $(1, 4)$ **17.** $(2, 0)$

5.4 Exercises (PAGE 231)

1. no solution **2.** infinitely many **3.** $(5, 1)$ **4.** $\left(5, \frac{3}{2}\right)$ **5.** $(1, 1)$ **6.** infinitely many solutions **7.** no solution **8.** $(1, -2)$ **9.** $(0, -3)$ **10.** $(-1, -3)$ **11.** $(10, -2)$ **12.** no solution **13.** $(-2, 0)$ **14.** $(3, -4)$ **15.** $(-2, 5)$

16. (1, 4) **17.** (1, 1) **18.** (5, 10) **19.** $x + 5 = 12$ **20.** $4(x + 2) = 60$ **21.** $x = 2x - 10$ **22.** $0.40x = 20$ **23.** $60 = x - 0.20x$

5.5 Exercises (PAGE 240)

1. 13, 26 **2.** Burford is 15, Mike is 13. **3.** 25°, 155° **4.** 20, 27 **5.** 11 yr, 8 yr **6.** 6 yr, 18 yr **7.** 18, 3 **8.** 12°, 78° **9.** 11 ft, 19 ft **10.** 65 **11.** 10 lb ($1.50), 20 lb (90¢) **12.** 11 nickels, 23 dimes **13.** 3 dimes, 10 quarters **14.** 10 lb (48¢), 10 lb (60¢) **15.** 210 adults, 240 children **16.** 18 gal of 20%, 6 gal of 60% **17.** Terry: 15 mph, wind: 5 mph **18.** Karin: 18 mph, wind: 6 mph **19.** $2000 at 10%, $8000 at 12% **20.** $7000 at 9%, $13,000 at 11% **21.** $14 per day, 10¢ per mile **22.** $20 per day, 12¢ per mile **23.** $(-2, -8)$ **24.** $(-5, 0)$

Chapter 5 Review Exercises (PAGE 244)

1. coinciding **2.** parallel **3.** intersecting **4.** $(2, -3)$ **5.** $(-1, 4)$ **6.** infinitely many solutions **7.** $(-3, 1)$ **8.** no solution **9.** $\left(8, -\frac{1}{2}\right)$ **10.** 17, 20 **11.** Barb is 10, Cindy is 7. **12.** 10 nickels, 15 dimes **13.** 15 pounds (80¢), 35 pounds ($1.00) **14.** 20 mph **15.** $2000 **16.** 6 liters of 50%, 4 liters of 25% **17.** 10 mph **18.** $(2, -4)$ **19.** $\left(\frac{1}{2}, 5\right)$ **20.** $\left(-\frac{2}{3}, \frac{3}{2}\right)$ **21.** 14°, 76° **22.** 12 years, 5 years **23.** true **24.** true **25.** false (sometimes have fractions) **26.** false (infinitely many) **27.** true **28.** true

Chapter 5 Test (PAGE 245)

1. intersecting lines **2.** no **3.** $(3, -1)$ **4.** no solution **5.** infinitely many **6.** 3, 15 **7.** 24°, 156° **8.** 30 nickels, 22 dimes **9.** 450 mph **10.** 40 lb candy, 60 lb nuts **11.** At some step an identity is obtained.

Chapter 5 Answers to Selected Enrichment Exercises

[5.2] **1.** $c = \frac{7}{3}$ **[5.3]** **2.** $(-70, 20)$ **[5.4]** **1.** $\left(3, \frac{13}{7}\right)$ **[5.5]** **2.** $14,000

CHAPTER 6 EXPONENTS AND POLYNOMIALS

6.1 Exercises (PAGE 256)

1. 8^4 **2.** 2^2y^3 **3.** $(2x)^4$ **4.** $2yyyy$ **5.** $(2y)(2y)(2y)(2y)$ **6.** $aa + bb$ **7.** x^7 **8.** a^9 **9.** $2y^{10}$ **10.** $a^1 = a$ **11.** $2y^2$ **12.** a^{12} **13.** $16x^{12}$ **14.** $2x^{12}$ **15.** $\frac{16}{x^{12}}$ **16.** cannot be simplified further **17.** 1 **18.** undefined **19.** 1 **20.** $\frac{1}{2x}$ **21.** $\frac{2}{x}$ **22.** $\frac{2}{x^2}$ **23.** $\frac{3}{y^3}$ **24.** $\frac{1}{9y^2}$ **25.** $\frac{3}{y^2}$ **26.** $\frac{27}{y^6}$ **27.** $\frac{x^6}{4y^2}$ **28.** $\frac{a^4}{b^2}$ **29.** $\frac{b^4}{a^4}$ **30.** $\frac{b^5}{a^6}$ **31.** $12x^3y^5$ **32.** $108x^{10}y^7$ **33.** $-8x^5y^5$ **34.** $\frac{y}{x}$ **35.** $\frac{a^2}{b^{12}}$ **36.** $\frac{x^5}{3y^7}$ **37.** x^4y^2 **38.** $\frac{y^{12}}{x^8}$ **39.** $\frac{x^2}{9y^2}$ **40.** $\frac{a^5}{b}$ **41.** $\frac{a^6b^6}{4}$ **42.** $\frac{b^9}{8a^{24}}$ **43.** 12 **44.** 36 **45.** -12 **46.** 36 **47.** -9 **48.** 9 **49.** -5 **50.** 25 **51.** $\frac{1}{4}$ **52.** 4 **53.** -4 **54.** $\frac{13}{36}$ **55.** 1 **56.** $-\frac{9}{2}$ **57.** $-\frac{1}{8}$ **58.** $\frac{1}{8}$ **59.** $-\frac{1}{6}$ **60.** $-\frac{1}{6}$

6.2 Exercises (PAGE 260)

1. 3.7×10^2 **2.** 3.7×10^{-3} **3.** 9.8×10^4 **4.** 7.56×10^{-11} **5.** 2.65×10^9 **6.** 1×10^{-2} **7.** 230 **8.** 0.023 **9.** 0.000087 **10.** 4,580,000 **11.** 0.0000000751 **12.** 66,400,000,000 **13.** 4×10^{11} **14.** 8×10^{11} **15.** 5×10^{-3} **16.** 6.6×10^{-4} **17.** 3×10^{14} **18.** 2×10^{-5} **19.** 2.78×10^{-7} **20.** 5.87×10^{12} mi **21.** $-\frac{1}{2}$ **22.** $\frac{1}{4}$ **23.** 4 **24.** $\frac{1}{3}$ **25.** $\frac{1}{49}$ **26.** $\frac{21}{100}$

6.3 Exercises (PAGE 266)

1. (a) binomial (b) $-3x^2$, 2 (c) -3, 2 **2.** (a) monomial (b) $2a$ (c) 2 **3.** (a) polynomial (b) $-4y^2$, $2y^3$, $-7y$, 1 (c) -4, 2, -7, 1 **4.** (a) trinomial (b) x^2, $-2xy$, y^2 (c) 1, -2, 1 **5.** 2 **6.** 1 **7.** 0 **8.** 14 **9.** 4 **10.** 0 **11.** 4 **12.** $5x$ **13.** $-3y$ **14.** $15a^2 - 4a$ **15.** $-10b^2 + 3$ **16.** $-x^4 - x^3 + 2$ **17.** 0 **18.** 8 **19.** $\frac{5}{8}y^2$ **20.** $0.27b^3$

21. $-3xy$ **22.** $5x^2 + 2y^2$ (no like terms) **23.** $7xy - 2y^2$ **24.** $2a^2b^2$ **25.** $-7x^2y + 2xy^2 + x^2$ **26.** 0 **27.** 17 **28.** 27 **29.** -221 **30.** 7 **31.** \$37.50 **32.** $2x + 10$, \$210 **33.** 2.65×10^5 **34.** 9.02×10^{-7} **35.** 0.000675 **36.** 106,000,000 **37.** x **38.** $-x + 1$ **39.** $x + 1 - a$ **40.** $-a - x + 2$

6.4 Exercises (PAGE 272)

1. $-5x - 1$ **2.** $8x^2 + 4$ **3.** $-2x^5 + 8x^4 - 2x^3 - 2x^2$ **4.** $2x^7 - 2x^6 + 2x^4 + 5x^2 + 2$ **5.** $-2x^3 - x^2 + 10x + 7$ **6.** $11x^5 + 7x^4 + 40x^3 - 17x^2 + 13x - 21$ **7.** $y^2 + 9$ **8.** $7x^5 - 8x^4 - 6x^3 + 6x^2 - 2x$ **9.** $-x^4 + 6x^3 + 7x^2 - 8x - 6$ **10.** $0.09y^3 - 0.88y^2 + 2y + 2.3$ **11.** $x - 11$ **12.** $-2x^2 + 7$ **13.** $-5y^2 - y - 2$ **14.** $y^2 - y - 7$ **15.** $7a^5 - 3a^4 - 5a^3 + 2a^2 + 3a$ **16.** $-7x^{10} - x^6 + 7x^5 - 3x^2$ **17.** $-15y^2 + 7$ **18.** $-3a + 4$ **19.** $6y^7 + 5y^5 - 3y^2 - 3y + 4$ **20.** $-3y^{12} + 6y^{10}$ **21.** $2y^2 - 3y - 13$ **22.** $-4a^2 + 4a + 4$ **23.** $-x^2y^2 - 11xy$ **24.** $9x^2 + 5$ **25.** $4a^2b + ab$ **26.** $-8a^2b + ab - 8ab^2$ **27.** $9x^2y - 5xy - 2xy^2$ **28.** $3x^2y - 5xy + 12xy^2$ **29.** $2n^2 - 5n + 7$ **30.** $n^2 + 6n - 4$ **31.** \$157 **32.** \$156 **33.** $24x + 6$ **34.** $-3x^2 - 3x + 186$ **35.** 5 **36.** 0 **37.** 30 **38.** 17 **39.** -1 **40.** \$370 **41.** $-6x^2$ **42.** $6x^2$ **43.** $4x^3$ **44.** $-10x^4$

6.5 Exercises (PAGE 280)

1. $12x$ **2.** $8y^4$ **3.** $-72y^5$ **4.** $56y^{11}$ **5.** $2x + 6$ **6.** $3x^2 - 12x$ **7.** $-4y^2 - 32y$ **8.** $6x^2 - 9x + 3$ **9.** $-10x^7 + 60x^5 - 70x^4$ **10.** $-36a^7 + 27a^5 - 18a^3$ **11.** $x^2 + 12x + 32$ **12.** $6a^2 - 13a + 6$ **13.** $x^3 - 8x^2 + 17x - 10$ **14.** $6y^3 + 23y^2 + 5y - 7$ **15.** $a^6 + 1$ **16.** $2x^4 + 7x^3 - 5x^2 + 14x - 6$ **17.** $x^2 + 12x + 20$ **18.** $a^2 - 36$ **19.** $y^2 + 2y - 15$ **20.** $x^2 - 10x + 21$ **21.** $x^2 - 8x - 48$ **22.** $a^2 - 16a + 64$ **23.** $5a^2 - 38a + 21$ **24.** $2y^2 + 13y - 70$ **25.** $6a^2 + 19a + 15$ **26.** $8y^2 - 26y + 15$ **27.** $15x^2 + 14x - 8$ **28.** $18a^2 - 59a - 14$ **29.** $40y^2 + 46y - 5$ **30.** $21x^2 - 41x - 40$ **31.** $2z^4 - 3z^2 - 2$ **32.** $3a^3 - 12a^2 + 5a - 20$ **33.** $14a^5 - 31a^3 + 15a$ **34.** $9a^4 - 30a^2 + 25$ **35.** $49y^6 - 4$ **36.** $40x^6 - 11x^4 - 21x^2$ **37.** $3x^3 + 7x^2 - 18x + 8$ **38.** $48a^5 + 84a^4 - 12a^3 + 11a^2 + 56a$ **39.** $84a^5 - 78a^3 + 28a^2 + 18a - 12$ **40.** $0.15x^3 - 0.21x^2 + 0.10x - 0.14$ **41.** $\frac{1}{3}y^3 + \frac{10}{3}y^2 - \frac{3}{8}y - \frac{15}{4}$ **42.** $3y^4 - 4y^3 - 15y^2 + 28y - 12$ **43.** $-24x^5 + 4x^4 + 8x^3 - 32x^2 + 7x - 5$ **44.** $2x^3y + 4x^2y^2$ **45.** $3a^4b^2 + 6a^3b^2 - 3a^3b^3$ **46.** $10a^2 - 13ab - 3b^2$ **47.** $14a^2 - 39ab + 10b^2$ **48.** $6x^3 - x^2y + 6xy^2 + 4y^3$ **49.** $a^4b^2 + a^3b - 3a^2 - a^2b^4 - ab^3 + 3b^2$ **50.** $x^3 + 2x^2 - x - 2$ **51.** $y^3 + 3y^2 - 4y - 12$ **52.** $(6x^2 - x - 2)$ ft^2 **53.** $(2y^3 + 5y^2 + 3y)$ cm^3 **54.** $R = 5000p - 100p^2$; \$40,000; \$60,000; \$22,500 **55.** $A = w^2 + 300w$; 13,600 m^2; 40,000 m^2; 400,000 m^2 **56.** $y^3 - 5y^2 - 3y + 5$ **57.** $-6x^2 + 3y^2$ **58.** $x^2 - 10x + 25$ **59.** $9x^2 - 4y^2$ **60.** $9x^2 + 12xy + 4y^2$

6.6 Exercises (PAGE 286)

1. $x^2 - 9$ **2.** $x^2 + 10x + 25$ **3.** $x^2 - 10x + 25$ **4.** $y^2 - 64$ **5.** $49a^2 - 1$ **6.** $4x^2 - 28x + 49$ **7.** $16y^2 - 81$ **8.** $25a^2 - 49$ **9.** $9a^2 - 6a + 1$ **10.** $25x^2 - 9$ **11.** $36a^2 + 84a + 49$ **12.** $16x^2 + 64x + 64$ **13.** $9y^2 - 54y + 81$ **14.** $25a^2 - 100$ **15.** $25y^4 - 10y^2 + 1$ **16.** $4x^4 - 9x^2$ **17.** $4y^4 + 12y^3 + 9y^2$ **18.** $4y^4 - 12y^3 + 9y^2$ **19.** $0.49y^2 - 4.2y + 9$ **20.** $\frac{1}{4}a^2 - \frac{1}{9}$ **21.** $25x^2 - 4y^2$ **22.** $25x^2 + 20xy + 4y^2$ **23.** $25x^2 - 20xy + 4y^2$ **24.** $x^4 - y^4$ **25.** $4x^4 - 4x^2y + y^2$ **26.** $64x^2 + 48xy + 9y^2$ **27.** $a^4 + 4a^2b + 4b^2$ **28.** $4x$ **29.** $2a^2 + 8b^2$ **30.** $-8z - 32$ **31.** $(2a^2 + 5a - 7)$ mi^2 **32.** $x^3 + 8$ **33.** $x^3 - 8$ **34.** $y^3 - 125$ **35.** $y^3 + 125$ **36.** $27x^3 + y^3$ **37.** $27x^3 - y^3$ **38.** $-3a^3b^2 + 3a^3b - 21a^2$ **39.** $15a^2 - 19a - 56$ **40.** $2x^3 - 3x^2y + 2xy^2 - y^3$ **41.** $5x$ **42.** $2x$ **43.** $-\frac{y^3}{x}$

6.7 Exercises (PAGE 292)

1. $x^3 - 3x^2 + 9x + 1$ **2.** $2x^4 - x^2 + 4$ **3.** $5a^2 - 4a + 3$ **4.** $y^5 - y^3 + y^2$ **5.** $\frac{1}{2}x^3 - \frac{5}{2}x^2 + 1$ **6.** $x - 8$ **7.** $4x^2 - 3x + 2$ **8.** $-40x^2 + 30x - 20$ **9.** $-4y^2 + 8y - \frac{2}{y}$ **10.** $-2xy^2 + 3x$ **11.** $3xy - 2y^3 + 4$ **12.** $2xy - \frac{7}{xy}$ **13.** $x - 2$ **14.** $a + 2$ **15.** $y + 1$ **16.** $y - 4 - \frac{22}{y - 4}$ **17.** $3a - 8$ **18.** $-2y + 10$ **19.** $7x^2 - 4x - 5 - \frac{6}{4x + 6}$ **20.** $5x^3 - 4$ **21.** $2a^2 + 2a + 19 + \frac{148}{3a - 12}$ **22.** $y^4 - 2y^3 + 4y^2 - 8y + 16$ **23.** $3x + 10 - \frac{5x + 30}{3x^2 + 2}$ **24.** $x^2 + 1$ **25.** $3x + 5$ **26.** $x - 6$ **27.** $16x^2 - 1$ **28.** $36x^2 - 60x + 25$ **29.** $4a^2 + 52a + 169$ **30.** $a^4 - 25$ **31.** $y^6 - 4y^3 + 4$ **32.** $4y^4 + 28y^2 + 49$ **33.** $3 \cdot 3 \cdot 5$ **34.** $2 \cdot 3 \cdot 5 \cdot 7$ **35.** $2 \cdot 2 \cdot 11 \cdot 17$ **36.** $5 \cdot 5 \cdot 5 \cdot 13$

Chapter 6 Review Exercises (PAGE 295)

1. a^5 **2.** $(3z)^3$ **3.** $(a+b)^2$ **4.** $bbbbbbb$ **5.** $-2xxx$ **6.** $(-2x)(-2x)(-2x)$ **7.** $2y^9$ **8.** $27x^6$ **9.** 1 **10.** $\frac{5}{a}$
11. $\frac{1}{5a}$ **12.** $\frac{b}{a}$ **13.** $\frac{b^6}{a^4}$ **14.** $\frac{b^8}{a^9}$ **15.** $\frac{2y^2}{x^4}$ **16.** 4.11×10^{-7} **17.** 5.49×10^{11} **18.** 6,150,000,000,000
19. 0.00000004 **20.** monomial **21.** binomial **22.** trinomial **23.** 7 **24.** 10 **25.** 8 **26.** $-x+2$
27. $11y^2 - y + 5$ **28.** $6a^2 - 5a$ **29.** $6x^5 - 8x^4 - 7x^2 - 7x - 5$ **30.** $4xy - 3$ **31.** $4a^2b^3 - 6a^2b^2 - ab^2$ **32.** $360
33. $-2x^2 - 3$ **34.** $x^3 - 3x^2 + 15$ **35.** $-3x^4 + 3x^3 + 6x^2 + 14x + 1$ **36.** $3x^2y^2 - xy - 2$
37. $29x^4 - 20x^3 + 2x^2 + 8x - 44$ **38.** $0.4x^3 + 0.9x^2 + 1.1x + 6$ **39.** $x^2 - 2x - 80$ **40.** $6x^2 - 5x - 4$ **41.** $16a^2 - 24a + 9$
42. $20y^2 - 59y + 42$ **43.** $\frac{9}{16} - 4y^6$ **44.** $2x^3 + 9x^2 + x - 12$ **45.** $3x^4 + x^3 - 7x^2 + 5x - 2$ **46.** $2x^3 + 9x^2y + xy^2 - 12y^3$
47. $12x^3y^3 - 20x^2y^2 + 13xy - 15$ **48.** $28a^2 + 17ab - 3b^2$ **49.** $16x^2 - y^2$ **50.** $64x^2 + 16xy + y^2$ **51.** $3x^2y^2 - xy + 5$
52. $2a^2 - 3b^2 + \frac{5}{a}$ **53.** $x + 7$ **54.** $4x + 3$ **55.** $7x^3 + 3x^2 - 2x - 5$ **56.** $x^2 + 5x + 25 + \frac{25}{x-5}$
57. $R = 1200p - 100p^2$; $2000 **58.** 1.86×10^5 mi per sec. **59.** $10x^2 + x - 2$ **60.** $8x^2y^2 - 3xy - 1$ **61.** $x + 3$
62. $25a^2 - 10ab + b^2$ **63.** $2x^3$ **64.** $12a^5b^5 - 15a^4b^2 - 6a^3b^2$ **65.** $\frac{y^4}{x^6}$ **66.** $\frac{y^6}{x^6}$ **67.** $\frac{1}{a^4b}$ **68.** 5 **69.** 3
70. binomial **71.** trinomial **72.** true **73.** false ($-3^2 = -9$ and $(-3)^2 = 9$) **74.** false (can have any degree) **75.** true
76. true **77.** false ($(a+b)^2 = a^2 + 2ab + b^2 \neq a^2 + b^2$) **78.** false (binomials) **79.** true **80.** true

Chapter 6 Test (PAGE 297)

1. 5^2a^3 **2.** $2y^7$ **3.** a^4 **4.** $-8x^6$ **5.** $\frac{1}{z^3}$ **6.** $\frac{y^7}{x^8}$ **7.** $-\frac{1}{64}$ **8.** 3×10^{-2} **9.** binomial **10.** 4
11. $-6y^5 + 4y^3 - 6y + 6$ **12.** $-4x^2y^2 + 5x^2y - 4x^2$ **13.** $285 **14.** $-2x + 10$ **15.** $3x^4 + 10x^3 - 3x^2 + 7$
16. $7a^2b^2 + 6ab + 2$ **17.** $-7x + 7$ **18.** $-4x^4 - x^3 + 6x^2 + 1$ **19.** $4a^2b - 4ab^2 - ab$ **20.** $-12x^4 + 16x^3 - 4x^2$
21. $x^2 - 3x - 40$ **22.** $8a^2 + 22a - 21$ **23.** $3y^3 + 22y^2 - 15y + 8$ **24.** $4x^2 - y^2$ **25.** $9x^2 - 24xy + 16y^2$
26. $4x^2 + 20x + 25$ **27.** $6x^3 - 5x^2 + 6x + 8$ **28.** $x^4 - 9$ **29.** $5x^2 - 2x - 3$ **30.** $3x^2 - 2x + 4$
31. false ($(x+y)^2 = x^2 + 2xy + y^2 \neq x^2 + y^2$) **32.** false ($(-w)^2 = (-w)(-w) = w^2 \neq -w^2$)

Chapter 6 Answers to Selected Enrichment Exercises

[6.1] **9.** $\frac{3y^4}{4x^5z}$ **12.** $\frac{a^{14}}{b^2}$ **[6.2]** **2.** 3×10^7 **[6.3]** **3.** 3 **5.** $8x^4y^4 - 4x^2y + 7xy^3$
[6.4] **1.** $\frac{4}{9}x^4 - \frac{5}{4}x^3 + \frac{2}{3}x^2 + \frac{4}{3}x + \frac{5}{4}$ **3.** $-0.32a^3 - 2.13a^2 + 5.35a + 6.06$ **[6.5]** **1.** $x^3 + y^3$
4. $2a^3 - a^2b + ab^2 - 2b^3$ **[6.6]** **4.** $a^{2n} - 2a^nb^n + b^{2n}$ **[6.7]** **2.** $2x^3 + 3$ **4.** $3x^4 - 5x^2 + 7$

CHAPTER 7 FACTORING POLYNOMIALS

7.1 Exercises (PAGE 305)

1. 5 **2.** 14 **3.** 1 **4.** $5x$ **5.** $14y$ **6.** y^2 **7.** 2 **8.** 1 **9.** $2y^2$ **10.** $6x^2$ **11.** $6y^3$ **12.** 1 **13.** $5xy$
14. $4xy^2$ **15.** x^3 **16.** 4 **17.** $8y$ **18.** $3a^2$ **19.** $9y^2$ **20.** $2x$ **21.** $a + 2$ **22.** $2x^2y$ **23.** $5ab^2$ **24.** $a + b$
25. $3(x+3)$ **26.** $7(3x-2)$ **27.** $y(18y+11)$ **28.** cannot be factored **29.** $x^6(x^4 - x^2 + 1)$ **30.** $6y(y^3 - 4y + 2)$
31. $5x(12x^2 + 10x - 5)$ **32.** $-2y^5(3y^5 + 4y^3 + 2)$ **33.** cannot be factored **34.** $xy(xy+1)$ **35.** $2ab(3a-b)$
36. $9xy^2(3x^2+5)$ **37.** $5xy(3x^2y^2 + xy + 2)$ **38.** $(a+2)(a^2+3)$ **39.** $(a+b)(x^2+y^2)$ **40.** $(a+2)(a^2+3)$
41. $(a+b)(x^2+y^2)$ **42.** $(b-1)(a^2+5)$ **43.** $(x+2)(x^2-7)$ **44.** $(b^2+1)(a^3+2)$ **45.** $(y-3)(x^2+1)$
46. $(ab+1)(a^3-b^2)$ **47.** $-(x^2+3)(y+1)$ **48.** $A = P(1 + 0.09) = P(1.09)$; **(a)** $109 **(b)** $1090 **(c)** $4945.71
49. He did not factor out the GCF. The answer should be $4x^2(x+2)$ **50.** The answer should be $-3x^2y(y-2)$.
51. $2x$; $5y$; $10xy$; the GCF of the product is the product of GCFs. **52.** $x^2 - 4x - 21$ **53.** $x^2 - 10x + 21$
54. $x^2 + 7xy + 12y^2$ **55.** $x^2 + xy - 12y^2$

7.2 Exercises (PAGE 313)

1. $(x+1)(x+3)$ **2.** $(x-1)(x+3)$ **3.** $(x+1)(x-3)$ **4.** $(x-1)(x-3)$ **5.** $(u-5)(u-7)$ **6.** $(u+5)(u-7)$ **7.** $(y+3)(y+7)$ **8.** cannot be factored **9.** $(x-3)(x-9)$ **10.** $(y+7)(y-8)$ **11.** $(x+7)(x-9)$ **12.** $(x+10)(x-12)$ **13.** $(x-7)(x+11)$ **14.** $(x+y)(x+3y)$ **15.** $(x-y)(x+3y)$ **16.** $(x+y)(x-3y)$ **17.** $(x-y)(x-3y)$ **18.** $(u-4v)(u+5v)$ **19.** $(x-2y)(x+15y)$ **20.** $(x+3y)(x+8y)$ **21.** $(u-3v)(u-5v)$ **22.** $(u-8v)(u+5v)$ **23.** $(x-4y)(x-6y)$ **24.** $(x+5y)(x+6y)$ **25.** $2(u+6v)(u+6v)$ **26.** $-2(u+6v)(u-7v)$ **27.** $y(x-9y)(x+10y)$ **28.** $3(x+4y)(x-8y)$ **29.** $v^2(u-11v)(u-11v)$ **30.** $-5(u+7v)(u+11v)$ **31.** $h=-16(t-3)(t+1)$; **(a)** 64 ft **(b)** 48 ft **(c)** 0 ft (the rock has hit the water) **32.** The GCF 2 has been left off in the answer. **33.** $35(x-2)$ **34.** $7a^2b^2(4a^2b^2-2ab-3)$ **35.** $(x+y)(2a-3b)$ **36.** $(x-6)(x^2+5)$ **37.** $(5a+2b)(x^2+y^2)$ **38.** $2x^2+7x+3$ **39.** $6x^2-13x+5$ **40.** $10x^2+x-2$

7.3 Exercises (PAGE 320)

1. $(2x+5)(x+1)$ **2.** $(2x-3)(x-1)$ **3.** $(2u+1)(u-3)$ **4.** $(2u-1)(u+7)$ **5.** $(2y-3)(y+8)$ **6.** $(2y+3)(y+8)$ **7.** $(2z-7)(3z+4)$ **8.** $(5x-8)(x-5)$ **9.** $(-3)(2x+9)(x+2)$ **10.** $7(u-1)(u-1)$ **11.** $4(2u-1)(2u-1)$ **12.** cannot be factored **13.** $y(3y+5)(y+2)$ **14.** $(-5)(3x-5)(3x-5)$ **15.** $3(2x^2-x+7)$; the trinomial cannot be factored **16.** $(2u-5)(3u-4)$ **17.** $(2x+5y)(x+y)$ **18.** $(2u+v)(u-3v)$ **19.** $(2u-v)(u+7v)$ **20.** $(3x-y)(x-3y)$ **21.** $(3x+7y)(x+2y)$ **22.** $(3u-v)(2u+v)$ **23.** $(-3)(x-4y)(x-2y)$ **24.** cannot be factored **25.** $(2u+v)(2u-v)$ **26.** $uv(3u-v)(u+5v)$ **27.** $(6x+y)(x-6y)$ **28.** $(3x+10y)(2x+3y)$ **29.** $2(7x+8y)(x+y)$ **30.** $xy(3x+y)(x-y)$ **31.** $(x-3y)(x+9y)$ **32.** $(x-9y)(x-9y)$ **33.** $-3(x+5)(x-8)$ **34.** $16u^2+40u+25$ **35.** $16u^2-40u+25$ **36.** $16u^2-25$

7.4 Exercises (PAGE 326)

1. $(x+5)^2$ **2.** $(x-5)^2$ **3.** $(x+5)(x-5)$ **4.** cannot be factored **5.** $(u-7)^2$ **6.** $(x-12)^2$ **7.** $(x+11)(x-11)$ **8.** $(3u+1)^2$ **9.** $(3u-1)^2$ **10.** $(2y-3)^2$ **11.** $(2x+5)^2$ **12.** $(3u+5)(3u-5)$ **13.** $(-3)(2y-5)^2$ **14.** $(2y-9)^2$ **15.** $(3x+5)^2$ **16.** cannot be factored **17.** $8u(u+1)(u-1)$ **18.** $(u^3+4)(u^3-4)$ **19.** $5y(y-10)^2$ **20.** $7(y^2+3)(y^2-3)$ **21.** $(x+3y)^2$ **22.** $(5x-y)^2$ **23.** $(8u+3v)(8u-3v)$ **24.** $(u^2+v^2)(u+v)(u-v)$ **25.** $(x+3)(x+6)$ **26.** $(x-6)^2$ **27.** $(u+2)(u+8)$ **28.** $(2y-7)^2$ **29.** $-6(x+9)(x-9)$ **30.** $(5u-2)^2$ **31.** $(4u+3)(4u-3)$ **32.** $(2y-3)(2y-5)$ **33.** $(8y-1)(5y+2)$ **34.** $3x^3(x^3+7)(x^3-7)$ **35.** $2(7x^3+3)(7x^3-3)$ **36.** $(3x+2y)(x-7y)$ **37.** $2(3u+7v)(3u-7v)$ **38.** $x^3(10x-3y)^2$ **39.** $(x+y+5)(x+y-5)$ **40.** $-\frac{5}{2}$ **41.** $\frac{1}{6}$ **42.** 0

7.5 Exercises (PAGE 331)

1. 5, −7 **2.** −6, −1 **3.** −2, 2 **4.** 0.5, −0.2 **5.** $\frac{1}{2}, -\frac{2}{5}$ **6.** 8 **7.** $-\frac{2}{3}$, 6 **8.** $-\frac{1}{5}, \frac{3}{2}$ **9.** $\frac{5}{8}, \frac{8}{3}$ **10.** $0, -\frac{7}{3}$ **11.** $\frac{5}{2}$, −12 **12.** 2, 3 **13.** −2, 3 **14.** 1, 7 **15.** −5, 4 **16.** −5 **17.** 5, 8 **18.** −6, 7 **19.** −4, 4 **20.** 0, 2 **21.** $-\frac{3}{2}$ **22.** $\frac{7}{3}, -\frac{7}{3}$ **23.** 6 **24.** 2, −5 **25.** −5, 7 **26.** 5, −7 **27.** $\frac{1}{8}, \frac{5}{2}$ **28.** 3, 2, −1 **29.** 0, −1, −5 **30.** 0, −1, 3 **31.** $7(y-5)^2$ **32.** $(2x-y)(x+5y)$ **33.** $5(3x+4y)(3x-4y)$ **34.** \$32,000

7.6 Exercises (PAGE 335)

1. −5 or 3 **2.** −11 or 4 **3.** 3 cm, 8 cm **4.** 7 ft by 12 ft **5.** 2 cm **6.** 4 in, 1 in **7.** 8 in, 14 in **8.** 28 cm, 7 cm **9.** \$750 **10.** 8 **11.** 21 **12.** 8 **13.** 5 **14.** \$7 or \$10 **15.** $-\frac{1}{3}$ **16.** $-\frac{4}{5}, \frac{4}{5}$ **17.** $-\frac{2}{3}$, 5 **18.** 0 **19.** undefined **20.** −1 **21.** 3 **22.** −18 **23.** −50 **24.** $\frac{2}{5}$ **25.** $\frac{3}{4}$ **26.** $\frac{4}{7}$

Chapter 7 Review Exercises (PAGE 339)

1. $2(4x+1)$ **2.** $3y^2(y^2-3)$ **3.** $(a+b)(a^2+5)$ **4.** $(x-3)(x^2+2)$ **5.** $(y^2+1)(x^2+6)$ **6.** $(x+5)(x-2)$ **7.** $(3y+1)^2$ **8.** $(y-7)(y-1)$ **9.** $(2x+3)(2x-3)$ **10.** $(2y-3)^2$ **11.** $(y-3)(y+15)$ **12.** $(5x-3)(x+3)$ **13.** $2(y+5)(y-5)$ **14.** $(x^2+5)(x^2-5)$ **15.** $(y^2+9)(y+3)(y-3)$ **16.** $(3x-1)(2x+5)$ **17.** $(3y+7)(2y-9)$ **18.** $(x-5y)^2$ **19.** $(x-6y)(x-7y)$ **20.** $(9x+8y)(9x-8y)$ **21.** cannot be factored **22.** $5(x-9y)^2$ **23.** $(3x-4y)(2x+7y)$ **24.** $\frac{1}{2}, -\frac{5}{12}$ **25.** $-\frac{1}{3}, \frac{1}{3}$ **26.** $-\frac{1}{4}$, −1 **27.** 2 **28.** $0, -\frac{1}{2}$ **29.** −7, 12 **30.** 2, 3

31. $-16, -14$; $14, 16$ **32.** 6 cm by 30 cm **33. (a)** \$45 **(b)** 17 **34.** $0, 3, -8$ **35.** $-\frac{5}{2}, \frac{3}{2}$ **36.** $-\frac{1}{3}, 4$ **37.** \$10
38. $(3x + 5)^2$ **39.** $(x + 6)(x - 4)$ **40.** $(2x + a)(x - 5)$ **41.** true **42.** true **43.** false $((a + b)^2 = a^2 + 2ab + b^2)$
44. true **45.** true

Chapter 7 Test (PAGE 340)

1. $4(5x + 3)$ **2.** $7(5y - 1)$ **3.** $6x^2(4x^2 - 2x + 3)$ **4.** $5x^3y^2(y + 8)$ **5.** $(y^2 + 2)(7x^2 - 1)$ **6.** $(x + 7)(x + 8)$
7. $(x - 8)^2$ **8.** $3(y + 5)(y - 5)$ **9.** $(x + 2)(x - 10)$ **10.** $(2x - 3)(x + 8)$ **11.** $(3x + y)(x + 5y)$ **12.** $\frac{5}{4}, -\frac{3}{2}$
13. $6, -5$ **14.** 1 or -4 **15.** 4 cm, 6 cm **16. (a)** \$332 **(b)** 12 **17.** No. The zero-product rule does not apply when the product is not equal to zero. The correct solution is 2 or -4.

Chapter 7 Answers to Selected Enrichment Exercises

[7.1] **14.** $(3ab - 2c)(2abc - 5)$ **[7.2]** **3.** $x(x - 6)$ **[7.5]** **4.** $-\frac{5}{3}$ **[7.6]** **1.** no solution

CHAPTER 8 RATIONAL EXPRESSIONS

8.1 Exercises (PAGE 348)

1. -1 **2.** $0, -3$ **3.** -4 **4.** $1, -4$ **5.** -1 **6.** none **7.** yes **8.** yes **9.** yes **10.** no **11.** no **12.** yes
13. $\frac{7}{10}$ **14.** $\frac{1}{5y}$ **15.** $\frac{2x^2}{y}$ **16.** $\frac{1}{7x^4z}$ **17.** $\frac{z + 9}{z^2 + 9}$ **18.** $\frac{w}{w - 7}$ **19.** $\frac{x + 2}{x - 1}$ **20.** 1 **21.** $-(x + 3)$ **22.** $\frac{y + 4}{y - 4}$
23. $a + b$ **24.** $\frac{x - y}{x + 2y}$ **25.** He divided out (canceled) terms, not factors of the entire numerator and entire denominator.
26. $\frac{1}{x - y}$; both values are 1 **27.** -1 **28.** 1 **29.** $\frac{1}{12}$ **30.** $\frac{3}{2}$ **31.** $\frac{2}{5}$ **32.** $2 \cdot 2 \cdot 3 \cdot 5 \cdot 5$

8.2 Exercises (PAGE 354)

1. $\frac{1}{3x}$ **2.** $\frac{5}{2y^2}$ **3.** $\frac{1}{2x(x + 1)}$ **4.** 1 **5.** $\frac{5(x - 2)}{x - 1}$ **6.** $\frac{y + 2}{y - 2}$ **7.** $\frac{1}{z + 5}$ **8.** $\frac{y + 1}{(y - 3)(y + 5)}$ **9.** $\frac{x(4 + x)}{4 - x}$ **10.** $\frac{a - 7}{a^2}$
11. $(2x - 3y)(x + y)$ **12.** 1 **13.** $\frac{x - y}{x - 2y}$ **14.** $\frac{7}{3}$ **15.** $x + 1$ **16.** $\frac{x + 5}{2x - 3}$ **17.** $\frac{3}{x + 2}$ **18.** $\frac{3}{2}$ **19.** 3
20. $\frac{y(y + 1)}{y - 1}$ **21.** x **22.** $\frac{5(z - 2)}{z - 1}$ **23.** $a + 5$ **24.** $\frac{y + 5}{2}$ **25.** $\frac{1}{6}$ **26.** $\frac{1}{(x + 2y)(x + y)}$ **27.** $\frac{1}{x - y}$ **28.** $(x + 5)^2$
29. $\frac{2a + y}{a - 2y}$ **30.** $0, -2$ **31.** none **32.** 0 **33.** no **34.** yes **35.** no **36. (a)** $\frac{5x}{10}$ **(b)** $\frac{x^2}{2x}$ **(c)** $\frac{x^3}{2x^2}$ **(d)** $\frac{x(x + 1)}{2(x + 1)}$
(e) $\frac{x(2x - 1)}{2(2x - 1)}$ **(f)** $\frac{x(x^2 - 1)}{2(x^2 - 1)}$ **37.** The numerator is 1 not 0 when the common factors are divided out. $\frac{1}{a + 1}$ **38.** $\frac{1}{2}$ **39.** $\frac{9}{14}$
40. $\frac{17}{3}$

8.3 Exercises (PAGE 359)

1. 2 **2.** $\frac{9}{x}$ **3.** 0 **4.** $\frac{y - 1}{y + 2}$ **5.** $\frac{-z}{z + 1}$ **6.** $\frac{3x^2}{3x^2 - 1}$ **7.** $\frac{1}{a + 1}$ **8.** $\frac{7 - 2a}{a}$ **9.** $\frac{x + 7}{3}$ **10.** $\frac{3z + 8}{2z}$ **11.** $\frac{-a}{a - 1}$
12. $\frac{4x + 1}{1 - x}$ **13.** $\frac{1}{a + 1}$ **14.** $\frac{x + 4}{6(x - 2)}$ **15.** $\frac{1}{z - 1}$ **16.** $\frac{1}{x - 2}$ **17.** $\frac{x - 5}{x + 1}$ **18.** $\frac{2(x + y)}{x - y}$ **19.** $\frac{4x - 1}{x + 1}$ **20.** $\frac{-2x}{2x - y}$
21. $\frac{3}{2}$ **22.** 1

8.4 Exercises (PAGE 366)

1. 60 **2.** 1365 **3.** $3y^2$ **4.** $3x(x + 1)$ **5.** $(a + 5)(a - 5)$ **6.** $3(x + 2)(x - 2)$ **7.** $(x - 1)(x + 1)^2$
8. $(z - 3)(z + 3)(z - 2)$ **9.** $(a - 3)(a + 3)(a - 1)$ **10.** $(x + y)(x - y)$ **11.** $6(x + y)$ **12.** $15xy(2x - y)$ **13.** $\frac{23}{42}$

14. $\frac{1}{20}$ **15.** $\frac{2(5x+6)}{45x^2}$ **16.** $\frac{2(y-20)}{(y+5)(y-5)}$ **17.** $\frac{1}{15(x+7)}$ **18.** $\frac{56}{(7-a)(7+a)}$ **19.** $\frac{3-5x}{2x(x-1)}$ **20.** $\frac{3z+5}{3(z+2)}$
21. $\frac{3y+7}{(y-1)(y+1)(y+3)}$ **22.** $\frac{4}{(z-3)(z+3)(z-1)}$ **23.** $\frac{a-1}{(a-4)(a+3)(a-3)}$ **24.** $\frac{12x-11}{(x-3)(x-1)(x+2)}$ **25.** $\frac{-3y}{(y-4)(y+4)}$
26. $\frac{3a+2}{(a-1)(a+1)}$ **27.** $\frac{8}{x+1}$ **28.** $\frac{3x^2-xy+6y^2}{(x+y)(x-y)}$ **29.** $\frac{-y(3y+19)}{(y+5)(y-2)}$ **30.** $\frac{y^2+3xy-2x^2}{xy(x+y)(x-y)}$ **31.** $\frac{1}{z+1}$ **32.** $\frac{a+5}{a-5}$
33. $\frac{2x^2+y^2}{x-y}$ **34.** -1 **35.** 3 or -2 **36.** 0 or -5 **37.** \$96.25 **38.** 2.6 hr

8.5 Exercises (PAGE 378)

1. $\frac{1}{3}$ **2.** $-\frac{1}{6}$ **3.** $\frac{7}{2}$ **4.** $\frac{1}{5}$ **5.** $-\frac{2}{5}$ **6.** no solution **7.** 4 **8.** no solution **9.** -2 **10.** 1, -6 **11.** 2, -12
12. -1, -3 **13.** 3 **14.** 4 **15.** $\frac{7}{11}$ **16.** Mary is 14, Ruth is 10 **17.** $\frac{30}{36}$ **18.** 6 **19.** $2\frac{1}{10}$ hr **20.** 36 days
21. 6 weeks **22.** 10 hr, 40 hr **23.** 8 min **24.** 12 days **25.** 12 min, 24 min **26.** $1\frac{7}{8}$ hr **27.** Jess: 4 mph; Ernie: 5 mph
28. 22 mph **29.** $\frac{5(2y+7)}{(y+5)(y-5)(y+2)}$ **30.** $\frac{x+19}{(x-2)(x+1)(x+5)}$ **31.** $\frac{4xy}{(x+y)(x-y)}$

8.6 Exercises (PAGE 387)

1. \$2.50 per lb **2.** 35 mpg **3.** 50 trees per acre **4.** $\frac{2}{3}$ **5.** $\frac{19}{2}$ **6.** $\frac{29}{11}$ **7.** 615 votes **8.** 35 gal **9.** 24 lb
10. 120 mi **11.** 42 **12.** 2511 lb **13.** 216 votes **14.** $33\frac{1}{3}$ gal **15.** 45 cm, 27 cm **16.** 6 in **17.** 5 cm
18. approximately 46 **19.** \$113.75 **20.** 500 fish **21.** 28 **22.** 80 **23.** 8 **24.** \$26.40 **25.** 40 **26.** 150 gal
27. \$17,368 **28.** \$2520 **29.** 18 **30.** 200 **31.** 2.5 hours **32.** 80 km/hr **33.** 32 in^3 **34.** 2 amps **35.** $-\frac{3}{8}$
36. $\frac{1}{2}$ **37.** 1, -7 **38.** $1\frac{1}{5}$ hr **39.** Steve $6\frac{2}{3}$ hr; Randy 20 hr **40.** $\frac{11}{7}$ **41.** $\frac{1}{4}$ **42.** $\frac{3}{2}$ **43.** $\frac{36}{5}$

8.7 Exercises (PAGE 395)

1. $\frac{11}{2}$ **2.** 8 **3.** $\frac{a-1}{3a}$ **4.** $\frac{y}{y+1}$ **5.** -1 **6.** $\frac{4+2a^2}{3a^2}$ **7.** $\frac{2+3y}{2y-3}$ **8.** $\frac{1+x}{1-x}$ **9.** $\frac{2a+1}{a}$ **10.** $\frac{y-3}{y}$
11. $\frac{x-2}{x-3}$ **12.** $\frac{a+3}{3-a}$ **13.** $V=\frac{3S_1S_2}{S_1+S_2}$; $\frac{30}{7}$ **14.** $R=\frac{2rg}{r+g}$ **15.** 133 mi **16.** 7 **17.** \$139.50 **18.** 7.5 cups
19. 9 **20.** -9 **21.** 100 **22.** 100 **23.** 4 **24.** -1

Chapter 8 Review Exercises (PAGE 400)

1. 0, 1 **2.** none **3.** 5, -1 **4.** no **5.** yes **6.** no **7.** $x+2$ **8.** $x-3$ **9.** $x+y$ **10.** $\frac{y(y-2)}{y+2}$
11. $\frac{2y(y-1)}{y+1}$ **12.** $(3x-y)(x-y)$ **13.** $\frac{3x+2}{(x-1)(x+1)}$ **14.** $\frac{2x}{x-3}$ **15.** $\frac{-1}{(a+1)(a-1)}$ **16.** $\frac{3x+5}{x-2}$ **17.** $\frac{9-x}{(x+3)(x-3)}$
18. $\frac{x^2+y^2}{x^2-y^2}$ **19.** -15 **20.** 1 **21.** -2 **22.** $\frac{6}{4}$ **23.** Diane: 15 mph; Don: 18 mph **24.** $2\frac{5}{14}$ days **25.** 8 hr
26. 30 mpg **27.** 200 trees per acre **28.** \$1.50 per lb **29.** -10 **30.** no solution **31.** $-\frac{1}{2}$ **32.** 225 votes **33.** 45 lb
34. 70 **35.** \$15.60 **36.** $\frac{1}{2}$ **37.** $2x+1$ **38.** $y-1$ **39.** 12 days **40.** 15 **41.** 1 **42.** 2 or 3 **43.** $-\frac{1}{2}$
44. $\frac{7x+1}{(x-2)(x+3)}$ **45.** 1 **46.** $\frac{x+5}{x-3}$ **47.** $8\frac{4}{7}$ minutes **48.** 8 mph **49.** false (does not reduce) **50.** true **51.** true
52. false (never find the LCD when multiplying or dividing) **53.** true **54.** true **55.** false (xy) **56.** true **57.** true
58. false ($a=\frac{c}{b}$) **59.** true **60.** false (proportional)

Chapter 8 Test (PAGE 403)

1. 0, −5 **2.** yes **3.** $\frac{1}{a}$ **4.** $\frac{5(x+4)}{x}$ **5.** $\frac{1}{y-3}$ **6.** $\frac{1}{a-b}$ **7.** $\frac{2x}{x+2}$ **8.** $\frac{y-5}{(y-1)(y+1)(y-2)}$ **9.** no solution **10.** 2 mph **11.** 37 gallons **12.** \$13.80 **13.** $1\frac{7}{8}$ days **14.** $\frac{1}{1+y}$ **15.** 5 **16.** 35 ft **17.** $\frac{1-2x}{2x-1} = \frac{(-1)(2x-1)}{(2x-1)} = -1$

Chapter 8 Answers to Selected Enrichment Exercises

[8.1] **2.** $\frac{3x-y}{2}$ **6.** $\frac{y+2}{y-2}$ **8.** $\frac{20}{W}$ feet **[8.2]** **1.** $\frac{x(x+1)}{x-6}$ **3.** $\frac{(a+b)^3}{a-b}$ **[8.3]** **1.** $\frac{2-x}{x-5}$ **4.** $\frac{b}{2a-b}$ **[8.4]** **1.** $\frac{-4(x^2+2y^2)}{(x+y)^2(x-y)^2}$ **4.** $\frac{x-3y}{(x-y)^2}$ **5.** $\frac{2(y-1)}{(y+1)(y-3)}$ **[8.5]** **2.** 0 **4.** 18 hr **12.** $a = \frac{3}{3c-1}$ **[8.6]** **1.** 24 **4.** 100 ft^3 **[8.7]** **2.** 1 **3.** $\frac{-a^2}{1-2a}$

CHAPTER 9 RADICALS AND RATIONAL EXPONENTS

9.1 Exercises (PAGE 409)

1. 2 **2.** 0 **3.** 1 **4.** 2 **5.** 6 **6.** 6 **7.** not a real number **8.** −11 **9.** ±11 (11 and −11) **10.** $\frac{3}{2}$ **11.** $\pm\frac{3}{2}$ $\left(\frac{3}{2} \text{ and } -\frac{3}{2}\right)$ **12.** 10 **13.** 5 **14.** $x-1$ **15.** $7a$ **16.** xy **17.** not a real number **18.** $-xy$ **19.** $x+5$ **20.** $y-4$ **21.** 5 **22.** 144 **23.** no value for p when w is negative **24.** 6.403 **25.** 5.148 **26.** 25.057 **27.** 23.304 **28.** 32.3% **29.** 22.0% **30.** $36x^{10}$ **31.** $4x^4$ **32.** $\frac{25y^2}{x^4}$

9.2 Exercises (PAGE 416)

1. $5\sqrt{3}$ **2.** $\sqrt{10}$ **3.** $4\sqrt{2}$ **4.** $30\sqrt{2}$ **5.** $7\sqrt{7}$ **6.** $25\sqrt{5}$ **7.** $5y\sqrt{3}$ **8.** $5x\sqrt{x}$ **9.** $5y\sqrt{3y}$ **10.** $3y\sqrt{3y}$ **11.** $7x^2\sqrt{3x}$ **12.** $3xy$ **13.** $3xy\sqrt{3x}$ **14.** $4xy\sqrt{3y}$ **15.** $5x^4y^2\sqrt{3xy}$ **16.** $\frac{5\sqrt{3}}{7}$ **17.** $\frac{5}{4}$ **18.** $\frac{5x}{y}$ **19.** $\frac{4x^2}{y^2}$ **20.** $\frac{5x\sqrt{3}}{y}$ **21.** $5xy^2$ **22.** $\frac{xy\sqrt{xy}}{7}$ **23.** $\frac{8\sqrt{7}}{7}$ **24.** $\frac{3\sqrt{5}}{5}$ **25.** $\frac{5xy\sqrt{3}}{z}$ **26.** $\frac{6y\sqrt{x}}{x}$ **27.** $\frac{5x\sqrt{xy}}{y^2z^2}$ **28.** $\frac{4}{xy}$ **29.** $2\sqrt{2}$ **30.** $5\sqrt{3}$ **31.** $4\sqrt{2}$ **32.** 4 sec **33.** 2.5 sec **34.** 3.1 sec **35.** 6.8 sec **36.** −11 **37.** not a real number **38.** $x-5$

9.3 Exercises (PAGE 422)

1. 10 **2.** $5\sqrt{3}$ **3.** 42 **4.** $\sqrt{42}$ **5.** $6\sqrt{5}$ **6.** $24\sqrt{7}$ **7.** $35\sqrt{6}$ **8.** $9x$ **9.** $5\sqrt{3y}$ **10.** $6a\sqrt{a}$ **11.** $3x^2$ **12.** $4xy$ **13.** $2xy\sqrt{3xy}$ **14.** $7x^2y^3\sqrt{6}$ **15.** $15xy$ **16.** $6xy\sqrt{3xy}$ **17.** 5 **18.** $\frac{7}{3}$ **19.** $\frac{\sqrt{3}}{5}$ **20.** $\frac{3\sqrt{3}}{5}$ **21.** $\frac{2\sqrt{3}}{3}$ **22.** $\frac{2\sqrt{7}}{7}$ **23.** 5 **24.** $\frac{\sqrt{3}}{2}$ **25.** $3x$ **26.** $\frac{2}{y}$ **27.** $\frac{3x}{2}$ **28.** $5xy$ **29.** $\sqrt{2y}$ **30.** $\frac{3\sqrt{xy}}{y}$ **31.** $\frac{5\sqrt{x}}{x}$ **32.** $\frac{y\sqrt{10x}}{5x}$ **33.** 6 **34.** $10\sqrt{2}$ **35.** no value for m if q is negative **36.** $7x\sqrt{3y}$ **37.** $\frac{7x\sqrt{2}}{5}$ **38.** $\frac{6x\sqrt{5y}}{5y}$ **39.** $9x$ **40.** $-\frac{1}{8}y$ **41.** $2x-6y$

9.4 Exercises (PAGE 427)

1. $10\sqrt{2}$ **2.** $-\sqrt{5}$ **3.** $-25\sqrt{xy}$ **4.** $3\sqrt{2}+2\sqrt{3}$ (cannot be simplified) **5.** $12\sqrt{2}$ **6.** $\sqrt{2}$ **7.** $2\sqrt{3}$ **8.** $41\sqrt{2}$ **9.** $9\sqrt{2}-10\sqrt{3}$ **10.** $-3\sqrt{3}$ **11.** $18\sqrt{11}$ **12.** $10\sqrt{3}-15\sqrt{5}$ **13.** $25\sqrt{x}$ **14.** $46\sqrt{2y}$ **15.** $2xy\sqrt{y}$ **16.** $14\sqrt{2}$ **17.** $-8\sqrt{3}$ **18.** $-43\sqrt{6}$ **19.** 0 **20.** $\sqrt{x}$ **21.** $-17\sqrt{5x}$ **22.** $56ab$ **23.** $-31b\sqrt{ab}$ **24.** $\frac{4\sqrt{3}}{3}$ **25.** $\frac{7\sqrt{5}}{5}$ **26.** $\frac{20\sqrt{7}}{7}$ **27.** $\frac{-24\sqrt{5}}{5}$ **28.** $\frac{-4\sqrt{5}}{5}$ **29.** $\frac{-5\sqrt{6}}{3}$ **30.** $4\sqrt{15}$ **31.** $2\sqrt{7}$ **32.** $3a\sqrt{5a}$ **33.** $5\sqrt{2}$ **34.** $\frac{2x\sqrt{15y}}{5y}$ **35.** $x^2+6xy-7y^2$ **36.** $x^2-6xy+9y^2$ **37.** x^2-16y^2 **38.** $9x^2-49y^2$

9.5 Exercises (PAGE 433)

1. $-\sqrt{5}$ **2.** $6x$ **3.** $\frac{5x\sqrt{3y}}{3y}$ **4.** $\sqrt{3}$ **5.** $-\sqrt{5}$ **6.** 0 **7.** $\frac{\sqrt{6}-\sqrt{10}}{2}$ **8.** $8x\sqrt{2}$ **9.** $2\sqrt{xy}$ **10.** $\frac{4\sqrt{5x}}{5}$ **11.** $-8\sqrt{3}$ **12.** $2x\sqrt{xy}$ **13.** $3+\sqrt{6}$ **14.** 10 **15.** $-4\sqrt{35}$ **16.** $2\sqrt{3}-\sqrt{6}$ **17.** 8 **18.** 4 **19.** $\frac{5\sqrt{2}}{2}$ **20.** $7-2\sqrt{10}$ **21.** -3 **22.** $7+3\sqrt{3}$ **23.** $-\sqrt{2}$ **24.** $16+\sqrt{6}$ **25.** $\sqrt{2}+1$ **26.** $\sqrt{7}-\sqrt{5}$ **27.** $3\sqrt{5}+6$ **28.** $6\sqrt{5}-12$ **29.** $2\sqrt{3}+2\sqrt{7}$ **30.** $3+\sqrt{3}$ **31.** $2-\sqrt{2}$ **32.** $5+\sqrt{15}$ **33.** $\sqrt{x}+1$ **34.** $3x$ **35.** $9(2x-5)$ **36.** $2x+2$ **37.** $4\sqrt{3}$ **38.** $5\sqrt{5x}$ **39.** -3 **40.** 4 *or* -1 **41.** 0 *or* -2

9.6 Exercises (PAGE 438)

1. 16 **2.** $\frac{9}{2}$ **3.** 7 **4.** no solution **5.** $\frac{5}{8}$ **6.** 2 **7.** 1 **8.** 3 **9.** $\frac{4}{3}$ **10.** 5 **11.** 9 **12.** 2 **13.** 3 **14.** $-\frac{1}{2}$ **15.** -4 **16.** no solution **17.** 0 **18.** 7 **19.** 5 **20.** 1 **21.** -1 **22.** $1+\sqrt{15}$ **23.** $5+\sqrt{10}$ **24.** 5 **25.** 12

9.7 Exercises (PAGE 445)

1. 13 **2.** $\sqrt{51}$ **3.** $2\sqrt{14}$ **4.** 10 **5.** $2\sqrt{6}$ **6.** $10\sqrt{3}$ **7.** $\sqrt{55}$ m (approximately 7.4 m) **8.** $6\sqrt{2}$ cm (approximately 8.5 cm) **9.** $10\sqrt{13}$ in (approximately 36.1 in) **10.** 50 ft **11.** 4 **12.** 9 **13.** $\frac{5}{3}$ **14.** 3 **15.** \$600 **16.** \$1000 **17.** $\$500\sqrt{3}$ (approximately \$866) **18.** 364 **19.** 400 mi **20.** $20\sqrt{10}$ mi (approximately 63.2 mi) **21.** 1.8 mi **22.** 0.05 mi (264 ft) **23.** 25 **24.** 24 **25.** The Pythagorean theorem does not apply since the triangle is not a right triangle. **26.** 5 **27.** hypotenuse 14; leg $7\sqrt{3}$ **28.** 6; $6\sqrt{3}$ **29.** hypotenuse $2\sqrt{2}$; leg 2 **30.** hypotenuse $3\sqrt{2}$; leg 3 **31.** $\frac{3}{4}$ **32.** 5 **33.** true **34.** false $(a^4 = a^3a)$ **35.** true **36.** false $\left(\frac{16x^6}{2x^2} = 8x^4\right)$

9.8 Exercises (PAGE 456)

1. 3 **2.** 1 **3.** not a real number **4.** 2 **5.** 1 **6.** 2 **7.** y **8.** $-2x$ **9.** $2a$ **10.** $2\sqrt[3]{3}$ **11.** $\frac{3\sqrt[3]{2}}{2}$ **12.** $x\sqrt[3]{x^2}$ **13.** $2\sqrt[3]{5}$ **14.** $2\sqrt[4]{5}$ **15.** $2a$ **16.** $2a\sqrt[3]{a}$ **17.** $2a$ **18.** $2a$ **19.** $\frac{\sqrt[3]{6}}{2}$ **20.** $\frac{\sqrt[4]{6}}{2}$ **21.** $\frac{3\sqrt[3]{a}}{a}$ **22.** $\frac{\sqrt[3]{20}}{2}$ **23.** $\frac{\sqrt[4]{22}}{2}$ **24.** $\frac{\sqrt[3]{ax}}{x}$ **25.** $4\sqrt[3]{2}$ **26.** $5\sqrt[3]{2}$ **27.** $5\sqrt[3]{2}$ **28.** $2a\sqrt[3]{a}$ **29.** $2y\sqrt[3]{y}$ **30.** $2a\sqrt[4]{a}$ **31.** 50 boxes **32.** 3 **33.** 3 **34.** 27 **35.** 4 **36.** $2\sqrt[3]{2}$ **37.** $2\sqrt[4]{2}$ **38.** $5^{1/2}$ **39.** $4^{1/3}$ **40.** $2^{1/4}$ **41.** $2^{2/3}$ **42.** $2^{2/3}$ **43.** $3^{2/5}$ **44.** $\frac{1}{5}$ **45.** $\frac{1}{64}$ **46.** $-\frac{1}{2}$ **47.** 27 **48.** 4 **49.** 2 **50.** $\frac{1}{w^{2/3}}$ **51.** y **52.** $\frac{1}{w^{1/2}}$ **53.** ab^3 **54.** $m^{7/4}$ **55.** $\frac{a^3}{b^2}$ **56.** $\sqrt{53}$ **57.** 4, $2\sqrt{3}$ **58.** $6\sqrt{2}$, $6\sqrt{2}$ **59.** 1.25 mi **60.** $(x-2)(x+8)$ **61.** $(x+3)^2$ **62.** $x(x-7)$

Chapter 9 Review Exercises (PAGE 460)

1. 2 **2.** 0 **3.** 1 **4.** 9 **5.** ± 12 (12 and -12) **6.** $\frac{5}{4}$ **7.** not a real number **8.** $2a$ **9.** $x+1$ **10.** $10\sqrt{2}$ **11.** 9 **12.** $2y\sqrt{2}$ **13.** $5xy\sqrt{2y}$ **14.** $\frac{4\sqrt{2}}{9}$ **15.** $\frac{4y}{x}$ **16.** $\frac{xy\sqrt{y}}{9}$ **17.** $\frac{6\sqrt{7}}{7}$ **18.** $\frac{5x\sqrt{2y}}{y}$ **19.** 12 **20.** 7 **21.** $3\sqrt{35}$ **22.** $6y$ **23.** $xy\sqrt{6y}$ **24.** $5xy\sqrt{5}$ **25.** 3 **26.** $\frac{5}{2}$ **27.** $\frac{3\sqrt{7}}{2}$ **28.** $\frac{5\sqrt{2}}{2}$ **29.** $\frac{3x}{2}$ **30.** $\frac{5x\sqrt{3y}}{3y}$ **31.** $17\sqrt{7}$ **32.** $-5\sqrt{5}$ **33.** $20\sqrt{2}$ **34.** $36\sqrt{x}$ **35.** $-7\sqrt{7}$ **36.** $8\sqrt{3x}$ **37.** $16x\sqrt{3}$ **38.** $\frac{6\sqrt{5}}{5}$ **39.** $-\frac{\sqrt{6}}{2}$ **40.** 34 **41.** $\sqrt{15}-5$ **42.** 6 **43.** 6 **44.** $1+\sqrt{6}$ **45.** $2+2\sqrt{5}$ **46.** $\sqrt{3}-1$ **47.** $-2\sqrt{7}-2\sqrt{5}$ **48.** $3+\sqrt{6}$ **49.** $\frac{7+\sqrt{7}}{6}$ **50.** $\frac{2}{3}$ **51.** 7 **52.** -1 **53.** $6\sqrt{5}$ **54.** 12 **55.** $4\sqrt{13}$ ft (approximately 14.4 ft) **56.** 8 **57.** \$6500 **58.** 256 **59.** 20 mi **60.** 0.8 mi **61.** $b = 10\sqrt{3}$; $c = 20$ **62.** $b = 7$; $c = 7\sqrt{2}$ **63.** 5 **64.** $2\sqrt[4]{5}$ **65.** $w\sqrt[4]{w^3}$

66. $\frac{3}{5}$ **67.** $2\sqrt[3]{5}$ **68.** $2x$ **69.** $3a\sqrt[3]{3}$ **70.** $\frac{3\sqrt[3]{a}}{a}$ **71.** $\frac{\sqrt[4]{6}}{2}$ **72.** $\frac{\sqrt[3]{15}}{5}$ **73.** $7\sqrt[3]{3}$ **74.** $y\sqrt[4]{y}$ **75.** 3 **76.** 16 **77.** 81 **78.** $\frac{1}{32}$ **79.** 4 **80.** $2\sqrt{x}$ **81.** $5xy\sqrt{2x}$ **82.** $y\sqrt{2x}$ **83.** $\frac{3\sqrt{5}}{5}$ **84.** $\sqrt{7} + \sqrt{2}$ **85.** $8xy\sqrt{2}$ **86.** $1 - 2\sqrt{10}$ **87.** $4y\sqrt{x}$ **88.** 8 **89.** $\frac{1}{5^{3/5}}$ **90.** 3 **91.** $\frac{1}{x^{3/4}}$ **92.** ab^2 **93.** $\frac{1}{ab^2}$ **94.** 60 mph **95.** 70 mph **96.** 7.5 lb/ft^2 **97.** 0.675 lb/ft^2 **98.** 16 **99.** 5 **100.** $b = 12\sqrt{3}$ cm; $c = 24$ cm **101.** 7 ft **102.** true **103.** true **104.** false ($\sqrt{16} + \sqrt{9} = 4 + 3 = 7$ but $\sqrt{16 + 9} = \sqrt{25} = 5$) **105.** false ($3\sqrt{x} + 2\sqrt{x} = 5\sqrt{x}$) **106.** true **107.** true **108.** false (side opposite 30° angle) **109.** true **110.** false ($y^{3/4} = \sqrt[4]{y^3}$)

Chapter 9 Test (PAGE 463)

1. 2 **2.** 5 **3.** ± 11 **4.** $\frac{9}{4}$ **5.** $4x$ **6.** $12\sqrt{3}$ **7.** $\frac{2\sqrt{2x}}{y}$ **8.** $\frac{7x\sqrt{2y}}{y}$ **9.** 24 **10.** $2x^2\sqrt[4]{2}$ **11.** $3x$ **12.** $6\sqrt{5}$ **13.** $-16\sqrt{2}$ **14.** $10\sqrt{3x}$ **15.** 0 **16.** $\frac{12\sqrt{11}}{11}$ **17.** 10 **18.** 2 **19.** $-3 + \sqrt{14}$ **20.** $\frac{5 + \sqrt{5}}{4}$ **21.** $\frac{7}{2}$ **22.** -3 **23.** 10 cm **24.** **(a)** $10\sqrt{5}$ **(b)** 20 **25.** $b = 20\sqrt{3}$, $c = 40$ **26.** $4\sqrt{2}$ **27.** -243 **28.** $\frac{x^2}{y^3}$

Chapter 9 Answers to Selected Enrichment Exercises

[9.1] **3.** $2x$ **6.** $-|y|$ **9.** cannot be determined, x could be either, or x could be 0 **12.** when $x \le 0$ **[9.2]** **3.** $\frac{5\sqrt{3yz}}{3x^2y^3z^4}$ **6.** $\frac{2x\sqrt[3]{3xy^2}}{y}$ **[9.3]** **3.** $\frac{2y^4z\sqrt{6xy}}{3x}$ **6.** $\frac{2x\sqrt[3]{25x^2y^2}}{5y^2}$ **[9.4]** **2.** $3(x - 5y)\sqrt{2}$ **4.** $12a^2b^2\sqrt[3]{a^2}$ **[9.5]** **2.** $x\sqrt{x} - y\sqrt{y}$ **4.** $\frac{4\sqrt{4 - x^2}}{4 - x^2}$ **5.** $\frac{1}{3 - 2\sqrt{2}}$ **9.** $x + 2\sqrt{x} + 1$ **[9.6]** **1.** $1 + 4\sqrt{x - 3} + x$; 4 **[9.7]** **2.** $b = x(a^2 - 1)$; 4

CHAPTER 10 QUADRATIC EQUATIONS

10.1 Exercises (PAGE 472)

1. $2x^2 + x - 5 = 0$; $a = 2$, $b = 1$, $c = -5$ **2.** $x^2 - 3x = 0$; $a = 1$, $b = -3$, $c = 0$ **3.** $x^2 + 1 = 0$; $a = 1$, $b = 0$, $c = 1$ **4.** $\frac{1}{2}y^2 - 3 = 0$; $a = \frac{1}{2}$, $b = 0$, $c = -3$ or $y^2 - 6 = 0$ (multiply by 2 to clear fractions and make a, b, and c integers); $a = 1$, $b = 0$, $c = -6$ **5.** $2x^2 + 2x + 5 = 0$; $a = 2$, $b = 2$, $c = 5$ **6.** not a quadratic equation **7.** No; multiplying the original equation on both sides by -1 yields a general form with the given constants. **8.** 7, -4 **9.** 7, -5 **10.** $-\frac{1}{2}$, 3 **11.** $\frac{4}{3}$, -1 **12.** 0, $\frac{7}{4}$ **13.** 5 **14.** 0, -5 **15.** 1, 3 **16.** $\frac{1}{3}$, -7 **17.** $\frac{4}{3}$, $-\frac{1}{2}$ **18.** 3, $\frac{3}{2}$ **19.** $\sqrt{3}$, $-\sqrt{3}$ **20.** ± 9 **21.** ± 8 **22.** $\pm\frac{3}{2}$ **23.** ± 3 **24.** $\pm 5\sqrt{3}$ **25.** ± 5 **26.** $\pm\sqrt{2}$ **27.** $\pm\sqrt{3}$ **28.** ± 2 **29.** 5, -1 **30.** 6, -8 **31.** $1 \pm \sqrt{5}$ **32.** 1, -2 **33.** 6, -10 **34.** 7.5 yd **35.** 6 ft **36.** 18 ft by 9 ft **37.** 3.5 in **38.** 15% **39.** 8.5% **40.** The solution 1 has been lost by dividing both sides by an expression containing the variable, $x - 1$. **41.** The product is 2, *not* zero. Do not try to use the zero-product rule at this point. **42.** $x^2 + 12x + 36$ **43.** $x^2 - 20x + 100$ **44.** $x^2 + \frac{2}{9}x + \frac{1}{81}$ **45.** $(x - 2)^2$ **46.** $(x + 5)^2$ **47.** $\left(x + \frac{1}{2}\right)^2$ **48.** $2\sqrt{2}$ **49.** $\frac{7}{2}$ **50.** $\frac{\sqrt{7}}{2}$

10.2 Exercises (PAGE 479)

1. 16 **2.** $\frac{49}{4}$ **3.** $\frac{1}{4}$ **4.** $\frac{1}{36}$ **5.** $\frac{1}{16}$ **6.** $\frac{4}{9}$ **7.** -3, -5 **8.** $1 \pm \sqrt{2}$ **9.** $\frac{1}{2}$, -1 **10.** 2, $\frac{1}{2}$ **11.** $-8 \pm \sqrt{14}$ **12.** $5 \pm \sqrt{3}$ **13.** 3, $-\frac{1}{2}$ (factor) **14.** $\frac{3 \pm \sqrt{17}}{4}$ (complete the square) **15.** $\pm\sqrt{10}$ (take roots) **16.** **(a)** 16 feet **(b)** 400 feet **(c)** 2 seconds **17.** 4 **18.** 16 **19.** 8 **20.** 8 **21.** $2\sqrt{2}$ **22.** $4 + 2\sqrt{2}$ **23.** 2 **24.** no solution (-2 does not check) **25.** $2\sqrt{13}$ **26.** $\sqrt{2}$

10.3 Exercises (PAGE 486)

1. 4, -5 **2.** 3, -3 **3.** $\frac{1}{5}$, $-\frac{2}{3}$ **4.** 1, $\frac{2}{3}$ **5.** $\frac{1 \pm \sqrt{21}}{10}$ **6.** $\frac{2 \pm \sqrt{2}}{2}$ **7.** $\frac{-9 \pm \sqrt{33}}{8}$ **8.** $-1 \pm \sqrt{6}$ **9.** $3 \pm \sqrt{10}$ **10.** $\frac{3 \pm 3\sqrt{5}}{2}$ **11.** 1, -4 **12.** $\frac{1 \pm \sqrt{17}}{2}$ **13.** no real number solution **14.** $\frac{1}{2}$, $-\frac{1}{2}$ **15.** $\frac{9}{2}$, -1 **16.** 3, $\frac{1}{2}$

17. $\frac{-5 \pm 2\sqrt{7}}{3}$ **18.** 2, −2 **19.** $\frac{1}{3}$, −2 **20.** $\frac{-1 \pm \sqrt{5}}{2}$ **21.** $\frac{1 \pm \sqrt{5}}{-2}$ **22.** Same $\left(\text{Multiply numerator and denominator of } \frac{-1 \pm \sqrt{5}}{2} \text{ by } -1 \text{ to obtain } \frac{1 \pm \sqrt{5}}{-2}\right)$. The equations are equivalent (multiply both sides of 20 by −1 to get 21). **23.** $\frac{3}{2}$, −1 **24.** $-1 \pm \sqrt{3}$ **25.** 1, −3 **26.** 0.56, −0.36 (using $\sqrt{21} \approx 4.6$) **27.** 1.7, 0.3 (using $\sqrt{2} \approx 1.4$) **28.** 1.6 cm, 2.6 cm **29.** 5.7 yards **30.** 3 seconds (on the way up) then again at 5 seconds (on the way down) **31.** The solutions are $3 + \sqrt{10}$ and $3 - \sqrt{10}$. Their sum is $(3 + \sqrt{10}) + (3 - \sqrt{10}) = 6 = -\frac{-6}{1} = -\frac{b}{a}$. **32.** $\pm\sqrt{13}$ **33.** $\frac{-1 \pm \sqrt{7}}{2}$ **34.** $\frac{7}{3}$ **35.** 6

10.4 Exercises (PAGE 492)

1. 6, −8 **2.** 1, −3 **3.** −3, 2 **4.** 0, −6 **5.** 12, −15 **6.** −1 **7.** 6, 10 **8.** $\pm\sqrt{5}$ **9.** $-1 \pm \sqrt{7}$ **10.** 5 **11.** 6 **12.** 5, 1 **13.** 25, 13 **14.** no solution **15.** −3 **16.** $\frac{1}{2}$ **17.** −1, 8 **18.** $\sqrt{5}$ **19.** 2, $\frac{1}{2}$ **20.** 2 **21.** $4 \pm 2\sqrt{2}$ **22.** $\frac{1 \pm \sqrt{10}}{3}$ **23.** 9 **24.** 8

10.5 Exercises (PAGE 498)

1. 6, −6 **2.** 12 years old **3.** 5, −2 **4.** 9 years old **5.** 10, −10 **6.** 7 years old **7.** 8 packages or 12 packages **8.** about 7 fountains **9.** 1 year old or 7 years old **10.** 14 cm, 10 cm **11.** 7 in **12.** 5 ft, 12 ft **13.** 11 cm **14.** 12 ft, 4 ft **15.** 10 in, 18 in **16.** 20 cm **17.** 11 ft, 5 ft **18.** 17 in, 14 in **19.** 6 hr, 12 hr **20.** 36 hr, 45 hr **21.** 3 in **22.** 25 mph **23.** 10 mph **24.** 2 mph **25.** 7 **26.** 1, −2 **27.** no solution **28.** 30 years old

29.

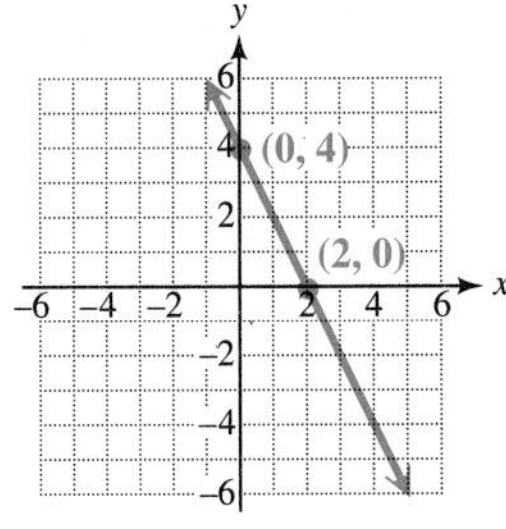

30.

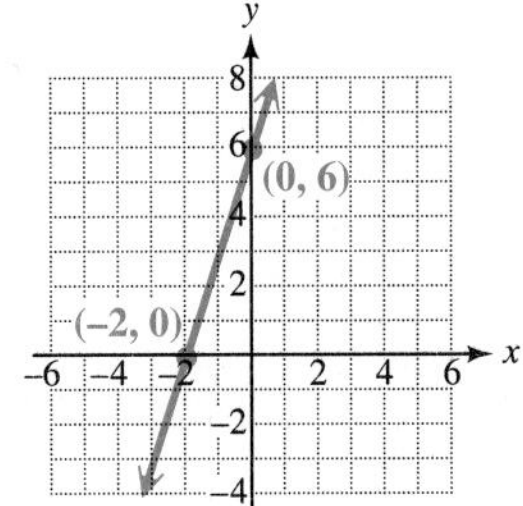

10.6 Exercises (PAGE 507)

1.

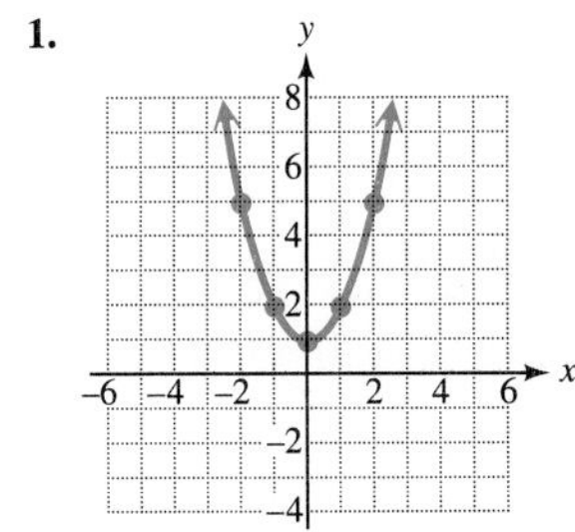

2.

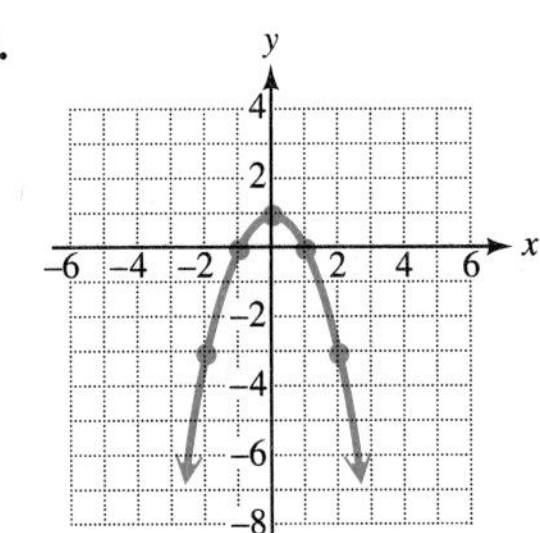

3.

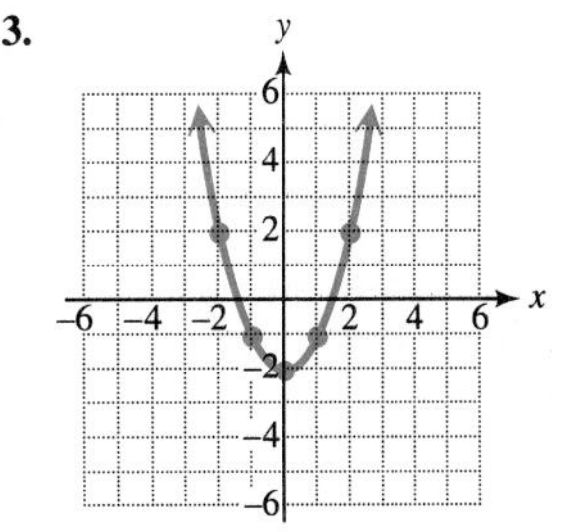

4.

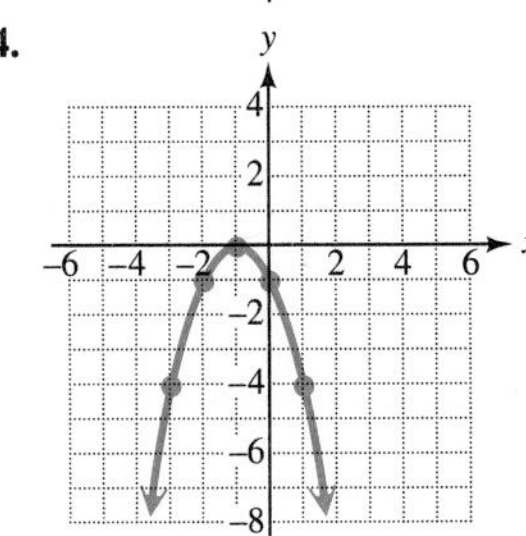

5.

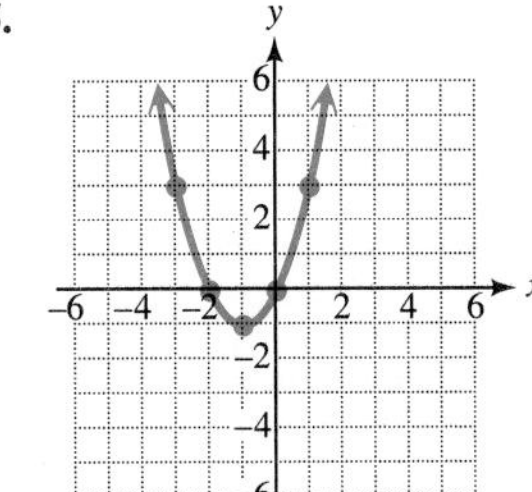

6.

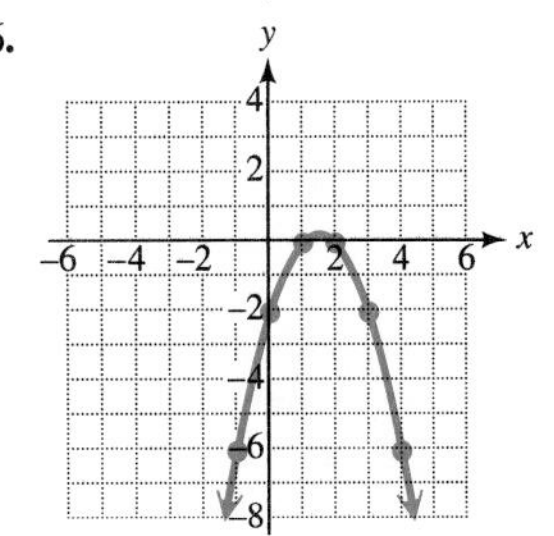

7. (4, 2) **8.** (−10, −9)

9. (0, −3) **10.** −14, 13 **11.** 3 cm, 4 cm **12.** 12 ft, 4 ft **13.** $1\frac{3}{5}$ days **14.** $2\sqrt{5}$ **15.** $\frac{\sqrt{3}}{3}$ **16.** $24\sqrt{2}$

10.7 Exercises (PAGE 512)

1. $\pm i$ **2.** $\pm 4i$ **3.** ± 1 **4.** $\pm 2i\sqrt{3}$ **5.** $\pm 5i\sqrt{2}$ **6.** $\pm 2\sqrt{3}$ **7.** $-1 \pm 2i$ **8.** $1 \pm 2i$ **9.** $\frac{1 \pm i\sqrt{3}}{2}$ **10.** $\frac{3 \pm i\sqrt{55}}{4}$ **11.** $\frac{2 \pm i\sqrt{21}}{5}$ **12.** $\frac{-2 \pm i\sqrt{21}}{5}$ **13.** up; $(2, -4)$;

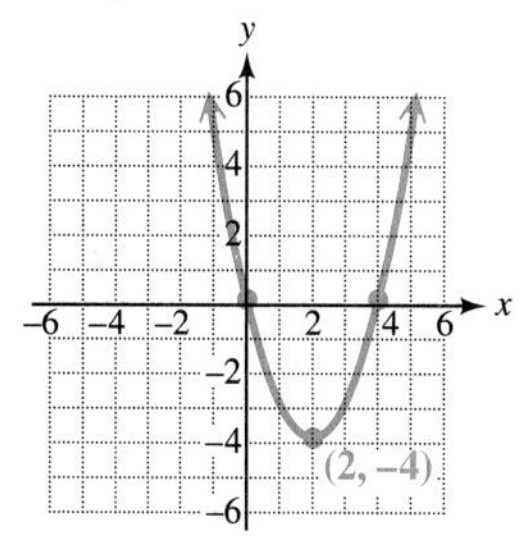

14. down; $(2, 4)$;

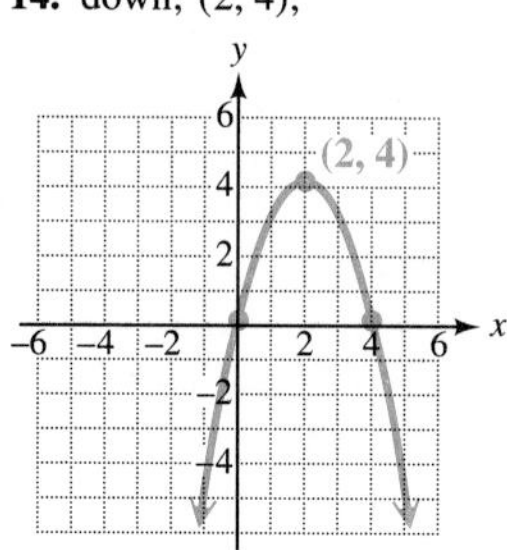

Chapter 10 Review Exercises (PAGE 514)

1. $6, -12$ **2.** $0, 10$ **3.** $\frac{4}{3}, -\frac{8}{7}$ **4.** $\frac{1}{4}$ **5.** $\frac{1}{64}$ **6.** $\frac{3 \pm \sqrt{5}}{2}$ **7.** $\frac{-1 \pm \sqrt{41}}{4}$ **8.** $-1, -5$ **9.** $-1 \pm \sqrt{6}$ **10.** $-1, -4$ **11.** $2, -3$ **12.** $0, 8$ **13.** $7, 12$ **14.** 3 years old **15.** 1 in or 3 in **16.** $6, -3$ **17.** 35 mph **18.** 10% **19.** 12 units or 20 units **20.** 4 mph **21.** **(a)** up **(b)** down **22.**

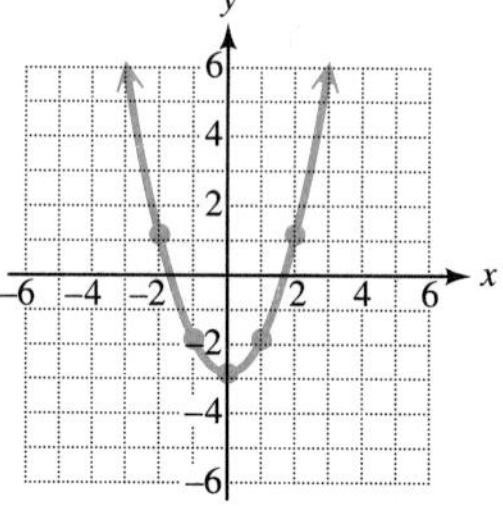

23.

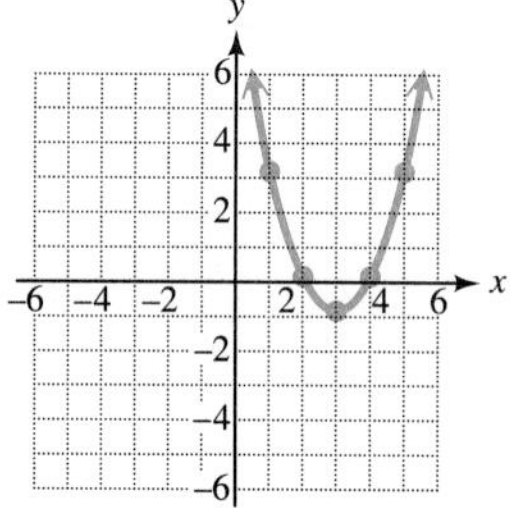

24. $(-4, -3)$ **25.** $(0, 6)$ **26.** $\pm 10i$ **27.** $\frac{1 \pm i\sqrt{13}}{2}$ **28.** $\frac{2 \pm 3i\sqrt{2}}{2}$ **29.** 15% **30.** 5 mph **31.** $4, -4$ **32.** 7 **33.** 16.8 yd (using $\sqrt{2} \approx 1.4$) **34.** Peter: 12 hr, Bill: 24 hr **35.** $1 \pm \sqrt{6}$ **36.** $3 \pm \sqrt{7}$ **37.** $\frac{-7 \pm \sqrt{73}}{2}$ **38.** $\pm 11i$ **39.** $0, -121$ **40.** $2 \pm i\sqrt{2}$ **41.** $(0, -8)$; down **42.** $(2, 5)$; down **43.** 49 **44.** $\frac{1}{36}$ **45.** true **46.** false (could have 1 solution) **47.** true **48.** true **49.** false (add 9 to both sides) **50.** true **51.** true **52.** false $\left(x = \frac{-b \pm \sqrt{b^2 - 4ac}}{2a}\right)$ **53.** true **54.** false ($x - 3$ mph) **55.** true **56.** false ($5i$) **57.** true **58.** false (down) **59.** true **60.** false (5, 8)

Chapter 10 Test (PAGE 516)

1. $-4, -9$ **2.** $3, -3$ **3.** $0, 5$ **4.** $\pm 2i\sqrt{6}$ **5.** $2 \pm \sqrt{3}$ **6.** $1 \pm i\sqrt{2}$ **7.** $\frac{1}{16}$ **8.** $3, \frac{1}{2}$ **9.** 2 **10.** 10% **11.** large pipe: 4 hours, small pipe: 12 hours **12.** 12 mph **13.** 9 items or 15 items **14.** **(a)** parabola **(b)** up **(c)** $(0, 2)$ **(d)**

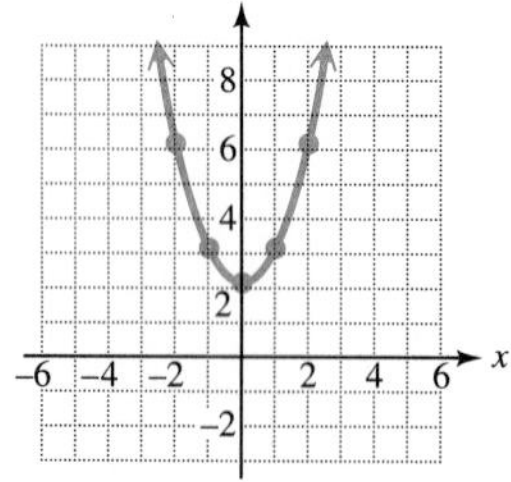

15. true **16.** false (the vertex is (6, 5)) **17.** false (imaginary number)

Chapter 10 Answers to Selected Enrichment Exercises

[10.1] **2.** $5, -2$ **6.** $5 \pm \sqrt{a}$ **[10.2]** **2.** $-1 \pm \sqrt{1 - c}$ **4.** $\frac{-b \pm \sqrt{b^2 - 4c}}{2}$ **[10.3]** **2.** $\frac{-y(3 \pm \sqrt{5})}{2}$ **3.** $3.54, -1.42$ **[10.4]** **1.** $\frac{1 \pm \sqrt{101}}{2}$ **4.** $x = \pm\frac{\sqrt{w}}{T}$ **[10.5]** **1.** 15 mph, 20 mph **[10.6]** **1.** $(-5, -5)$

APPENDIX A A REVIEW OF GEOMETRY

Appendix A Exercises (PAGE 530)

1. false (right angle) **2.** true **3.** true **4.** true **5.** false (complementary) **6.** true **7.** false ($\overleftrightarrow{CD}$ and $\overleftrightarrow{HI}$ intersect at C) **8.** true **9.** false (only one side equal) **10.** true **11.** 58 cm; 180 cm^2 **12.** 21.4 ft; 27.3 ft^2 **13.** 12.8 mi; 10.24 mi^2 **14.** 58.9 m^2 **15.** 198 in^2 **16.** 26 m **17.** 7.85 in **18.** $3150 **19.** 42.7 km; 145.2 km^2 **20.** 69.1 in; 379.9 in^2 **21.** 53.4 ft; 226.9 ft^2 **22.** 21.12 ft^3 **23.** 9152 cm^3 **24.** 4096 m^3 **25.** 551.368 in^3 **26.** 53.96 ft^2 **27.** 3472 cm^2 **28.** 1536 m^2 **29.** 403.44 in^2 **30.** 2411.52 cm^3 **31.** 5.7 in^3 **32.** 1004.8 cm^2 **33.** 17.96 in^2 **34.** 4186.7 ft^3 **35.** 356.6 m^3 **36.** 1256 ft^2 **37.** 243.2 m^2 **38.** 200 g **39.** 170 cm^2 **40.** $741 **41.** 16-in costs less (12-in: $0.044 per square inch, 16-in: $0.040 per square inch) **42.** yes; congruent by ASA **43.** $904.32

APPENDIX B INTRODUCTION TO FUNCTIONS

Appendix B Exercises (PAGE 539)

1. all real numbers **2.** all real numbers $x \geq 2$ **3.** all real numbers except -5 **4.** all real numbers $x \leq 4$ **5.** all real numbers except 1 **6.** all real numbers **7. (a)** 5 **(b)** 7 **(c)** 9 **(d)** -1 **(e)** $2b + 5$ **(f)** $-2a + 5$ **8. (a)** -1 **(b)** 1 **(c)** 15 **(d)** -55 **(e)** $2b^3 - 1$ **(f)** $-2a^3 - 1$ **9. (a)** -7 **(b)** -7 **(c)** -7 **(d)** -7 **(e)** -7 **(f)** -7 **10. (a)** 1 **(b)** 4 **(c)** 7 **(d)** -8 **(e)** $-3a + 1$ **(f)** $-3b + 4$ **11. (a)** 1 **(b)** 8 **(c)** 23 **(d)** 28 **(e)** $4a^2 - 3a + 1$ **(f)** $4b^2 - 11b + 8$ **12. (a)** 0 **(b)** 1 **(c)** 2 **(d)** -3 **(e)** $-a$ **(f)** $1 - b$ **13.** linear function **14.** constant function **15.** quadratic function **16.** $f(x) = (11.95)x$; $179.25 **17.** $g(x) = 55x$; 440 miles **18.** not the graph of a function **19.** graph of a function **20.** not the graph of a function **21.** 11 **22.** -31 **23.** -136 **24.** $-\frac{3}{4}$ **25.** -23 **26.** -35

FINAL REVIEW EXERCISES

Final Review Exercises (PAGE 541)

1. $\frac{11}{10}$ **2.** $\frac{2}{3}$ **3.** $\frac{3}{7}$ **4.** $\frac{10}{9}$ **5.** $\frac{14}{5}$ **6.** $\frac{1}{28}$ **7.** 32.715 **8.** 7.88 **9.** 0.35872 **10.** 55 **11.** $2\frac{7}{18}$ **12.** $\frac{107}{13}$ **13.** 19 **14.** $6\frac{1}{16}$ **15.** 37.5% **16.** $2\frac{18}{25}$ **17.** $2.31 **18.** 0.01 ml **19.** 33 **20.** $2332.80 **21.** $-\frac{4}{3}$ **22.** 8 **23.** $>$ **24.** $>$ **25.** 12 **26.** -10 **27.** $\frac{1}{12}$ **28.** -3 **29.** 0 **30.** -16 **31.** $2(y + 6)$ **32.** $-7(2x + 3)$ **33.** $-12a + 2b - 5$ **34.** $5y + 8$ **35.** -8 **36.** $-5xxxx$ **37.** -12 **38.** $\frac{2}{5}$ **39.** 9 **40.** $\frac{1}{4}$ **41.** 4 **42.** -6 **43.** 39 **44.** 9 **45.** 4 **46.** $\frac{11}{2}$ **47.** -10 **48.** $a = b - 2c$ **49.** $31,000 **50.** $128 **51.** 17 in **52.** 45 mph, 75 mph **53.**

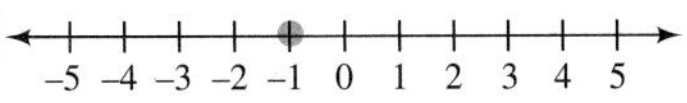

54.

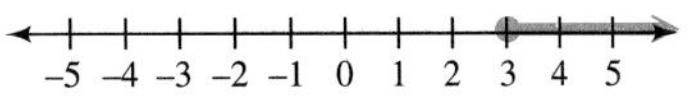

55. $x > 1$ **56.** $-2 \leq x < 2$ **57.** third **58.** (5, 0) **59.** $1850 **60.** true **61.** $\frac{4}{5}$, $4x - 5y = 33$ **62.** $y = \frac{3}{4}x - 3$, $\frac{3}{4}$, $(0, -3)$ **63.** $4x + 5y = 35$ **64.** perpendicular **65.**

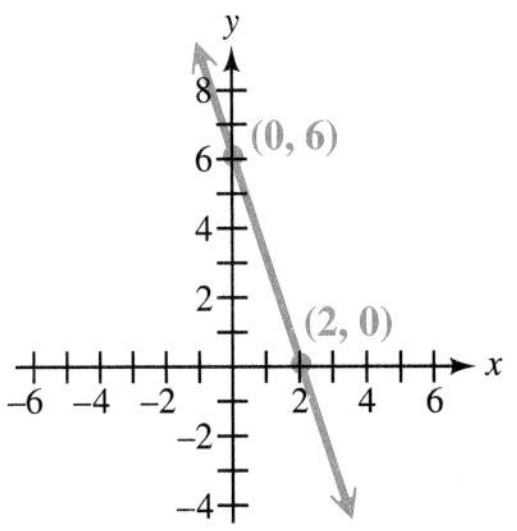

66.

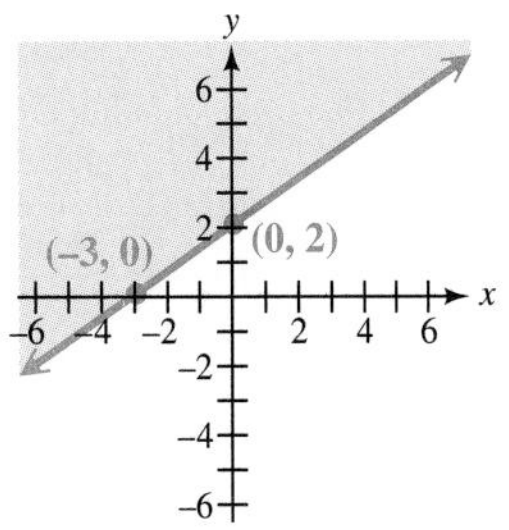

67. parallel

68. exactly one **69.** (1, 5) **70.** (4, 0) **71.** (−3, −6) **72.** $\left(\frac{1}{4}, -\frac{2}{3}\right)$ **73.** 5 mph **74.** \$5000 **75.** (6, 1) **76.** 20 lb of 95¢ candy and 40 lb of 65¢ candy **77.** $3x^5$ **78.** y^4 **79.** $9a^6$ **80.** $\frac{1}{a^2}$ **81.** 3.62×10^7 **82.** 0.00072 **83.** $6.3 \times 10^0 = 6.3$ **84.** 5×10^{-12} **85.** monomial **86.** 5 **87.** $x^7 - 6x^5 - 4x^3 + 4x^2 + 3x$ **88.** \$67 **89.** $a + 1$ **90.** $-4x^2y^2 - 4xy - 3$ **91.** $11y - 8$ **92.** $-x^2 - 11x + 11$ **93.** $5a - 2$ **94.** $4x^2y - 5xy^2 - 6xy$ **95.** $-12a^3 + 6a^2$ **96.** $27x^2 + 30xy - 8y^2$ **97.** $3a^3 - 4a^2 - 9a + 10$ **98.** $25x^2 + 70x + 49$ **99.** $4x^2 - 25y^2$ **100.** $x^4 - 4x^2 + 4$ **101.** $3y^7 - y^4 + 5y$ **102.** $2x^2 - 8x + 5$ **103.** $8(3x - 2)$ **104.** $3x^2y^2(2x - y + 3)$ **105.** $(x^2 + 2)(3x + 2)$ **106.** $(a^2 + 3)(b + 1)(b - 1)$ **107.** $(x + 8)(x + 5)$ **108.** $(y - 9)^2$ **109.** $6(x + 2y)(x - 2y)$ **110.** $(x - 4y)(x + 5y)$ **111.** $(2x + 1)(x - 5)$ **112.** $(3x + 2y)^2$ **113.** $\frac{1}{4}, -8$ **114.** −2, 10 **115.** 6 cm, 24 cm **116.** 7 **117.** −1, 8 **118.** $\frac{a + b}{a - b}$ **119.** $\frac{x(x - 2)}{x + 2}$ **120.** $\frac{y + 1}{y}$ **121.** $\frac{12y - 11}{(y + 2)(y - 3)(y - 1)}$ **122.** $\frac{-x - 3}{x + 2}$ **123.** $x + 1$ **124.** $\frac{1}{2}$ **125.** 1025 mi **126.** $\frac{3}{8}$ **127.** \$200 **128.** 4 in^3 **129.** 16 **130.** ±13 **131.** $9x$ **132.** $10xy\sqrt{2}$ **133.** $\frac{3x\sqrt{3}}{2y}$ **134.** $\frac{7y\sqrt{x}}{x}$ **135.** $75\sqrt{3}$ **136.** $2x\sqrt{2}$ **137.** $12\sqrt{2}$ **138.** $6\sqrt{5}$ **139.** $-\sqrt{7x}$ **140.** $\frac{\sqrt{3}}{3}$ **141.** $3 - \sqrt{14}$ **142.** $3\sqrt{2} + 2\sqrt{3}$ **143.** 6 **144.** no solution **145.** 5 m **146.** 20 **147.** $b = 22\sqrt{3}$, $c = 44$ **148.** $a = 45$ cm, $c = 45\sqrt{2}$ cm **149.** $5\sqrt[3]{5}$ **150.** $3x\sqrt[4]{3x}$ **151.** $\frac{2\sqrt[3]{x}}{x}$ **152.** $a\sqrt[4]{a}$ **153.** 4 **154.** $\frac{1}{4}$ **155.** 5, 7 **156.** −7 **157.** $\frac{1}{2}, 5$ **158.** $\frac{3 \pm \sqrt{13}}{2}$ **159.** $\frac{5}{2}, -1$ **160.** $\frac{5 \pm \sqrt{41}}{2}$ **161.** 3 **162.** 2, −1 **163.** 3 in, 1 in **164.** Al needs 3 hr and Joe 6 hr **165.**

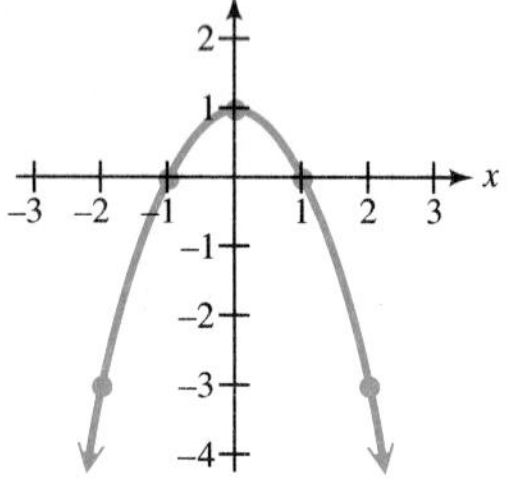

166. ±8i **167.** $1 \pm i$ **168.** $-2 \pm i$

Index

Rules of Exponents (6.1)

Let a and b be any two numbers, m and n any two integers.

1. $a^m \cdot a^n = a^{m+n}$
2. $\frac{a^m}{a^n} = a^{m-n} \quad (a \neq 0)$
3. $(a^m)^n = a^{mn}$
4. $(ab)^n = a^n b^n$
5. $\left(\frac{a}{b}\right)^n = \frac{a^n}{b^n} \quad (b \neq 0)$
6. $a^0 = 1 \quad (a \neq 0)$
7. $a^{-n} = \frac{1}{a^n} \quad (a \neq 0)$
8. $\frac{1}{a^{-n}} = a^n \quad (a \neq 0)$

The Language of Problem Solving (3.5)

Symbol	**Stands for**
$+$	and, sum, sum of, added to, increased by, more than
$-$	minus, less, subtracted from, less than, diminished by, difference between, difference, decreased by
$\cdot$	times, product, product of, multiplied by, of
$\div$	divided by, quotient of, ratio
$=$	equals, is equal to, is as much as, is, is the same as, gives, yields

Slope of a Line (4.3)

The slope of a line through (x_1, y_1) and (x_2, y_2) is

$$m = \frac{y_2 - y_1}{x_2 - x_1}$$

Forms of Equation of a Line (4.4)

Standard $ax + by = c$

Point-Slope $y - y_1 = m(x - x_1)$

Slope-Intercept $y = mx + b$

Properties of Equality (3.1, 3.2)

If a, b, and c are real numbers and $a = b$, then

$a + c = b + c$

$a - c = b - c$

$ac = bc \quad (c \neq 0)$

$\frac{a}{c} = \frac{b}{c} \quad (c \neq 0)$

Properties of Inequality (3.7)

If a, b, and c are real numbers and $a < b$, then

$a + c < b + c$

$a - c < b - c$

$$\left.\begin{array}{l} ac < bc \\ \frac{a}{c} < \frac{b}{c} \end{array}\right\} (c > 0)$$

$$\left.\begin{array}{l} ac > bc \\ \frac{a}{c} > \frac{b}{c} \end{array}\right\} (c < 0)$$